Biochemical Actions of Hormones

VOLUME VI

Contributors

FRANCESCO BRESCIANI

RONALD H. COOPER

RANDALL T. CURNOW

JENNY P. GLUSKER

RUSSELL HILF

R. J. B. KING

JOSEPH LARNER

IVAN LIEBERBURG

BRUCE S. MCEWEN

A. FRANCES PEARLMUTTER

ARUN K. ROY

RUTH Y. SCHMITZ

VINCENZO SICA

FOLKE SKOOG

MELVYN S. SOLOFF

DONAL A. WALSH

ALESSANDRO WEISZ

Biochemical Actions of Hormones

Edited by GERALD LITWACK

Fels Research Institute and Department of Biochemistry
Temple University, School of Medicine
Philadelphia, Pennsylvania

VOLUME VI

ACADEMIC PRESS   New York San Francisco London 1979

A Subsidiary of Harcourt Brace Jovanovich, Publishers

ACADEMIC PRESS, INC.
111 Fifth Avenue, New York, New York 10003

United Kingdom Edition published by
ACADEMIC PRESS, INC. (LONDON) LTD.
24/28 Oval Road, London NW1 7DX

Library of Congress Cataloging in Publication Data

Main entry under title:

Biochemical actions of hormones.

    Includes bibliographies.
    1. Hormones. I. Litwack, Gerald, ed. II. Axelrod,
Julius, Date   [DNLM: 1. Hormones. 2. Physiology.
WK102 B615]
QP571.B56   574.1'927   70–107567

PRINTED IN THE UNITED STATES OF AMERICA
79 80 81 82   9 8 7 6 5 4 3 2 1

Contents

1. The Physiological Regulation and Function of cAMP-Dependent Protein Kinases

Donal A. Walsh and Ronald H. Cooper

2. Hormonal and Metabolic Control of Phosphoprotein Phosphatase

Randall T. Curnow and Joseph Larner

3. Structural Aspects of Steroid Hormones and Carcinogenic Polycyclic Aromatic Hydrocarbons

Jenny P. Glusker

4. Modulation of Chemical Carcinogenesis by Hormones

Russell Hilf

5. How Important Are Steroids in Regulating the Growth of Mammary Tumors?

R. J. B. King

6. Biochemical Actions of Neurohypophysial Hormones and Neurophysin

Melvyn S. Soloff and A. Frances Pearlmutter

List of Contributors

Numbers in parentheses indicate the pages on which the authors' contributions begin.

Francesco Bresciani* (461), Department of Pathology, University of Toronto, Toronto, Ontario, Canada

Ronald H. Cooper (1), Department of Biological Chemistry, School of Medicine, University of California, Davis, California 95616

Randall T. Curnow (77), Departments of Internal Medicine and Pharmacology, University of Virginia School of Medicine, Charlottesville, Virginia 22901

Jenny P. Glusker (121), The Institute for Cancer Research, The Fox Chase Cancer Center, Philadelphia, Pennsylvania 19111

Russell Hilf (205), Department of Biochemistry and University of Rochester Cancer Center, University of Rochester, Rochester, New York 14642

R. J. B. King (247), Hormone Biochemistry Department, Imperial Cancer Research Fund, P.O. Box 123, Lincoln's Inn Fields, London WC2A 3PX, England

Joseph Larner (77), Department of Pharmacology, University of Virginia School of Medicine, Charlottesville, Virginia 22901

Ivan Lieberburg (415), The Rockefeller University, New York, New York 10021

Bruce S. McEwen (415), The Rockefeller University, New York, New York 10021

*Present Address: Istituto Patologia Generale, I Facoltà di Medicina e Chirurgia, Università degli Studi di Napoli, Napoli, Italy.

A. Frances Pearlmutter (265), Department of Biochemistry, Medical College of Ohio, Toledo, Ohio 43699

Arun K. Roy (481), Department of Biological Sciences, Oakland University, Rochester, Michigan 48063

Ruth Y. Schmitz (335), Institute of Plant Development and Department of Botany, Birge Hall, University of Wisconsin, Madison, Wisconsin 53706

Vincenzo Sica* (461), Department of Pathology, University of Toronto, Toronto, Ontario, Canada

Folke Skoog (335), Institute of Plant Development and Department of Botany, Birge Hall, University of Wisconsin, Madison, Wisconsin 53706

Melvyn S. Soloff (265), Department of Biochemistry, Medical College of Ohio, Toledo, Ohio 43699

Donal A. Walsh (1), Department of Biological Chemistry, School of Medicine, University of California, Davis, California 95616

Alessandro Weisz† (461), Department of Pathology, University of Toronto, Toronto, Ontario, Canada

*Present Address: Istituto Patologia Generale, I Facoltà di Medicina e Chirurgia, Università degli Studi di Napoli, Napoli, Italy.

†Present Address: Istituto Patologia Generale, I Facoltà di Medicina e Chirurgia, Università degli Studi di Napoli, Napoli, Italy.

Preface

There seems to be no need for rationalizing the increased frequency of appearance of new volumes in this series. With the continued progress in molecular biology and molecular genetics, research in endocrinology continues at a blistering pace.

In this volume there are up-to-date critical summaries of the regulation of protein kinases and phosphoprotein phosphatases. There is emphasis on the relationship of the endocrines to cancer. In particular, an extensive review on the precise structures of steroid hormones and carcinogens is presented by a crystallographer and some conclusions have been drawn from this analysis which bear on steroid receptors. Other reports cover hormonal regulation of chemical carcinogenesis, the question of the importance of steroid hormones as growth factors for mammary tumors, the effects of steroid hormones in the central nervous system, and properties of the purified estrogen receptor. A contribution summarizes recent work on the biochemical actions of neurohypophysial hormones and neurophysin. Plant hormone action is represented by a report on the biochemistry and physiology of cytokinins. Multihormonal systems are exemplified by control of the α_{2u} globulin produced in the liver.

As in previous volumes, this treatise is organized by presenting articles of general interest first and then to proceed to more specialized subject matter, although when topics have similar subjects they are grouped together in preference to the aforementioned organization.

GERALD LITWACK

xi

Contents of Previous Volumes

CHAPTER 1

The Physiological Regulation and Function of cAMP-Dependent Protein Kinases

Donal A. Walsh and Ronald H. Cooper

I. INTRODUCTION

The elegant second messenger hypothesis of cAMP action proposed by Sutherland and Rall (1960) has served as a cornerstone upon which has been built our understanding of the mechanism of hormonal action. Since that time, it has been shown that a wide range of polypeptide hormones, the catecholamines, and a number of other cellular stimuli elicit the formation of cAMP, and that cAMP promotes all, or some, of the physiological events characteristic of the particular response. The elegance of this hypothesis is not compromised by recognition of the facts that (a) not all hormonal effects are mediated by this mechanism and (b) not all physiological responses initiated by the hormone are necessarily promoted through the elevation of cAMP concentration. For the latter, two primary examples are the independent regulation of K^+ release and amylase secretion from the parotid (Selinger *et al.*, 1973) and the regulation of hepatic glycogenolysis (Cherrington *et al.*, 1976).

The regulation of hepatic glycogenolysis by catecholamines provided the experimental framework on which the cAMP second messenger hypothesis was founded. These studies had in their turn been built on the earlier extensive investigations from the Coris's laboratory which provided not only our first understanding of the regulation of enzyme activity by covalent modification (Cori, 1956) but the training ground for a substantial number of the leading investigators in this area. Studies by E. G. Krebs, who received his training from the Coris, concentrated on the molecular mechanisms of skeletal muscle glycogenolysis and resulted in the identification of phosphorylase kinase, the enzyme which catalyzes the phosphorylation and activation of phosphorylase (Krebs *et al.*, 1958), and subsequently of the cAMP-dependent protein kinase, the enzyme which catalyzes the phosphorylation and activation of phosphorylase kinase (Walsh *et al.*, 1968). These enzymes are fundamental components of the glycogenolytic cascade (Fig. 1); we now know that many additional complexities are imposed on this system, and a discussion in greater depth is presented as the conclusion of this review.

The initial study of the cAMP-dependent protein kinase (Walsh *et al.*, 1968) demonstrated that this enzyme catalyzed the phosphorylation of other proteins in addition to phosphorylase kinase, that the enzyme was activated by cAMP within the concentration range that was physiologically appropriate ($K_a = 2 \sim 10 \times 10^{-8}\ M$), and that a stoichiometric binding of cAMP to the protein occurred (Fig. 2). Thus the cAMP-dependent protein kinase was recognized as a primary site of action of the cyclic nucleotide. Kuo and Greengard (1969) extended this concept by identifying this enzyme in both a wide range of mammalian tissues and at least nine animal phyla, and they

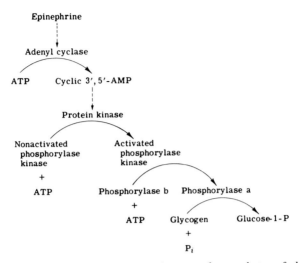

FIG. 1. The mechanism of action of epinephrine in the regulation of skeletal muscle glycogenolysis (from Walsh and Krebs, 1973).

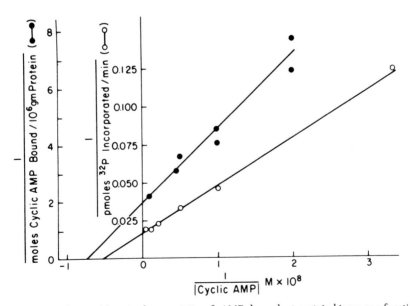

FIG. 2. Binding and kinetic characteristics of cAMP-dependent protein kinase as a function of cAMP concentration. Binding was determined by equilibrium gel filtration; the cAMP dependence of protein kinase activation was determined from the stimulation of casein phosphorylation (from Walsh and Ashby, 1973).

proposed that all the wide variety of effects elicited by cAMP are mediated through the stimulation of protein kinase. Although the hormonal regulation of glycogenolysis is a feature of essentially all eukaryotic cell types, the breadth of the postulate of cAMP action, as mediated by the activation of protein kinase, has since been supported by the identification of a wide range of phosphoproteins that serve as substrates for this enzyme. Subsequently, the cAMP-dependent protein kinase has been identified in all mammalian tissues in which it has been sought; in consequence an often-quoted (and albeit accepted) mechanism of cAMP action is as presented in Fig. 3. As this and other reviews (Walsh and Krebs, 1973; Langan, 1973a; Rubin and Rosen, 1975) clearly document, there is now substantial evidence that the mechanism shown in Fig. 3 is the primary mechanism by which cAMP mediates the action of hormones. It is important to recognize that this is probably not the only mechanism by which the cyclic nucleotide promotes intracellular events. As documented elsewhere (Walsh, 1978), evidence of other cAMP receptors is beginning to accumulate.

The purpose of this review is to examine the role of the cAMP-dependent protein kinase and its regulation. It will concentrate on the properties of the enzyme that currently appear germane to an understanding of its physiological function, and will not attempt to document or correlate the myriad other properties that cannot as yet be placed within a physiological context. This chapter is not a review of cAMP action; only those aspects of cAMP for which a role for protein phosphorylation appears justified will be considered. Con-

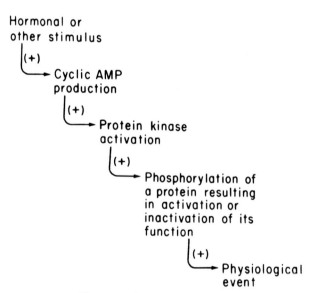

FIG. 3. Model of cAMP action.

versely, this chapter will not attempt to present an encyclopedic description of potential roles of protein phosphorylation, but will concentrate only on those systems which may provide a more generalized insight into the function and regulation of protein kinase. At the end of the chapter we have selected four specific systems for more detailed presentation because they appear to illustrate certain facets of regulation by protein kinase. It is well beyond the scope of this chapter to discuss many of the other systems in which protein phosphorylation may be involved; if we offend anyone by our selectivity, we apologize.

II. PROPERTIES OF THE cAMP-DEPENDENT PROTEIN KINASE

A. CATALYTIC PROPERTIES

cAMP-Dependent protein kinase catalyzes the phosphorylation of proteins according to the reaction of Eq. (1).

$$ATP—Mg + Protein \rightarrow ADP—Mg + Protein—PO_4 \tag{1}$$

For the enzyme from a wide range of tissues the reported K_m for ATP is within the range 5–50 μM but predominantly at close to 20 μM; this value, which is 200-fold less than the typical concentration within the cell, would appear to exclude any possibility of the regulation of the protein kinase by restriction of cellular ATP. The reaction requires Mg^{2+} in the physiological concentration range typical of that for many kinases. Singh and Wang (1977) have reported that the degree of phosphorylation and, in consequence, activation of phosphorylase kinase catalyzed by the cAMP-dependent protein kinase, is increased at high Mg^{2+} concentrations. Enzyme activation is 2–3 times higher when activation is studied at 10 mM as compared to 2 mM Mg^{2+}, with phosphate incorporation increased from 2 to 7 moles/mole. Similar changes in Mg^{2+} concentration did not affect the phosphorylation of either casein or histone; thus it is concluded that high Mg^{2+} alters the conformation of phosphorylase kinase, rendering more phosphorylation sites accessible to the protein kinase. It is doubtful that this per se is physiologically significant, but it is becoming increasingly apparent that regulation of protein kinase activity by many ligands may occur through interactions of the ligand with the substrate rather than with the enzyme. Pyruvate kinase, as discussed below (Section IV, A), is currently the best example of such a regulatory process; it is to be anticipated that other examples will also be discovered, because such a mechanism provides for a specificity with respect to a specific substrate.

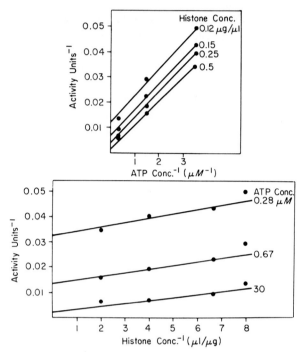

Fig. 4. Kinetic evaluation of the mechanism of brain cAMP-dependent protein kinase (from Moll and Kaiser, 1976).

A detailed kinetic mechanism for the catalytic function has so far been provided only for the brain enzyme (Moll and Kaiser, 1976). The data (Fig. 4) are compatible with a double displacement (ping-pong) mechanism. Such an observation is compatible with the observation of a phosphohistidine at the active site (Kochetkov *et al.*, 1976) and would explain the observed ATPase activity that is apparently an integral component of the cAMP-dependent protein kinase (Moll and Kaiser, 1976; Shizuta *et al.* 1975). In contrast to this proposed mechanism, J. R. Feramisco and E. G. Krebs (personal communication) find that the kinetic data for the skeletal muscle enzyme with synthetic peptide substrates are only compatible with a sequential mechanism. The latter has more corollaries with catalytic mechanisms proposed for other kinases (see Boyer, 1973).

B. Subunit Composition and Mechanism of cAMP Activation

Extensive evidence from many laboratories has documented that the cAMP-dependent protein kinase is comprised of two nonidentical subunits:

one subunit, designated C, possesses the catalytic function, while the second subunit, designated R, contains the binding site for cAMP. The holoenzyme comprising both R and C is catalytically inactive, and the binding of cAMP to R perturbs the interaction between R and C such that even mild physicochemical techniques can separate the two subunits. The skeletal muscle enzyme has a molecular weight of 170,000 and is comprised of two catalytic subunits each of molecular weight 40,900 and a regulatory subunit dimer of two polypeptide chains covalently linked by disulfide bond(s). Each regulatory monomer binds cAMP and thus activation occurs according to the reaction of Eq. (2).

$$R_2C_2 + 2 \text{ cAMP} \rightleftharpoons R_2\text{cAMP}_2 + 2C \tag{2}$$

Ogez and Segel (1976) have provided a critical appraisal of the possible mechanisms by which activation of the protein kinase by cAMP could occur. The nine specific models that were considered can be divided into the two general categories indicated* in Eqs. (3) and (4).

$$RC + \text{cAMP} \rightleftharpoons \text{RcAMPC} \rightleftharpoons \text{RcAMP} + C \tag{3}$$

$$\begin{array}{l} RC \rightleftharpoons R + C \\ \quad\ \ \Big\} \rightleftharpoons R \cdot \text{cAMP} \\ \text{cAMP} \end{array} \tag{4}$$

Ogez and Segel (1976) have also provided an experimental protocol that would delineate which model is correct, but sufficient data are not yet available. The solution of which of these mechanisms is correct is crucial to a full physiological understanding of the transducer role of the cAMP-dependent protein kinase in mediating the actions of cAMP. The mechanism of Eq. (4) encompasses the concepts of protein kinase function as currently generally envisaged (*vide infra*), but that of Eq. (3) prompts consideration of whether an active ternary complex exists and, if so, whether dissociation of the protein kinase is a necessary physiological event.

It is of particular interest that the recently characterized cGMP-dependent protein kinase from lung (Lincoln *et al.*, 1977; Gill *et al.*, 1977) has many characteristics that are similar to the cAMP-dependent protein kinase, prompting the suggestion of teleological identity (Gill, 1977; Lincoln and Corbin, 1977). The cGMP-dependent protein kinase holoenzyme has a molecular weight of 150,000 and is composed of two 74,000 molecular weight subunits which are linked by disulfide bridge(s). One mole of cGMP is bound per subunit; however, the activation of the enzyme does not require dissociation of the subunits. For the cGMP-dependent enzyme the binding

---

*For the purposes of this presentation, the stoichiometry of subunits that comprise the protein kinase or the regulatory subunit–cAMP complex, as indicated in Eq. (2), will not be given throughout the text.

of the cyclic nucleotide ligand promotes a conformational change in the enzyme sufficient to permit the full expression of catalytic function. By corollary, it can be presupposed that the binding of cAMP to the cAMP-dependent protein kinase produces a conformational change that permits the expression of catalytic function; a second consequence of this conformational change may be to weaken the interaction of the subunits. The weakened interaction of the subunits and the potentiation of catalytic activity may be either related or unrelated events. In consequence, a putative RcAMP–C ternary complex may have full catalytic function. Both cGMP and cAMP activate their respective protein kinases by modifying V_{max} and not affecting K_m, in accord with the "V" type allosteric system of Monod, Wyman, and Changeux. Activation of an enzyme by a dissociation mechanism should not be considered as one that is discrete from the classical concerted allosteric model of Monod *et al.* (1965) but rather as representing an extreme example of a conformational interaction. Nevertheless, a dissociation mechanism has many potential physiological consequences additional to those of the classical allosteric mechanism.

C. Isozymes of Soluble cAMP-Dependent Protein Kinase

As a general rule for intracellular systems, and with few exceptions, an enzyme only catalyzes a single reaction. cAMP controls a broad spectrum of physiological events, but the search for discrete cAMP-dependent protein kinases which would catalyze the phosphorylation of each potential phosphoprotein has led to the conclusion that a single enzyme species must catalyze the phosphorylation of at least several different protein substrates in mediating the diverse actions of cAMP. It was initially discovered in skeletal muscle and liver (Reimann *et al.*, 1971; Chen and Walsh, 1971) and later determined for a range of tissues (Corbin *et al.*, 1975a; Hofmann *et al.*, 1975) that there exist two principal isozymes of the soluble cAMP-dependent protein kinase. These have been designated types I and II on the basis of gradient elution from DEAE-cellulose (Fig. 5). Both isozymes display the same subunit composition; they differ in respect to the regulatory subunit component, but the catalytic subunits of each are identical by all tested physiological or enzymological criteria. Both types of isozymes have two species of catalytic subunit which can be separated by isoelectric focusing (Fig. 6) (Chen and Walsh, 1971; Bechtel *et al.*, 1977). The two isoelectric focusing species are identical in size, chromatographic properties, and enzymological characteristics. The isoelectric focusing profiles of catalytic subunit from either Type I or II are indistinguishable. The catalytic properties of the Type I and II isozymes have been examined by many investigators and

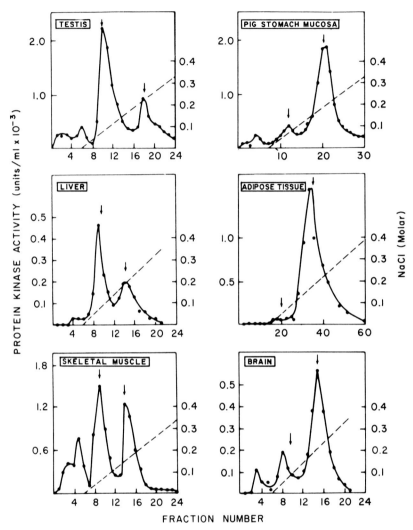

FIG. 5. Isozyme tissue distribution of cAMP-dependent protein kinase: DEAE-cellulose column profiles of protein kinases from various mammalian tissues. Fresh rat tissues and pig stomach mucosa were homogenized in 4 ml/gm of cold 5 mM Tris (pH 7.5) containing 1 mM EDTA (liver = 10 ml/gm, adipose tissue = 2 ml/gm) and extracts (all tissues 2 ml except adipose tissue = 4 ml) were applied to DEAE-cellulose columns (0.9 × 3.5 cm) equilibrated in the same above buffer. After applying the sample, the column was washed with approximately 50 ml of buffer and a linear gradient of NaCl to 0.35 or 0.4 M was begun. Fractions (~6 ml) were collected and were assayed for protein kinase activity in the presence of 2 μM cAMP. The arrows in the figure represent the positions of the peaks of types I and II heart protein kinases, respectively. (From Corbin *et al.*, 1975a.)

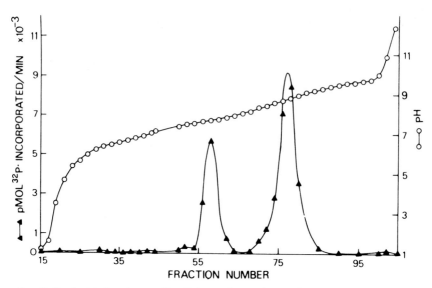

FIG. 6. Isoelectric focusing profile of the catalytic subunit of Type I isozyme of cAMP-dependent protein kinase. Protein kinase activities were determined using mixed histones as the substrate (from Bechtel *et al.*, 1977).

no significant differences have been detected. The difference between Type I and II isozymes of the cAMP-dependent protein kinase appears to reside solely in differences in the regulatory subunits. The two types are designated R_I and R_{II}. R_I is smaller than R_{II} (49,000 *cfr* 55,000), but although it has been shown that both types of regulatory subunit are particularly sensitive to proteolytic degradation, sufficient physicochemical evidence is now available to assure that R_I is not artifactually derived from R_{II}.

The difference in R_I and R_{II} results in changes in the regulatory subunit–catalytic subunit interaction. Type I and II isozymes of the protein kinase are not distinguishable on the basis of simple cAMP dependence of activation of enzyme activity, but such dependence is modified differentially for the two isozymes. The affinity of cAMP binding to the Type I isozyme is lowered by the presence of ATP—Mg^{2+} (Fig. 7); this property is ascribed to the binding of ATP to the holoenzyme (Beavo *et al.*, 1975). The binding of ATP to the holoenzyme occurs with an affinity constant of 50 nM (Fig. 8), a value that is substantially lower than the K_m of ATP required for catalytic activity. Free R_I does not bind ATP. Presumably, the ATP that affects cAMP affinity could bind either at a site comprised of components of both catalytic subunit and regulatory subunit moieties or at the active site of the enzyme, the affinity of which would have been modified by the binding of the regulatory subunit.

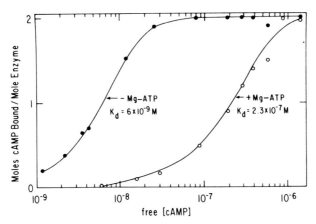

FIG. 7. Effect of Mg—ATP on the binding of cAMP to protein kinase. Assays were carried out in the absence or presence of 4 mM ATP, as indicated (from Beavo *et al.*, 1974).

Hoppe *et al.* (1977) have recently provided initial evidence that the latter is probably the correct explanation.

The association–dissociation characteristics of the Type II isozyme are not regulated by simple binding of ATP but are modified by an ATP-dependent phosphorylation of R_{II} (Rosen *et al.*, 1977). This phosphorylation occurs either by an intramolecular reaction catalyzed by unphosphorylated (undis-

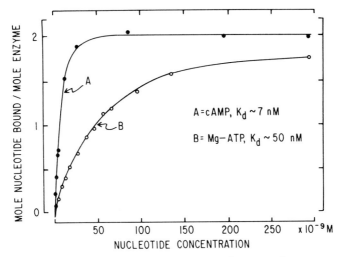

FIG. 8. Binding of [^{3}H]cAMP or Mg-[^{14}C]ATP to protein kinase. Binding assays were carried out at pH 6.9 in the presence of 4 mM magnesium acetate by the Millipore filter technique (from Beavo *et al.*, 1974).

sociated) holoenzyme or by an intermolecular reaction catalyzed by free
catalytic subunit (i.e., in the presence of cAMP). The phosphorylation of R_{II}
results in a decrease in the rate of reassociation of subunits (Fig. 9); thus the
phosphorylation produces an "apparent" enhancement of cAMP sensitivity
of the Type II isozyme. The Type I isozyme is not a substrate for auto- or
C-catalyzed phosphorylation. The physiological role of the regulation of
Type I isozyme by ATP, or of the Type II isozyme by phosphorylation, is
obscure. It is difficult to envisage a practical circumstance under which
regulation could occur by a variation in ATP at a concentration that is a factor
of 10^6 lower than the physiological level. From similar reasoning Rosen *et al.*
(1977) concluded that the Type II isozyme is quite probably always in the
phosphorylated state. A simple explanation of these mechanisms has inherent possibilities of physiologically consequential effects.

The interaction between the regulatory and the catalytic subunits is modified by ionic strength. For Type I heart enzyme, preincubation with 0.5 *M*
salt promotes dissociation, whereas the Type II (cardiac II or adipose) enzyme is minimally affected (Fig. 10). When reassociation is studied at 0°, the
Type II enzyme (adipose) rapidly recombines in the absence of salt, but this
is prevented by high salt (Fig. 11). In contrast, reassociation of the Type I
enzyme (cardiac) does not occur at a significant rate at 0° in either the
presence or the absence of high salt (Fig. 11). Reassociation of Type I en-

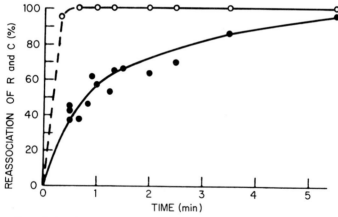

FIG. 9. Effect of phosphorylation on subunit reassociation of Type II isozyme of cAMP-
dependent protein kinase. Equimolar amounts of C and R [phospho (●————●) or dephospho
(○---○)] were mixed at a final concentration of 0.03 μM in 20 μl of 50 m*M* potassium
phosphate, pH 7.0, containing 4 m*M* 2-mercaptoethanol, 75 m*M* NaCl, 1 mg/ml bovine serum
albumin, and preincubated for different times at 4°. The indicated times refer to the time of
preincubation plus the 30 seconds required to separate C from holoenzyme and R (from
Rangel-Aldao and Rosen, 1976).

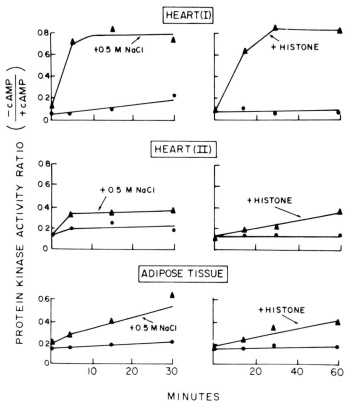

FIG. 10. Effect of prior incubation with 0.5 *M* NaCl or histone on activity of partially purified protein kinases of heart (Type I and II) and adipose tissue (Type II) (from Corbin *et al.*, 1975a).

zyme will occur at 30° in the absence of salt. These results show that high salt in general favors the dissociated state of either Type I or Type II enzyme, but that the Type I enzyme is markedly more sensitive; the degree of this sensitivity is indicated in Fig. 12. Expressed in alternate terms, high salt makes the enzyme more sensitive to cAMP-stimulated dissociation (Fig. 13).

The Type I isozyme is also more sensitive to histone-promoted dissociation (Fig. 10) and, in comparison to other substrates, histone increases the sensitivity of the protein kinase to cAMP-stimulated dissociation (Fig. 14). This property has caused confusion in the past literature because, as often quoted, the activation constant for the protein kinase by cAMP was reported to be significantly lower than the normal physiological concentration range of the cyclic nucleotide. This confusion, which has often resulted in searches for putative pools of inactive or bound cAMP, arose because of the widespread use of histone as an assay tool. In fact, for glycogen synthase (Fig. 14)

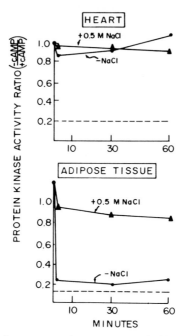

FIG. 11. Comparison of reassociation (i.e., activity ratio) of heart (Type I) and adipose tissue (Type II) protein kinase subunits. Homogenates of fresh heart (4 ml/g) and adipose tissue (1 ml/g) were prepared in cold 10 mM potassium phosphate, 10 mM EDTA, and 0.5 mM 1-methyl-3-isobutylxanthine, pH 6.8. After centrifugation at 27,000g for 40 minutes, cAMP was added to the supernatant fractions to 10 μM. Aliquots (200 μl) were chromatographed on a Sephadex G-25 column (0.9 × 10 cm) which had been equilibrated at 0° in the same above buffer in the absence and presence of 0.5 M NaCl, as indicated. The chromatography step required less than 2 minutes. Fractions (~0.5 ml) were collected, and 10 μl aliquots of the peak fraction containing the breakthrough protein were assayed for protein kinase in the presence and absence of 2 μM cAMP at the indicated times at 0° following the chromatography step. The ordinate shows the protein kinase activity ratio. The total activity (presence of cAMP) of the adipose tissue enzyme was 75% that of the heart enzyme following the chromatography. The total activities did not change significantly during incubation. Dashed lines indicate the activity ratios in the extracts before adding 10 μM cAMP. The zero time samples were assayed after addition of 10 μM cAMP but before chromatography (from Corbin *et al.*, 1975a).

or for casein as reported in the first description of the cAMP-dependent protein kinase (Walsh *et al.*, 1968), the enzyme is sensitive to cAMP in a concentration range (0.2–1.0 μM) which very closely parallels that observed in tissues in response to hormones.

The function of the two isozymes of the cAMP-dependent protein kinase remains obscure; as stated above, there is no indication of a difference in substrate preference. A study of the tissue distribution of the isozymes (for example, see Fig. 5) or of the species variation for a given tissue (Fig. 15)

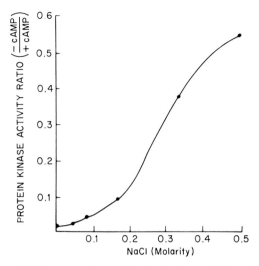

FIG. 12. Effect of NaCl concentration on dissociation (i.e., activity ratio) of the heart Type I protein kinase (from Corbin *et al.*, 1975a).

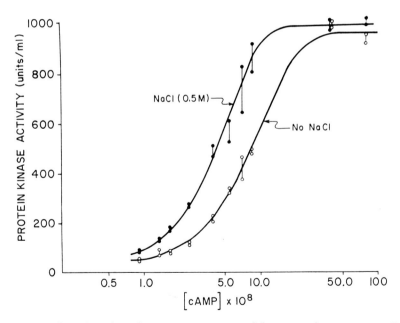

FIG. 13. Effect of NaCl on the cAMP requirement of the protein kinase, Type II (from Corbin *et al.*, 1973).

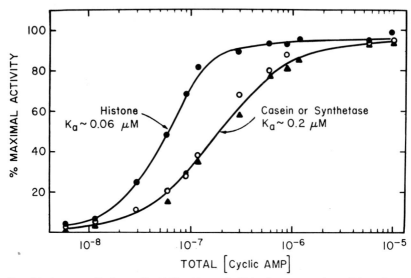

FIG. 14. Apparent K_a for cyclic AMP with casein (▲), glycogen synthase (○), or histone mixture Type IIA (●), as substrate (from Beavo *et al.*, 1974).

suggests no apparent trend that could be related to physiological function. M. Costa *et al.* (1976b) have presented the intriguing finding that the pattern of isozymes changes during the cell cycle of Chinese hamster ovary cells, with Type I predominant during mitosis and Type II at the G_1/S boundary (Fig. 16). Russell proposes that the Type I isozyme is a positive effector of growth whereas the activation of the Type II enzyme represents a mechanism by which a negative influence can be imposed on the proliferative process (Russell, 1977; Byus *et al.*, 1977b). In support of this proposition, Russell notes that the amount of the Type I enzyme increases during isoproterenol-induced cardiac hypertrophy (Byus *et al.*, 1977a), that Type I protein kinase is induced in 3T3 cells after viral transformation (Gharrett *et al.*, 1976), and that the activation profiles of these isozymes are compatible with this conclusion. This proposal is difficult to prove but deserves further examination; it seems doubtful, however, that this can be the sole explanation of isozyme distribution in view of the existence of a large percentage of the Type I isozyme in tissues such as skeletal muscle and heart (rat) with a virtually zero rate of proliferation.

D. SUBSTRATE SPECIFICITY OF THE cAMP-DEPENDENT PROTEIN KINASE: *IN VITRO* AND *IN VIVO* CRITERIA

As indicated above, the cAMP-dependent protein kinase catalyzes the phosphorylation of a widely diverse range of proteins. Bylund and Krebs

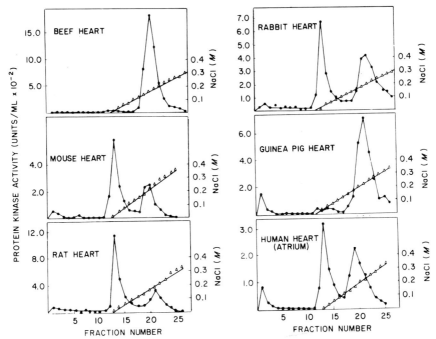

FIG. 15. Variation in the patterns of cAMP-dependent protein kinase isozymes in hearts from several species. Except for mouse and human hearts, crude extracts were prepared by homogenizing tissues at 4° in 10 mM potassium phosphate (4 ml/g), pH 6.8, containing 1 mM EDTA followed by centrifugation at 20,000g for 45 minutes. The rat heart had been perfused 15 minutes (no hormones) before freezing and homogenizing. For mouse and human heart tissues, 8 ml/g homogenates were prepared. DEAE-cellulose columns (0.9 × 4 cm) were equilibrated in the same buffer and 2 ml of supernatant (human = 1.2 ml) were applied. The rat heart extract was always chromatographed simultaneously on an identical column as a control for other extracts using a split delivery from a simple gradient delivery system. After washing each column with ~ 50 ml of buffer, a linear gradient (0–0.4 M) of NaCl was started. Each gradient flask contained 100 ml. A 20 μl aliquot of each fraction (~5 ml) was assayed for protein kinase (●————●) in the presence of 2 μM cAMP. Sodium ion (△————△) was measured by a Beckman cationic electrode. (From Corbin and Keely, 1977.)

(1975) reported that either thermal denaturation or chemical modification converted lysozyme into a substrate for the cAMP-dependent protein kinase. An example of the thermal denaturation effect is illustrated in Fig. 17; the native protein is quite inert, but upon denaturation it becomes an efficient substrate.

Reduced-carboxymethylated (RCMM) lysozyme has an affinity for the protein kinase quite comparable to histone (Table I). The experiments of Bylund and Krebs make an important contribution by emphasizing that the phosphorylation of a protein by the cAMP-dependent protein kinase *in vitro* is a far from reliable guide that the protein is regulated by such a process *in vivo*.

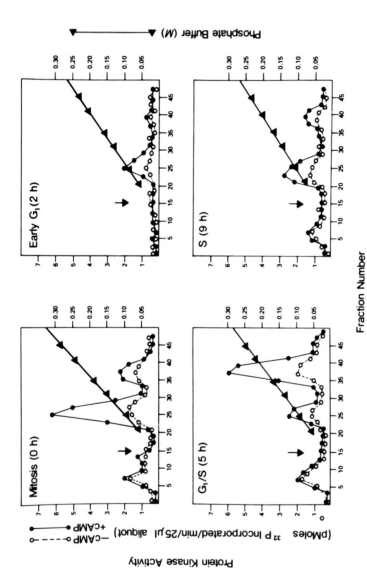

FIG. 16. Elution profile after DEAE-cellulose chromatography of cAMP-dependent protein kinase obtained from synchronized CHO cells at various stages of the cell cycle. Cells were synchronized in mitosis by selective detachment of mitotic cells and cold-acclimated for 3 hours to obtain at least 60×10^6 mitotic cells. The approximate cell cycle position and time after release from mitosis is noted in the figure on the basis of labeling index and mitotic index. Cells, 15×10^6, were harvested at each time indicated. Cells collected at zero hour were harvested directly from the cold-acclimated cells, and the rest of the cells were plated into plastic Petri dishes at low densities and harvested at the times indicated by scraping the cell monolayer with a rubber policeman. A cell extract was applied to a DEAE-52 chromatography column and eluted with a salt gradient. Cell extracts were applied to the columns within 1 hour of the time they were harvested. The arrow in each graph indicated initiation of the gradient. (From M. Costa et al., 1976.)

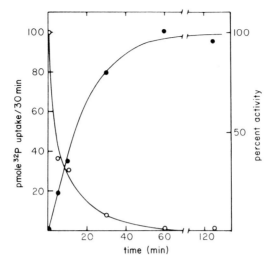

FIG. 17. The effect of thermal denaturation on the activity (O———————O) and phosphorylation (●————————●) of lysozyme. A lysozyme solution [10 mg/ml in 1 mM 2-(N-morpholino)ethane-sulfonic acid, pH 6.5] was heated at 98°. At various times, aliquots were removed, added to an equal volume of the same buffer on ice, and then assayed for enzyme activity and [32] P incorporation. (From Bylund and Krebs, 1975.)

It is of interest, for example, that three of the first proteins used extensively to measure protein kinase activity (histone, casein, and protamine) are prepared by harsh extraction conditions.

Extending from the work of Bylund and Krebs, Kemp *et al.* (1975, 1976) and Engströms' group (Zetterqvist *et al.*, 1976) have utilized synthetic peptides to study the parameters that define substrate specificity. Initially, these

TABLE I

COMPARISON OF KINETIC CONSTANTS OF PROTEIN
SUBSTRATES FOR cAMP-DEPENDENT PROTEIN KINASE[a]

Protein[b]	V_{max} (μmoles ^{32}P/minute/mg enzyme)	K_m (μM)
RCMM–lysozyme (8)	1.28 ± 0.09	22 ± 4
Unfractionated histone (3)	3.95 ± 0.28	33 ± 4
Histone F2b (2)	15.3 ± 1.0	32 ± 17
Whole casein (2)	0.28 ± 0.04	60 ± 6

[a] From Byland and Krebs, 1975.
[b] The number of determinations is given in parentheses.

results suggested that one of the primary features was the presence of a diargininyl peptide on the N-terminal side of the phosphorylatable serine. As indicated (Table II), substitution of one of the arginines by alanine increased the apparent K_m by 300-fold and depressed the V_{max}. Lysine, histidine, and homoarginine (HA) were each found unsatisfactory as a substitute for one of the arginines. Hexapeptides compared favorably as substrates to intact proteins (cf. Tables I and II), but less than six amino acids proved insufficient. An interesting hexapeptide has been synthesized by Kemp *et al.* (1976) in which the key serine is replaced by alanine; the peptide serves as an effective inhibitor of the cAMP-dependent protein kinase. This type of approach may be very useful as a physiological probe if such a peptide were transported into the cell or could be incorporated into liposomes.

The conclusion that substrate specificity is determined by the diargininyl residue has been recently compromised by the elucidation of several of the peptide sequences containing the phosphorylation site from intact proteins (Table III). The diargininyl sequence is present in pyruvate kinase, in the α subunit of phosphorylase kinase, and in a phosphatase inhibitor, but in the β subunit of phosphorylase kinase and histone H1 one of the arginines is substituted by lysine. A basic residue located two amino acids from the phosphoserine on the N-terminal side is a characteristic feature of all the protein substrates, but obviously a full characterization of the structure that defines a protein as a substrate for the protein kinase awaits elucidation.

TABLE II

KINETIC CONSTANTS FOR SYNTHETIC PEPTIDE SUBSTRATES OF cAMP-DEPENDENT PROTEIN KINASE[a]

Peptide	V_{max} (μmoles/minute/mg)	K_m^{app} (μM)
Leu-Arg-Arg-Ala-Ser-Leu-Gly	20.2 ± 0.5	16.0 ± 0.9
Leu-Ala-Arg-Ala-Ser-Leu-Gly	8.7 ± 0.6	4900.0 ± 700
Leu-Arg-Ala-Ala-Ser-Leu-Gly	5.3 ± 0.2	6300.0 ± 400
Leu-Lys-Arg-Ala-Ser-Leu-Gly	17.1 ± 0.4	1400.0 ± 100
Leu-Arg-Lys-Ala-Ser-Leu-Gly	16.9 ± 0.3	260.0 ± 10
Leu-His-Arg-Ala-Ser-Leu-Gly	12.1 ± 0.3	415.0 ± 22
Leu-Arg-His-Ala-Ser-Leu-Gly	6.5 ± 0.1	1340.0 ± 50
Leu-HA-Arg-Ala-Ser-Leu-Gly	10.0 ± 0.3	350.0 ± 20
Leu-Arg-HA-Ala-Ser-Leu-Gly	7.3 ± 0.7	440.0 ± 40
Leu-Arg-Arg-Ala-Ser-Leu-Gly	20.2 ± 0.5	16.0 ± 0.9
Arg-Arg-Ala-Ser-Leu-Gly	17.9 ± 0.5	26.0 ± 2
Arg-Ala-Ser-Leu-Gly	10.2 ± 0.5	4400.0 ± 400
Leu-Arg-Arg-Ala-Ser-Leu	18.1 ± 0.4	57.0 ± 4
Leu-Arg-Arg-Ala-Ser	Negligible	

[a] Adapted from Kemp *et al.*, 1977.

TABLE III

AMINO ACID SEQUENCES AT THE PHOSPHORYLATION SITE OF SUBSTRATES FOR cAMP-DEPENDENT PROTEIN KINASE[a]

Substrate	Sequence
Phosphorylase kinase (β subunit)	Ala-Arg-Thr-Lys-Arg-Ser-Gly-Ser(P)-$\begin{smallmatrix}\text{Val}\\\text{Ile}\end{smallmatrix}$-Tyr-Glu-Pro-Leu-Lys
Histone H1	Ala-Lys-Arg-Lys-Ala-Ser(P)-Gly-Pro-Pro-Val-Ser
Phosphorylase kinase (α subunit)	Phe-Arg-Arg-Leu-Ser(P)-Ile-Ser-Thr-Glu-Ser-Glx-Pro
Pyruvate kinase (rat liver)	Gly-Val-Leu-Arg-Arg-Ala-Ser(P)-Val-Ala-Glx-Leu
Phosphatase inhibitor	Ile-Arg-Arg-Arg-Arg-Pro-Thr(P)-Pro-Ala-Thr
Glycogen synthase (site 2)	$\begin{smallmatrix}\text{Lys}\\\text{Arg}\end{smallmatrix}$ Arg-Ala-Ser(P)-
Glycogen synthase (site 1)	$\begin{smallmatrix}\text{Lys}\\\text{Arg}\end{smallmatrix}$ Ser-Asn-Ser(P)-Val-Asp-Thr-Ser-Ser-Leu-Ser
Histone H2B	Lys-Lys-Arg-Lys-Arg-Ser(P)-Arg-Lys-Glu-Ser(P)-Tyr-Ser-Val-Tyr-Val-Tyr-Lys
β Casein B	Phe-Thr-Glu-Arg-Gln-Ser(P)-Leu-Thr-Leu-Thr-Asp
Myelin basic protein	Lys-Gly-Arg-Gly-Leu-Ser(P)-Leu-Ser-Arg-Phe
	Ser-Gln-Arg-His-Gly-Ser(P)-Lys-Thr-Leu-Ala

[a]Data from Proud *et al.*, 1977, and references cited therein, and Kemp *et al.*, 1975.

It is not possible to evaluate whether the protein is indeed regulated physiologically by cAMP solely from the observation that a protein is phosphorylated *in vitro* by the cAMP-dependent protein kinase. In 1960 Sutherland and Rall defined four criteria that should be met to establish that the actions of a hormone are mediated by cAMP (Sutherland and Rall, 1960). These criteria have served as an invaluable guide over the years, and with these as a model we (Krebs, 1974; Walsh and Ashby, 1973) have defined five criteria that should be satisfied before it can be accepted that a given function of cAMP is mediated by a protein phosphorylation mechanism. These criteria are as follows:

A. A protein that bears a functional relationship to the cAMP-mediated process is phosphorylated *in vitro*.
B. *In vitro* phosphorylation of the protein leads to modified function.
C. A stoichiometric correlation should exist between *in vitro* phosphorylation and modified function.
D. Phosphorylation of the protein should be demonstrated *in vivo* in response to a cAMP signal.
E. Modified function *in vivo* should be demonstrated in response to a cAMP signal.

The importance of these criteria is manifest by the degree of uncertainty that exists for many potential phosphoproteins. Of all the suggested substrates, only one—phosphorylase kinase—fulfills all five criteria. As indicated in Fig. 18, phosphorylase kinase can be phosphorylated *in vitro* by the cAMP-dependent protein kinase (criterion A), phosphorylation is associated with modified function (criterion B), and there is a close correlation between the degree of phosphorylation and the degree of activation (criterion C). In Fig. 19 is shown the results of a study of the phosphorylation (critierion D) and activation (criterion E) of phosphorylase kinase in perfused rat heart in response to a cAMP signal. A close correlation is observed for both these functions (i.e., activity and phosphorylation) both *in vitro* and *in vivo*. It is important that the indications from *in vitro* experiments should be confirmed by experiments with intact cells. It should be appreciated that the chemical modification of a protein often leads to a variation in the function of that protein; studies with many chemical modification reagents have repeatedly emphasized this point. The action of the cAMP-dependent protein kinase results in the chemical modification of the protein; thus, by corollary, it can be expected that such phosphorylation may modify one or several of the catalytic properties of the enzyme. Caution must therefore be exercised in inferring a physiological consequence of such an *in vitro* action.

Nevertheless, a growing number of proteins are beginning to be found to meet one or several of the above criteria. As an example, ribosomal proteins

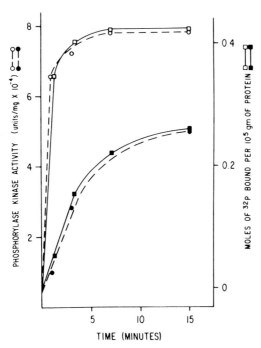

FIG. 18. The effect of cyclic AMP-dependent protein kinase on the phosphorylation and activation of phosphorylase kinase. A reaction mixture containing purified, nonactivated phosphorylase kinase (3.68 mg) was incubated at 20° in the presence (open symbols) or absence (filled symbols) of purified cyclic AMP-dependent protein kinase. (From Walsh and Ashby, 1973.)

and histone H1 have each been shown to be phosphorylated in response to cAMP both *in vitro* (criterion A) and *in vivo* (criterion D). The major question which remains with these proteins is to identify the function modified by phosphorylation (criteria B and E). As an example of a second type of currently common situation, it has been shown that both glycogen synthase and triglyceride lipase are phosphorylated *in vitro* (criterion A), that such *in vitro* phosphorylation leads to a change in activity (criterion B), and that a close correlation exists between the modification of activity and the degree of phosphorylation (criterion C). Changes in activity have been observed *in vivo* in response to a cAMP signal (criterion E), but as yet phosphorylation of the protein has not been demonstrated *in vivo* (criterion D). In this situation, a second element is beginning to be appreciated. As documented below, there are two sites phosphorylated in glycogen synthase, each of which modifies activity but only one of which is apparently regulated in response to cAMP (see Section IV,D). Thus it may not always be easy to attribute a modified function to a direct effect of cAMP.

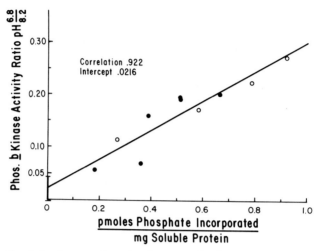

FIG. 19. Correlation between the epinephrine-stimulated activation and phosphorylation of cardiac phosphorylase kinase. Rat hearts were perfused with 1.5 mCi of ^{32}P for 30 minutes before stimulation with 1 μM epinephrine. Data points were obtained at various times post-epinephrine addition or removal. [^{32}P]Phosphorylase kinase was determined by antibody pre-cipitation. (From T. E. McCullough and D. A. Walsh, unpublished observations.)

III. APPROACHES FOR EVALUATING THE FUNCTION OF cAMP-DEPENDENT PROTEIN KINASE

A. ACTIVATION OF THE PROTEIN KINASE *IN VIVO*

As indicated above (Section II,B), it is still uncertain as to whether dissoci-ation of the protein kinase is necessary for activation. Nevertheless, a pri-mary effort, spearheaded by the group of Corbin and Park, has been made to evaluate the dissociation and corollary activation of the protein kinase in *in vivo* (i.e., intact cell) situations. The approach makes use of the property that activation of the enzyme is not simply the binding of a ligand to a protein but involves a secondary reaction of dissociation. In consequence, inactivation requires not only the removal of ligand but the reassociation of subunits. It is virtually inconceivable that conditions could be found to "freeze" the bind-ing of a ligand to a protein so that the activity of an enzyme, as modified by a simple allosteric activation *in vivo*, would be reflected by the assay of that enzyme under *in vitro* conditions following extraction. Thus, no studies are pursued to examine the state of allosteric activation *in vivo* from subsequent *in vitro* type assays. For the protein kinase, however, conditions have been sought that would "freeze" the association–dissociation state of the enzyme during extraction. Subsequent assay of extracts, assuming that the association-dissociation state had been stabilized, could, by measuring the degree of cAMP dependence, reflect the amount of holoenzyme and the amount of free catalytic subunit. This is often presented on the basis of the activity ratio of

$$\frac{\text{activity} - \text{cAMP}}{\text{activity} + \text{cAMP}}$$

This type of measurement is valid providing the following criteria apply:

1. During the extraction procedure no reassociation of the subunits occurs.
2. During the extraction procedure no dissociation of the subunits occurs.
3. The assay conditions are established such that the measured activity or activity ratio does not reflect the concentration of endogenous components of the extraction media other than the protein kinase.

In general, the techniques that are required to meet the first criterion have received the greatest attention. This is a pragmatic approach, but as such it should be appreciated that an understanding of the action of the hormone can be inferred only on the assumption that dissociation of the protein kinase is essential for activation. Such an approach does not provide evidence that dissociation is the mechanism of protein kinase activation; an often preconceived assumption (*vide* Section II,B).

The initial studies of *in vivo* activation occurred coincidentally with the identification of the parameters that affect association–dissociation (see Section II,c), and Corbin *et al.* (1975b) recognized that the procedures of tissue extraction should be chosen dependent on whether the tissue contained primarily Type I, Type II, or both types I and II isozymes (see Figs. 5 and 15). For the tissues containing Type II isozyme, Corbin *et al.* (1975a) proposed that tissue extraction should be performed in media containing 0.05 M NaF and 0.5 M NaCl. Under these conditions, reassociation of the enzyme at 0° is substantially blocked (see Fig. 11, lower curve), whereas in the absence of the high salt a rapid reassociation occurs. Under such extraction conditions, the assay of protein kinase for either control or hormone-pretreated tissue is linear with time, and the degree of cAMP dependence is independent of the dilution of extract used (Fig. 20). This is an important criterion because it infers that carry-over of endogenous components, such as cAMP, into the assay either are at too low a concentration to affect the assay or are sufficiently high to be saturating at all tissue concentrations measured. For most tissues with respect to cAMP it is probably the former, but this should not be assumed for any new parameter or tissue stimulation under investigation.

It is also evident, however, that the activation of protein kinase may be regulated by more than just cAMP, the best current example being hemin (see Section IV,B). In consequence, the conditions of assay must be carefully

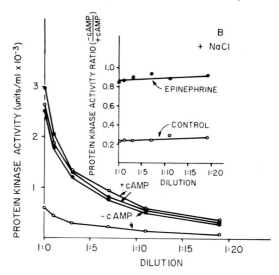

FIG. 20. Effect of dilution on the cAMP dependence of the protein kinase in crude extracts. Fat pads were incubated for 15 minutes without hormone and then incubated in fresh medium for 10 minutes in the presence (●————●) or absence (○————○) of $11 \mu M$ epinephrine. The tissues were homogenized (1 ml per gm) in cold 10 mM potassium phosphate, 10 mM EDTA, 0.5 M NaCl, and 0.5 mM 1-methyl-3-isobutylxanthine. After centrifugation for 5 minutes at 12,000g, the clear infranatant fractions were diluted as indicated in the above buffer (plus NaCl). In the undiluted extracts the cAMP was $\sim 2 \times 10^{-7}$ M in the absence and $\sim 6 \times 10^{-7}$ M in the presence of epinephrine. Inset: activity ratios plotted as functions of dilution. (From Corbin *et al.*, 1973.)

evaluated for each new tissue investigated. Extraction conditions for the Type I isozyme differ from those used for the Type II because the former is dissociated by high salt (Fig. 10). Maintenance of the dissociated state relies primarily on the property that association is relatively slow at 0°. For tissues that contain both isozymes, some compromise salt concentration is generally used (Cherrington *et al.* 1976). Corbin *et al.* (1975a) proposed that conditions should be chosen to minimize cAMP phosphodiesterase activity in the extract because, as stated by them, hydrolysis of cAMP in extracts after homogenization but before assay of the protein kinase can introduce a source of error in determination of the activation state of the enzyme. In consequence, the extraction media in their studies include the phosphodiesterase inhibitor 1-methyl-3-isobutylxanthine. In a subsequent paper (Cherrington *et al.*, 1976) this group indicated that the omission of methyl isobutylxanthine from the extraction media resulted in lower expressed protein kinase activities in glucagon-stimulated liver cells (Table IV). These observations emphasize that many such "activation measurements" may well be a reflection more of cAMP concentrations in the homogenized extract and not of protein kinase activation in the tissue.

TABLE IV

EFFECT OF 1-METHYL-3-ISOBUTYLXANTHINE ON DETERMINATION OF cAMP-DEPENDENT
PROTEIN KINASE ACTIVITY RATIO[a]

	Protein kinase activity ratio (−cAMP/+cAMP)			
Additions	Saline	Glucagon		
Methylisobutylxanthine (0.5 mM) + EDTA (10 mM)	0.28	0.70,	0.61,	0.50
Methylisobutylxanthine (0.5 mM)	0.29	0.58,	0.62,	0.51
None	0.26	0.38,	0.48,	0.32

[a] Homogenates (40 ml/gm) of liver cells previously exposed to saline or glucagon (2–5×10^{-10} M) for 2 minutes were prepared in buffer containing both Na_2EDTA and methylisobutylxanthine, methylisobutylxanthine alone, or neither agent. Homogenates were assayed after 30 minutes at 0° for protein kinase activity. Data in each vertical column are from one experiment. (Adapted from Cherrington *et al.*, 1976.)

Corbin *et al.* (1973) have also shown that the addition of cAMP to a control extract maintained at 0° resulted in the activation of the protein kinase, thus minimizing the effects of hormone added to the intact tissue. These data indicate that the conditions of extraction are not sufficient to prevent cAMP-induced dissociation of the enzyme during the homogenization. It has, however, been shown that the protein kinase activity ratio of the subsequent homogenates remains stable for at least 1 hour even for intermediary levels of protein kinase activation (Fig. 21). This type of control and the linearity of the subsequent assay thus provides confidence that, following the initial homogenization period, spurious dissociation or association is not a significant factor.

There remains, however, the always difficult problem of attempting to evaluate whether the disruption of the tissue by homogenization perturbs the equilibrium of the system. The history of measurements of the activation state of phosphorylase and phosphorylase kinase speaks to the complications of attempting to establish conditions for maintaining an enzyme in an active or inactive state, especially the latter. It is worth noting that different procedures are required to measure these parameters in smooth muscle, cardiac muscle, and skeletal muscle. Corbin *et al.* (1975b) have attempted to address this problem. As indicated in Table V, they have provided evidence that if charcoal is added to the extraction media, the effect of addition of exogenous cAMP is eliminated. Under these conditions an epinephrine effect is still manifest. Thus it is argued that the activation of the protein kinase, observed upon addition of epinephrine, must occur while the cell is intact and not as a result of a cAMP-stimulated event occurring during extraction. The data are consistent with that conclusion, but neither in subsequent papers from that laboratory nor in those from others has this seemingly very important control

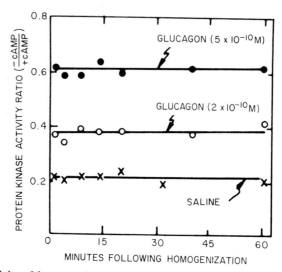

FIG. 21. Stability of the protein kinase activity ratio in whole homogenates of liver cells made from hepatocytes previously exposed to saline or glucagon for 2 minutes (from Cherrington *et al.*, 1976).

been performed. It would appear to these reviewers to be incautious to assume that under the wide variety of conditions of hormonal stimulation of tissues which have been studied by Corbin and other workers, no interaction of cAMP with protein kinase would occur during the extraction period. The investigation (Table V), as presented by Corbin, was designed to eliminate the possibility that a restricted pool of cAMP became available to the protein kinase upon tissue disruption. Equally important should be the consideration that protein kinase located in association with different organelles may be activated to different degrees by a cAMP signal because of heterogeneous distribution of cAMP throughout the cell.

The number of experiments utilizing the charcoal extraction control (Table V) has been limited. In the primary experiment presented (Table V), the interpretation is complicated by the observation that the addition of charcoal increased both cAMP-dependent and cAMP-independent activities by more than 50%. Although the activity ratio is unaffected, such a number is compromised if the denominator in the calculation is not constant. In preliminary experiments, we (W. K. Palmer and D. A. Walsh, unpublished observations) have observed that if exogenous protein kinase holoenzyme (inactive) is added to the tissue homogenate of glucagon-stimulated liver, the exogenous protein kinase is activated by the extraction procedure. This control therefore indicates that the protein kinase activity of the extract reflects the cAMP concentration. The interpretation of data of "*in vivo* activated protein kinase" would be far

TABLE V

EFFECT OF ADDING CHARCOAL TO THE HOMOGENIZING MEDIUM ON PROTEIN KINASE ACTIVATION BY
EPINEPHRINE IN PERFUSED HEARTS[a]

Perfusate additions	Additions to homogenizing medium	Protein kinase activity (units/ml)		Activity ratio (−cAMP/+cAMP)
		−cAMP	+cAMP	
0	None	683	3250	0.21
0	Charcoal (10 mg/ml)	1020	4960	0.21
0	cAMP (0.1 μM)	2030	3270	0.62
0	Charcoal (10 mg/ml) (+cAMP 0.1 μM added later)	1020	4400	0.23
Epinephrine (0.4 μM)	None	1495	3030	0.49
Epinephrine (0.4 μM)	Charcoal (10 mg/ml)	1660	4120	0.41

[a] Homogenization (10 mg/gm) was performed using one up and one down turn of the homogenizer in cold 10 mM potassium phosphate (pH 6.8), 10 mM EDTA, and 0.5 M MIX. Either charcoal (10 mg/ml) or cAMP (final concentration, 0.1 μM) was added to the medium before homogenization as indicated. In one case cAMP was added after homogenization. The homogenates were immediately centrifuged at 20,000g for 5 minutes, and 10 μl aliquots of the supernatant fractions were assayed for protein kinase activity in the presence and absence of 2 μM cAMP (5 minute assay). Where indicated, epinephrine was present for 2 minutes (from Corbin *et al.*, 1975b).

more secure if extraction conditions could be found such that endogenously added protein kinase was not activated during the extraction even upon addition of exogenous cAMP, and that exogenous protein kinase was not activated by endogenous cAMP. Until such conditions are established (i.e., criterion 2 above) the interpretations of "*in vivo* activation" must be made only with extreme caution.

If one assumes that the reservations expressed above can be eliminated, then the methodology permits the establishment of an additional link in the chain of events between hormonal stimulation and the resultant physiological event. Soderling *et al.* (1973) and Skala and Knight (1977) have studied the relationship between protein kinase activation and adipocyte lipolysis. Both epinephrine-stimulated elevation of cAMP and insulin depression of the epinephrine effect are coordinated with equivalent changes in protein kinase activation (Fig. 22). When this is expressed as a relationship between activity ratio and concentration of cAMP, simple saturation kinetics are observed (Fig. 23). Interestingly, however, half-maximal activation of protein kinase is achieved at a concentration corresponding to 1.5 μM cAMP, a value considerably higher than the *in vitro* half-maximal effective concentra-

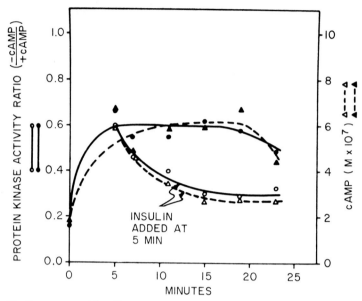

FIG. 22. Time course of the effects of epinephrine and insulin on protein kinase activity ratio and cAMP concentration. Two groups of fat pad incubations were both exposed to 11 μM epinephrine for the designated periods of time. After 5 minutes, 6.9 nM insulin (final concentration) was added to one group. The protein kinase activity in the infranatant fractions was assayed in the absence and presence of 1.33 μM exogenous cAMP. Symbols: ($\bullet$, $\blacktriangle$), incubation with epinephrine; ($\circ$, $\triangle$), epinephrine plus insulin (from Soderling *et al.*, 1973).

tion with either histone or glycogen synthase as substrate (see discussion relating to Fig. 14).

Skala and Knight (1977) suggested that the significant linear regression between the reciprocal values of cAMP and protein kinase activation (insert, Fig. 23) implied that the tissue does not contain a pool of bound cAMP which is unavailable to activate the protein kinase. This conclusion is valid if it could be assumed that the relative concentration of available cAMP did not reflect the concentration of cAMP in the pool.

Skala and Knight (1977) also showed that there was a good correlation between glycerol release and the protein kinase activity ratio at low levels of stimulation but that stimulation of the protein kinase above an activity ratio of 0.52 did not result in further glycerol release (Fig. 24). This result suggests either that the potential to stimulate protein kinase exceeds the actual need to modulate the physiological event and/or that not all processes in the cell are regulated over the same range of protein kinase activation. These data, indicating the role of protein kinase activation in lipolysis, serve to substantiate the extensive work that has occurred primarily in Steinberg's laboratory

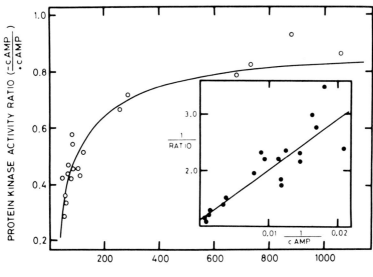

FIG. 23. The relationship between protein kinase activity ratio and the concentration of cyclic AMP in brown fat from 24-day-old rats. Pieces of brown fat were incubated for 20 minutes at 37° in Krebs–Ringer bicarbonate buffer, pH 7.4, containing 3% bovine serum albumin and 5 mM glucose, with or without 10 mM theophylline and with varying concentrations of norepinephrine (from Skala and Knight, 1977).

(see Steinberg, 1976, for review) showing that triglyceride lipase exists in phospho- (active) and dephospho- (inactive) forms (Fig. 25).

An integral relationship has been proposed from a substantial number of laboratories supporting a key role for cyclic AMP in the regulation of cellular proliferation and differentiation (for review, see Pastan *et al.*, 1975; Friedman *et al.*, 1976; Ryan and Heidrick, 1974). Changes in the activation of protein kinase have been proposed to be associated with cAMP-induced modification of cellular growth patterns. Thus, Li *et al.* (1977) have shown that morphological changes in Chinese hamster ovary cells can be induced with exogenous addition of dibutyryl cAMP and that such induction is associated with a prolonged activation of the protein kinase. In these same cells prostaglandin E_1 elevated cAMP and maximally activated the protein kinase, but the duration of the response for both was short and no morphological transformation occurred. Li *et al.* (1977) proposed that the limited duration of the prostaglandin response was insufficient for the sustained modifications required for the morphological effects, thus implying that one method by which different processes could be regulated differentially in the cell is by the duration of protein kinase activation.

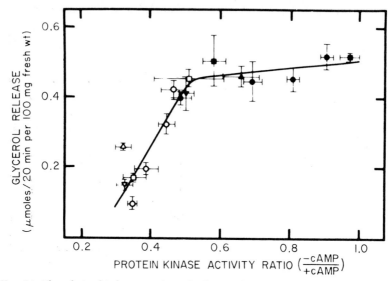

FIG. 24. The relationship between glycerol release and protein kinase activity ratio in brown fat from 24-day-old rats. The points represent the mean ± S.E.M. of results obtained with tissue from different animals within a given set of incubation conditions. The conditions are represented as follows (with the number of incubations in parentheses): (∇), no additions (6); (O), plus $0.05\,\mu M$ (3); $0.5\,\mu M$ (3); $5.0\,\mu M$ (3); or $50\,\mu M$ (5) norepinephrine; ($\square$), plus insulin, with or without $50\,\mu M$ norepinephrine (4); ($\triangle$), plus propranolol in the presence of $50\,\mu M$ norepinephrine (3). Closed symbols represent the same conditions and number of incubations in the presence of 10 mM theophylline. (From Skala and Knight, 1977.)

Russell's group (Byus *et al.*, 1976, 1977a,b) has proposed that the activation of the Type I isozyme is a primary parameter for regulation of cell growth, presenting evidence (although still preliminary) that isoproterenol-induced cardiac hypertrophy occurs consequentially to an elevation of the Type I isozyme and that the activation of the Type I isozyme is a positive component in events promoted in lymphocytes stimulated by a mitogenic signal. In contrast, activation of the Type II isozyme is proposed to represent a mechanism by which a negative influence can be imposed on the proliferative response.

Data of this type emphasize a primary problem of interpretation: It is difficult to establish that the activation of either or both of the isozymes of protein kinase is a *necessary* event for changes in the growth pattern of the cells or any other physiological event. Possibly the best way to establish the cause–effect relationships will be with genetically manipulated cells. This approach will be discussed below (Section III,D).

The specific activation of one of the two isozymes of protein kinase has also been observed by Means *et al.* (1976) for Sertoli cells in response to

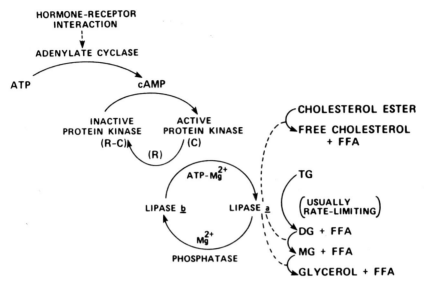

FIG. 25. Mechanism of activation of hormone-sensitive lipase in adipose tissue. Solid arrows: well-characterized steps. Dotted lines: uncertainty as to whether or not a single enzyme protein (hormone-sensitive lipase) is responsible for catalyzing the several acyl hydrolase reactions demonstrated or whether there are multiple enzyme proteins all bound in a common lipid-rich particle (from Steinberg, 1976).

FSH. It is not known how differential activation of isozymes could be achieved; presumably, some parameter, such as those discussed above (Section II,C), must be involved in establishing a modified range of cAMP sensitivity.

Byus *et al.* (1977b) have also examined the activation of protein kinase as a function of time following partial hepatectomy. The biphasic pattern that has been observed for cAMP levels (as a function of time after hepatectomy) was also seen for changes in protein kinase. For this and other systems, Russell's group has proposed that one of the actions of the activation of protein kinase is to modulate ornithine decarboxylase by stimulation of its synthesis. Russell's and many other laboratories support the concept that the regulation of this enzyme is a key to the modulation of cell growth. Again in this system one is faced with the tricky proposition of evaluating cause–effect relationships.

In a variety of endocrine organs, steroidogenesis is regulated by polypeptide hormones. In a substantial number of these, cAMP has been implicated as the second messenger, and the systems have been shown to obey the four criteria defined by Sutherland. More recently, the conclusion of cAMP involvement has been questioned based on data that showed a marked disparity between dose–response curves for cAMP production and steroidogenesis; correlations between these parameters and protein kinase activation have been examined by several groups (Cooke *et al.*, 1976; Richardson and Schulster, 1973; Podesta *et al.*, 1976; Sharma *et al.*, 1976; Clark *et al.*, 1976). Two examples are presented in Figs. 26 and 27 for the regulation of corticosterone production by ACTH and of testosterone production by LH, respectively. In these systems it is observed that at low concentrations of polypeptide hormone significant steroid production occurs without either elevation of cAMP or activation of protein kinase. Higher doses of the stimulating hormone generally do elevate both these latter parameters.

There are many possible explanations of these data, and there is no additional information that permits a clear delineation between the alternatives. The simplest explanation is that protein kinase activation is not involved in steroidogenesis. Among more extreme alternatives is the possibility that the protein kinase and cAMP are, by some means, compartmentalized. For Leydig cells, protein kinase activation and cAMP production are not coincident; apparently, in these as in some other systems, cAMP production appears to exceed that needed for maximum protein kinase activation. A

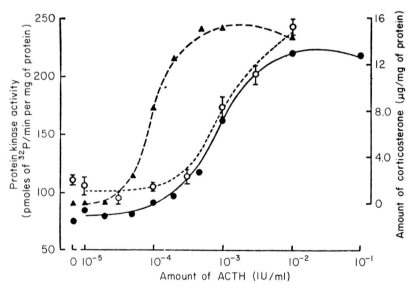

FIG. 26. Variation of protein kinase activity with ACTH concentration in isolated adrenal cells. Protein kinase activity was measured in the sonicates derived from isolated adrenal cells that had been exposed to ACTH for 2 minutes (○) and 20 minutes (●). Corticosterone production (▲) was estimated after 20 minutes of exposure to the hormone. Where shown, vertical bars refer to S.E.M. of estimates on quadruplicate incubates. Other values shown are means of estimates on duplicate incubations (from Richardson and Schulster, 1973).

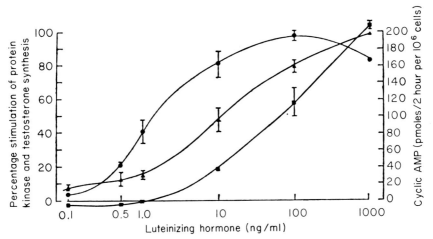

FIG. 27. Luteinizing hormone dose–response curves for protein kinase activation, production of cyclic AMP, and testosterone in Leydig cells. For testosterone (●) and protein kinase (▲) the results presented are the means ± S.E.M. of four separate experiments carried out with Leydig cells prepared from 16 rats (four rats/experiment). The cells were preincubated for 2 hours at 32° under CO_2+O_2 (5:95) and then incubated for a further 20 minutes (for protein kinase assay) and 2 hours (for testosterone and cyclic AMP assays) with different amounts of luteinizing hormone without changing the incubation medium. Results are expressed as percentage of maximum stimulation obtained with luteinizing hormone. The means ± range of duplicates for cyclic AMP production (■) with different amounts of luteinizing hormone are given from one typical experiment (from Cooke *et al.*, 1976).

second example of this latter phenomenon has been described by Field *et al.* (1975) for the stimulation of thyroid cells by TSH. Full activation of protein kinase of these cells is obtained by approximately a 5-fold increase in cAMP, whereas higher levels of TSH result in up to a 17-fold increase in cyclic nucleotide levels with no apparent additional effect on the protein kinase. Evidently, some (possibly all) cells have the potential to be stimulated so that levels of cAMP exceed that needed for protein kinase activation. It is not known whether this infers that there is "spare cAMP" as there have been suggested to be "spare hormone receptors," or whether higher levels of cAMP may modulate cellular events by a process not involving protein phosphorylation.

In a recent paper from Corbin's laboratory (Corbin *et al.*, 1977), the following statement was made: "The theory (a proposal presented concerning activation of membrane protein kinases) obviously assumes that cAMP causes physical dissociation of the holoenzyme into regulatory and catalytic subunits in the cell. Although such *in vivo* dissociation has not been established with certainty, its physiological sense is made clear from . . . [reference to previous discussion in the paper]." This statement sums up the current state of the art. The criteria expressed at the beginning of this section have yet to be fully met and, in consequence, experimental data on activation *in vivo* must be viewed with reservation. Currently, the "physiological sense" directs us into accepting these observations, but we must be cautious not to permit a mass of data accumulated within these limitations to obscure its validation.

B. Translocation of the Subunits of cAMP-Dependent Protein Kinase *In Vivo*

Hofmann *et al.* (1977) have provided an accurate determination of the total amount of each of the subunits of the cAMP-dependent protein kinase in tissues. Their data (Table VI) clearly establish that for most tissues the concentrations of the regulatory subunit and the catalytic subunit are present in essentially an equimolar ratio. These data provide for the important consideration that in unstimulated tissue there exist essentially no free subunits. If dissociation of the protein kinase is essential for activation, it is relevant to evaluate whether the isolated subunit has a specific function that it could not perform as a component of a larger macromolecular complex.

TABLE VI

CATALYTIC AND REGULATORY SUBUNIT CONCENTRATIONS IN RABBIT TISSUES BASED ON MEASUREMENTS OF ENZYME ACTIVITY AND CYCLIC AMP BINDING CAPACITY[a]

Tissue	N	Catalytic subunit		Regulatory subunit	R/C
		Activity (units/kg w.wt.)	Concentration (μmoles/kg w.wt.)	Concentration (μmoles/kg w.wt.)	
Skeletal muscle	6	134 ± 7	0.32 ± 0.01	0.30 ± 0.02	0.94
Heart	6	162 ± 9	0.38 ± 0.02	0.31 ± 0.02	0.82
Kidney	6	144 ± 4	0.34 ± 0.01	0.31 ± 0.02	0.77
Liver	8	120 ± 7	0.28 ± 0.02	0.25 ± 0.01	0.89
Brain (extract)	6	180 ± 12	0.42 ± 0.07	0.40 ± 0.01	0.95
Brain (particulate)	4	146 ± 15	0.36 ± 0.01	0.36 ± 0.01	1.00
Brain (total)		331	0.78	0.76	0.97

[a]Molar concentrations of catalytic subunit were calculated utilizing as a basis (a) the known specific activity and molecular weight of the C subunit, 10.3 μmole/minute/mg and 40,000 daltons, respectively, and (b) the extent of tissue dilution occurring in the homogenization procedure. Molar concentrations of R were calculated assuming that 1 mole of cyclic AMP binds to 1 mole of R. The values are expressed as means $\pm$ S.E.M. N = number of animals used. The abbreviation w.wt. stands for wet weight of tissue. For skeletal muscle, heart, kidney, and liver, the molar concentrations are arbitrarily based on the amount of subunits in the soluble fraction. (From Hofmann *et al.*, 1977.)

Initial studies in Korenman's, Jungmann's, and our own laboratories have provided a potential rationale for dissociation. If, for example, liver is perfused with dibutyryl cAMP, then a substantial component of the catalytic activity of the protein kinase becomes associated with the nuclear fraction (Fig. 28; Castagna et al., 1975). The association is time-dependent, with maximum activity being associated with the nuclei at 8 minutes and then slowly returning to normal values (Fig. 29). From a detailed characterization of the protein kinase activities based on many criteria, it has been validated that the protein kinase activity that becomes associated with the nucleus on stimulation of the tissue is free ca¹alytic subunit derived from the cytosol. Identical results have been obtained with glucagon stimulation of liver (Palmer et al., 1974). Under similar activation conditions, no regulatory subunit becomes bound to the nucleus.

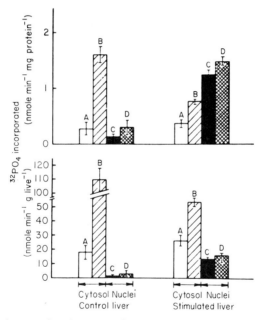

FIG. 28. Cytoplasmic and nuclear protein kinase activity in control and Bt₂-cAMP-stimulated perfused rat liver. Livers were removed 8 minutes after addition of either water or of $100 \mu M$ Bt₂-cAMP addition to the perfusate. Protein kinase activity in cytoplasmic and nuclear extracts were determined in either the absence (A, C) or presence (B, D) of $2.5 \mu M$ cAMP, respectively. Protein kinase activity was corrected for incorporation in the absence of exogenous substrate. Data are presented on the basis of nmoles ³²PO₄ incorporated per minute into histone either per mg of cytoplasmic or nuclear protein (top) or per gm of liver (bottom). The data is given ± S.E.M. calculated from 3 livers per point, 2 enzyme concentrations per liver, 2 determinations per enzyme concentration (from Castagna et al., 1975).

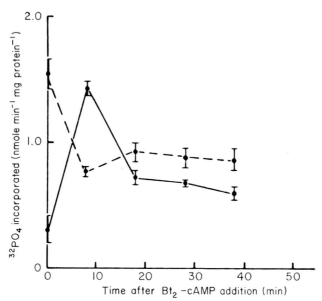

FIG. 29. Time course of the effect of Bt$_2$-cAMP addition to perfused rat liver on nuclear and cytoplasmic protein kinase activity. The protein kinase activity in cytoplasmic (●----●) and nuclear (●————●) extracts is expressed in nmoles ^{32}PO$_4$ incorporated per minute per mg of cytoplasmic or nuclear protein, respectively. Data are corrected for incorporation in the absence of endogenous substrate. The bars represent ± S.E.M. calculated from each of three animals for the 0, 18, 28 and 38 minute time points and from 6 animals for the 8 minute time point (from Castagna *et al.*, 1975).

As a consequence of these results, the attractive theory has been proposed that hormones stimulate the activation of cytosolic cAMP-dependent protein kinase, the protein kinase dissociates, and a portion of the free catalytic subunit migrates to the nucleus where it is responsible for the phosphorylation of proteins involved in the regulation of gene activity. One possible candidate for the latter is histone H1 which, as Langan (1969, 1973b) has previously indicated, is phosphorylated in liver in response to glucagon. This mechanism is presented schematically in Fig. 30.

Keely *et al.* (1975) have questioned whether the association of the catalytic subunit with nuclei and other subcellular organelles occurs in the intact cell or as an artifact during preparation. In support of the latter, they have provided evidence that the binding of catalytic subunit to the particulate fraction of cardiac muscle was not decreased by either trypsin treatment or boiling of the membrane fractions, but that it could be decreased by the addition of 150 m*M* KCl. In addition, catalytic subunit derived from heart also bound membrane fractions derived from *Escherichia coli*, thus raising the question of whether there was any specificity and/or selectivity of the

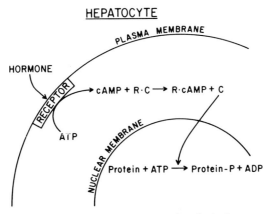

FIG. 30. Schematic representation of the mechanism by which glucagon may influence nuclear protein kinase.

process. The results of Keely *et al.* (1975) definitely demand that caution be exercised in evaluating possible phenomena concerning the translocation of protein kinase subunits to subcellular fractions.

Support of the idea that translocation of catalytic subunit is of physiological consequence has come from the studies of Steiner's laboratory (see Steiner *et al.*, 1977, for review). This group has pursued a long sequence of studies on immunocytochemical determination of cyclic nucleotide function. They have determined that, following the injection of glucagon into rats, an enhanced fluorescence was detected in the nucleus at 2 and 10 minutes postglucagon injection by the use of catalytic subunit specific antibody. Because very little cAMP-dependent protein kinase is present in control nuclei, Steiner's data would support, by an entirely different experimental approach, the hypothesis that translocation of catalytic subunit to the nucleus from the cytoplasm occurs following hormonal stimulation of the tissue. This group has also reported that levels of catalytic subunit in the nucleus are enhanced during the process of liver regeneration, presumably as a consequence of elevated cAMP.

It is apparent that studies of potential translocation of protein kinase subunits are not easy and that measurement of activities in cellular fractions may well be compromised by the difficulty of determining the extent of nonspecific association. The results of this type of study are presented below, but must be interpreted within the reservations expressed above.

The translocation of the catalytic subunit of cytosolic protein kinase has been reported to occur in porcine ovaries in response to exogenous 8-*p*-chlorophenylthio cAMP (Spielvogel *et al.*, 1977). This result was observed with nuclei isolated by both aqueous and nonaqueous methods, thus providing additional support to the theory that the event occurs in the intact cell. Translocation of the catalytic subunit to the nucleus has also been reported for glial tumor cells stimulated by norepinephrine (Salem and De Vellis, 1976), and during the transsynaptic induction of tyrosine hydroxylase (E. Costa *et al.* 1976a). In the latter system a defined sequence of events has been detailed, as indicated in Fig. 31. The activation of protein kinase (as indicated by the activity measured in the absence of cAMP) is initiated by an elevation of cAMP [in Fig. 31 this is expressed as cAMP/cGMP ratio, but this reflects an elevation of cAMP (E. Costa *et al.*, 1976a)]. Subsequent to protein kinase activation, total cytosol activity is decreased as the catalytic subunit is transferred to the particulate fraction.

It should be noted that the change in activity of particulate protein kinase does not exactly mirror the time course of protein kinase activation but that the peak effect is offset by several hours. If "apparent translocation" was

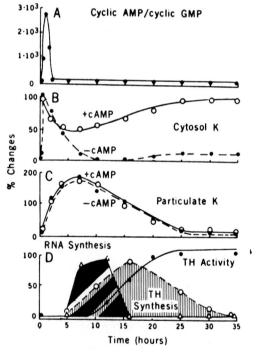

FIG. 31. Sequence of molecular events taking place in chromaffin cells during the trans-synaptic induction of tyrosine hydroxylase (TH) elicited by exposure to 4°C for 2 hours. The adrenal medullas were dissected stereomicroscopically. A, Percent of change in the ratio of cyclic AMP to cyclic GMP concentrations (fundamentally an indication of changes in cAMP levels); B, activity of cytosol kinase (K); C, activity of particulate kinase (K); D, Synthesis of RNA, TH molecules, and activity of TH measured *in vivo*. (From Kurosawa *et al.*, 1976.)

simply a reflection of artifactual binding, then this time offset would not be expected to be observed. Presumably, translocation to the particulate fraction is a time-dependent, and potentially regulated, process. The accumulation of maximum levels of protein kinase in the particulate (nuclear) fractions coincides with the onset of RNA synthesis. Subsequent elevation of tyrosine hydroxylase activity is a result of enhanced synthesis. The data presented provide for a logical time sequence of events, but additional evidence is still required to establish the cause–event relationship of the various observations.

Corbin *et al.* (1977) have studied the distribution of cardiac cAMP-dependent protein kinase in response to epinephrine stimulation. They observed that either epinephrine alone, or epinephrine plus 1-methyl-3-isobutylxanthine, increased the cAMP content of both particulate and supernatant fractions, and also that the increase was associated with the translocation of a large percentage of the catalytic subunit from the particulate to the supernatant fraction (Table VII). In contrast, distribution of the regulatory subunit was not significantly affected by this treatment. A schematic representation of the mechanism (Fig. 32) has been proposed, and it has been suggested that the purpose of such a mechanism would be to permit a differential regulation of populations of protein kinase such that protein kinase in the vicinity of the adenyl cyclase might be preferentially activated in comparison to the cytosolic enzyme.

C. cAMP ANALOGS AS PROBES OF cAMP ACTION

The use of analogs of cAMP to probe the mechanism of action of the cyclic nucleotide was first described by Posternak *et al.* (1962) with the synthesis of dibutyryl cAMP. Subsequently, Miller's group (for review, see Miller, 1977) has synthesized a very large number of these compounds and characterized their properties as both activators of the cAMP-dependent protein kinase and as substrates of phosphodiesterase. This has provided a tool for examining the role of protein kinase as a mediator of cAMP action in the intact cell. Miller *et al.* (1975) have proposed the use of an equation of the type:

$$\log[\text{cAMP analog}]_{50} = a + b \log(S) + c \log(K_a)$$

in which $[\text{cAMP analog}]_{50}$ is the concentration of cAMP analog added to the system to produce 50% of a maximum effect of an observed physiological event, (S) is the value of

$$\frac{\text{rate of hydrolysis of cAMP}}{\text{rate of hydrolysis of analog}}$$

TABLE VII

CONCENTRATIONS OF cAMP, R SUBUNIT, AND C SUBUNIT IN SUPERNATANT AND PARTICULATE FRACTIONS OF PERFUSED RABBIT HEART[a]

Experiment no.	Addition to perfusate	cAMP		R subunit (RC + free R-cAMP)		C subunit (RC + free C)	
		Supernatant	Particulate	Supernatant	Particulate	Supernatant	Particulate
1	None	0.07 ± 0.01	0.09 ± 0.01	0.27 ± 0.03	0.14 ± 0.03	0.30 ± 0.02	0.14 ± 0.02
	Epi (1 μM)	0.11 ± 0.01	0.15 ± 0.01	0.24 ± 0.00	0.14 ± 0.03	0.42 ± 0.02	0.10 ± 0.00
2	None	0.08 ± 0.02	0.16 ± 0.03	0.33 ± 0.02	0.31 ± 0.04	0.24 ± 0.03	0.18 ± 0.01
	Epi (1 μM) + 2 mM MIX	0.82 ± 0.13	0.33 ± 0.02	0.30 ± 0.02	0.31 ± 0.06	0.37 ± 0.06	0.09 ± 0.01

[a] Homogenates (60 ml/g of tissue for experiment 1 and 5 ml/g of tissue for experiment 2) were prepared from frozen hearts from 0.5 kg rabbits which had been perfused for 2 minutes in the absence or presence of epinephrine (Epi) or epinephrine plus 1-methyl-3-isobutylxanthine (MIX), as indicated. The homogenization buffer was 10 mM potassium phosphate (pH 6.8), 10 mM EDTA, 0.5 mM 1-methyl-3-isobutylxanthine, and 0.25 M NaCl. In experiment 1, the particulate fraction was washed three times in the same volume and buffer in the absence of NaCl. In experiment 2, the homogenate was centrifuged once at 20,000g for 10 minutes at 4°. The particulate fraction was resuspended in the same volume of the buffer above, and the supernatant and particulate fractions were diluted 12 times in the same buffer. The protein kinase activity (+2 μM cAMP) was determined immediately, and the cAMP-binding protein (R subunit) was determined the following day. Aliquots (0.4 ml) were placed in a boiling water bath for 1 minute and then centrifuged for cAMP determination. The concentration of catalytic subunit (C) was calculated from the specific activity and molecular weight of pure liver catalytic subunit monomer (3×10^6 units/mg) (26). Results are range of duplicates for two hearts in experiment 1 or mean ± S.E.M. for four hearts in experiment 2. Units: nmoles/g tissue. (From Corbin et al., 1977.)

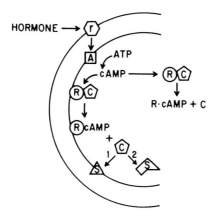

FIG. 32. Possible mechanism for the activation of membrane bound cAMP-dependent protein kinase (adapted from Corbin *et al.*, 1977).

by phosphodiesterase, and (K_a) is the activation constant of the cAMP-dependent protein kinase for the cAMP analog. The values of a, b, and c are determined by regression analysis for a series of substituted analogs.

This type of expression permits a calculation of [cAMP analog]$_{50}$ which can then be compared to observed results. Miller *et al.* (1975) have used this approach to evaluate the role of protein phosphorylation in the induction of hepatic tyrosine aminotransferase (TAT). As indicated in Table VIII, this approach, with the exception of a few analogs, does provide a reasonable basis for prediction of the concentration of analog required for induction of half-maximum (Ind$_{50}$) of TAT activity.

Obviously, other parameters, such as rate of transport of analog into the cell, must be included in a more complete equation, but this approach does provide for an assessment of the role of protein kinase in a particular physiological event that, because of its complexity, is not amenable to more direct evaluation. The primary weakness in the rationale is the assumption that the binding site for cAMP of protein kinase will have a molecular architecture quite different from the cAMP binding site of other putative cAMP receptors. There is no reason *a priori* to assume this, and the many studies of drug receptor sites suggest that often different receptor sites for the same ligands are chemically quite similar in the immediate microenvironment of the binding site.

In a slight modification of this approach, Wicks *et al.* (1975) have examined the correlation of 8-hydroxy cAMP stimulation of TAT induction and, for the catalysis of the phosphorylation of histone H1 at serine 37 *in vivo*, the site specific for the cAMP-dependent protein kinase. A reasonable correlation was observed (Fig. 33), thus providing additional evidence for the role of protein phosphorylation in TAT induction.

TABLE VIII

ACTIVITIES OF 6- AND 8-SUBSTITUTED DERIVATIVES OF cAMP AS ACTIVATORS OF RAT LIVER
cAMP-DEPENDENT PROTEIN KINASE, SUBSTRATES FOR RAT LIVER PHOSPHODIESTERASE, AND
INDUCERS OF RAT LIVER TYROSINE AMINOTRANSFERASE[a]

cAMP Derivative	K_a for rat liver protein kinase (nM)	S value for rat liver phosphodiesterase (relative rate)	Ind$_{50}$ for tyr transaminase induction (mg/kg)	
			Observed	Calculated
cAMP	21	1.0	—	—
N^{6}Bt-cAMP	26	0.06	12	11.8
8-Substituent on cAMP				
—NH$_2$	12	0.90	58	21.6
—NHMe	11	0.07	90	—
—NHCH$_2$Ph	240	0.06	160	69.2
—OH	9.6	0.09	3.8	6.4
—OMe	84	0.06	57	30.0
—SH	5.4	0.10	2.1	4.2
—SMe	10	0.08	2.8	6.3
—SCH$_2$Ph	9.1	0.06	0.90	—
—SPhpCl	0.22	0.05	0.45	0.24
—Br	7.0	0.11	1.6	5.4
N^6-Substituent on cAMP				
—Et	30	0.29	13	—
—Et$_2$	13	0.14	14	9.9
—CH$_2$Ph	19	0.40	22	21.6
—OEt	42	0.46	46	43.3
—OCH$_2$Ph	17	0.55	25	22.8
—OCOEt	100	0.12	56	47.1
6-Substituent on cAMP				
—SH	70	1.20	47	100.3
—SMe	1.2	0.60	5.5	2.9
—SCH$_2$Ph	10	0.72	16	16.9
—OH	43	0.63	40	50.9
—OMe	47	0.68	50	56.5

[a] The K_a values for protein kinase were determined from Lineweaver–Burk plots. The S value is the rate of hydrolysis of cAMP/rate of hydrolysis of the analog. Ind$_{50}$ refers to the dose of compound that produces 50% of maximal tyrosine aminotransferase induction. (From Miller *et al.*, 1975.)

Expanding this concept, Wicks' group (Wagner *et al.*, 1975) compared the effect of 6- and 8-substituted analogs of cAMP on induction of phosphoenolpyruvate carboxykinase and TAT. The correlation obtained (Fig. 34) suggests that each of these is regulated by a similar mechanism, presumably via protein phosphorylation. A similar study has been presented by O'Neill *et*

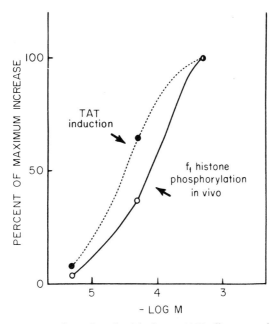

FIG. 33. Dose–response relationships for 8-hydroxy-cAMP effects on induction of tyrosine aminotransferase and the phosphorylation of histone f_1 at the site specific for cAMP-dependent protein kinase in intact H35 cells. The analog was added at the concentrations indicated for 2 hours. Each value for histone phosphorylation represents two observations at $5 \mu M$, four at 50 μM, and one at 500 μM. The observed increase in histone phosphorylation at 500 μM was 9.8-fold more than the control. Tyrosine aminotransferase (TAT) activity was determined in separate experiments 3 hours after analog addition. Each value represents four observations, and the observed increase in enzyme activity at 500 μM was 4.4-fold over the control (from Wicks *et al.*, 1975).

al. (1977) in which the relationship between the ability of cAMP analogs to stimulate changes in cellular morphology of CHO cells (cell elongation) with changes in the activation ratio of the protein kinase has been examined. A clear correlation is seen (Table IX) between those analogs that activated protein kinase and those that affected cellular morphology. The data presented in Table IX also report the concentration of cAMP in the cell. It is clear that some of the effective analogs in fact elevate the concentration of cAMP in the cell.

These data provide one of the several reports available which show that cAMP analogs may function by one or more of several routes. These are:

1. The analog may directly stimulate cAMP-dependent protein kinase.
2. The analog may be metabolized in the cell to yield cAMP.
3. The analog may be metabolized to a compound other than cyclic AMP but one which stimulates protein kinase.

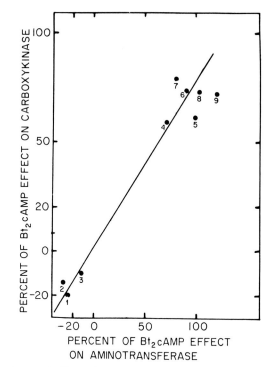

FIG. 34. Correlation of effects of cAMP analogs on tyrosine aminotransferase and phosphoenolpyruvate carboxykinase activities in H35 cells. The analogs were all added at 0.5 mM, and cells were harvested for assay at 5 hours. Each value is the mean of at least three observations, with standard errors of 10–20%. The average increase in activity generated by Bt_2-cAMP was 2.9-fold for the aminotransferase and 2.0-fold for the carboxykinase. The values for analogs 1, 2, and 3 are given as percentage of decrease in control activity. 1, 8HOEtHN-cAMP; 2, $8H_2N$-cAMP; 3, 6HS-cAMP; 4, 6MeS-cAMP; 5, 8HOEtS-cAMP; 6, 8Br-cAMP; 7, $8PhCH_2S$-cAMP; 8, 8EtS-cAMP; 9, 8MeS-cAMP. (From Wagner *et al.*, 1975.)

4. The analog, or a derivative of it, may inhibit phosphodiesterase and result in an increase in the production of endogenous cAMP from ATP.

As indicated in the data of Table IX, many analogs act by increasing endogenous cAMP levels, whereas others result in a more direct activation of the protein kinase. Interestingly, we (Castagna *et al.*, 1977; Dills *et al.* 1977) have recently reinvestigated the mechanism of action of dibutyryl cAMP, the analog that has been used extensively for more than a decade. In contrast to previous belief, we have shown (in liver) that cAMP is not a direct product of metabolism (Fig. 35) and that, as others had proposed, the dibutyryl cAMP acts as a result of the formation of N^6-monobutyryl cAMP, an effective activator of the protein kinase, and as an inhibitor of phosphodies-

TABLE IX
ACTIVITY OF CYCLIC NUCLEOTIDES IN CHO CELLS IN CULTURE[a]

Cyclic nucleotide	Cell elongation activity	Protein kinase activation ratio	Net endogenous cyclic AMP increase
Nothing	−	—	—
Nothing	−	—	—
cAMP	−	0.43	2.4
cAMP	−	0.52	1.0
$O^{2'}$-Monobutyryl cAMP	−	0.33	1.1
N^6-Monobutyryl cAMP	+	0.86	26.4
N^6-Monobutyryl cAMP	+	0.99	14.8
$N^6,O^{2'}$-Dibutyryl cAMP	+	0.95	28.9
$N^6,O^{2'}$-Dibutyryl cAMP	+	1.09	12.5
8-Benzylthio cAMP	+	0.95	−0.2
8-Benzylthio cAMP	+	0.82	0.1
8-Bromo cAMP	+	0.83	0.1
8-Bromo cAMP	+	1.01	1.3
cGMP	−	0.39	−0.1
cGMP	−	0.26	−0.2
$N^2,O^{2'}$-Dibutyryl cGMP	−	0.32	−0.2
$N^2,O^{2'}$-Dibutyryl cGMP	−	0.31	0.1
8-Bromo cGMP	−	0.40	0.0
8-Bromo cGMP	−	0.33	0.1

[a]Modified from O'Neill et al., 1977.

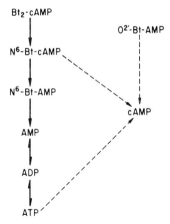

FIG. 35. Pathway of metabolism of N^6, O'_2-dibutyryl cAMP in liver. Predominant pathway shown in heavy arrows. Possible sources of cAMP shown in dotted arrows (from Dills et al., 1977).

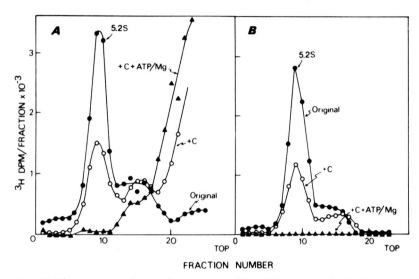

FIG. 36. The sucrose gradient sedimentation profiles of the macromolecular binding fractions prelabeled by perfusion with [³H]Bt₂-cAMP: Effect of the addition of the catalytic subunit of cAMP-dependent protein kinase. Livers were perfused for 30 minutes with an initial concentration of 0.32 μM [³H]Bt₂-cAMP, and cytoplasmic macromolecular fractions were prepared from unfrozen tissue. Immediately prior to applying the macromolecular fraction (approximately 2 mg of protein) to the gradient, the solution was incubated for 5 minutes at 0° at pH 6.8 with the following: (●), no additions; (○), 18 μg of pure skeletal muscle cAMP-dependent protein kinase catalytic subunit; (▲), 18 μg of catalytic subunit 5 mM magnesium chloride and 1 mM ATP. At the termination of the ultracentrifugation, an aliquot of each fraction was counted directly (A) or the amount retained by a Millipore membrane was determined (B). (From Castagna *et al.*, 1977.)

terase. In a continuation of this study, [³H]dibutyryl cAMP has been used as an effective marker of protein kinase activation. If, following perfusion of liver with [³H]dibutyryl cAMP, the tissue is rapidly extracted, [³H]N⁶-monobutyryl cAMP is found bound to a protein with the sedimentation characteristics of the regulatory subunit of the protein kinase (Fig. 36). Subsequent incubation with either catalytic subunit or catalytic subunit plus ATP–Mg²⁻ permits unambiguous identification that the binding protein is regulatory subunit. This method provides another technique by which the degree of protein kinase activation can be evaluated. As an example (Fig. 37), binding (and presumably protein kinase activation) is illustrated as a function of time for liver perfused with 8.8 μM dibutyryl cAMP.

D. GENETIC PROBES OF cAMP ACTION

A powerful approach to the study of cAMP action and the role of protein phosphorylation, of which so far only the "very tip of the iceberg" has been

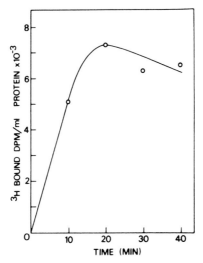

FIG. 37. Time course of the binding of [³H]N⁶-Bt-cAMP by hepatic cytosol protein. At zero time [³H]Bt₂-cAMP was added to liver perfusate media to a final concentration of 8.8 μM. At the indicated points tissue was removed and rapidly fractionated by gel filtration (from Castagna *et al.*, 1977).

exposed, is the use of genetic manipulations. Studies emanating from the Tomkins laboratory by Coffino (Steinberg *et al.*, 1977; Lemaire and Coffino, 1977) have examined S49 mouse lymphoma cells with selected resistance to cAMP-induced cytolysis. These cells have been shown to have a variety of defects in cAMP-dependent protein kinase (and cAMP receptors). The mutants fall into the 4 classes: (a) cells with no detectable protein kinase activity (designated kin⁻), (b) cells with kinase that has a reduced apparent affinity for cAMP (designated K_m mutants), (c) cells with a reduced amount of activity (designated V_{max} mutants), and (d) cells with normal kinase activity that respond to cAMP normally except that they are resistant to cAMP-induced cytolysis (designated D⁻). Principal studies to date have been with K_m mutants, which probably arise from a structural alteration in the R subunit. The D⁻ mutant appears to reflect a change(s) in a step distal to the protein kinase, such as a modification of a phosphoprotein substrate.

E. MICROINJECTION OF PROTEINS AS PROBES OF cAMP ACTION

The large amphibian oocyte has provided the opportunity for a unique sequence of experiments by Maller and Krebs (1977). Meiotic cell division of such oocytes is stimulated by progesterone, and this maturation process is associated with bursts of protein phosphorylation. In contrast to a wide range of other known steroid hormone effects, the progesterone action on the

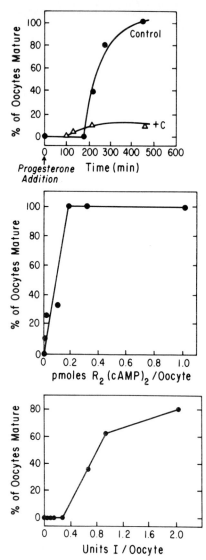

FIG. 38. Top: Effect of protein kinase catalytic subunit (C) on frequency of germinal vesicle breakdown of oocytes from *Xenopus laevis*. Approximately 50 ml of either C (1.54 mg/ml) (△) or its diluant (25 mM Mes, 0.5 mg/ml of bovine serum albumin, pH 6.5) (●) was microinjected into each of 25 oocytes. The oocytes were exposed to 30 μM progesterone 10–15 minutes later. The frequency of germinal vesicle breakdown was recorded as a function of time, and oocytes were defined as mature after experiencing germinal vesicle breakdown. Center: Dose–response of oocytes from a single female to microinjection of R_2-cAMP$_2$. The percentage of germinal vesicle breakdown was scored 5 hours after injection. Bottom: Induction of maturation of oocytes by microinjection of the heat-stable inhibitor protein of the cAMP-dependent protein kinase. (From Maller and Krebs, 1977.)

oocyte is mediated via a receptor on the cell membrane and occurs extragenomally. Maller and Krebs (1977) have shown that the microinjection of catalytic subunit into these cells blocks progesterone action, whereas, by contrast, microinjection of either the regulatory subunit or of the heat-stable inhibitor protein of the cAMP-dependent protein kinase can mimic progesterone action (Fig. 38). This effect of the regulatory subunit is apparently specific for that derived from the Type II isozyme. Maller and Krebs (1977) have proposed a model (Fig. 39) which suggests that a high steady-state level of a protein phosphorylated by the cAMP-dependent protein kinase blocks entry of the cell into meiotic cell division and that the addition of the regulatory subunit, by blocking catalytic subunit activity, results in dephosphorylation of the key protein and in consequence permits oocyte maturation. [Progesterone has been reported to depress cAMP levels in the oocyte (Speaker and Butcher, 1977), hence mimicking the action of the regulatory subunit.] This approach of microinjection, possessing unique advantages, is unfortunately limited to but a few systems.

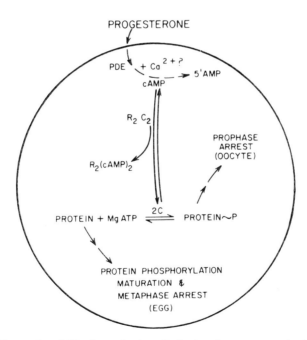

FIG. 39. Proposed model for the mechanism of induction of oocyte maturation by microinjection of R_2-$cAMP_2$, or the heat-stable inhibitor protein, or of blocking of progesterone-induced induction by microinjection of catalytic subunit of the protein kinase (from Maller and Krebs, 1977).

IV. SPECIFIC SYSTEMS

Regulation of activity by phosphorylation–dephosphorylation has now been described both *in vitro* and *in vivo* for a number of enzymes. In this section we have chosen to concentrate on four specific systems the consideration of which we believe is of special help in understanding the regulatory role of the cAMP-dependent protein kinase.

A. Regulation of Liver Pyruvate Kinase (Type L) Activity by cAMP-Dependent Protein Kinase

Pyruvate kinase has long been known to be one of the key enzymes of metabolism and is one of the foci of allosteric regulation. Recently, the liver isozyme (but not that from skeletal muscle) has been shown to be a substrate of the cAMP-dependent protein kinase. Presumably, regulation by cAMP reflects the response to extracellular stimuli. Impinging on this regulation are a range of intracellular modulators whose effects determine both the phosphorylation state of the enzyme and the activity of the phospho- and dephospho- forms. A brief description of this complexity is presented here to emphasize the scope of potential control.

The main isozyme of pyruvate kinase in liver, the L type, shows complex regulatory properties, with fructose 1,6-diphosphate as the major positive effector and ATP and some amino acids as negative effectors (Seubert and Schoner, 1971). Recently, Engstrom and co-workers have demonstrated that phosphorylation of pyruvate kinase, catalyzed by the cAMP-dependent protein kinase, results in the alteration of the response of the enzyme to its substrate and allosteric effectors (Ljungström *et al.*, 1974, 1976; Berglund *et al.*, 1977). As shown in Fig. 40, at low assay concentrations of phosphoenolpyruvate, the activity of the phosphorylated enzyme is markedly depressed; phosphorylation reduced the affinity of the enzyme for phosphoenolpyruvate with the $S_{0.5}$ for this substrate being increased from 0.3 to 0.9 mM upon phosphorylation of the enzyme. In the liver cell the concentration of phosphoenolpyruvate is 0.02–0.5 mM, a concentration range which is nonsaturating and over which the effect of phosphorylation on pyruvate kinase is presumably of physiological consequence. The activation of pyruvate kinase by fructose diphosphate is observed with both the phospho- and dephospho- enzymes, and in the presence of this metabolite the two forms are kinetically indistinguishable. Phosphorylation of the enzyme apparently does not modify the V_{max} of the enzyme. Both phospho- and dephospho- enzymes are sensitive to inhibition by ATP and by alanine. In addition to phosphoenolpyruvate, fructose diphosphate, ATP, and amino

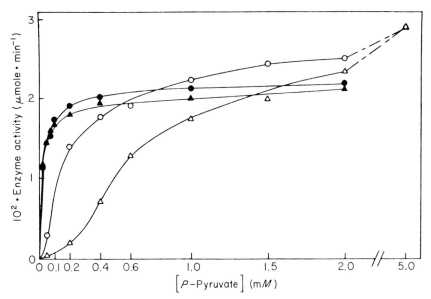

FIG. 40. Dependence of pyruvate kinase activity on the concentration of phosphoenolpyruvate. Symbols: (△————△), phosphorylated enzyme; (▲————▲), phosphorylated enzyme in
the presence of 20 μM fructose 1,6-bisphosphate; (○————○), unphosphorylated enzyme;
(●————●), unphosphorylated enzyme in the presence of 20 μM fructose 1,6-bisphosphate.
(From Ljungström *et al.*, 1976.)

acids modifying the activity of the phospho- and dephospho- forms of pyruvate kinase, each of these metabolites also affects the interconversion between the two forms.

Féliu *et al.* (1977) have shown that the rate of phosphorylation (and in
consequence inactivation) catalyzed by the cAMP-dependent protein kinase
was decreased by physiological concentrations of phosphoenolpyruvate and
by micromolar concentrations of fructose diphosphate, and that these inhibitory effects are counteracted by Mg—ATP and by several amino acids
(cysteine, alanine, serine, phenylalanine). As examples, the rate of cAMP-
dependent inactivation is blocked more than 80% by either 0.5 mM phosphoenolpyruvate or 5 μM fructose diphosphate, but it is enhanced between
20 to 40% by 0.5 mM amino acids. No direct evidence is yet available, but
presumably these metabolites modify the phosphorylation reaction by interaction with the substrate. Féliu *et al.* (1977) have therefore proposed an
extension of the allosteric model of pyruvate kinase (Fig. 41). The more
active conformation, which occurs upon binding of either fructose diphosphate or phosphoenolpyruvate, is a poor substrate for cAMP-dependent
inactivation; the less active conformation, produced by ligand binding of
Mg—ATP or amino acids, is a good substrate for the cAMP-dependent

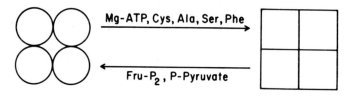

More active conformation:
Poor substrate for cyclic AMP-
dependent inactivation

Less active conformation:
Good substrate for cyclic AMP-
dependent inactivation

FIG. 41. Model for the regulation of pyruvate kinase (from Féliu *et al.*, 1977). Abbreviations: fru-P_2, fructose-1,6-diphosphate; P-pyruvate, phosphoenolpyruvate.

inactivation. This produces a two-tier system of metabolic control, amounting to almost "overkill," and poses the question of why it would be physiologically advantageous to regulate not only by ligand binding but by covalent modification in response to the same signal. Nevertheless, Féliu *et al.* (1977) have provided evidence that this type of control does occur. In a study of the

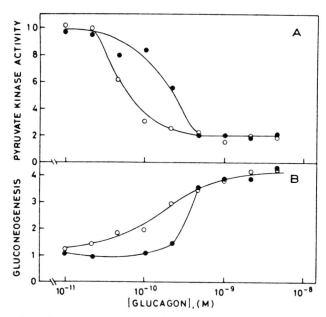

FIG. 42. Effect of various concentrations of glucagon on the activity of pyruvate kinase (A) and on the rate of gluconeogenesis (B) of hepatocytes incubated with (●) or without (○) 10 n*M* insulin. Pyruvate kinase was measured at 0.15 m*M* phosphoenolpyruvate in aliquots of cells taken 5 minutes after the addition of glucagon and is expressed in units/g cells. Gluconeogenesis was measured by the conversion of [^{14}C]pyruvate into glucose and glycogen over a period of 20 minutes and is expressed in μmoles of pyruvate converted per 20 minutes/gm of cells (from Féliu *et al.*, 1976).

pyruvate kinase activity in normal-fed, sucrose-fed, starved, and diabetic rats, Féliu *et al.* (1977) showed that there was a definite inverse relationship between the activity state of the pyruvate kinase and the cellular concentration of phosphoenolpyruvate.

The activation state of pyruvate kinase is also regulated by hormonal control. Evidence for a physiological role of pyruvate kinase phosphorylation has come from studies of isolated rat hepatocytes (Féliu *et al.*, 1976). Figure 42 shows the effect of various concentrations of glucagon on the activity of pyruvate kinase and on the rate of gluconeogenesis of hepatocytes incubated with or without 10 nM insulin. There is an inverse relationship between the activity of pyruvate kinase and the extent of gluconeogenesis. Figure 43 shows the rapid decrease in activity of pyruvate kinase in response to 0.3 nM glucagon, after which there is a gradual return to the initial activity. However, the prior addition of 10 nM insulin caused a rapid, complete reactivation following a short latency period. Obviously, a close interrelationship occurs between the extracellular and intracellular controls, and Féliu *et al.* (1977) have shown that glucagon stimulation of pyruvate kinase inactivation is depressed in animals in which cellular levels of phosphoenolpyruvate had been elevated. Thus, pyruvate kinase has become a prime example of regulation by an interdigitating sequence of controls which includes each of the following: (a) allosteric regulation of the enzyme; (b) covalent modification of the enzyme; (c) covalent modification altering the response to allosteric ac-

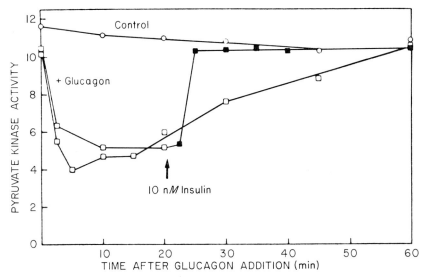

FIG. 43. Time course of the effect of 0.3 nM glucagon on the activity of pyruvate kinase and of its reversal by 10 nM insulin. Glucagon (□) and insulin (■) were added as indicated. Pyruvate kinase activity is expressed in units/gm of cells (from Féliu *et al.*, 1976).

tivators; and (d) allosteric modification altering the response to covalent
modifiers. It is to be expected that this degree of complexity will be observed
in other systems.

B. REGULATION OF GLOBIN SYNTHESIS

Wicks (1974) has reviewed in detail the substantial evidence that indicates
that cAMP regulates protein synthesis at the translational level. As indicated
by the type of data presented in Figs. 33 and 34 and in Table VIII, it is
probable that protein phosphorylation is involved. Evidence from both *in
vitro* and *in vivo* experiments that has been provided by many excellent
laboratories has shown that both ribosomal proteins and various initiation
factors are substrates for both cAMP-dependent and cAMP-independent
protein kinases. This larger area will not be reviewed here, but consideration
of the regulation of globin synthesis by hemin potentially provides a special
insight into our understanding of regulation mechanisms of protein kinase.

The recent review by Revel (1977) summarizes the results that have established that hemin regulates globin synthesis and provided a detailed understanding of the protein synthetic machinery. In the absence of hemin there is
a rapid cessation of protein synthesis in reticulocyte lysates. This is due to
the inactivation of a polypeptide chain initiation factor, designated eIF-2.
This inactivation has been shown to be due to modification of eIF-2 by phosphorylation catalyzed by a cAMP-independent protein kinase (Weissbach
and Ochoa, 1976; Staehelin *et al.*, 1975). It has been proposed that the eIF-2
protein kinase also exists in phospho-dephospho forms, its phosphorylation
being potentially catalyzed by the cAMP-dependent protein kinase resulting in
the activation of catalytic activity (Datta *et al.* 1977a; Delaunay *et al.* 1977).
The suggested cascade of reactions is shown in Fig. 44, although this scheme
requires substantial verification and the results obtained are controversial.
The scheme has many similarities to the regulation of glycogenolysis and is the
only other example so far elucidated of a two-stage phosphorylation cascade.

Assuming this system is general for the regulation of protein synthesis in
other cells, the mechanism in Fig. 44 would provide a means whereby cAMP
would inhibit protein synthesis. It is probable that such a mechanism could
account for a decrease in general protein synthesis that occurs in response to
the typical catabolic signal associated with the metabolic actions of cAMP.
[In the systems studied by Wicks and others (see Wicks, 1974), cAMP promotes the specific synthesis of selected proteins (such as TAT or phosphoenolpyruvate carboxykinase, Figs. 33 and 34).] Datta *et al.* (1977b) have
also recently shown that hemin blocks the binding of cAMP to the protein
kinase and decreases cAMP-dependent protein kinase activity (Fig. 45). Pre-

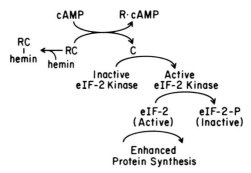

FIG. 44. Model for the regulation of globin synthesis by hemin control of cAMP-dependent protein kinase (adapted from Datta *et al.*, 1977a).

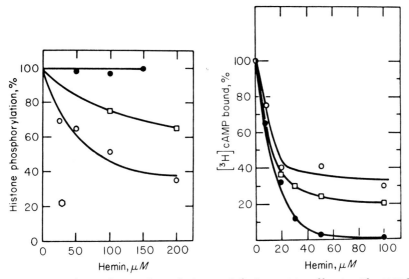

FIG. 45. Regulation of protein kinase by hemin. Left: Competition of hemin with cAMP for binding to the regulatory subunit of cAMP-dependent protein kinase. Binding of [^{3}H]cAMP to cAMP binding protein (kinase holoenzyme or regulatory subunit) as a function of the hemin concentration. Symbols: (○), homogenous bovine heart protein kinase, 1.0 μg; (□), bovine heart protein kinase regulatory subunit, 0.4 μg; (●), cAMP-dependent rabbit reticulocyte protein kinase (pkIIb), 4.8 μg. The [^{3}H]cAMP binding in the absence of hemin was taken as 100%. Right: Effect of hemin on histone phosphorylation by cAMP-dependent protein kinase. Standard 50 μl assay with reticulocyte protein kinase pkIIb (2 μg of protein) (○), bovine heart protein kinase (0.4 μg) (□), or bovine heart protein kinase catalytic subunit (0.154 μg) (●). The phosphorylation rate in the absence of hemin was taken as 100%. When the histone concentration was reduced from 50 to 5 μg/50 μl, the 100% phosphorylation rate with 3 μg of pkIIb protein (12.4 pmoles of ^{32}P/minute) was reduced to 3 pmoles/minute, or 22%, by 30 μM hemin (○) (from Datta *et al.*, 1977b).

sumably, what is occurring is a binding of hemin to the holoenzyme (Fig. 44). This observation would fully satisfy the role of hemin as a stimulator of globin synthesis. If the proposal from Ochoa's lab is correct, it is so far a unique example of a process with specific regulation occurring by interaction with the cAMP-dependent protein kinase.

The potential ramifications of such a mechanism for the regulation of cellular function are many; it also poses many complexities. For example, such a mechanism would infer that hemin would regulate all other processes in which cAMP-dependent protein kinase were involved. Possibly in the highly specialized reticulocyte this would be an acceptable circumstance, but in a tissue such as liver with a broad diversity of cAMP action, such a mechanism would on the surface appear to be counterproductive. The proposed type of regulation of the protein kinase by hemin is so far a unique example that is difficult to rationalize on the basis of our knowledge of the virtual identity of protein kinases between tissues (isozyme distribution ignored; see Section II). It remains to be evaluated whether other such similar modifiers will be detected. Teleologically, such a mechanism can be rationalized only with difficulty.

C. The Role of cAMP-Dependent Protein Kinase in Muscle Contraction

Increases in cardiac contractility under the influence of β-adrenergic agents are associated with elevated intracellular levels of cAMP. These observations suggested a regulatory role for cAMP in cardiac contractile processes, presumably mediated by cAMP-dependent protein kinases and involving modification of proteins by phosphorylation. Consideration of protein phosphorylation in muscle serves as a focus for recognizing that a given physiological event may be mediated by the phosphorylation of more than one protein. It also emphasizes the need to recognize that not all regulatory protein phosphorylation reactions are mediated by the cAMP-dependent enzyme.

Contractile and regulatory proteins of muscle which have been shown to be phosphorylated *in vitro* by various phosphokinases are listed in Table X. The enzyme myosin light-chain kinase is highly specific for phosphorylation of the P light chain, and there is some evidence that changes in the phosphorylation of this light chain in the perfused rabbit heart (Frearson *et al.*, 1976) and in rabbit skeletal muscle *in vivo* (Stull and High, 1977) can be correlated with modified physiological function. The light-chain kinase is activated by Ca^{2+} and is not regulated by cAMP.

TABLE X

PHOSPHORYLATION OF CONTRACTILE AND REGULATORY PROTEINS OF MUSCLE BY PHOSPHOKINASES

Substrate	Tissue	Kinase	Reference
Troponin I (M.W. 28,000)	Skeletal muscle	cAMP-Dependent protein kinase	Bailey and Villar-Palasi, 1971 Stull et al., 1972 Pratje and Heilmeyer, 1972 England et al., 1974 Perry and Cole, 1973
	Skeletal muscle	Phosphorylase b kinase	Stull et al., 1972
	Cardiac muscle	cAMP-Dependent kinase	Cole and Perry, 1975 Rubio et al., 1975
	Cardiac muscle	cGMP-Dependent protein kinase	Blumenthal et al., 1978
	Cardiac muscle	Phosphorylase b kinase	Cole and Perry, 1975
Troponin T (M.W. 37,000)	Skeletal muscle	Phosphorylase b kinase	Stull et al., 1972 Perry and Cole, 1973, 1974 Moir et al., 1977
Myosin light-chain (M.W. 18,000)	Skeletal muscle	Myosin light-chain kinase	Perrie et al., 1972, 1973
	Cardiac muscle	Myosin light-chain kinase	Frearson and Perry, 1975
Phospholamban (M.W. 22,000)	Cardiac sarcoplasmic reticulum	cAMP-Dependent protein kinase	Kirchberger et al., 1972, 1974 Tada et al., 1974
24,000 M.W. protein	Cardiac sarcolemma	cAMP-Dependent protein kinase	Krause et al., 1975 Sulakhe and St. Louis, 1976

1. Troponin

Troponin is composed of three subunits: a Ca^{2+}-binding subunit (troponin C), an inhibitory subunit (troponin I), and a tropomyosin-binding subunit (troponin T). In the presence of all three subunits, actomyosin ATPase activity is inhibited in the absence of Ca^{2+} and stimulated in the presence of Ca^{2+}.

Troponin T has been shown to be phosphorylated *in vitro* by phosphorylase kinase. On prolonged incubation with phosphorylase kinase, a total of 3 moles of phosphate per mole of troponin T (rabbit skeletal muscle) can be incorporated. When troponin T is phosphorylated by phosphorylase kinase in the presence of troponin C, the extent of phosphorylation at each site is considerably decreased (approximately 90% inhibition at molar ratios of 1:1; Moir *et al.*, 1977). There is no significant rate of phosphorylation by cAMP-dependent protein kinase of troponin T from either skeletal (Pratje and Heilmeyer, 1972) or cardiac (Moir *et al.*, 1977; Stull and Buss, 1977) muscle.

Troponin I from both cardiac and skeletal muscle has been shown to be phosphorylated by cAMP-dependent protein kinase and by phosphorylase kinase. The major site of troponin I phosphorylation by phosophorylase kinase was shown to be threonine #11. The main site of phosphorylation of troponin I by bovine cardiac cAMP-dependent protein kinase is serine #118 (Moir *et al.*, 1974), while with rabbit skeletal cAMP-dependent protein kinase 2 moles of ^{32}P per mole of troponin I were incorporated (Huang *et al.*, 1974), the second site of phosphorylation being identical to a minor site also phosphorylated by phosphorylase kinase. An important difference in the phosphorylation of troponin I from cardiac and skeletal muscle, with respect to physiological implications, is that phosphorylation of cardiac troponin I by cAMP-dependent protein kinase is much more rapid than that of skeletal troponin I (Cole and Perry, 1975; Stull and Buss, 1977). Furthermore, phosphorylation of cardiac troponin I by cAMP-dependent protein kinase is not blocked by troponin C, as is the case with troponin I from skeletal muscle (Cole and Perry, 1975).

The differences between the phosphorylation of cardiac and skeletal muscle troponin may be of special significance for the metabolism of cardiac muscle. A hypothesis has been proposed in which phosphorylation of troponin I in response to catecholamine stimulation of cardiac muscle could cause an increase in contraction by modifying the properties of troponin (Stull *et al.*, 1972; England *et al.*, 1974). Further support for this hypothesis was provided by experiments showing that in intact rat hearts perfused with ^{32}P, troponin I (isolated by affinity chromatography) was phosphorylated on stimulation with epinephrine (England, 1975). As shown in Fig. 46, following administration of 10^{-6} *M* epinephrine to perfused rat heart, there was a delay of 5 seconds, after which contraction gradually increased reaching a

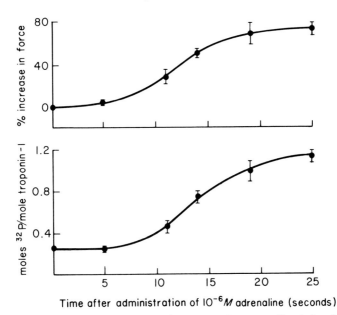

FIG. 46. Time course of changes in force of contraction (upper panel) and phosphorylation of troponin-I (lower panel) following administration of 10^{-6} M adrenaline. Rat hearts were initially perfused with ^{32}P during a control period. The hearts were freeze-clamped at the times shown following continuous perfusion with adrenaline. The increase in force of contraction is expressed as a percentage of that during the control period. Each point is the mean of three hearts, and the vertical bars represent 2 S.E.M. (from England, 1975).

maximum after 20 seconds. The amount of ^{32}P in troponin I followed an identical time course, increasing from a control value of 0.2 mole ^{32}P per mole troponin I to a maximum of 1.2 moles/mole. By using I strain mice that are deficient in phosphorylase kinase, England (1977) established that the phosphorylation that he observed in the perfused heart was catalyzed by the cAMP-dependent protein kinase.

Figure 47 (England, 1976) shows that the plot of increase in contractile force vs. troponin I phosphorylation appears biphasic. Where the amount of phosphate in troponin I was less than 1.0 mole/mole there was a linear correlation between increase in contractile force and troponin I phosphorylation. Further incorporation of phosphate was not accompanied by increased contraction.

At present, the effect of phosphorylation on troponin activity is not well understood, but Ray and England (1976) have observed that phosphorylation of troponin I caused a decrease in the Ca^{2+} sensitivity of the actomyosin ATPase from bovine and rat cardiac muscle (Fig. 48). Buss and Stull (1977) have studied the effects of phosphorylation by cAMP-dependent protein kinase on the calcium binding parameters of the cardiac troponin–

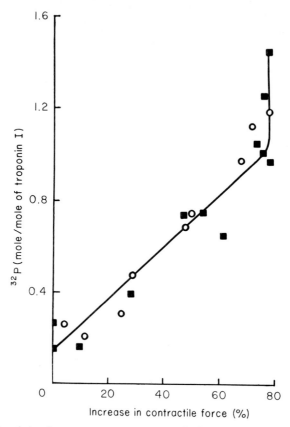

FIG. 47. Correlation between increase in contractile force and incorporation of ^{32}P into troponin I in perfused rat hearts. Symbols: (■), the hearts perfused with DL-isoprenaline; (○), hearts perfused with adrenaline (from England, 1976).

tropomyosin complex. Two classes of calcium binding sites differing in their affinity constants by three orders of magnitude were observed, but phosphorylation had no marked effect on either the affinity or the amount of calcium bound to the protein. In the perfused rat heart (England, 1976), two situations were observed in which troponin I phosphorylation was not correlated with contractile force. Perfusion with glucagon caused an increase in contractile force preceding any significant increase in phosphorylation. Pulse perfusions with isoprenaline showed that when contractile force was decreasing after prior stimulation, there was no corresponding fall in troponin I phosphorylation. Apparently, therefore, the phosphorylation of troponin may be one of the "on" signals for enhanced contractility, but not the "off" signal. This then points to the possibility that the phosphorylation of other

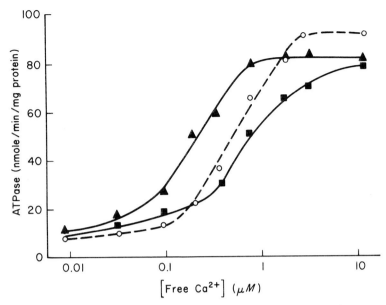

FIG. 48. The effect of phosphorylation and dephosphorylation on the Ca^{2+} sensitivity of cardiac myofibril ATPase. Myofibrils were phosphorylated with protein kinase (■), dephosphorylated with phosphoprotein phosphatase (▲), or untreated (○). Myofibril ATPase was measured in the presence of Ca/EGTA buffers at various free Ca^{2+} concentrations. (From Ray and England, 1976.)

proteins may be a significant factor in the regulation of different phases of the physiological response.

2. Sarcoplasmic Reticulum

The possibility that cAMP mediates the effects of catecholamines through regulation of intracellular calcium is an attractive hypothesis, because the contraction–relaxation cycle of muscle depends on changes in the intracellular concentration of Ca^{2+}. The sarcoplasmic reticulum plays a key role as a calcium-sequestering membrane system responsible for muscle relaxation. Transport of calcium across sarcoplasmic reticulum involves a calcium-activated ATPase (for review, see Tada *et al.*, 1978). Calcium uptake by cardiac sarcoplasmic reticulum has been shown to be stimulated by catecholamines (Shinebourne *et al.*, 1969; Entman *et al.*, 1969). Kirchberger *et al.* (1972) first reported that preincubation of canine cardiac microsomes (consisting primarily of sarcoplasmic reticulum) with exogenous cAMP-dependent protein kinase and cAMP led to a doubling of the rate of calcium uptake. This effect of cAMP-dependent protein kinase on calcium transport has since been confirmed by several other investigators (LaRaia and Morkin, 1974; Sulakhe and Drummond, 1974; Nayler and Berry, 1975; Schwartz *et al.*, 1976).

Further studies (Kirchberger *et al.*, 1974) indicated that there is a linear relationship between the rate of calcium uptake by sarcoplasmic reticulum and the phosphorylation of microsomes over a wide range of cAMP-dependent protein kinase concentrations (Kirchberger *et al.*, 1974). Fractionation of the cardiac sarcoplasmic reticulum by SDS gel electrophoresis has led to the identification of a 22,000 dalton protein (phospholamban) whose phosphorylation is catalyzed by cAMP-dependent protein kinase (Tada *et al.*, 1975). As shown in Fig. 49, there is a close correlation between phosphorylation of the 22,000 dalton protein and increased calcium uptake by cardiac sarcoplasmic reticulum (Kirchberger and Chu, 1976). Dephosphorylation of the 22,000 dalton phosphoprotein of cardiac sarcoplasmic reticulum was catalyzed by an intrinsic phosphoprotein phosphatase and was associated with a decrease in the rate of calcium transport by these membranes (Kirch-

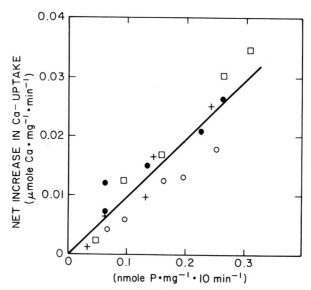

FIG. 49. Correlation between protein kinase-induced increase in oxalate-facilitated calcium transport by cardiac sarcoplasmic reticulum and net increase in phosphorylation of 22,000 dalton protein phospholamban. Microsomes were incubated in the presence of cyclic AMP, varying concentrations of protein kinase, and either [γ-^{32}P]ATP or unlabeled ATP for measurements of phosphorylation or calcium uptake, respectively. Plotted are increases in calcium uptake vs. increases in phosphorylation over control values. Symbols (●, ○, □, +) denote data from each of four independent experiments. (From Kirchberger and Chu, 1976.)

berger and Raffo, 1977). Stimulation of calcium uptake when cardiac microsomes are phosphorylated by cAMP-dependent protein kinase is accompanied by stimulation of the Ca^{2+}-activated ATPase activity associated with the Ca^{2+} transport process (Kirchberger *et al.*, 1974).

3. Sarcolemma

An alternative possibility for modulating the amount of Ca^{2+} delivered to the cardiac contractile proteins is to change Ca^{2+} fluxes across the sarcolemma. Catecholamines have been shown to increase calcium flux across sarcolemma in the heart (Grosmann and Furchgott, 1964; Vassort *et al.*, 1969). Sulakhe and Drummond (1974) demonstrated that skeletal muscle sarcolemma was phosphorylated by exogenous cAMP-dependent protein kinase and that this was accompanied by stimulation of calcium uptake and Ca^{2+}-stimulated ATPase activity. Similar findings have recently been reported in cardiac sarcolemma (Sulakhe *et al.*, 1976; Hui *et al.*, 1976). Such membranes were shown to contain an endogenous protein kinase activity capable of membrane phosphorylation, and this phosphorylation was increased on addition of cAMP (Sulakhe *et al.*, 1976). Membrane phosphorylation catalyzed by endogenous kinase in response to cAMP was shown to be associated with small but significant increases in calcium uptake relative to control preparations in the absence of added cAMP.

Using sarcolemma-enriched membranes of pig heart muscle, Krause *et al.* (1975) were able to demonstrate, by SDS gel electrophoresis, phosphorylation of an endogenous substrate of 24,000-dalton molecular weight by either endogenous or exogenous cAMP-dependent protein kinase. In their studies, high and low affinity sites for calcium binding were detected; phosphorylation had no effect on the total binding capacity but caused an increase in the affinity for Ca^{2+} of both sites. Support for a physiological role for the phosphorylation of sarcolemma in modulating myocardial contractility must await a fuller understanding of the molecular mechanisms involved. However, evidence that such phosphorylation occurs *in vivo* has recently been obtained in studies with rat hearts perfused with ^{32}P (M. S. Clippinger and D. A. Walsh, unpublished observations). In the latter study, the epinephrine-stimulated phosphorylation occurred after the onset of the inotropic effect.

It appears, therefore, that the regulation of contraction by epinephrine may involve the independent phosphorylation of at least three proteins. The onset may be associated with troponin I phosphorylation, but the phosphorylation of sarcoplasmic reticulum and sarcolemma may play an important role in either the maintenance or termination of this effect. With this as a model, it is to be anticipated that other physiological events modulated by cAMP will also involve multiple cAMP-regulated protein phosphorylations.

D. The Role of cAMP-Dependent Protein Kinase in Glycogen Metabolism

The so-called glycogenolytic cascade (previously referred to in Fig. 1), in which hormonal activation of cAMP-dependent protein kinase leads in turn to phosphorylation and activation of phosphorylase kinase, activation of phosphorylase, and thus to glycogen breakdown, has, since its initial postulate, been shown to be considerably more complex and capable of regulation at numerous points. The ramifications of many of these findings have yet to be fully appreciated; however, in Fig. 50 we present a summary of the current state of the art, emphasizing the complexities of the system. It is beyond the scope of this review to list the many contributions from a large body of literature that give primary support to the scheme presented. For several of the findings it is not possible to rate the relative importance of the observations in governing the physiological consequence, nor to present sufficient justification as to why this level of complexity is necessary. For clarity of presentation the scheme is presented as a sequence of interlinking boxes, and it is left to the reader to evaluate how the parameters in each box interdigitate. In box A are summarized the controls that exist at the level of the cAMP-dependent protein kinase; these have been primarily reviewed in Section II of this chapter. As discussed, the physiological significance of the two isozymes, or the self-catalyzed phosphorylation of the Type II isozyme, is at present unknown.

The identification of a protein inhibitor (designated I) of cAMP-dependent protein kinase (Walsh *et al.*, 1971) has proved a useful tool in the study of reactions catalyzed by cAMP-dependent protein kinase. This inhibitor protein interacts with the catalytic subunit, but not the holoenzyme, to produce an inactive C-I complex. The finding that the inhibitor is present in skeletal muscle and cardiac muscle in sufficient amounts to block approximately 20% of the amount of cAMP-dependent protein kinase in those tissues, and that it may be elevated in response to insulin in perfused heart (Walsh and Ashby, 1973), suggests that it may have a physiologically important role but this remains to be proven.

The regulation of phosphorylase kinase is illustrated in box B of Fig. 50; most of the studies have been carried out on the enzyme from rabbit skeletal muscle. Activation by cAMP-dependent protein kinase causes phosphorylation of the β subunit which is correlated with the increase in enzyme activity; after a lag, when the β subunit is already substantially phosphorylated, phosphorylation of the α subunit occurs (Cohen, 1973; Hayakawa *et al.*, 1973). It appears that phosphorylation of the α subunit is necessary to permit dephosphorylation and inactivation of the molecule (Cohen and Antoniw, 1973). The delay in phosphorylation of the α subunit relative to the β subunit

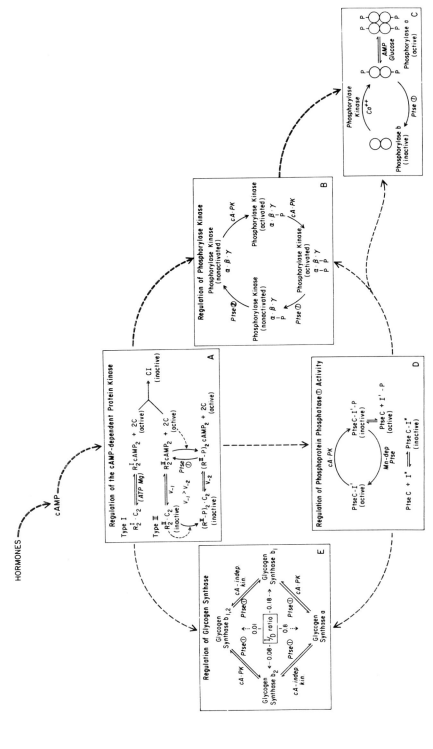

Fig. 50. Regulation of the glycogen cascade by phosphorylation-dephosphorylation reactions. See text.

and the fact that dephosphorylation of the β subunit does not occur until after α subunits have been phosphorylated could provide a specific time interval for the conversion of phosphorylase b to a.

Implicit in this control mechanism is the idea that the cAMP-dependent protein kinase not only activates the enzyme (through phosphorylation of the β subunit) but may also control its subsequent inactivation (through phosphorylation of the α subunit). Dephosphorylation of the β subunit is catalyzed by a general phosphoprotein phosphatase that is arbitrarily designated phosphatase (1) in this scheme. Regulation of this phosphatase is presented in box D of Fig. 50 and discussed below.

Dephosphorylation of the α subunit, in contrast to that of the β, has been reported to be catalyzed by a specific α-phosphorylase kinase phosphatase (Antoniw and Cohen, 1976). Regulation of this latter phosphatase would provide a mechanism for an alternate signal to sustain or diminish the hormonal activation mediated by cAMP. The relationship of this phosphatase to the more general phosphoprotein phosphatase [Ptse (1)] still requires clarification; it is characterized primarily by a requirement for Mn^{2+}, but as yet no effectors of this enzyme are known.

The phosphorylase kinase-catalyzed conversion of phosphorylase b to a is depicted in box C of Fig. 50. The concept of the regulation of protein function by reversible covalent modification of its structure originated with the identification of the two forms of phosphorylase. By comparison with the complex multisite phosphorylations observed with phosphorylase kinase and glycogen synthase, phosphorylation of phosphorylase is relatively simple, occurring at a single unique serine residue.

Phosphorylase kinase activity is also regulated by Ca^{2+}, a mechanism believed to be of special consequence in the regulation of glycogenolysis upon nerve stimulation in skeletal muscle. The requirement of phosphorylase kinase for Ca^{2+} is of particular significance with respect to the coupling of glycogenolysis to muscle contraction. Recent studies in liver suggest that α-adrenergic activation of glycogenolysis in that tissue may be mediated by an elevation of intracellular calcium, thereby leading to activation of phosphorylase kinase, and may occur independently of the activation of cAMP-dependent protein kinase (Cherrington *et al.*, 1976; Birnbaum and Fain, 1977; Keppens *et al.*, 1977; Exton *et al.*, 1977). It should be borne in mind that the classical studies of Sutherland, Rall, and co-workers were carried out in species in which β receptors appear to be more important than α receptors in catecholamine-induced glycogenolysis.

The regulation of glycogen synthase is presented in box E of Fig. 50. Classically, this enzyme has been referred to as synthase I or D, as defined by its dependence on glucose 6-phosphate for activity. The active species (I) is nonphosphorylated; the inactive species (D) is a phosphoprotein, and this phosphorylation was shown to be catalyzed by the cAMP-dependent protein kinase. Recently, as an added complexity, it has been recognized that phosphorylation can occur at more than one site catalyzed by more than one enzyme (Schlender and Reimann, 1975; Huang *et al.*, 1975; Nimmo *et al.*, 1976; Soderling, 1975; Soderling *et al.*, 1977). Presented in box E is the nomenclature of Cohen's group for the various synthase forms. Although there are some differences concerning exact values of I/D ratios for each species, there is general agreement between groups regarding the basic scheme. Active glycogen synthase, designated a, has an I/D ratio of 0.8 and can be inactivated by phosphorylation at site (1) by the cAMP-dependent protein kinase to give synthase b_1 or by phosphorylation at site (2) by a cAMP-independent protein kinase to give synthase b_2. Synthases b_1 and b_2 have I/D ratios of 0.13 and 0.08, respectively; each is substantially, although not totally, inactivated. Synthase b_1 or synthase b_2 can be converted to synthase $b_{1,2}$, that is, phosphorylated in both sites by the cAMP-independent and cAMP-dependent protein kinases, respectively. [Synthase b_1 can also be converted to synthase $b_{1,2}$ by action of the cAMP-dependent protein kinase, not shown; Soderling *et al.*, 1977]. Synthase $b_{1,2}$ is fully inactive.

It will be of interest to see whether the activity of the independent glycogen synthase kinase is altered by hormonal treatment, for it has been observed that glycogen synthase activity ratios can be altered by insulin (Miller and Larner, 1973) and by α-adrenergic agents (Hutson *et al.*, 1976) without concomitant changes in cAMP levels. The dephosphorylation of each site is catalyzed by the general phosphoprotein phosphatase designated Ptse (1) (box D, Fig. 50). Recent evidence has been obtained showing that dephosphorylation of muscle glycogen synthase phosphorylated in either sites (1) or (2) occurred at a low rate, whereas the presence of phosphate in site (1) increased the rate of dephosphorylation of site (2) by the phosphatase (Hutson *et al.*, 1978). Thus the phosphorylation–dephosphorylation of the b_1 site may play a regulatory role in determining the rate of synthase conversion. Thus for both phosphorylase kinase and glycogen synthase, the phosphorylation of a site on the enzyme other than the site(s) directly concerned with enzyme activation or inactivation may influence the control of enzyme activity.

The present state of knowledge concerning the apparent specificity of the phosphorylation–dephosphorylation reactions of the various enzymes of glycogen metabolism appears somewhat paradoxical. The same phosphoprotein phosphatase [Ptse (1)] catalyzes the dephosphorylation of sites in the β subunit of phosphorylase kinase, phosphorylase, and glycogen synthase; these are phosphorylated by three different phosphokinases. In contrast, a distinct phosphoprotein phosphatase catalyzes the dephosphorylation of the α subunit of phosphorylase kinase, a substrate for the cAMP-dependent enzyme. A problem in interpreting the evidence that the activities designated as phosphorylase phosphatase, β-phosphorylase kinase phosphatase, and glycogen synthase phosphatase are indeed identical arises from the fact that multiple forms of the enzyme have been described, of varying molecular weights, generally larger than the molecular weight of approximately 35,000 found for purified rabbit liver (Brandt *et al.*, 1975) and muscle phosphorylase phosphatase (Gratecos *et al.*, 1974). A plausible explanation for the occurrence of multiple forms involving a single catalytic subunit has come from the work of Lee and co-workers, indicating that liver phosphorylase phosphatase in crude extracts may be converted from multiple molecular weight forms to a single form of molecular weight 35,000 by treatment with trypsin or ethanol.

It has therefore been proposed that the existence of inactive or less active forms of the enzyme may represent enzyme–inhibitor complexes in which a unique catalytic subunit of molecular weight 35,000 (designated Ptse C, box D, Fig. 50) is complexed with inhibitor proteins. This hypothesis provides an intriguing parallel to the protein kinase catalytic–regulatory subunit complex, the enzyme whose function opposes that of the phosphoprotein phosphatases. Huang and Glinsmann (1975) have provided evidence that the general phosphoprotein phosphatase exists in active and inactive forms (box D, Fig. 50) and that the conversion of the active form to the inactive forms occurs as a result of the cAMP-dependent protein kinase-catalyzed phosphorylation of the inhibitor subunit. Thus the Ptse C-I′ species is active, whereas the Ptse C-I′-P form is inactive. With mild physicochemical perturbation, the subunits can be separated to give Ptse C, which is catalytically active, and I′-P, which is an inhibitor of Ptse C. Nonphosphorylated I′ does not inhibit Ptse C. Dephosphorylation of I′-P is probably catalyzed by a Mn^{2+}-dependent phosphatase that may be similar to the Mn^{2+}-dependent α-phosphorylase kinase phosphatase. Glinsmann's group has also identified a second inhibitor, I″, which is not regulated by phosphorylation (Huang and Glinsmann, 1976).

Figure 50 presents a bewildering sequence of interrelated phosphorylations and dephosphorylations in which the cAMP-dependent protein kinase and the general phosphoprotein phosphatase play multiple roles. To dissect the ramifications of such controls and their physiological consequences is not possible at this time. It is probable, however, that this degree of complexity is not unique to the cAMP-dependent regulation of glycogen metabolism but will prove of widespread occurrence in other systems.

ADDENDUM

A recent paper by Walkenbach *et al.* (1978) (*Mol. Cell. Biochem.* **19,** 31) has described the effect of insulin on the cAMP-dependent protein kinase of diaphragm. Insulin added to the intact cell resulted in the decrease in the total amount of cAMP-dependent protein kinase, a decrease in the cAMP binding activity, but no significant increase in the amount of free catalytic subunit. This interesting observation suggests the possibility that an action of insulin is to modify the holoenzyme form of the protein kinase such that it is refractory to activation by the normal concentrations of cAMP. This is so far a unique observation indicating that the protein kinase may be modified by specific interaction with the holoenzyme that decreases its sensitivity to cAMP-stimulated disassociation.

ACKNOWLEDGMENTS

The authors wish to acknowledge the support of the National Institutes of Health (Grants AM 13613 and AM 21019). The authors are indebted to the many investigators in the field who have courteously provided manuscripts prior to their publication.

REFERENCES

Antoniw, J. F., and Cohen, P. (1976). *Eur. J. Biochem.* **68**, 45–54.

Bailey, C., and Villar-Palasi, C. (1971). *Fed. Proc., Fed. Am. Soc. Exp. Biol.* **30**, 1147.

Beavo, J. A., Bechtel, P. J., and Krebs, E. G. (1974). *Proc. Natl. Acad. Sci. U.S.A.* **71**, 3580–3583.

Beavo, J. A., Bechtel, P. J., and Krebs, E. G. (1975). *Adv. Cyclic Nucleotide Res.* **5**, 241–251.

Bechtel, P. J., Beavo, J. A., and Krebs, E. G. (1977). *J. Biol. Chem.* **252**, 2691–2697.

Berglund, L., Ljungström, O., and Engström, L. (1977). *J. Biol. Chem.* **252**, 613–619.

Birnbaum, M. J., and Fain, J. N. (1977). *J. Biol. Chem.* **252**, 528–535.

Blumenthal, D. K., Stull, J. T., and Gill, G. N. (1978). In press.

Boyer, P. D., ed. (1973). "The Enzymes," 3rd ed., Vol. 8. Academic Press, New York.

Brandt, H., Capulong, Z. L., and Lee, E. Y. C. (1975). *J. Biol. Chem.* **250**, 8038–8044.

Buss, J. E., and Stull, J. T. (1977). *FEBS Lett.* **73**, 101–104.

Bylund, D. B., and Krebs, E. G. (1975). *J. Biol. Chem.* **250**, 6355–6361.

Byus, C. V., Chubb, J. M., Huxtable, R. J., and Russell, D. H. (1976). *Biochem. Biophys. Res. Commun.* **73**, 694–702.

Byus, C. V., Hedge, G. A., and Russell, D. H. (1977a). *Biochim. Biophys. Acta* **498**, 39–45.

Byus, C. V., Klimpel, G. R., Lucas, D. O., and Russell, D. H. (1977b). *Nature (London)* **268**, 63–64.

Castagna, M., Palmer, W. K., and Walsh, D. A. (1975). *Eur. J. Biochem.* **55**, 193–199.

Castagna, M., Palmer, W. K., and Walsh, D. A. (1977). *Arch. Biochem. Biophys.* **181**, 46–60.

Chen, L. J., and Walsh, D. A. (1971). *Biochemistry* **10**, 3614–3621.

Cherrington, A. D., Assimacopoulos, F. D., Harper, S. C., Corbin, J. D., Park, C. R., and Exton, J. H. (1976). *J. Biol. Chem.* **251**, 5209–5218.

Clark, M. R., Azhar, S., and Menon, K. M. J. (1976). *Biochem. J.* **158**, 175–182.

Cohen, P. (1973). *Eur. J. Biochem.* **34**, 1–14.

Cohen, P., and Antoniw, J. F. (1973). *FEBS Lett.* **34**, 43–47.

Cole, H. A., and Perry, S. V. (1975). *Biochem. J.* **149**, 525–533.

Cooke, B. A., Lindh, M. L., and Janszen, F. H. A. (1976). *Biochem. J.* **160**, 439–446.
Corbin, J. D., and Keely, S. L. (1977). *J. Biol. Chem.* **252**, 910–918.
Corbin, J. D., Soderling, T. R., and Park, C. R. (1973). *J. Biol. Chem.* **248**, 1813–1821.
Corbin, J. D., Keely, S. L., and Park, C. R. (1975a). *J. Biol. Chem.* **250**, 218–225.
Corbin, J. D., Keely, S. L., Soderling, T. R., and Park, C. R. (1975b). *Adv. Cyclic Nucleotide Res.* **5**, 265–279.
Corbin, J. D., Sugden, P. H., Lincoln, T. M., and Keely, S. L. (1977). *J. Biol. Chem.* **252**, 3854–3861.
Cori, C. F. (1956). *In* "Enzymes: Units of Biological Structure and Function" (O. M. Gaebler, ed.), p. 573. Academic Press New York.
Costa, E., Kurosawa, A., and Guidotti, A. (1976). *Proc. Natl. Acad. Sci. U.S.A.* **73**, 1058–1062.
Costa, M., Gerner, E. W., and Russell, D. H. (1976). *J. Biol. Chem.* **251**, 3313–3319.
Datta, A., deHaro, C., Sierra, J. M., and Ochoa, S. (1977a). *Proc. Natl. Acad. Sci. U.S.A.* **74**, 1463–1467.
Datta, A., deHaro, C., Sierra, J. M., and Ochoa, S. (1977b). *Proc. Natl. Acad. Sci. U.S.A.* **74**, 3326–3329.
Delaunay, J., Ranu, R. S., Levin, D. H., Ernst, V., and London, I. M. (1977). *Proc. Natl. Acad. Sci. U.S.A.* **74**, 2264–2268.
Dills, W. L., West, T. D., and Walsh, D. A. (1977). *J. Biol. Chem.* **252**, 4287–4292.
England, P. J. (1975). *FEBS Lett.* **50**, 57–60.
England, P. J. (1976). *Biochem. J.* **160**, 295–304.
England, P. J. (1977). *Biochem. J.* **168**, 307–310.
England, P. J., Stull, J. T., Huang, T. S., and Krebs, E. G. (1974). *In* "Metabolic Interconversion of Enzymes" (E. H. Fischer *et al.*, eds.), pp. 175–184. Springer-Verlag, Berlin and New York.
Entman, M. L., Levey, G. S., and Epstein, S. E. (1969). *Circ. Res.* **25**, 429–438.
Exton, J. H., Cherrington, A. D., Hutson, N. J., and Assimacopoulos-Jeannet, F. D. (1977). *In* "Glucagon: Its Role in Physiology and Clinical Medicine" (P. Foa, J. Bajaj, and N. L. Foa, eds.), pp. 321–348. Springer-Verlag, Berlin and New York.
Féliu, J. E., Hué, L. F., and Hers, H. G. (1976). *Proc. Natl. Acad. Sci. U.S.A.* **73**, 2762–2766.
Féliu, J., Hué, L., and Hers, H. G. (1977). *Eur. J. Biochem.* (in press).
Field, J. B., Bloom, G., Kerins, M. E., Chayoth, R., and Zor, U. (1975). *J. Biol. Chem.* **250**, 4903–4910.
Frearson, N., and Perry, S. V. (1975). *Biochem. J.* **151**, 99–107.
Frearson, N., Solaro, R. J., and Perry, S. V. (1976). *Nature (London)* **264**, 801–802.
Friedman, D. L., Johnson, R. A., and Zeilig, C. E. (1976). *Adv. Cyclic Nucleotide Res.* **7**, 69–114.
Gharrett, A. J., Malkinson, A. M., and Sheppard, J. R. (1976). *Nature (London)* **264**, 673–675.
Gill, G. N. (1977). *J. Cyclic Nucleotide Res.* **3**, 153–162.
Gill, G. N., Walton, G. M., and Sperry, P. J. (1977). *J. Biol. Chem.* **252**, 6443–6449.
Gratecos, D., Detwiler, T., and Fischer, E. H. (1974). *In* "Metabolic Interconversion of Enzymes" (E. H. Fischer *et al.*, eds.), pp. 43–52. Springer-Verlag, Berlin and New York.
Grosmann, A., and Furchgott, R. F. (1964). *J. Pharmacol. Exp. Ther.* **145**, 162–172.
Hayakawa, T., Perkins, J. P., and Krebs, E. G. (1973). *Biochemistry* **12**, 574–580.
Hofmann, F., Beavo, J. A., Bechtel, P. J., and Krebs, E. G. (1975). *J. Biol. Chem.* **250**, 7795–7801.
Hofmann, F., Bechtel, P. J., and Krebs, E. G. (1977). *J. Biol. Chem.* **252**, 1441–1447.
Hoppe, J., Marutzky, R., Freist, W., and Wagner, K. G. (1977). *Eur. J. Biochem.* **80**, 369–372.
Huang, F. L., and Glinsmann, W. H. (1975). *Proc. Natl. Acad. Sci. U.S.A.* **72**, 3004–3008.
Huang, F. L., and Glinsmann, W. H. (1976). *Eur. J. Biochem.* **70**, 419–426.

Huang, K. P., Huang, F. L., Glinsmann, W. H., and Robinson, J. C. (1975). *Biochem. Biophys. Res. Commun.* **65**, 1163–1169.

Huang, T. S., Bylund, D. B., Stull, J. T., and Krebs, E. G. (1974). *FEBS Lett.* **42**, 249–252.

Hui, C. W., Drummond, M., and Drummond, G. I. (1976). *Arch. Biochem. Biophys.* **173**, 415–427.

Hutson, N. J., Brumley, F. T., Assimacopoulos, F. D., Harper, S. C., and Exton, J. H. (1976). *J. Biol. Chem.* **251**, 5200–5208.

Hutson, N. J., Khatra, B. S., and Soderling, T. R. (1978). *J. Biol. Chem.* **253**, 2540–2545.

Keely, S. L., Jr., Corbin, J. D., and Park, C. R. (1975). *Proc. Natl. Acad. Sci. U.S.A.* **72**, 1501–1504.

Kemp, B. E., Bylund, D. B., Huang, T. S., and Krebs, E. G. (1975). *Proc. Natl. Acad. Sci. U.S.A.* **72**, 3448–3452.

Kemp, B. E., Benjamini, E., and Krebs, E. G. (1976). *Proc. Natl. Acad. Sci. U.S.A.* **73**, 1038–1042.

Kemp, B. E., Graves, D. J., Benjamini, E., and Krebs, E. G. (1977). *J. Biol. Chem.* **252**, 4888–4894.

Keppens, S., Vandenheede, J. R., and de Wulf, H. (1977). *Biochim. Biophys. Acta* **496**, 448–457.

Kirchberger, M. A., and Chu, G. (1976). *Biochim. Biophys. Acta* **419**, 559–562.

Kirchberger, M. A., and Raffo, A. (1977). *J. Cyclic Nucleotide Res.* **3**, 45–53.

Kirchberger, M. A., Tada, M., Repke, D. I., and Katz, A. M. (1972). *J. Mol. Cell. Cardiol.* **4**, 673–680.

Kirchberger, M. A., Tada, M., and Katz, A. M. (1974). *J. Biol. Chem.* **249**, 6166–6173.

Kochetkov, S. N., Bulargina, T. V., Sashchenko, L. P., and Severin, E. S. (1976). *FEBS Lett.* **71**, 212–214.

Krause, E. G., Will, H., Schirpke, B., and Wollenberger, A. (1975). *Adv. Cyclic Nucleotide Res.* **5**, 473–490.

Krebs, E. G. (1974). *Endocrinol. Proc. Int. Congr., 4th, 1972* pp. 17–29.

Krebs, E. G., Kent, A. B., and Fischer, E. H. (1958). *J. Biol. Chem.* **231**, 73–83.

Kuo, J. F., and Greengard, P. (1969). *Proc. Natl. Acad. Sci. U.S.A.* **64**, 1349–1355.

Kurosawa, A., Guidotti, A., and Costa, E. (1976). *Science* **193**, 691–693.

Langan, T. A. (1969). *J. Biol. Chem.* **244**, 5763–5765.

Langan, T. A. (1973a). *Adv. Cyclic Nucleotide Res.* **3**, 99–136.

Langan, T. A. (1973b). *J. Biol. Chem.* **248**, 6289–6291.

LaRaia, P. J., and Morkin, E. (1974). *Circ. Res.* **35**, 298–306.

Lemaire, I., and Coffino, P. (1977). *Cell* **11**, 149–154.

Li, A. P., O'Neill, J. P., Kawashima, K., and Hsie, A. W. (1977). *Arch. Biochem. Biophys.* **182**, 181–187.

Lincoln, T. M., and Corbin, J. D. (1977). *Proc. Natl. Acad. Sci. U.S.A.* **74**, 3239–3243.

Lincoln, T. M., Dills, W. L., and Corbin, J. D. (1977). *J. Biol. Chem.* **252**, 4269–4275.

Ljungström, O., Hjelmquist, G., and Engström, L. (1974). *Biochim. Biophys. Acta* **358**, 289–298.

Ljungström, O., Berglund, L., and Engström, L. (1976). *Eur. J. Biochem.* **68**, 497–506.

Maller, J. L., and Krebs, E. G. (1977). *J. Biol. Chem.* **252**, 1712–1718.

Means, A. R., Fakunding, J. L., and Tindall, D. J. (1976). *Biol. Reprod.* **14**, 54–63.

Miller, J. (1977). *In* "Cyclic 3′,5′-Nucleotides: Mechanisms of Action" (H. Cramer and J. Schultz, eds.), pp. 77–105. Wiley, New York.

Miller, J. P., Beck, A. H., Simon, L. N., and Meyer, R. B., Jr. (1975). *J. Biol. Chem.* **250**, 426–431.

Miller, T. D., Jr., and Larner, J. (1973). *J. Biol. Chem.* **248**, 3483–3488.

Moir, A. J. G., Wilkinson, J. M., and Perry, S. V. (1974). *FEBS Lett.* **42**, 253–256.
Moir, A. J. G., Cole, H. A., and Perry, S. V. (1977). *Biochem. J.* **161**, 371–382.
Moll, G. W., and Kaiser, E. T. (1976). *J. Biol. Chem.* **251**, 3993–4000.
Monod, J., Wyman, J., and Changeux, J. P. (1965). *J. Mol. Biol.* **12**, 88–118.
Nayler, W. G., and Berry, D. (1975). *J. Mol. Cell Cardiol.* **7**, 387–395.
Nimmo, H. G., Proud, C. G., and Cohen, P. (1976). *Eur. J. Biochem.* **68**, 31–44.
Ogez, J. R., and Segel, I. H. (1976). *J. Biol. Chem.* **251**, 4551–4556.
O'Neill, J. P., Li, A. P., and Hsie, A. W. (1977). *Biochim. Biophys. Acta* **497**, 35–45.
Palmer, W. K., Castagna, M., and Walsh, D. A. (1974). *Biochem. J.* **143**, 469–471.
Pastan, I. H., Johnson, G. S., and Anderson, W. B. (1975). *Annu. Rev. Biochem.* **44**, 491–522.
Perrie, W. T., Smillie, L. B., and Perry, S. V. (1972). *Biochem. J.* **128**, 105P–106P.
Perrie, W. T., Smillie, L. B., and Perry, S. V. (1973). *Biochem. J.* **135**, 151–164.
Perry, S. V., and Cole, H. A. (1973). *Biochem. J.* **131**, 425–428.
Perry, S. V., and Cole, H. A. (1974). *Biochem. J.* **141**, 733–743.
Podesta, E. J., Dufau, M. L., and Catt, K. J. (1976). *FEBS Lett.* **70**, 212–216.
Posternak, T., Sutherland, E. W., and Henion, W. F. (1962). *Biochim. Biophys. Acta* **65**, 558–560.
Pratje, E., and Heilmeyer, L. M. G., Jr. (1972). *FEBS Lett.* **27**, 89–93.
Rangel-Aldao, R., and Rosen, O. M. (1976). *J. Biol. Chem.* **251**, 3375–3380.
Ray, K. P., and England, P. J. (1976). *FEBS Lett.* **70**, 11–16.
Reimann, E. M., Walsh, D. A., and Krebs, E. G. (1971). *J. Biol. Chem.* **246**, 1986–1995.
Revel, M. (1977). *In* "Molecular Mechanisms of Protein Biosynthesis" (H. Weissbach and S. Pestka, eds.), p. 246. Academic Press, New York.
Richardson, M. C., and Schulster, D. (1973). *Biochem. J.* **136**, 993–998.
Rosen, O. M., Rangel-Aldao, R., and Erlichman, J. (1977). *Curr. Top. Cell. Regul.* **12**, 39–55.
Rubin, C. S., and Rosen, O. M. (1975). *Annu. Rev. Biochem.* **44**, 831–887.
Rubio, R., Bailey, C., and Villar-Palasi, C. (1975). *J. Cyclic Nucleotide Res.* **1**, 143–150.
Russell, D. (1977). *Adv. Cyclic Nucleotide Res.* **9** (in press).
Ryan, W. L., and Heidrick, M. L. (1974). *Adv. Cyclic Nucleotide Res.* **4**, 81–116.
Salem, R., and De Vellis, J. (1976). *Fed. Proc., Fed. Am. Soc. Exp. Biol.* **35**, 296.
Schlender, K. K., and Reimann, E. M. (1975). *Proc. Natl. Acad. Sci. U.S.A.* **72**, 2197–2201.
Schwartz, A., Entman, M. L., Kanike, K., Lane, L. K., Van Bornet, E. P. (1976). *Biochim. Biophys. Acta* **426**, 57–72.
Selinger, Z., Batzri, S., Eimerl, S., and Schramm, M. (1973). *J. Biol. Chem.* **248**, 369–372.
Seubert, W., and Schoner, W. (1971). *Curr. Top. Cell. Regul.* **3**, 237–267.
Sharma, R. K., Ahmed, N. K., and Shanker, G. (1976). *Eur. J. Biochem.* **70**, 427–433.
Shinebourne, E. A., Hess, M. L., White, R. J., and Hamer, J. (1969). *Cardiovasc. Res.* **3**, 113–117.
Shizuta, Y., Beavo, J. A., Bechtel, P. J., Hofmann, F., and Krebs, E. G. (1975). *J. Biol. Chem.* **250**, 6891–6896.
Singh, T. J., and Wang, J. H. (1977). *J. Biol. Chem.* **252**, 625–632.
Skala, J. P., and Knight, B. L. (1977). *J. Biol. Chem.* **252**, 1064–1070.
Soderling, T. R. (1975). *J. Biol. Chem.* **250**, 5407–5412.
Soderling, T. R., Corbin, J. D., and Park, C. R. (1973). *J. Biol. Chem.* **248**, 1822–1829.
Soderling, T. R., Jett, M. F., Hutson, N. J., and Khatra, B. S. (1977). *J. Biol. Chem.* **252**, 7517–7524.
Speaker, M. G., and Butcher, F. R. (1977). *Nature (London)* **267**, 848–850.
Spielvogel, A. M., Mednieks, M. I., Eppenberger, U., and Jungmann, R. A. (1977). *Eur. J. Biochem.* **73**, 199–212.

Staehelin, T., Trachsel, H., Erni, B., Boschetti, A., and Schreier, M. H. (1975). *Proc. FEBS Meet., 10th, 1975* Vol. 39, p. 309.

Steinberg, D. (1976). *Adv. Cyclic Nucleotide Res.* **7**, 157–198.

Steinberg, R. A., O'Farrell, P. H., Friedrich, U., and Coffino, P. (1977). *Cell* **10**, 381–391.

Steiner, A. L., Koide, Y., Earp, H. S., Bechtel, P. J., and Beavo, J. A. (1977). *Adv. Cyclic Nucleotide Res.* **9** (in press).

Stull, J. T., and Buss, J. E. (1977). *J. Biol. Chem.* **252**, 851–857.

Stull, J. T., and High, C. W. (1977). *Biochem. Biophys. Res. Commun.* **77**, 1078–1083.

Stull, J. T., Brostrom, C. O., and Krebs, E. G. (1972). *J. Biol. Chem.* **247**, 5272–5274.

Sulakhe, P. V., and St. Louis, P. J. (1976). *Gen. Pharmacol.* **7**, 313–319.

Sulakhe, P. V., and Drummond, G. I. (1974). *Arch. Biochem. Biophys.* **161**, 448–455.

Sulakhe, P. V., Leung, N. L. K., and St. Louis, P. J. (1976). *Can. J. Biochem.* **54**, 438–445.

Sutherland, E. W., and Rall, T. W. (1960). *Pharmacol. Rev.* **12**, 265–299.

Tada, M., Kirchberger, M. A., Repke, D. I., and Katz, A. M. (1974). *J. Biol. Chem.* **249**, 6174–6180.

Tada, M., Kirchberger, M. A., and Katz, A. M. (1975). *J. Biol. Chem.* **250**, 2640–2647.

Tada, M., Yamamoto, T., and Tonomura, Y. (1978). *Physiol. Rev.* **58** (in press).

Vassort, G., Rougier, O., Garnier, D., Sauviat, M. P., Coraboeuf, E. and Gargouïl, Y. M. (1969). *Pflugers Arch.* **309**, 70–81.

Wagner, K., Roper, M. D., Leichtling, B. H., Wimalasena, J., and Wicks, W. D. (1975). *J. Biol. Chem.* **250**, 231–239.

Walsh, D. A. (1978). *Biochem. Pharmacol.* **27**, 1801–1804.

Walsh, D. A., and Ashby, C. D. (1973). *Recent Prog. Horm. Res.* **29**, 329–359.

Walsh, D. A., and Krebs, E. G. (1973). *Enzymes* **8**, 555–581.

Walsh, D. A., Perkins, J. P., and Krebs, E. G. (1968). *J. Biol. Chem.* **243**, 3763–3774.

Walsh, D. A., Ashby, C. D., Gonzales, C., Calkins, D., Fischer, E. H., and Krebs, E. G. (1971). *J. Biol. Chem.* **246**, 1977–1985.

Weissbach, H., and Ochoa, S. (1976). *Annu. Rev. Biochem.* **45**, 191–216.

Wicks, W. D. (1974). *Adv. Cyclic Nucleotide Res.* **4**, 335–438.

Wicks, W. D., Koontz, J., and Wagner, K. (1975). *J. Cyclic Nucleotide Res.* **1**, 49–58.

Zetterqvist, O., Ragnarsson, U., Humble, E., Berglund, L., and Engström, L. (1976). *Biochem. Biophys. Res. Commun.* **70**, 696–703.

CHAPTER 2

Hormonal and Metabolic Control of Phosphoprotein Phosphatase

Randall T. Curnow and Joseph Larner

I. INTRODUCTION

The interconversion of enzymes between their active and inactive forms as a result of phosphorylation and dephosphorylation is well established as an important mechanism for metabolic control (Segal, 1973). Appreciation of this fundamental phenomenon has evolved mainly from the study of the enzymes of glycogen metabolism. Phosphorylation of phosphorylase (Krebs and Fischer, 1956) and phosphorylase kinase (Delange *et al.*, 1968) activates these enzymes, while phosphorylation of glycogen synthase (Friedman and Larner, 1963) results in its inactivation. The phosphorylation steps involving phosphorylase kinase and glycogen synthase are mediated by a cyclic AMP-dependent protein kinase (Schender *et al.*, 1969) and are therefore controlled by agents which modulate the intracellular concentration of this cyclic nucleotide. While extensive work has been carried out on the kinases,

77

until recently less attention has been paid to the phosphoprotein phosphatases which catalyze the reciprocal dephosphorylation reactions. In the past several years, however, significant progress has been made relative to purification, specificity, and regulation of this class of enzyme (Lee *et al.*, 1976). The purpose of this paper is to review this information in order to define the current state of our knowledge and to ascertain the direction of future research in this area.

While we clearly recognize that metabolite and hormonal control of the phosphoprotein phosphatase activities associated with metabolic pathways other than glycogen metabolism are undoubtedly very important, our knowledge in these areas is much less complete; therefore, they will not be discussed here.

II. ENZYME PROPERTIES

Despite the fact that phosphorylase phosphatase, the first known interconverting enzyme, was discovered more than 35 years ago by Cori and Green (1943), our understanding of its biochemistry has evolved slowly. These enzymes have been extremely difficult to study with precision because of difficulties encountered in their purification. In addition, the study of the phosphatases, which exert their catalytic action on substrates *in vitro* and are also intracellular enzymes from the same or similar tissues, poses special problems in enzyme kinetic analysis. Because the substrates are of high molecular weight, the molar ratio of enzyme to substrate under most assay conditions is necessarily quite high, thus making determination of standard Michaelis–Menton kinetics difficult. In order to establish a reference base for subsequent discussion, this section will describe the approaches used to characterize the enzymatic properties of phosphoprotein phosphatases from various tissues. Table I lists these properties for the major phosphoprotein phosphatases associated with glycogen metabolism.

A. METHODS OF PURIFICATION AND ENZYME PROPERTIES

Wosilait and Sutherland (1956) were the first to partially purify phosphorylase phosphatase from dog liver. Their procedure involved absorption of the enzyme from the homogenate onto calcium phosphate gel and subsequent elution with 0.3 M NaCl. The eluate was then precipitated with ammonium sulfate followed by ethanol. This procedure produced a 200- to 300-fold purification. Their studies focused on the quantitation of inorganic phosphate release from phosphorylase catalyzed by the phosphatase. The

TABLE I

CHARACTERISTICS OF PHOSPHOPROTEIN PHOSPHATASE REACTIONS RELATED TO GLYCOGEN METABOLISM FROM VARIOUS SOURCES USING PURIFIED SUBSTRATES[a]

Organ	Species	Cellular fraction	Molecular weight(s) ($\times 10^3$)	Purification	Substrates	References
Skeletal muscle	Rabbit	Glycogen	50 (SD)	2000× (AP, Am, CC, GF)	GP	Hurd et al. (1966)
	Rabbit	Cytosol	1000× (EP, CC, GF)	GS,H	Kato and Bishop (1972)
	Rabbit	Cytosol	300; 150 (GS)	—	GS,GP,H	Kato and Sato (1974)
	Rabbit	Cytosol	I, 300 (GF)	—	H>>GS=GP	Antoniw et al. (1977)
			II, 170 (GF)	—	αPK>>βPK	Antoniw et al. (1977)
			IIIA, 75 (GF)	—	GS,GP,βPK	Antoniw et al. (1977)
			IIIB, 45 (GF)	—	GS,GP,βPK	Antoniw et al. (1977)
	Rabbit	Cytosol	35 (SDS)	5000× (EP,GF, CC)	GP	Brandt et al. (1975)
	Rabbit	Glycogen	32 (SDS)	6000× (polylys-Sep)	GP,T	Gratecos et al. (1974)
	Rabbit	Cytosol	70	—	GS,GP,H	Huang and Glinsmann (1975)
	Rabbit	Cytosol	300<25 (GF)	—	GP,T,H	Ray and England (1976)

(continued)

TABLE I continued

Organ	Species	Cellular fraction	Molecular weight(s) (× 10³)	Purification	Substrates	References
Heart	Bovine	Cytosol	—	150 × (EP, CC)	GS,GP,H	Nakai and Thomas (1974)
Liver	Dog	Cytosol	—	200–300 × (CaPO$_4$ gel, AmP)	GP,PV	Wosilait and Sutherland (1956)
	Dog	Glycogen	51 (GF)	—	GP	Goris et al. (1975)
	Dog	8000g supernatant	—	—	GS	Bishop (1970)
	Rabbit (Rat)	Cytosol	34 (GF, SD)	25,000× (AP, AmP,EP,CC, GF, Hexs)	GP,GS,H PhK,RPK	Brandt et al. (1975)
	Rabbit	Cytosol	164→47 (GF)	451×	GP,H	Kobayashi et al. (1975)
	Rabbit	Cytosol	Peak I, 30. Peak II, 34 (GF, SDS)	4,610× (AP,HSC, IE,HS)	GS,GP,H,C	Khandelwal et al. (1976)
	Rat	Cytosol	—	—	GP,GS	Tan and Nuttall (1976)
	Rat	Cytosol	—	—	Distinct CC fx for GP and GS	Kiluchi et al. (1977)

[a] Abbreviations: GP, phosphorylase; GS, glycogen synthase; H, histone; αPK, α subunit of phosphorylase kinase; βPK, β subunit of phosphorylase kinase; T, inhibitory subunit of troponin; PV, phosvitin; RPK, R subunit of protien kinase; SD, sucrose density gradient centrifugation; GF, gel filtration; AP, acid precipitation; CC, DEAE-cellulose chromatography; EP, ethanol precipitation; SDS, SDS-polyacrylamide gel electrophoresis; polylys-Sep, polylysine-Sepharose chromatography; AMP, ammonium sulfate precipitation; HSC, high-speed centrifugation; Hexs, hexanediamine-Sepharose chromatography; HS, histone Sepharose chromatography; IE, focusing.

time course of liberation of phosphate from phosphorylase coincided with loss of enzymatic activity; the total amount of phosphate liberated during the complete inactivation of phosphorylase was calculated to be 1 mole per 100,000 g of phosphorylase. In addition to phosphorylase, this phosphatase preparation also dephosphorylated phosvitin and α-casein. This suggested the presence either of several specific phosphatases or, alternatively, of a nonspecific protein phosphatase. The major impact of this work was that it was the first to firmly establish the chemical difference between the two forms of phosphorylase in liver.

The next significant step was made by Hurd *et al.* (1966), who isolated phosphorylase phosphatase from the muscle glycogen particle. They subjected the 78,000*g* postacid (pH 6.1) precipitated glycogen–protein pellet to amylase digestion. This released approximately 75% of the phosphatase into the supernatant which was further purified by chromatography on DEAE-cellulose. The phosphorylase phosphatase and phosphorylase kinase were eluted together with 0.15 *M* NaCl and subsequently separated from one another by gel filtration on Sephadex G-200. This procedure allowed a much higher purification than previously attained and produced an enrichment of approximately 2000-fold. The enzyme had an apparent K_m for phosphorylase *a* of about 3 μM and a molecular weight of approximately 50,000, as determined by sucrose density gradient centrifugation. However, the purified enzyme was not homogeneous; polyacrylamide gel electrophoresis revealed several bands, of which fewer than half had phosphatase activity. The enzyme apparently exhibited a large degree of substrate specificity, being active only against phosphorylase *a* and phosphopeptides derived from it.

Subsequently, Gratecos *et al.* (1974) achieved further purification of this enzyme. After solubilizing the enzymes present in the glycogen particle with amylase, they made use of two unusual properties of the phosphatase, i.e., its stability in concentrated urea and its inhibition by polylysine. The enzyme was chromatographed on a polylysine-Sepharose 4B affinity column. After elution of phosphorylase kinase, phosphorylase, and other contaminating proteins with a low salt concentration, the phosphatase was eluted with 6 *M* urea, leading to a 700-fold purification. Further removal of nonspecific proteins by ammonium sulfate precipitation resulted in a final purification of 6000-fold. Polyacrylamide gel electrophoresis revealed several protein bands, with molecular weights ranging from 30,000 to 120,000. The enzyme was resistant to trypsin and chymotrypsin treatment.

This more highly purified enzyme exhibited the same substrate specificity as described by Hurd *et al.* (1966). It did not dephosphorylate histone, protamine, or phosphorylase kinase, and acted only on phosphorylase *a* or phosphopeptides derived from it and the inhibitory component of troponin (TN-I).

Another significant step in the purification and characterization of phosphoprotein phosphatase was made by Kato and Bishop (1972), who studied the phosphoprotein phosphatase derived from the 78,000 g supernatant of rabbit muscle extracts. The supernatant enzyme was purified by ethanol fractionation, chromatography on DEAE-cellulose, and gel filtration over Sephadex G-200. An important observation made in these studies was that Mn^{2+} stabilized the enzyme to freezing and thawing, which allowed for a marked increase in the yield and a purification of approximately 1000-fold. Villar-Palasi (1969) had previously described a similar method for purifying the enzyme but had achieved limited success, apparently because of the omission of Mn^{2+}. In contrast to the phosphatase preparations described by Hurd *et al.* (1966) and Gratecos *et al.* (1974), these studies suggested that phosphatase activities against several substrates were associated with the same protein peak. Phosphatase activities against purified rabbit muscle glycogen synthase D and [^{32}P]histone copurified in constant ratios. The enzyme possessed an apparent K_m of $0.12 \mu M$ for glycogen synthase.

Zieve and Glinsmann (1973) next examined the substrate specificity of this enzyme in greater detail using ^{32}P release as a marker. They demonstrated that the ratio of phosphorylase kinase phosphatase to glycogen synthase phosphatase activity remained constant through greater than a 1000-fold purification. In addition, they showed that the active, but not inactive, form of phosphorylase kinase was an effective competitive inhibitor of the glycogen synthase phosphatase.

Nakai and Thomas (1974) also used the method of Kato and Bishop to purify a phosphoprotein phosphatase from bovine heart. Their purification was only 150-fold as a result of their omission of the final Sephadex G-200 gel filtration step. The 0.25–0.30 M NaCl fraction from the DEAE-cellulose step was studied for phosphatase activity against phosphorylase, glycogen synthase, histone, and casein as substrates, using ^{32}P release. Dephosphorylation activities against the four substrates eluted together from Sephadex G-100 gel filtration and possessed the same isoelectric focusing characteristics. They also demonstrated that each of the various dephosphorylatable substrates was an effective competitive inhibitor of the others. Accordingly, the data of Kato and Bishop (1972), Zieve and Glinsmann (1973), and Nakai and Thomas (1974), taken together, suggested that the several phosphatase activities present in the post-78,000 g supernatant of muscle extracts may reside in a single protein species.

Antoniw *et al.* (1977), in contrast, have recently presented evidence indicating that certain muscle phosphoprotein phosphatases exhibit a high degree of substrate specificity. They examined the interrelationships among protein phosphatase activities of glycogen metabolism, i.e., phosphorylase phosphatase, glycogen synthase phosphatase, and the α- and β-phosphorylase kinase phosphatases. The fractions from the final gel filtration step (G-200) were assayed with these substrates using ^{32}P release. Three protein phosphatases with distinct specificities (termed I, II, and III) were resolved. Phosphatase I was active against phosphorylated histone but had only modest activity against the other substrates. This phosphatase species had an apparent molecular weight of 300,000 daltons. Phosphatase II possessed greater than 95% of the total extract phosphatase activity against the α subunit of phosphorylase kinase, with much less activity against the other substrates. The apparent molecular weight of this enzyme was 170,000 daltons.

Phosphatase III was found to be particularly interesting. It was the most active histone phosphatase of the three enzymes, possessing approximately 95% of the phosphorylase phosphatase and β-phosphorylase kinase phosphatase activities and approximately 80% of the phosphatase activity against glycogen synthase. The activities against the three copurified quite closely throughout the various steps. This latter enzyme exhibited sedimentation characteristics compatible with two molecular species, one of 75,000 daltons (IIIA) and the other of 45,000 daltons (IIIB). Cohen *et al.* (1977a) suggested that the major phosphatase activities against phosphorylase, glycogen synthase, and β-phosphorylase kinase are catalyzed by this enzyme. This assumption was based on the evidence showing the copurification of the various activities and the fact that these activities were inhibited in an identical manner by a heat-stable protein that is apparently specific for the protein phosphatase III (see Section II,B). While it has not been rigorously established that this enzyme is the same as the enzyme that was studied by Kato and Bishop (1972), Nakai and Thomas (1974), and Zieve and Glinsmann (1973), the data suggest that this may well be the case. The data are also in accord with the hypothesis that a common phosphoprotein phosphatase(s) catalyzes a number of protein dephosphorylations as determined by ^{32}P release. A major shortcoming of all these studies, however, is the fact that they were performed with nonhomogeneous enzyme preparations. In addition, in most cases the dephosphorylation reaction was quantitated by measuring ^{32}P release from noncharacterized sites, without evaluating substrate enzyme activity change. This latter consideration is conceivably very important, for it is now clear that several of these substrates are phosphorylated at multiple sites, the dephosphorylation of which does not closely correlate with enzymatic activity conversion (Roach and Larner, 1977).

In 1975, Brandt and co-workers achieved the purification and characterization of a homogeneous phosphoprotein phosphatase from rabbit liver. The initial steps involved precipitations of liver extracts with acid, then ammonium sulfate, and finally ethanol. The most important of these steps was the ethanol precipitation at room temperature. The specific activity of the enzyme extracted from the final precipitate was increased 5- to 10-fold and behaved as a monomeric species on subsequent purification steps which included chromatography on DEAE-Sephadex, Sephadex G-75, and two additional hydrophobic chromatographic separations on hexanediamine-Sepharose. This resulted in a 24,700-fold purification of the enzyme, which was homogeneous on polyacrylamide disc gel electrophoresis, with an apparent molecular weight of 34,000, as estimated by Sephadex G-75 chromatography.

They speculated that they were able to obtain a homogeneous enzyme because the ethanol precipitation had removed inhibitory proteins. As will be discussed subsequently, this idea was probably correct and has marked a major advance in our knowledge of the potential regulatory mechanisms for phosphoprotein phosphatases. The possibility that the multiple forms of the enzyme observed by others were generated from a single high molecular weight species by partial proteolysis was also investigated by Brandt and co-workers (1974). They found that when rat livers were extracted under conditions which minimized lysosomal damage, a single form of the enzyme was reproducibly obtained, with an apparent molecular weight of approximately 220,000, as determined by gel filtration on Bio-Gel A-0.2 m. Accordingly, it was concluded that the multiple forms of the liver enzyme that they and others had observed were an artifact of the preparative procedure probably generated by the attack of lysosomal enzymes.

Killilea *et al.* (1976) next examined the capacity of the homogeneous low molecular weight enzyme to dephosphorylate other substrates such as purified rabbit liver glycogen synthase and phosphorylase. Using enzyme activity conversion, they reported that, during purification, phosphorylase phosphatase and glycogen synthase phosphatase activities copurified at a relatively constant ratio. The possibility that these activities resided in a single enzyme was further supported by the findings that both substrates competitively interacted and that both activities were inhibited by lysine ethyl ester. The kinetic characteristics of two activities were compared. The apparent K_m for glycogen synthase b was found to be about $0.12 \mu M$, while that for phosphorylase was $2 \mu M$. The V_{max} for glycogen synthase b was 0.66 units/ml plus $MgCl_2$ and 0.06 units/ml with no additions. They were not able to determine a value of V_{max} for liver phosphorylase, but the relative rates at V_{max} of dephosphorylation of liver glycogen synthase b and muscle phosphorylase a were calculated to be approximately 1:100. Thus, the low V_{max} toward glycogen synthase b was offset by the fact that the K_m for phosphorylase a was approximately 20 times higher than that for glycogen synthase b.

The results of experiments in which a mixture of glycogen synthase b and phosphorylase a, at about physiological concentrations, were incubated with the phosphatase were in very close agreement with the kinetic findings; i.e., the relative rates of dephosphorylation of glycogen synthase and phosphorylase were found to be approximately 1–5. These observations are of importance in understanding potential mechanisms related to the more rapid rate of phosphorylase inactivation than glycogen synthase activation observed to occur in liver *in vivo* and *in vitro* following glucose administration (Curnow *et al.*, 1975). This topic is discussed in detail in Section II,B,2,c,i.

Khandelwal *et al.* (1976) also obtained a highly purified rabbit liver phosphoprotein phosphatase. ^{32}P-Labeled substrates were used in their studies. The steps of purification which yielded a 4610-fold purified product included acid precipitation -nd chromatography on DEAE-Sephadex A-50, Sephadex G-75, and finally on Sepharose-histone. The phosphoprotein phosphatases activity appeared in two distinct peaks from the Sepharose-histone column, termed phosphoprotein phosphatase I and II, respectively. On SDS polyacrylamide gel electrophoresis, each fraction migrated as a single diffuse band with apparent molecular weights of 30,500 daltons for I and 34,000 daltons for II. Similar to the results of Killilea *et al.* (1976), their purified phosphoprotein phosphatases I and II were both able to catalyze the dephosphorylation of a wide variety of substrates, including purified rabbit muscle ^{32}P-labeled glycogen synthase D, ^{32}P-labeled phosphorylase a, [^{32}P]histone, and [^{32}P]casein. Phosphatase II was also able to dephosphorylate the ^{32}P-labeled I component of troponin and activated rabbit muscle phosphorylase kinase (phosphatase I was not tested against these substrates). All substrates behaved as competitive inhibitors for the dephosphorylation of other substrates. The activity ratios of the phosphatases with respect to phosphorylase a, glycogen synthase D, histone, and casein remained fairly constant throughout purification. In addition, enzyme activities against all substrates tested demonstrated similar patterns of thermal inactivation. Accordingly, they concluded that these several properties supported the concept that dephosphorylation of all the substrates was catalyzed by either of the phosphatase fractions isolated in their study. The phosphorylated substrates used by these investigators were made using phosphorylase kinase (i.e., [^{32}P]phosphorylase and [^{32}P]troponin inhibitor subunit) and cyclic AMP-dependent protein kinase (i.e., [^{32}P]glycogen synthase, [^{32}P]casein, and [^{32}P]histone). These results clearly indicated that the same phosphoprotein phosphatase could dephosphorylate different substrates regardless of the type of protein kinase used in the phosphorylation reaction.

The substrate specificity of the phosphoprotein phosphatases reported in the literature and discussed above are also listed in Table I. The recurrent theme in the studies of Killilea *et al.* (1976) and Khandelwal *et al.* (1976) has been that a homogeneous phosphatase of low molecular weight may be the physiologically significant enzyme for several phosphoprotein substrates. The results of Kato and Bishop (1972), Zieve and Glinsmann (1973), Nakai and Thomas (1974), and Cohen *et al.* (1975) obtained using less purified enzyme have been interpreted in a similar way. In all these studies, it is clear that the purification procedures may have yielded the less labile but more nonspecific phosphatase. Several investigators have reported that phosphatase activities of glycogen metabolism may reside in different en- zymes. Villar-Palasi (1969) reported that synthase phosphatase and phos- phorylase phosphatase isolated from skeletal muscle were probably different enzymes. He drew this conclusion because he could demonstrate no compe- titive interactions between the two substrates. M. Laloux and W. Stalmans (unpublished observations 1974, quoted by Stalmans, 1976), Merlevede *et al.* (1976), and R. T. Curnow and K. Sato (unpublished observations, 1978) have found that hepatic synthase phosphatase is much more labile than phosphorylase phosphatase under several experimental conditions. In de- veloping rat liver, Devos and Hers (1974) found that synthase phosphatase activity emerged at day 18 of gestation while phosphorylase phosphatase did not appear until day 21. Goris and Merlevede (1974) noted that, during purification of phosphoprotein phosphatase from rat liver, synthase phos- phatase activity was lost. In contrast to the findings of Brandt *et al.* (1974), Tan and Nuttal (1976) noted that, while ethanol precipitation of crude liver extracts markedly activated phosphorylase phosphatase, the activity of synthase phosphatase was not appreciably changed.

More recently, Kikuchi *et al.* (1977) studied liver phosphoprotein phos- phatase activities of soluble liver extracts after chromatography on DEAE- cellulose. Under the conditions developed, synthase phosphatase activity emerged from the column as a sharp, single peak, followed by a similarly sharp peak of phosphorylase phosphatase activity. The latter peak also con- tained activity against glycogen synthase *D*. The synthase phosphatase activ- ity in the first peak was much more labile than the activities in the second peak. Ethanol precipitation inactivated synthase phosphatase but activated phosphorylase phosphatase. In addition, freezing inactivated the partially purified synthase phosphatase but did not affect phosphorylase phosphatase activity. They speculated that the difference between their results and the results of others, which indicated the presence of a single phosphoprotein phosphatase possessing activity against several substrates, could be ac- counted for by the loss of a more labile phosphoprotein phosphatase(s) dur- ing purification. Indeed, it is quite clear that such losses could readily occur when such relatively severe treatments as room temperature ethanol pre- cipitation, freezing and thawing in the presence of mercaptoethanol, or lim- ited trypsin digestion are used during purification.

It is evident that effort must be directed at purifying the less stable forms of phosphatase. In addition, the studies in which ^{32}P release has been monitored as an index of phosphatase activity should be repeated following enzyme activities, because these two methods may give different results (Roach and Larner, 1977). Nonetheless, it is evident that the low molecular weight, stable enzymes which withstand the various purification procedures all have broad substrate specificities.

B. CONTROL PROPERTIES

1. Protein Inhibitors of Phosphoprotein Phosphatases

A significant advance in our understanding of the biochemistry and regulation of the phosphoprotein phosphatases has been the recent appreciation that these enzymes are associated with regulatory proteins. These proteins inhibit the intrinsic activities of phosphoprotein phosphatases in many tissues. Furthermore, there is evidence that the activities of these inhibitory proteins are themselves subject to hormonal and metabolic control.

Baba and Tsuiki (1974) were the first to present evidence for a protein inhibitor of a phosphoprotein phosphatase. Their findings evolved from the study of certain unusual aspects of glycogen metabolism in Ehrlich ascites carcinoma cells. They had previously reported that these tumor cells were devoid of glycogen and failed to synthesize glycogen when incubated *in vitro* in the presence of glucose (Takeda and Tsuiki, 1967). Despite the fact that these cells theoretically possessed sufficient glycogen synthase to conduct glycogenesis at a substantial rate, it was found to be totally present in the inactive or *D* form. Furthermore, no *D* to *I* conversion could be demonstrated when crude homogenates were incubated *in vitro*. In an elegant series of experiments, they investigated the basis of this phenomenon and were able to demonstrate the following: (a) Unlike most tissues, the glycogen synthase *D* activity was totally sedimented by high-speed centrifugation, despite the fact that the tissue was devoid of glycogen; (b) in marked contrast to whole homogenates, a rapid synthase *D* to *I* conversion occurred in the pellet preparation; and (c) there was a factor in the high-speed supernatant which was responsible for the failure of *D* to *I* conversion in the homogenate. They assumed that the *D* to *I* conversion which occurred in the sediment fraction was due to a phosphatase because it was blocked by F^- and by glycogen and could be reversed by the addition of ATP—Mg^{2+}. The high-speed supernatant-inhibiting factor was found to be nondialyzable and to withstand heating for 3 minutes at 100°. However, it was approximately 70% inactivated upon incubation with trypsin (0.4 mg/ml) for 1 hour at 37°. The partially purified inhibitor also inhibited the synthase phosphatase reaction in rat liver extracts. Sephadex G-200 column chromatography indicated its molecular weight to be less than 50,000 daltons. The action of the inhibitor was blocked by glucose 6-P. It was also reversed by high-speed centrifugation under conditions where the enzyme was sedimented, thus indicating that the association between the inhibitor and the enzyme was weak. The inhibitor had some specificity, as it had no effect on the phosphorylase phosphatase reaction in the tumor cell. Baba and Tsuiki concluded that the presence of such an inhibitor of glycogen synthase phosphatase could account for the lack of glycogen synthesis found in tumor cell line.

Shortly after the initial report of Baba and Tsuiki, Brandt *et al.* (1974) independently described the presence of a protein inhibitor of phosphoprotein phosphatase in extracts derived from rat liver, skeletal muscle, and heart. During phosphatase purification, they found that large portions of the enzyme were present in inhibited or inactive forms. It was noted that a consistent, large increase (15- to 40-fold) in enzyme activity occurred during the ethanol precipitation step (see, e.g., Section II,A). This activation was associated with a concomitant conversion of the enzyme activity from multiple molecular weight forms to a single form with molecular weight of 34,000 daltons. They accordingly proposed that the inactive forms consisted of enzyme–inhibitor complexes and that the inhibitor moiety was a protein(s).

Brandt *et al.* (1974) subsequently demonstrated that the protein inhibitor was destroyed by precipitation with ethanol or by exposure to trypsin, but that it was stable when heated at 90° for 10 minutes. The last two characteristics were the same as those for the inhibitor described by Baba and Tsuiki (1974). The inhibitor preparation eluted over a wide region on a Biogel A-0.5 m agarose column, indicating the presence of multiple molecular weight forms of from 50,000 to 250,000 daltons. The kinetics of the inhibition were noncompetitive with respect to phosphorylase *a*. They also found that the inhibitor was active against the glycogen synthase phosphatase activity of their homogeneous rabbit liver phosphoprotein phosphatase. When the partially purified inhibitor was added to the homogeneous liver phosphatase, the complex formed was heterogeneous with respect to size, as was found for phosphatase activity prior to the ethanol treatment. They concluded that, because the inhibitor itself was polydisperse, its association with the phosphatase could account for the generation of multiple molecular weight forms of the inactive enzyme.

Huang and Glinsmann (1975) have also made a highly significant contribution to this area by elucidating a novel mechanism for the potential hormonal control of phosphoprotein phosphatase. This process involves the "activation" of a protein inhibitor of phosphoprotein phosphatase by means of phosphorylation catalyzed by the cyclic AMP-dependent protein kinase.

The original work of Riley and Haynes (1963), followed by that of Merlevede and Riley (1966) and Chelela and Torres (1970), had indicated that the phosphatase activities in crude extracts (adrenal cortex and skeletal muscle) could be inactivated by incubation with cyclic AMP in the presence of ATP—Mg^{2+}. The obvious implication of these data was that the reduction in phosphatase activity had been mediated through phosphorylation of some constituent of the phosphatase system via a cyclic AMP-dependent protein kinase. Accordingly, Huang and Glinsmann (1975) examined the effect of a combination of cyclic AMP, ATP—Mg^{2+}, and cyclic AMP-dependent protein kinase on a phosphoprotein phosphatase isolated from rabbit skeletal muscle by a procedure similar to that of Kato and Bishop (1972), except that Mn^{2+} was omitted from the buffers. It will be recalled that the presence of this ion stabilized and increased the yield of the enzyme during purification. On sucrose density gradient centrifugation and polyacrylamide disc gel electrophoresis, this phosphatase was found to be homogeneous, with a single protein species of 70,000 daltons.

Incubation of the phosphatase with activated protein kinase plus ATP—Mg^{2+} resulted in an approximate 80% inhibition of enzyme activity. Support for involvement of the cyclic AMP-dependent protein kinase was derived from several lines of evidence. First, when the ATP analog 5′-adenylyl imidodiphosphate was substituted for ATP, the reaction did not occur. ADP would not substitute for ATP, nor could AMP be substituted for cyclic AMP to observe a reduction in phosphatase activity. In addition, the inclusion either of the cyclic AMP binding protein (regulatory subunit of a cyclic AMP-dependent protein kinase) or of the protein kinase inhibitor of Walsh *et al.* (1968) inhibited the kinase-mediated diminution in phosphatase activity.

The activity of the inactivated phosphatase was not restored by dilution, dialysis, gel filtration over Sephadex G-25, or treatment with Norite to remove the ATP. However, reactivation did occur upon the addition of $MnCl_2$ or trypsin. As the $MnCl_2$ reactivation was prevented by potassium phosphate, Huang and Glinsmann reasoned that a Mn^{2+}-dependent phosphatase reaction was responsible for the reactivation. When they attempted to demonstrate direct phosphorylation of the enzyme with [^{32}P]ATP, they found that the phosphatase itself was not phosphorylated but that an associated protein inhibitor was phosphorylated.

Separation of the components by sucrose density gradient centrifugation or by polyacrylamide gel electrophoresis revealed that the protein kinase-inactivated phosphatase had changed in molecular weight from the starting value of 70,000 to a new molecular weight of 52,000 daltons. This occurred together with a reactivation of the enzyme. When the sucrose density gradient fractions were assayed, several fractions lower in molecular weight than the enzyme itself were found to contain inhibitory activity. The inhibitory activity was not decreased by heating at 90° for several minutes or by extensive dialysis. The inhibitor was, therefore, similar to the protein inhibitors of phosphatase described by Baba and Tsuiki (1974) and by Brandt *et al.* (1974). While the enzyme itself had not been phosphorylated in the kinase reaction, the inhibitory fractions had been. The phosphorylated inhibitor was found to have a molecular weight of 26,000 daltons as determined by SDS-polyacrylamide disc gel electrophoresis. It could be inactivated by an Mn^{2+}-dependent phosphatase coincident with loss of covalent phosphate. Interestingly, this phosphoinhibitor inhibited only the phosphatase activity directed against phosphorylase *a* and not the phosphatase activity against synthase or phosphorylated histone, the activities of which were also present in this particular phosphoprotein phosphatase(s). The results of this study, therefore, provided direct evidence for the inactivation of one of the activities of a muscle phosphoprotein phosphatase(s) by a reaction involving the cyclic AMP-dependent protein kinase via the formation of a potent phosphoprotein inhibitor of the phosphatase.

Thus, in a relatively short period of time, three apparently different protein inhibitors of phosphoprotein phosphatase(s) had been described; an inhibitor of synthase phosphatase activity (Baba and Tsuiki, 1974), an inhibitor of both synthase phosphatase and phosphorylase phosphatase activities (Brandt *et al.*, 1974), and an inhibitor which was apparently specific for phosphorylase phosphatase activity (Huang and Glinsmann, 1975).

Huang and Glinsmann (1976a,b) soon reported the presence of yet a second protein inhibitor associated with the partially purified muscle phosphatase. When the muscle phosphatase was chromatographed directly on Sephadex G-200, a single heat-stable inhibitor was observed; if the phosphatase was first treated with cyclic AMP-dependent protein kinase, two inhibitory peaks were now seen. One inhibitor, termed inhibitor-1, corresponded to the previously described phosphoinhibitor having a molecular weight of 26,000 daltons; the second inhibitor, denoted inhibitor-2, had an apparent molecular weight of 33,000 daltons by SDS polyacrylamide gel electrophoresis or 42,000 daltons as estimated by gel filtration. Removal of inhibitor-2 resulted in a further 2-fold increase in the specific activity of the phosphatase. Inhibitor-2 was as effective as inhibitor-1 in noncompetitively inhibiting phosphatase activity, and essentially complete inhibition could be obtained with either inhibitor. Because the activity of inhibitor-2 was not influenced by protein kinase or by the Mn^{2+}-dependent phosphatase activity which inactivated inhibitor-1, it was not regulated by a covalent phosphorylation mechanism. Inhibitor-2, in contrast to inhibitor-1, also inhibited the synthase phosphatase activity present in the partially purified phosphoprotein phosphatase. There remains a problem concerning the molecular weights: The total of the molecular weights of the two inhibitors is 59,000 daltons, and that of the original enzyme is 70,000 daltons.

Because various ligands such as nucleotides, hexoses, hexose phosphates, and glycogen affect the phosphorylase phosphatase reaction by interacting with phosphorylase *a*, (see, e.g., Section II,B,2), Huang and Glinsmann (1976b) evaluated whether the effect of either inhibitor-1 or -2 was altered by effectors which altered phosphorylase *a*. As others had demonstrated (Martensen *et al.*, 1973a), the adenine nucleotides inhibited the phosphatase. When added with maximally inhibiting concentrations of nucleotides, further inhibition was observed with inhibitor-2 but not with inhibitor-1. Glycogen or glucose 6-phosphate activated the phosphatase and partially reversed the inhibition of the phosphatase by AMP, but were ineffective in reversing the inhibition by either inhibitor.

These findings, taken together with those indicating that inhibitor-2, but not inhibitor-1, inhibited the dephosphorylation of glycogen synthase and histone, raised the possibility that these inhibitors could confer phosphatase specificity. Huang and Glinsmann (1976b) proposed the interesting hypothesis that the effects of ligands which influence the phosphatase reaction by changing the conformation of the substrate may be significantly modified by the presence of inhibitor.

Cohen *et al.* (1977a) achieved a 700-fold purification of a heat-stable, trypsin-labile protein inhibitor from rabbit muscle, using a procedure which included heat-treatment (95°), chromatography on DEAE-cellulose, and gel filtration over Sephadex G-100. This inhibitor protein was thought to be the inhibitor-2 described previously by Huang and Glinsmann (1976b), because prior phosphorylation was not necessary for full inhibiting activity to be demonstrated. The apparent molecular weight was 65,000, as determined by Sephadex G-200 gel filtration. Its activity was highly specific for protein phosphatase III (see Section II,A), inhibiting equally the phosphorylase phosphatase, β-phosphorylase kinase phosphatase, and glycogen synthase phosphatase activities of this enzyme. It was 200 times less effective in inhibiting the activity of their protein phosphatase I and protein phosphatase II.

Cohen *et al.* (1977b) also characterized the inhibitor-1 of Huang and Glinsmann. They purified this inhibitor to homogeneity as judged by SDS-acrylamide disc gel electrophoreais and estimated its molecular weight as 25,000 daltons. Phosphorylation of inhibitor-1 by cyclic AMP-dependent protein kinase resulted in the incorporation of one mole of covalently bound phosphate per mole protein. They next determined the complete amino acid sequence by the micro dansyl–Edman procedure. The structure of the phosphorylated site was very unusual, for it included a sequence of four consecutive arginines just N-terminal to the phosphorylated residue which was found to be threonine and not serine. The partial amino acid sequence was: Ile-Arg-Arg-Arg-Arg-Pro-Thr(P)-Pro-Ala-Thr. A sequence of four arginines has been previously observed only in the protamines. However, the chemical natures of the inhibitor and the protamines differ markedly. Protamines consist of nearly 70% arginine residues in the entire molecule.

More recently, Khandelwal and Zinman (1978) purified to homogeneity another heat-stable protein inhibitor of phosphoprotein phosphatase from rabbit liver. Following boiling of liver extracts, they chromatographed the resulting supernatant fraction first over DEAE-cellulose, Sephadex G-200, and finally over DEAE-cellulose a second time. The inhibitor following the final DEAE-cellulose elution was purified more than 800-fold. It migrated as a single band on a polyacrylamide disc gel electrophoresis and had a molecular weight of 14,200 by SDS-polyacrylamide disc gel electrophoresis. As with the other inhibitors of this type, it was found to be noncompetitive against phosphorylase a as substrate. The effect of this purified inhibitor on the dephosphorylation of [^{32}P]phosphorylase a by the phosphatases in crude extracts of rat brain, kidney, liver, heart, skeletal muscle, and adipose tissues was examined. The purified inhibitor was equally effective in inhibiting the phosphatase from all tissues tested.

Using the purified liver phosphoprotein phosphatase which they had previously described (Khandelwal *et al.*, 1976) (see Section II,A), they tested for the presence of inhibitory activity in a number of rat tissues. While the inhibitor activity in each of these tissues was not fully characterized, it was demonstrated in brain, kidney, heart, liver, adipose tissue and skeletal muscle. Thus, inhibitors of phosphoprotein phosphatase appear to be widely distributed among mammalian tissues.

The characteristics of the various heat-stable, trypsin-labile protein inhibitor of the phosphoprotein phosphatases are listed in Table II. The biochemical mechanisms for the action of these inhibitors of the phosphoprotein phosphatases and their physiological relevance are currently unknown. Nevertheless, there are certain common features of their actions which are informative. The inhibitors apparently interact with the enzyme and not the phosphoprotein substrates, because in all cases the inhibition has been found to be noncompetitive. In addition, the inhibitors described by several workers inhibit the phosphatase activities against multiple substrates. These findings accordingly suggested the possibility that inhibitor proteins may constitute "regulatory" subunits of certain phosphatases, inhibiting the activity of the catalytic subunits in the complex intracellular milieu. Indeed, as pointed out, the compelling data of Huang and Glinsmann (1976b) have clearly indicated that dynamic regulation of phosphoprotein phosphatase activities is possible through "activation" of such inhibiting factors by means of phosphorylation mediated by cyclic AMP-dependent protein kinase. In addition, it has been suggested that the inhibiting subunits may in some way confer specificity to the apparently nonspecific low molecular weight catalytic subunits.

TABLE II
Characteristics of the Heat-Stable, Trypsin-Labile Protein Inhibitors of Phosphoprotein Phosphatases[a]

Tissue	Species	Molecular weight ($\times 10^3$)	Substrate specificity	Activity blocked by	Reference
Erhlich ascites tumor	(Grown in mice)	<50 (GF)	GS	Glucose 6-phosphate	Baba and Tsuiki (1974)
Liver	Rabbit	50–250 (GF)	GP, GS	—	Brandt et al. (1974)
Skeletal muscle	Rabbit	Inhibitor-1, 26 (SDS)	GP	AMP	Huang and Glinsmann (1975, 1976)
		Inhibitor-2, 33 (SDS)	GP, GS		
		42 (GF)			
Skeletal muscle	Rabbit	"Inhibitor-2," 65 (GF)	GP, GS, βPK "Phosphatase III"		Cohen et al. (1977)
Liver	Rabbit	14.2 (SDS)	GP		Khandelwal and Zinman (1978)

[a]Abbreviations: same as in Table I.

2. Control by Low Molecular Weight Effectors and Glycogen

Considerable work has been done on the regulation of phosphoprotein phosphatases by divalent cations, nucleotides, hexoses, and glycogen. A role for these factors in the control of phosphatase activities seems likely, for modulation clearly can be shown *in vitro* at physiological concentrations. The study of these interactions has produced new concepts concerning enzyme regulation. These include an action of a ligand on a substrate protein, as well as the enzyme itself, and the fact that a low molecular weight "catalytic subunit" appears to be less sensitive to allosteric control factors than the higher molecular weight forms of the enzyme.

a. Role of Divalent Cations. It is of historical interest that Cori and Cori (1945) first observed that Mn^{2+} was required for maximal activity of a soluble muscle phosphorylase phosphatase (originally termed PR enzyme or prosthetic group-releasing factor) while Mg^{2+} inhibited the enzyme. Using purified glycogen synthase D as substrate, Kato and Bishop (1972) showed that phosphatase partially purified from the skeletal muscle was stimulated by Mn^{2+}, Ca^{2+}, and Mg^{2+}. Kato and Sato (1974) studied the same enzyme and made the important observation that the phosphatase activity was separable into two peaks on Sephadex G-150. Peak I enzyme (higher molecular weight) was not affected by divalent cations, but peak II (lower molecular weight) was totally dependent on Mn^{2+} or Ca^{2+} for activity. Nakai and Thomas (1974) examined the effect of divalent cations on partially purified phosphatase from bovine heart. This enzyme was stimulated by Mg^{2+}, Ca^{2+}, or Mn^{2+} with glycogen synthase D and phosphohistone as substrates, but it was inhibited with phosphorylase a as substrate. In contrast, Killilea *et al.* (1976), using homogeneous rabbit liver phosphatase, found that 10 mM Mg^{2+} inhibited the dephosphorylation of purified glycogen synthase D by 60%.

Martensen *et al.* (1973a) examined the inhibition of skeletal muscle phosphorylase phosphatase by divalent cations. The phosphatase was prepared from the glycogen pellet as described by Hurd *et al.* (1966). The inhibition by Mn^{2+} or Mg^{2+} was competitive with respect to both phosphorylase a and a phosphopeptide derived from phosphorylase a as substrate. Kinetic analysis revealed that the nature of this inhibition was complex, with apparent binding of the cations to both the enzyme and the substrate. The single binding site on the enzyme for divalent cations was apparently the one that interacts with the arginyl functions of the substrate, because the divalent cations were found to compete with m-propoxybenzamide, which is known to interact with this site on the substrate.

Recently, Khandelwal (1977) examined the influence of divalent cations on low molecular weight homogeneous liver phosphoprotein phosphatase against purified [^{32}P]phosphorylase, ^{32}P-Labeled glycogen synthase D, and

[32P]histone as substrates. Dephosphorylation of glycogen synthase was not influenced by Ca^{2+} or Mn^{2+}. Similarly, the dephosphorylation of phosphohistone was not influenced by Mg^{2+}. With these exceptions, the activity of liver phosphoprotein phosphatase was inhibited by all the cations tested with glycogen synthase *D*, phosphorylase *a*, and phosphohistone as substrates. In contrast to the results of Martensen, who used less purified enzyme, the inhibition was found to be noncompetitive with respect to all substrates. The cations also demonstrated varying degrees of inhibition with different substrates employed, the greatest occurring with phosphorylase *a*. These findings led Khandelwal (1977) to speculate that substrates may therefore also play a role in the inhibition of liver phosphoprotein phosphatase activity by divalent cations.

There is still confusion in this area for several reasons. The role of the metal in stability vs. activity of various enzyme forms has not been resolved. The state of purity and molecular heterogeneity of the various enzymes and substrates have made extrapolation from one study to another extremely difficult. Lastly, because different molecular forms vary in sensitivity to the metals (Kato and Sato, 1974), differing results would be expected, depending on which form was present in the particular study.

b. Role of Nucleotides. The adenine and uridine nucleotides have dramatic effects on phosphoprotein phosphatase activity against certain substrates in crude, partially purified, and purified preparations. The inhibition of phosphorylase phosphatase by AMP was first demonstrated by Sutherland (1951) in skeletal muscle extracts. The work of Nolan and co-workers (1964) was important in elucidating the mechanism of this effect. Their findings indicated that the site of AMP action was on the substrate, phosphorylase *a*, and not the phosphatase, because AMP did not affect the rate of dephosphorylation of the phosphorylated tetradecapeptide derived from phosphorylase *a* by means of limited proteolysis.

A fascinating aspect of AMP inhibition of the phosphorylase phosphatase reaction is that its presence depends on the tissue and the experimental conditions. In a series of studies of a glycogen–protein particle isolated from skeletal muscle, Haschke *et al.* (1970) demonstrated that the nucleotides AMP and IMP were without effect on the phosphatase reaction in the particle preparation. If the particles were dissociated by dilution, inhibition by the nucleotides could then be observed. In contrast to the muscle glycogen particle, AMP was found by Stalmans *et al.* (1971) to be inhibitory on the phosphorylase phosphatase reaction in a concentrated glycogen fraction isolated from rat liver. The physiological relevance of the inhibitory effect of AMP on phosphorylase phosphatase becomes more compelling when considered in relationship to the opposing effects of glucose or glucose 6-phosphate (see, e.g., Section II,B,2,c,ii).

The influence of ATP on glycogen synthase phosphatase activity in liver glycogen pellet preparations and muscle extracts has been investigated by Gilboe and Nuttall (1972, 1973). Their work revealed that ATP at physiological concentrations (2.5 mM) markedly inhibited the synthase D to I conversion. This inhibition could be overcome by glucose in the case of the liver enzyme and by glucose 6-phosphate with the muscle preparation. They proposed that such interactions could be the basis of a regulatory mechanism in which an increase in the hexose or hexose phosphate level could increase the synthase phosphatase reaction velocity by relieving the nucleotide inhibition. The physiological importance of such a mechanism for the control of synthase phosphatase is unclear, for most ATP within the cell is complexed with Mg^{2+}. In addition, Merlevede and co-workers (1976) have presented data indicating that the ATP—Mg^{2+} complex actually stimulates certain phosphoprotein phosphatase activities in many tissues.

The necessary studies concerning the effect of the various nucleotides on the dephosphorylation reactions catalyzed by a highly purified phosphatase and purified substrates were performed by Khandelwal (1977). Using a low molecular weight homogeneous liver phosphatase and ^{32}P-labeled substrates, he evaluated the effects of ATP, ADP, cyclic AMP, UTP, UDP, UMP, and UDPglucose at 0.1 and 1 mM concentrations. ATP and ADP were more effective in inhibiting the dephosphorylation of glycogen synthase than the dephosphorylation of phosphorylase, while AMP was a much more potent inhibitor of phosphorylase dephosphorylation. The uridine nucleotides were less effective as inhibitors, and UDPglucose did not inhibit any of the dephosphorylation reactions.

  c. Role of Glucose and Glucose 6-Phosphate.   It is now clear that glucose and glucose 6-phosphate probably play important regulatory roles in certain phosphoprotein phosphatase reactions. In the following sections we will review the evidence regarding the effects, physiological relevance, and mechanisms of actions of these agents on selected dephosphorylation reactions.

  i. Glucose control of hepatic phosphoprotein phosphatase activity.   Several lines of evidence indicate that glucose can directly modulate hepatic carbohydrate homeostasis, independent of glucoregulatory hormones. The studies of Soskin (1940) were the first to suggest that a major determinant of glucose homeostasis *in vivo* was the capacity of the liver to cease glucose production when the circulating glucose concentration was raised and to augment glucose production in the glucopenic situation. Studies using minced or sliced liver tissue (Soskin *et al.*, 1939), the isolated perfusion liver preparation (Woods and Krebs, 1971), and the isolated hepatocyte preparation (Hué *et al.*, 1975) have clearly demonstrated that glucose causes a concentration-dependent inhibition of glycogenolysis and/or stimulation of glycogen synthesis.

The work of Glinsmann *et al.* (1970) and Buschiazzo *et al.* (1970) clearly demonstrated that glucose can promote the inactivation of phosphorylase and activation of glycogen synthase in the isolated perfused liver. Because these glucose-induced effects occurred in the absence of detectable changes in cyclic AMP levels, it is possible that they were mediated through a mechanism involving activation of the phosphoprotein phosphatase(s) catalyzing the dephosphorylation of these enzymes.

The influence of glucose on hepatic glycogen metabolism has been studied extensively by Hers's group. They formulated an interesting hypothesis in which the interaction of glucose with phosphorylase *a* is considered to be the primary event leading to an enzyme cascade involving the obligatory inactivation of phosphorylase followed by the activation of glycogen synthase (Hers *et al.*, 1974). They propose that phosphorylase *a* controls synthase phosphatase activity by an inhibitory action. According to this scheme, glucose first binds to phosphorylase *a*, making it a "better" substrate for phosphorylase phosphatase and thus facilitating the conversion of phosphorylation *a* to *b*. Once phosphorylase *a* is decreased below a critical threshold, the inhibition of synthase phosphatase would be relieved and the conversion of synthase *D* to *I* could then proceed.

The experimental aspects which are central to this hypothesis are the following:

a. Glucose stimulates the conversion of phosphorylase *a* to *b* in various crude and partially purified tissue preparations.

b. The lag phase for hepatic synthase *D* to *I* conversion in tissue extracts corresponds to the time necessary for nearly complete conversion of phosphorylase from the *a* to the *b* form.

c. Phosphorylase *a* is an inhibitor of the synthase phosphatase reaction.

d. In intact tissues, glucose or other glycogenic effectors do not activate glycogen synthase unless the concentration of phosphorylase *a* is lowered below a threshold value approximately equal to 10% of total (*a* + *b*) phosphorylase.

With regard to point (a), glucose has been shown by many investigators to enhance the conversion of phosphorylase *a* to *b* in broken cell systems. The stimulation of the conversion of phosphorylase *a* to *b* by glucose was first demonstrated by Holmes and Mansour (1968) in muscle extracts. However, because the concentration of free glucose does not increase perceptibly in muscle (Kipnis *et al.*, 1959), this effect of glucose would seem to be of little physiological importance. Stalmans *et al.* (1971) subsequently demonstrated that glucose activated the phosphorylase phosphatase reaction in several liver preparations. The effect of glucose was apparently on the phosphorylase *a* substrate, as glucose also exposed the phosphorylated region of the enzyme to attack by trypsin, inhibited phosphorylase *a* directly, and protected the phosphorylase *a* against thermal inactivation. Furthermore, they found that a series of glucose analogs had the same relative potency in each of the reactions studied. It was concluded that the binding of glucose to liver phosphorylase *a* favors a conformation that is a better substrate for the phosphatase. As mentioned in Section II,B,3 of this chapter, AMP has been shown to have an effect opposite to that of glucose on the liver phosphorylase phosphatase reaction. Stalmans and co-workers (1971) found that the addition of 0.1 mM AMP increased the apparent K_a of glucose for a partially purified liver phosphorylase phosphatase (derived from the glycogen pellet) from 3 to 33 mM. Accordingly, they proposed that, in the presence of physiological concentrations of AMP, glucose (10–30 mM) would be expected to increase the velocity of the phosphorylase phosphatase reaction in a dose-dependent manner. Thus, there is general agreement that glucose stimulates the phosphorylase phosphatase reaction.

However, while the glucose effect on the phosphorylase phosphatase reaction is evident, there have been no reports, to the best of our knowledge, of the alternative mechanism—namely, the direct influence of glucose on the glycogen synthase phosphatase reaction using enzyme and substrate free from contamination with phosphorylase. This is a very important point, because the findings of several investigators (see e.g., Section II,B,2,c,ii) have shown that the phosphorylated hexose glucose 6-phosphate stimulates the synthase phosphatase reaction in many tissues. As both glucose and glucose 6-phosphate stimulate the phosphorylase phosphatase reaction, it is not unreasonable to assume that glucose should also stimulate the synthase phosphatase reaction directly.

Evidence leading to the formulation of hypothesis (b) above came from the observations of Gold and Segal (1967), who found that a lag phase occurred before synthase activation was manifest in crude liver homogenates incubated at room temperature. Stalmans *et al.* (1971) then demonstrated that this lag corresponds with the time required for nearly complete conversion of phosphorylase *a* to *b* by the phosphorylase phosphatase reaction. Furthermore, they were able to demonstrate that the lag phase of synthase activation could be increased or decreased by factors which similarly changed the time needed for the conversion of phosphorylase *a* to *b*.

However, there is a very significant problem in using the demonstration of a lag phase in crude preparations as evidence in support of the theory of obligatory phosphorylase control of the synthase phosphatase reaction. The ability to demonstrate a lag phase using crude or partially purified tissue extracts depends completely on the experimental conditions employed. While the lag phase of synthase activation is evident in glycylglycine buffer, it is not observed, nor is there any apparent relationship between synthase activation and phosphorylase inactivation, when either 50–100 mM imidazole or HEPES buffers are used (Stalmans, 1976). Thus, phosphorylase control of the synthase phosphatase reaction should not be inferred from experiments in which a multiplicity of poorly understood factors influences the results.

With regard to point (c), the inhibition of synthase phosphatase by phosphorylase a was first demonstrated in mouse liver extracts by Stalmans *et al.* (1971) and is the pivotal aspect of their scheme. Similar inhibitory effects of phosphorylase a on the synthase phosphatase in extracts from human polymorphonuclear leukocytes have been demonstrated (Wang *et al.*, 1977). The type of inhibition produced by phosphorylase a was not determined in these studies. Recently, Tan and Nuttal (1978) have reported that the phosphorylase a inhibition of the synthase phosphatase reaction in liver extracts was noncompetitive. Killilea *et al.* (1976) have recently investigated the interaction among purified liver phosphorylase a and synthase D and a homogeneous liver phosphatase. They found that (see, e.g., Section II,A) when phosphorylase a and synthase D were present together with the phosphatase at a physiological phosphorylase:synthase ratio of 10:1 (Maddaiah and Madsen, 1966), the rate of phosphorylase a dephosphorylation was 5 times that of synthase D. These findings were in excellent agreement with the kinetic data, which indicated that this phosphatase dephosphorylated phosphorylase a 100 times faster than synthase, which was partially offset by a K_m for synthase D 20 times lower than that for phosphorylase a. In contrast to the findings of Stalmans *et al.* (1971), no lag period in the synthase D to I conversion was observed, and the initial kinetics were linear. Accordingly, it follows that activation by glucose of a phosphatase acting on both substrates would inherently favor, *by virtue of the kinetics alone,* the more rapid inactivation of phosphorylase followed by the activation of glycogen synthase.

It is evident that, before these issues can be fully resolved, a more complete understanding will be required concerning whether or not the two enzymes are dephosphorylated by a common phosphatase or by two direct phosphatases. Nonetheless, it is evident that the phosphatase-catalyzed synthase D to I conversion can proceed at a linear rate without a lag phase when phosphorylase a and synthase D are present together in approximately physiological concentrations.

With regard to the fourth point above, Stalmans *et al.* (1974) analyzed the early changes in glycogen synthase and phosphorylase activities in successive liver biopsies taken from anesthetized, fed mice and rats after an intravenous glucose load. The results were clearly in support of their hypothesis. They found that phosphorylase inactivation was usually complete within 2 minutes and invariably preceded synthase activation. In those situations in which levels of phosphorylase a was not reduced below 10% of total phosphorylase activity following glucose, no synthase activation was seen. The rate of synthase activation was found by Hué *et al.* (1975) to be inversely proportional to the residual amount of phosphorylase *a* below the arbitrary threshold level of 10% in experiments with isolated hepatocytes. Above this level there was no relationship. Curnow *et al.* (1975) reported a similar pattern of hepatic synthase and phosphorylase response following glucose administration to anesthetized postabsorptive monkeys. While these data indirectly support the role of phosphorylase in the response of the hepatic synthase systems to glucose, they cannot obviate other complementary or alternative mechanisms.

In contrast to the above findings, Goldstein and Curnow (1978) have now reported that intravenous glucose administration to anesthetized rats fasted from 24 to 120 hours promoted large increases in hepatic synthase activities which were not associated with any measurable prior diminution of hepatic phosphorylase activities. Under these conditions, levels of phosphorylase *a* were 80–90%. However, in agreement with the findings of Stalmans *et al.* (1974), Goldstein and Curnow (1978) found that the administration of glucose to fed rats promoted very rapid inactivation of hepatic phosphorylase, followed by less rapid increases in synthase *I* activities. Since Hers (1976) had pointed out that the failure of other groups (Miller *et al.*, 1973; Nuttall *et al.*, 1972) to confirm that inactivation of phosphorylase precedes synthase activation may have been due to their use of an improper method for the determination of phosphorylase *a*, Goldstein and Curnow (1978) measured phosphorylase by the method of Stalmans and Hers (1975) using 0.5 *M* caffeine in the absence of AMP, the low–high-substrate method of Tan and Nuttall (1975), or in the presence or absence of AMP. The same qualitative results were found regardless of the method for measurement of liver phosphorylase activity.

Curnow *et al.* (1977) examined the effect of glucose administration on the hepatic phosphoprotein phosphatase activities of fed and 48-hour fasted anesthetized rats. In these studies liver biopsies were removed and immediately frozen between liquid nitrogen-cooled clamps at various times following glucose administration (1 gm/kg, i.v.). Phosphatase assay was performed using the frozen liver homogenized 1/3 (w/v) in 50 m*M* Tris (pH 7.4), 5 m*M* EDTA, 2 m*M* EGTA, 2 m*M* phenylmethylsulfonylfluoride, and 5 m*M* mercaptoethanol as the enzyme source and purified muscle glycogen synthase *D* as substrate. The synthase *D* was purified by the method of Takeda *et al.* (1975). While no change in hepatic phosphoprotein phosphatase activity was seen following glucose administration to fed rats in paired experiments, it did cause a dramatic increase in the enzyme activity from 48-hour fasted animals. Phosphatase increased almost 2-fold from baseline values of 51 ± 10 U/gm ($n = 6$) to 90 ± 20 U/gm ($p < 0.02$) at 1 minute with no change in phosphorylase activities. Increases in glycogen synthase *I* activities were seen by 5 minutes. Similar results (R. T. Curnow, J. N. Rowe, and D. F. Goldstein, unpublished observations, 1977) have also been found using an isolated perfused liver preparation. While the mechanism for these effects of glucose on the liver phosphoprotein phosphatase activity is not known, the data clearly indicate that a process(es) exists, other than that promulgated by Hers (1976) and co-workers, and suggest instead that the synthase phosphatase reaction is directly activated following glucose administration without the intermediate participation of phosphorylase.

It is concluded that while the evidence for the hypothesis formulated by Hers and co-workers concerning the mechanism of action of glucose on hepatic glycogen metabolism in the fed rat and mouse is compelling, it is nearly entirely circumstantial in nature. Furthermore, at each level of experimental evidence there exist alternative interpretations or important exceptions. The resolution of these vexing problems must await future well-controlled studies at the mechanistic level.

ii. Glucose 6-phosphate control of various phosphoprotein phosphatase reactions. Using a highly purified enzyme preparation from skeletal muscle, Martensen *et al.* (1973b) reported that glucose 6-phosphate increased phosphorylase phosphatase activity. The effect of the ligand was to increase the V_{max} by about 2-fold, but it had no effect on the K_m for the substrate. Because no activation could be demonstrated using a phosphorylated peptide derived from phosphorylase *a*, they concluded that the effects were on substrate and not enzyme-directed.

As with the effect of the interaction of glucose and AMP on the liver phosphorylase phosphatase reaction, the stimulatory effect of glucose 6-phosphate on the muscle system should be considered in conjunction with the inhibitory action of AMP. Bot and Dosa (1971) have shown that the inhibitory effect of physiological concentrations of AMP on the muscle phosphorylase phosphatase can be counteracted and the enzyme activity increased by glucose 6-phosphate. Thus, it is conceivable that one important determinant of phosphorylase phosphatase activity in muscle is the ratio of the concentration of AMP to glucose.

Hizukuri and Takeda (1971) demonstrated an increase in synthase phosphatase activity with glucose 6-phosphate using a partially purified enzyme preparation from bovine spleen. Subsequently, Kato and Bishop (1972) using purified enzymes from skeletal muscle, Nakai and Thomas (1974) using heart enzymes, Wang *et al.* (1977) using enzyme from human polymorphonuclear leukocytes, Lawrence and Larner (1978) using the adipocyte enzyme, and Killilea *et al.* (1976) using highly purified liver phosphatase also demonstrated stimulation of the phosphatase reaction by glucose 6-phosphate. Recently, S. Hizurki and J. Larner (unpublished observations, 1977) have found that glucose 6-phosphate stimulated the release of ^{32}P from purified rabbit skeletal muscle [^{32}P]glycogen synthase D. While the mechanism of glucose 6-phosphate action on the phosphatase reaction is unknown, the data of Kato and Bishop (1972) and Nakai and Thomas (1974) suggest that its effects are primarily on the protein substrate.

Most recently, Khandelwal (1977) examined the effect of glucose 6-phosphate on the dephosphorylation of the ^{32}P-labeled glycogen synthase, phosphorylase, and histone, using homogeneous low molecular weight liver phosphoprotein phosphatase (34,000 daltons). In contrast to the findings of others, glucose 6-phosphate either had no effect or partially inhibited the activity of this phosphatase for all three substrates. It is interesting to recall that Kato and Bishop (1972) were also unable to demonstrate activation by glucose 6-phosphate of the muscle phosphatase if ^{32}P-labeled substrate was used, with the effect apparent only when enzyme activity changes were followed.

d. Effect of Glycogen.   Because the enzymes of glycogen metabolism are closely associated with the glycogen–protein component of the cell, it would be expected that the polysaccharide might significantly influence the activity of the various phosphoprotein phosphatase reactions. The literature concerning the influence of glycogen on the phosphatase reactions in tissue extracts is confusing, for careful dose–response studies have not frequently been reported. The effect of glycogen on phosphoprotein phosphatase reactions is frequently reported to be biphasic, with various tissues having different thresholds for these effects.

In liver extracts the activities of both synthase phosphatase and phosphorylase phosphatase demonstrate a biphasic response with respect to glycogen concentration. DeWulf and Hers (1968) and Stalmans *et al.* (1971) have found that concentrations of about 1% stimulated these reactions, while concentrations of 5% or greater were inhibitory. Skeletal muscle phosphatases are more sensitive to the effects of glycogen. Villar-Palasi *et al.* (1970) reported that physiological concentrations of glycogen (0.2%) markedly inhibited the synthase phosphatase reaction but did not influence the phosphorylase phosphatase reaction. Kato and Bishop (1972) demonstrated that glycogen concentrations in the 0.05–0.15% range were optimal for the activity of their partially purified skeletal muscle phosphatase, whereas higher concentrations were inhibitory. That glycogen had no effect with histone as substrate was consistent with an action on the substrate and not the phosphatase. Martensen *et al.* (1973b) also examined the effects of glycogen on a partially purified muscle phosphatase preparation. Unlike the effects of glucose and glucose 6-phosphate, which did not change the affinity for substrate, glycogen caused a severalfold diminution in the apparent K_m for phosphorylase *a*. Because all these studies had been performed using crude or partially purified preparations, Khandelwal (1977) examined the influence of various glycogen concentrations on the dephosphorylation of substrates catalyzed by a highly purified low molecular weight liver phosphatase. In contrast to results obtained in less pure preparations, glycogen had very little effect on the phosphatase in this setting.

Thus, similar to other effectors of the phosphatase reactions, the effect of glycogen varies from tissue to tissue and with the stage of purity of the phosphatase and substrate. Similarly, it is reasonable to assume that the role of glycogen is significant in its capacity to modulate the action of other effectors, such as divalent cations, glucose, glucose 6-phosphate, and nucleotides which influence more directly the enzymatic dephosphorylation of proteins.

  e. Role of Antecedent Phosphorylation.   In their studies of the regulation of phosphorylase kinase activity purified from skeletal muscle, Cohen and Antoniw (1973) elucidated a potentially new regulatory mechanism for the control of a phosphoprotein phosphatase activity. They found that, while phosphorylation of the α subunit of phosphorylase kinase subsequent to phosphorylation of the β subunit did not additionally affect the activity of the enzyme, it did profoundly change the rate of dephosphorylation of the enzyme by phosphorylase kinase phosphatase. When phosphorylase kinase was phosphorylated to the extent of one mole of ^{32}P per mole $\alpha\beta\gamma$ unit (0.23 mole/α, 0.75 mole/β), inactivation of the enzyme with dephosphorylation of neither the α nor β subunit occurred in the absence of divalent cations. In contrast, if 2 moles of phosphate were incorporated per mole $\alpha\beta\gamma$ unit (1.05 mole/α, 1.05 mole/β), dephosphorylation of the β subunit took place selectively in the absence of divalent cations and the reaction proceeded 50- to 100-fold faster then in the preceding experiment. This left a unique product phosphorylated only in the α subunit. The dephosphorylation of the α subunits was now dependent on the presence of divalent cations. The decrease of kinase activity paralleled the loss of phosphate from the β subunits. It was postulated that phosphorylation of the α subunit alters the conformation of phosphorylase kinase, facilitating the action of phosphorylase kinase phosphatase on the β subunit.

The potential metabolic significance of these findings is that it is less likely that inactivation of the kinase would occur until phosphorylation of the α subunit had occurred. This latter process has been shown to be delayed *in vitro* until two β subunits per $(\alpha\beta\gamma)_4$ were phosphorylated by cyclic AMP-dependent protein kinase. Hypothetically, this would assure a finite period in which dephosphorylation would not occur and thus prevent needless competition with the phosphorylation process. This mechanism would also tend to regulate the duration of time the enzyme would exist in the phosphorylated or active state. Because phosphorylation of both the α and β subunits has been demonstrated by Yeaman and Cohen (1975) *in vivo*, it is possible that such a mechanism is functionally important.

III. HORMONAL CONTROL

Hypothetically, a hormone might perturb the balance between the phosphorylated and dephosphorylated state of an enzyme or other protein by increasing or decreasing the activity of the phosphorylation reaction catalyzed by a kinase or the dephosphorylation reaction catalyzed by a phosphatase or by affecting both processes simultaneously. While the biochemical events associated with the activation of the kinases by hormones have received much attention and are fairly well understood (Rubin and Rosen, 1975), only recently has firm evidence accumulated indicating hormonal control of the phosphatase reactions. It is the purpose of the remainder of this paper to review this evidence.

A. EFFECT OF INSULIN

It has been known for several years that insulin promotes the activation of glycogen synthase and the inactivation of phosphorylase in many tissues. These effects have been demonstrated both *in vivo* (Curnow *et al.*, 1975) and in isolated-intact cell systems (Miller and Larner, 1973). While evidence has been presented indicating this effect is mediated, in part, through the action of insulin to decrease the activity of the cyclic AMP-dependent protein kinase (Villar-Palasi *et al.*, 1971), the hormone has also been demonstrated to influence significantly the activities of certain phosphoprotein phosphatases. Evidence for the involvement of phosphatase in the action of insulin was simultaneously reported by Gold (1970) and by Bishop (1970), and later by Nuttal and co-workers (1976).

Gold (1970) observed that alloxan-induced diabetes in the rat resulted in a loss of the activity of liver glycogen synthase phosphatase the activity of which was assessed by measuring the conversion of endogenous glycogen synthase from the D to I form in concentrated extracts. Insulin treatment of diabetic animals 1 hour before sacrifice resulted in the complete restoration of the liver synthase phosphatase activity capacity for activation of glycogen synthase *in vitro*.

Nicholas and Goldberg (1972) confirmed and extended the observations of Gold (1970) concerning the effects of alloxan-induced diabetes on the hepatic "synthase-activating system." These workers observed a 60% diminution in hepatic glycogen synthase phosphatase activity in 3-day diabetic rats. Intravenous administration of insulin (2 units/kg) to the diabetic rats resulted in an increase in synthase phosphatase activity by 10 minutes to a level nearly 2-fold greater than nondiabetic controls. This increase was accompanied with a similarly larger increase in glycogen synthase *I* activity, Accordingly, the findings of these two groups clearly demonstrated a profound effect of chemically induced insulin deficiency on hepatic synthase phosphatase activity and the ability of insulin treatment to reverse this effect rapidly. Whether the effect of the diabetic state or insulin was at the level of the enzyme, the substrate, or some other indirect effector, such as phosphorylase, was not assessed.

In an effort to determine the mechanism by which insulin administration was less effective in activating hepatic glycogen synthase in pancreatectomized dogs deprived of insulin for 2–4 days compared to normal dogs (Bishop *et al.*, 1971), Bishop (1970) examined the hepatic phosphoprotein phosphatase activity of pancreatectomized dogs maintained on variable amounts of insulin. Phosphatase activity was assessed in extracts by serial liver biopsy samples using purified muscle glycogen synthase *D* as substrate. In dogs whose diabetes was controlled by daily insulin injections, insulin with glucose (3.2 U/kg/hour and 2.5 gm/kg/hour, respectively) promoted a 2- to 4-fold increase in phosphatase activity within 5–15 minutes. The addition of glucagon (20 μg/kg) to the insulin-plus-glucose infusion brought phosphatase activity back to or below control levels within 6 minutes.

In the light of current knowledge, the interpretation of these data is complex. It is possible, as Bishop suggested, that the changes in phosphatase activity were the result of an enzymatic interconversion process, i.e., a phosphorylation-dephosphorylation of the enzyme or associated proteins as described by Huang and Glinsmann (1975). Alternatively, the changes in synthase phosphatase activity in the crude extract could have reflected the changes in phosphorylase *a* (Stalmans *et al.*, 1974). In contrast to the dogs maintained on daily insulin, those animals deprived of insulin for from 2 to 4 days showed no change in synthase phosphatase activity with insulin administration for 30–120 minutes. These findings suggested to the author that in prolonged insulin deficiency the activating factor for liver synthase phosphatase was either lacking or ineffective.

Tan and Nuttall (1976) have investigated the glycogen synthase phosphatase and phosphorylase phosphatase activities in liver extracts from alloxan-diabetic rats. This study was the first to evaluate simultaneously both the phosphorylase and synthase phosphatase activities in diabetic liver and to assess the phosphatase reactions by following the conversion of both endogenous and exogenous substrates. The exogenous substrates were purified glycogen synthase D and phosphorylase a from rabbit liver. Another important consideration in this study was that when exogenous substrates were used, the liver extracts were preincubated in order to convert the endogenous substrates to products, to degrade known modifiers of the phosphatases such as AMP and ATP, and to allow for the conversion of endogenous phosphorylase a to b. They found that the extent of synthase D to I conversion in liver extracts using endogenous substrate varied with nutritional state. Extracts derived from diabetic-fed rats showed markedly decreased synthase phosphatase activities. In contrast, endogenous hepatic synthase D to I conversions from diabetic rats fasted 16 hours were rapid and complete. Phosphorylase phosphatase activities could not be accurately assessed using endogenous phosphorylase because of low levels of substrate in diabetic animals. The nutritional status of the animal also had a highly significant effect on phosphatase activities which were measured using exogenous substrates. Fasting for 24 hours significantly reduced hepatic synthase and phosphorylase phosphatase activities in normal rats. Both synthase and phosphorylase activities were significantly decreased in diabetic rats in the fed state when compared to nondiabetic-fed rats. In contrast, the hepatic phosphatase activities of 24-hour fasted diabetic animals were not different from those of similarly fasted nondiabetic animals.

Tan and Nuttal (1976) were able to increase synthase phosphatase activities with insulin administration in their alloxan-diabetic rats to only 50% of controls. In contrast, phosphorylase phosphatase activities were increased by insulin administration to levels not different from controls. These findings were considered consistent with the existence of two phosphatases, with both enzymes being under the same set of physiological controls.

Khandelwal *et al.* (1977) examined the effect of streptozotocin-induced diabetes and insulin supplementation on phosphoprotein phosphatase in rat liver. They employed phosphatase assays measuring both endogenous synthase D to I and phosphorylase a to b conversions and dephosphorylation of the exogenous substrates, ^{32}P-labeled phosphorylase, and histone. Hepatic phosphatase activity measured using all these substrates was diminished in the diabetic animals.

In studies directed at determining potential mechanisms responsible for the diminutions of hepatic phosphatase activities found in the diabetic animal, Khandelwal and co-workers (1977) measured the activity of a heat-stable protein inhibitor of phosphoprotein phosphatase in extracts of normal and diabetic rat liver. They made the exciting observation that inhibitor activities were significantly increased in the livers of diabetic animals. Insulin treatment of diabetic rats for 7 days resulted in complete normalization of phosphatase activity and reduction in the activity of the heat-stable phosphatase inhibitor to nondiabetic levels. Accordingly, their results indicated that increased activities of the newly defined protein inhibitors are mechanistically important in the reduction in phosphatase activities found in diabetic liver.

Another significant contribution in this area was recently made by Nuttall and co-workers (1976). They have presented evidence that insulin activates a phosphoprotein phosphatase reaction in tissues of nondiabetic as well as diabetic animals. In studies of the rat heart synthase phosphatase and phosphorylase phosphatase systems, they found that synthase phosphatase activities in normal-fasted and alloxan-diabetic rats were approximately 50% of the activities of fed controls. These activities were measured in concentrated homogenates by means of following interconversion of endogenous substrate. Administration of insulin to fasted and diabetic rats increased synthase phosphatase activities to fed levels by 15 and 30 minutes, respectively. In order to determine whether the insulin effect was due to a change in the phosphatase or its protein substrate and not due to some small molecular weight effector, Sephadex G-25 chromatography and ammonium sulfate precipitation of heart extracts were performed prior to assay. Because insulin activation of the synthase phosphatase activity was still present after these treatments, it was concluded that insulin administration had produced a stable modification of the phosphatase, its substrate, or both. Intravenously administered glucose, presumably associated with insulin release from the pancreas, also activated the heart synthase phosphatase; thus, increases in the circulating insulin concentration within the normal range were also effective.

The phosphorylase phosphatase activity in the heart extracts was not affected by fasting or the diabetic state. Furthermore, a role for phosphorylase *a* in the alterations in enzyme activities found in this study seemed extremely unlikely, for basal phosphorylase *a* activities were the same in all groups studied. Accordingly, these studies clearly demonstrated an impressive effect of insulin on the activity of the heart synthase phosphatase system both in diabetic and nondiabetic animals without an apparent role of phosphorylase in the process.

The recent work of Lawrence and Larner (1978) using isolated fat cells also indicates that activation of the synthase phosphatase system is an important event in the leading to activation of glycogen synthase promoted by insulin and other agents which increase hexose transport. It was shown that the insulin-stimulated conversion of glycogen synthase *D* to *I* in these cells occurred by two mechanisms. One process was independent of hexose transport, while the other was dependent upon it. It was found that insulin (100μ U/ml), in the absence of glucose, provoked an increase in the percent synthase in the *I* form from 9.2% to 15.3%, while with insulin plus glucose (5 m*M*) the increase was to 30%. Glucose alone caused only a slight increase in the percent *I*. No temporal relationship was found between the synthase *I* increments and changes in phosphorylase *a* levels. The insulin-plus-glucose combination produced an approximate 10-fold increase in glucose 6-phosphate levels in these cells, while insulin alone had little effect.

It was reasoned that the potentiation of the insulin effect by glucose on the synthase *D* to *I* conversion was mediated by stimulation of synthase phosphatase by the increased hexose phosphate levels. To test this possibility, the effect of glucose 6-phosphate on the synthase phosphatase activity in fat cell extracts was examined using endogenous enzyme as substrate. They found that the activity of the phosphatase was significantly increased by glucose 6-phosphate at concentrations comparable to those measured in the cells in the presence of glucose and insulin. Thus, it was concluded that the insulin-induced alterations in the glucose 6-phosphate level could play an important role in mediating the intracellular effects of the hormone on the glycogen synthase system via activating synthase phosphatase.

In recent work, A. H. Gold, D. Dickemper, and D. M. Haverstick (personal communication, 1978) have separated an insulin-sensitive synthase phosphatase activity from an insulin-insensitive phosphorylase phosphatase activity in liver extracts by means of DE-52/Sephadex G-25 chromatography. In these experiments partially purified liver glycogen synthase *D* and phosphorylase *a* were used as substrates, and changes in their activities were followed to estimate phosphatase activities. Chromatography of liver extracts from nondiabetic-fed rats yielded synthase phosphatase activity which eluted following 0.15 *M* NaCl, while phosphorylase phosphatase activity was eluted completely free of synthase phosphatase activity with 0.25 *M* NaCl. In contrast, chromatography of liver extracts from alloxan-diabetic rats revealed nearly complete loss of synthase phosphatase activity without any apparent change in phosphorylase phosphatase activity. Treatment of the diabetic rat with insulin 3 hours before sacrifice (4 U i.p.) completely reversed the diminution in synthase phosphatase activity.

Thus, Gold and co-workers have reproduced the findings of Kikuchi *et al.* (1977) (see, e.g., Section II,A) with regard to the separation of synthase and phosphorylase phosphatase activities by chromatographic techniques. In addition, they have made the potentially significant observation that hepatic synthase phosphatase activity, but not hepatic phosphorylase phosphatase activity, is profoundly affected by insulin *in vivo*. These findings have added new and compelling evidence to the argument that the phosphoprotein phosphatases play an important role in determining the metabolic expression of insulin action on the cell.

B. ROLE OF GLYCOGENIC STEROIDS

Adrenal glucocorticoids have long been recognized as activators of hepatic glycogen synthesis (Long *et al.*, 1940). DeWulf and Hers (1968) subsequently demonstrated that this process involved activation of hepatic glycogen synthase. Evidence was soon forthcoming which indicated that steroid activation of synthase was mediated via activation of the hepatic phosphoprotein phosphatase(s). Stalmans *et al.* (1971) found that treatment of mice with prednisone 3–5 hours before sacrifice increased the activity of the hepatic phosphorylase phosphatase reaction 3- to 10-fold. Mersmann and Segal (1969) demonstrated that the effect of adrenalectomy on the hepatic synthase phosphatase reaction in liver extracts was profoundly influenced by the nutritional status of the animal; the activity of synthase phosphatase was completely lost in the livers of adrenalectomized 48-hour fasted rats, but was not changed in livers from fed adrenalectomized rats. Furthermore, they found that steroid administration 4–5 hours before sacrifice returned the phosphatase activity to control levels associated with increased hepatic glycogen concentrations and synthase I activities.

The possible relationship between insulin and the glucocorticoid-promoted activation of hepatic glycogen synthase was examined by Nicholas and Goldberg (1972). They found that the steroid-induced activation of hepatic synthase in adrenalectomized rats which were fasted for 12 hours was rapid and correlated closely with the activation of synthase phosphatase. Phosphatase activities were measured using endogenous synthase *D* as substrate. In contrast, they found that the enzyme activities were not changed by steroid administration in adrenalectomized rats made diabetic by alloxan treatment. On the other hand, insulin administration to the diabetic-adrenalectomized animals fasted 12 hours produced marked increases in both the glycogen synthase activity and the synthase phosphatase activity of these livers.

Nichols and Goldberg (1972) concluded from these results that the apparent steroid activation of glycogen synthase and synthase phosphatase *in vivo* was dependent on the release of insulin. Such an interpretation seems dangerous, for insulin levels were not measured and endogenous synthase was used as substrate. Nonetheless, the results clearly indicate a potentially significant interaction between glucocortical hormones and insulin in the control of the hepatic glycogen synthase phosphatase reaction. In addition, their findings further strengthened the concept that the phosphoprotein phosphatases play a significant role in the mediation of hormone action on metabolic processes.

Tan and Nuttal (1976) have studied the effect of adrenalectomy on the synthase phosphatase and phosphorylase phosphatase activities in liver extracts of fed and 48-hour fasted rats using both endogenous and highly purified liver enzymes as substrates. They found that both hepatic phosphatase activities were markedly depressed in fasted rats when exogenous enzymes were used as substrates, while only synthase phosphatase activity was reduced when conversions of endogenous substrates were assessed. A physiologically important role for synthase phosphatase in mediating the effect of glucose was suggested by the findings that glucose administration to fasted-adrenalectomized rats failed to promote synthase activation.

In an effort to determine a chemical mechanism for the diminished hepatic phosphatase activities in fasted-adrenalectomized animals, Tan and Nuttall (1976) subjected the liver extracts to ethanol precipitation. It was of interest that this procedure activated hepatic phosphorylase phosphatase activities in fed control and fasted adrenalectomized rats to nearly identical levels. In contrast, this procedure inactivated the synthase phosphatase in normal-fed liver and modestly activated that in fasted-adrenalectomized rats, with the resulting activities about the same. Because the ethanol precipitation dissociates an inhibitor protein from phosphorylase phosphatase (see, e.g., Sections II,A and II,B), they concluded that a modification in the inhibitory rather than the catalytic subunit of phosphorylase phosphatase was responsible for the decreased enzyme activities in adrenalectomized-fasted rats. Accordingly, in light of these findings and those of Khandelwal *et al.* (1977) in diabetic liver (see Section III,A), an important role is emerging for these putative regulatory proteins of phosphatases in the alterations in metabolism found in perturbed endocrine states.

C. Effect of Epinephrine and Autonomic Control

As described previously (Section II,B,1), Huang and Glinsmann (1975) demonstrated that activation of cyclic AMP-dependent protein kinase resulted in the phosphorylation and concomitant "activation" of a relatively heat-stable inhibitor of phosphorylase phosphatase in muscle extracts. Following up on these observations, Tao *et al.* (1978) demonstrated that the administration of epinephrine-induced activation of phosphorylase in an isolated rat hind-limb preparation was associated with a decrease in muscle phosphorylase phosphatase activity. Concomitant increases in cyclic AMP levels were also present. In these experiments, muscle samples were excised and immediately frozen 2 minutes after intravenous bolus injection of epinephrine (100 μg/kg BW). Phosphorylase phosphatase was measured using exogenous muscle phosphorylase *a* as substrate. Associated with the decrease in phosphorylase phosphatase activity was an increase in the activity of a heat-stable and trypsin-labile phosphorylase phosphatase inhibitor.

These findings are highly significant, for they are the first to provide firm experimental evidence that the sequence of events following epinephrine stimulation of adenylate cyclase in muscle may involve the cyclic AMP-dependent protein kinase-catalyzed phosphorylation and "activation" of a protein inhibitor of phosphorylase phosphatase. These findings, together with those of Tan and Nuttall (1975) and Khandelwal *et al.* (1977), further emphasize the potential importance of these regulators of phosphatase activities both in the abnormalities in metabolism associated with altered endocrine states and in the physiological action of hormones.

The studies of Shimazu and Amakawa (1975) revealed another potential mechanism for the control of liver phosphorylase phosphatase activity. They found that electrical stimulation of a sympathetic nerve (splanchnic nerve) to the abdominal viscera of the rabbit increased hepatic phosphorylase activity through a mechanism involving the rapid inactivation of phosphorylase phosphatase rather than the activation of phosphorylase kinase. The effects of nerve stimulation on hepatic cyclic AMP levels, phosphorylase kinase activities, phosphorylase activities, and glycogen synthase activities were examined and compared with those of epinephrine and glucagon administration on these same parameters. Splanchnic nerve stimulation produced a 2-fold increase in hepatic phosphorylase activity within 30 seconds associated with a 50% diminution of phosphorylase phosphatase activity but caused no significant change in the hepatic cyclic AMP level or phosphorylase kinase activity. In marked contrast, the administration of either glycogenolytic hormone promoted a rapid increase in phosphorylase activity which was associated with increases in the cyclic AMP level and phosphorylase kinase activity. Accordingly, the authors proposed that hepatic phosphorylase phosphatase plays a key role in mediating the neural influences on hepatic glycogen metabolism. Further studies are necessary to elucidate the mechanisms whereby these effects of nerve stimulation are mediated.

D. Effect of Somatostatin

A potential role for somatostatin in the control of hepatic carbohydrate homeostasis, in addition to its well-established role in inhibiting polypeptide hormone secretion (Guillemin and Gerich, 1976), is suggested by the findings that somatostatin (a) is present within the islets of Langerhans in the D-cells (Arimura *et al.*, 1975); (b) is released into the pancreatic effluent by effectors which also stimulate insulin release (Patton *et al.*, 1976); and (c) possibly inhibits glucagon-stimulated cyclic AMP accumulation in isolated hepatocytes (Oliver *et al.*, 1976). Curnow and Rowe (1977) have studied this possibility by examining the effect of intravenous somatostatin administration (25 μg/kg followed by a 1 μg/kg/minute infusion) on hepatic cyclic AMP and glycogen levels and the activities of hepatic glycogen synthase, phosphorylase, and phosphoprotein phosphatase. In these studies, liver biopsies were serially obtained from pentobarbital-anesthetized 17-hour fasted rabbits and immediately frozen in liquid nitrogen. Phosphatase activities were determined using the frozen liver homogenized 1/3 (w/v) in 50 mM Tris (pH 7.4), 5 mM EDTA, 2 mM EGTA, 2 mM PMSF, and 5 mM mercaptoethanol as the enzyme source, while a highly purified dog muscle synthase D was used as substrate. Changes in the liver parameters were correlated with simultaneous measurements of arterial glucose and immunoreactive insulin and glucagon concentrations. Liver and arterial blood samples were taken at $-15, 0, 1, 5, 10, 20, 30, 75$, and 90 minutes in relationship to a somatostatin infusion given between $t=0$ and $t=30$ minutes.

Somatostatin administration produced immediate approximately 2-fold increases in phosphoprotein phosphatase activities (35 ± 4 to 67 ± 8 U/g protein, $n=6$, $p<0.02$) by 1 minute (Fig. 1), which preceded both decreases in phosphorylase activities and increases in synthase I activities that occurred simultaneously. Diminutions in insulin, glucagon, and glucose levels were not apparent until after 5 minutes. Hepatic cyclic AMP levels decrease significantly during somatostatin infusion but only after 10 minutes. It is of interest that these effects of somatostatin have been found only in the rabbit, although its effect on these parameters has also been studied in the dog and rat. Nonetheless, the findings indicate that somatostatin may be a significant hormone in the regulation of hepatic carbohydrate homeostasis mediated

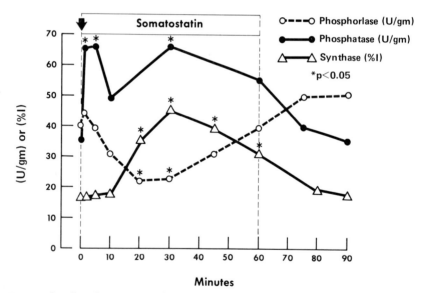

FIG. 1. The effect of somatostatin administration (25 μg/kg i.v. bolus followed by a 1 μg/kg/ min i.v. infusion) to pentobarbital-anesthetized, 3–4 kg rabbits ($n=6$) on hepatic phosphoprotein phosphatase, glycogen synthase, and phosphorylase activities. Asterisks indicate $p<0.05$ compared to $t=0$ by paired analysis. No changes from baseline values were noted in rabbits given saline.

through a mechanism involving activation of a phosphoprotein phosphatase activity.

III. CONCLUSIONS

It is clear from the foregoing that a multiplicity of factors undoubtedly interact cooperatively or antagonistically to regulate the activity of phosphoprotein phosphatase(s). In Fig. 2 we present a hypothetical scheme whereby hormonal and metabolic influences might modulate phosphoprotein phosphatase activity. The model is based on the work of the following investigators: Brandt *et al.* (1975) and Khandelwal *et al.* (1976), who have purified to homogeneity a low molecular weight phosphatase; Baba and Tsuiki (1974), Brandt *et al.* (1974), Huang and Glinsmann (1975, 1976a,b) and Khandewal (1977), who identified and purified proteins which are apparently inhibitory subunits of the phosphatase; and Tan and Nuttall (1976), Huang and Glinsmann (1975), Khandelwal and Zinman (1978), and Tao *et al.* (1978), who have revealed that these inhibitory proteins may be sites through which regulation of this enzyme is effected. In Fig. 2 the hypothetical phosphatase holoenzyme is shown consisting of three line figures representing simple polypeptide chains; these represent a catalytic 34,000 dalton subunit (Brandt *et al.*, 1975) designated c, and two inhibitory subunits designated i_1 and i_2 which represent the phosphorylatable 26,000 dalton inhibitor-1 and the nonphosphorylatable 33,000 dalton inhibitor-2 of Huang and Glinsmann (1976a,b), respectively. Because the chemical nature of the relationships among these constituents of the putative phosphatase holoenzyme is not known, the activity of c is depicted as being relative to the free surface of the line not impinged upon by either i_1 or i_2. Thus, conformational changes of either i_1 or i_2 would result in either an increased or decreased activity of c.

The relative activities of c are depicted in Fig. 2 by the subscript number, with 1 being the state of least catalytic activity and 8 being the most active catalytic state. Nine hypothetical states of the enzyme are shown. Although all conformations are theoretical, experimental evidence for states I–VII has been reported, while states VIII and IX remain more speculative. The data of Huang and Glinsmann (1975, 1976a,b) and Tao *et al.* (1978) indicate that the activity of c in the intrinsic situation could be determined to a significant extent by the phosphorylation of i_1, which would in turn be a reflection of the balance between the activities of cyclic AMP-dependent protein kinase and a Mn^{2+}-dependent phosphatase. Accordingly, hormones which affect the activity of either the kinase or the phosphatase could determine if the activity of the enzyme were in either state I or II. For the sake of argument, the phosphatase activity catalyzing the dephosphorylation of i_1 could be that

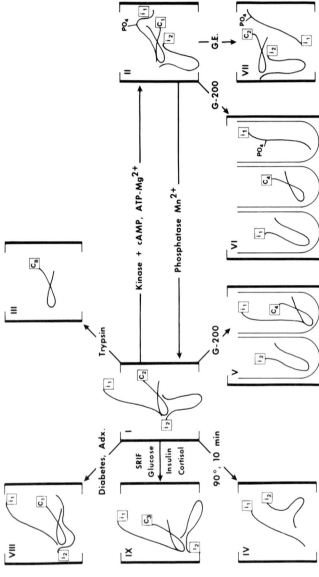

FIG. 2. A hypothetical model for relationships among the 34,000 dalton catalytic subunit, shown as c (relative activity depicted by the adjoining number); the 26,000 dalton phosphorylatable inhibitor, shown as i_1; and the 33,000 dalton non-phosphorylatable inhibitor, shown as i_2. Other abbreviations: Adx, adrenalectomized; SRIF, somatostatin; G-200, Sephadex G-200 chromatography; G. E., polyacrylamide gel electrophoresis. For explanation, see text.

activity associated with residual nonphosphorylated i_1 in state I. States III and IV, respectively, represent the effect of trypsin treatment which results in the degradation of both inhibitory subunits and full activation of the catalytic subunit and heat treatment which destroys the catalytic unit but has no apparent effect on the inhibitory subunits. States V, VI, and VII represent the consequences of Sephadex G-200 gel filtration and polyacrylamide gel electrophoresis of the enzyme in states I or II (Huang and Glinsmann, 1976a,b) and demonstrate the potential to dissociate the components of the holoenzyme.

The studies of Tan and Nuttall (1976) and Khandelwal *et al.* (1977) have indicated that the diminutions in liver phosphoprotein phosphatase activities found in diabetic and adrenalectomized animals may be due to increased activity of the phosphatase protein inhibitor. Because the presence of the phosphorylatable i_1 has not been demonstrated in liver, and in order to maintain a unitary hypothesis, we suggest, as indicated by state VIII, that an increase in i_2 *activity* could account for the diminished phosphatase activity found in diabetic and adrenalectomized rat liver. Similarly, it is possible, as illustrated in state IV, that the effects of somatostatin (SRIF in Fig. 2) described by Curnow and Rowe (1977), the effects of insulin reported by Nuttall *et al.* (1976) and Khandelwal *et al.* (1977), and the effects of hydrocortisone described by Mersmann and Segal (1969) are related to hormone-promoted diminutions in the *activity* of this inhibitor. While the existence of a mechanism whereby phosphatase activity could be controlled by alterations in i_2 activity is speculative, methods are currently available to test for alterations in activity and/or configuration of this protein in perturbed endocrine states and following exposure of tissues to hormones or other metabolic effectors. It is possible that ligands such as nucleotides, divalent cations, hexoses, or hexose phosphatases could influence the conformation of the protein, and thus its activity, in a fashion analogous to their effects on phosphorylase *a*.

While conformational changes in i_1 and i_2 are suggested by Fig. 2, it is equally possible that changes in intrinsic phosphatase activities are related to the degree of association of holoenzyme units. Indeed, Brandt *et al.* (1974) have demonstrated clearly that the combination of inhibitory protein(s) with a low molecular weight homogeneous enzyme leads to a polydisperse pattern of enzyme activity on gel filtration. Thus, the presence or absence of hormones or other metabolic effectors might modulate phosphatase activity by influencing the polymeric association of the tripartite units.

The presence of regulatory subunits such as i_1 and i_2 is also apparently important in determining the effect of ligands which influence enzyme activity (Khandelwal, 1977). Accordingly, the conversion of the enzyme to the various states depicted in Fig. 2 could conceivably profoundly influence response of the enzyme activity to agents such as nucleotides, sugars, and metals.

This model does not obviate the existence of more than a single protein holoenzyme unit which could catalyze the dephosphorylation of the enzymes of glycogen metabolism. Undoubtedly, there exist more than one phosphoprotein phosphatase controlled by this or other mechanisms. Thus, while there has been considerable and dramatic progress made in the past several years, it is quite clear that we have only scratched the surface in this area and that further investigation is needed to establish the biochemical nature and regulation of the phosphoprotein phosphatases and their roles in mediating the intracellular effects of hormone and other metabolic effectors.

ACKNOWLEDGMENTS

Supported in part by USPHS Research Grants AM 18471, AM 20787, and AM 14335; USPHS Diabetes–Endocrinology Center Grant AM 17042; and a grant from the American Diabetes Association. Randall T. Curnow, M.D., is the recipient of a USPHS Research Career Development Award AM 477. Joseph Larner, M.D., Ph.D., is an Establish Investigator of the American Diabetes Association.

REFERENCES

Antoniw, J. F., Nimmo, H. G., Yeaman, S. J., and Cohen, P. (1977). *Biochem. J.* **162**, 432–433.

Arimura, A., Sato, H., DuPont, A., Nishi, N., and Schally, A. V. (1975). *Science* **189**, 1007–1009.

Baba, T., and Tsuiki, S. (1974). *Biochim. Biophys. Acta* **370**, 419–430.

Bishop, J. S. (1970). *Biochim. Biophys. Acta* **208**, 208–218.

Bishop, J. S., Goldberg, N. D., and Larner, J. (1971). *Am. J. Phys.* **220**, 499–506.

Bot, G., and Dosa, I. (1971). *Acta Biochim. Biophys. Acad. Sci. Hung.* **6**, 73–87.

Brandt, H., Killilea, J. D., and Lee, E. Y. C. (1974). *Biochem. Biophys. Res. Commun.* **61**, 548–554.

Brandt, H., Capulong, Z. L., and Lee, E. Y. C. (1975). *J. Biol. Chem.* **250**, 8038–8044.

Buschiazzo, H., Exton, J. H., and Park, C. R. (1970). *Proc. Natl. Acad. Sci. U.S.A.* **65**, 383–387.

Chelala, C. A., and Torres, H. N. (1970). *Biochim. Biophys. Acta* **198**, 504–513.

Cohen, P., and Antoniw, J. F. (1973). *FEBS Lett.* **34**, 43–47.

Cohen, P., Antoniw, J. F., Nimmo, H. C., and Proud, G. M. (1975). *Biochem. Soc. Trans.* **3**, 849–854.

Cohen, P., Nimmo, G. A., and Antoniw, J. F. (1977a). *Biochem. J.* **162**, 435–444.

Cohen, P., Rylatt, D. B., and Nimmo, G. A. (1977b). *FEBS Lett.* **76**, 182–186.

Cori, G. T., and Cori, C. F. (1945). *J. Biol. Chem.* **158**, 21–26.

Cori, G. T., and Green, A. A. (1943). *J. Biol. Chem.* **151**, 31–38.

Curnow, R. T., and Rowe, J. N. (1977). *Clin. Res.* **25**, 389A.

Curnow, R. T., Rayfield, E. F., George, D. T., Zenser, T. V., and DeRubertis, F. R. (1975). *Am. J. Physiol.* **228**, 80–87.

Curnow, R. T., Rowe, J. N., and Goldstein, D. E. (1977). *Diabetes* **22**, Suppl. 1, 393.

DeLange, R. J., Kemp, R. G., Riley, W. D., Cooper, R. A., and Krebs, E. G. (1968). *J. Biol. Chem.* **243**, 2200–2208.

Devos, P., and Hers, H. G. (1974). *Biochem. J.* **140**, 331–340.

DeWulf, H.. and Hers, H. G. (1968). *Eur. J. Biochem.* **6**, 558–564.

Freidman, D. L., and Larner, J. (1963). *Biochemistry* **2**, 669.

Gilboe, D. P., and Nuttall, F. Q. (1972). *Biochem. Biophys. Res. Commun.* **48**, 898–906.

Gilboe, D. P., and Nuttal, F. Q. (1973). *Biochem. Biophys. Res. Commun.* **53**, 164–171.

Guillemin, R., and Gerich, J. (1976). *Annu. Rev. Med.* **27**, 379–388.

Glinsmann, W., Pauk, G., and Hern, E. (1970). *Biochem. Biophys. Res. Commun.* **39**, 774–782.

Gold, A. H. (1970). *J. Biol. Chem.* **245**, 905–906.

Gold, A. H., and Segal, H. L. (1967). *Arch. Biochem. Biophys.* **120**, 359–364.

Goldstein, D. E., and Curnow, R. T. (1978). *Metab., Clin. Exp.* **27**, 315–323.

Goris, J., and Merlevede, W. (1974). *FEBS Lett.* **48**, 184–187.

Goris, J., Defreyn, G., and Merlevede, W. (1975). *Arch. Int. Physiol. Biochim.* **82**, 988–990.

Gratecos, D., Detwiler, T., and Fischer, E. H. (1974). *In* "Metabolic Interconversion of Enzymes" (E. H. Fischer *et al.*, eds.), pp. 43–51. Springer-Verlag Berlin and New York.

Haschke, R. H., Heilmeyer, L. M. G., Meyer, F., and Fischer, E. H. (1970). *J. Biol. Chem.* **245**, 6657–6663.

Hers, H. G. (1976). *Annu. Rev. Biochem.* **45**, 187–189.

Hers, H. G., Stalmons, W., DeWulf, H., Lalous, M., and Hué, L. (1974). *In* "Metabolic Interconversion of Enzymes" (E. H. Fischer *et al.*, eds.), pp. 89–98. Springer-Verlag, Berlin and New York.

Hizurkuri, S., and Takeda, Y. (1971). *Biochim. Biophys. Acta* **212**, 179–181.

Holmes, P. A., and Mansour, T. E. (1968). *Biochim. Biophys. Acta* **156**, 275–284.

Huang, F. L., and Glinsmann, W. H. (1975). *Proc. Natl. Acad. Sci. U.S.A.* **72**, 3004–3008.

Huang, F. L., and Glinsmann, W. A. (1976a). *FEBS Lett.* **62**, 326–329.

Huang, F. L., and Glinsmann, W. H. (1976b). *Eur. J. Biochem.* **70**, 419–426.

Hué, L., Bontemps, F., and Hers, H. G. (1975). *Biochem. J.* **152**, 105–114.

Hurd, S. S., Nova, W. B., Hickenbottom, J. P., and Fischer, E. H. (1966). *In* "Methods in Enzymology" (E. F. Neufeld and V. Ginsburg, eds.), Vol. 8, pp. 546–550. Academic Press, New York.

Kato, K., and Bishop, J. S. (1972). *J. Biol. Chem.* **247**, 7420–7429.

Kato, K., and Sato, S. (1974). *Biochim. Biophys. Acta* **358**, 299–307.

Keller, P. J., and Cori, G. T. (1955). *J. Biol. Chem.* **214**, 127–134.

Khandelwal, R. L. (1977). *Biochim. Biophys. Acta* **248**, 379–390.

Khandelwal, R. L., and Zinman, S. M. (1978). *J. Biol. Chem.* **253**, 560–565.

Khandelwal, R. L., Vandenheede, J. R., and Krebs, E. G. (1976). *J. Biol. Chem.* **251**, 4850–4858.

Khandelwal, R. L., Zinman, S. M., and Zebrowski, E. J. (1977). *Biochem. J.* **168**, 541–548.

Kikuchi, K., Tamura, S., Hiraga, A., and Tsuiki, S. (1977). *Biochem. Biophys. Res. Commun.* **75**, 29–37.

Killilea, S. D., Brandt, H., Lee, E. Y. C., and Whelan, W. J. (1976). *J. Biol. Chem.* **251**, 2363–2368.

Kipnis, D. M., Helmreich, E., and Cori, C. F. (1959). *J. Biol. Chem.* **234**, 165–170.

Kobayashi, M., Kato, K., and Sato, S. (1975). *Biochim. Biophys. Acta* **377**, 343–355.

Krebs, E. G., and Fischer, E. H. (1956). *Biochim. Biophys. Acta* **20**, 150–157.

Lawrence, J. C., and Larner, J. (1978). *J. Biol. Chem.* **253**, 2104–2113.

Lee, E. Y. C., Brandt, H., Capulong, Z. L., and Killilea, S. D. (1976). *Recent Adv. Enzymol.* **14**, 467–490.

Long, C. N. H., Katzin, B., and Fry, E. G. (1940). *Endocrinology* **26**, 309–315.

Maddaiah, V. T., and Madsen, N. B. (1966). *J. Biol. Chem.* **241**, 3873–3881.

Martensen, T. M., Brotherton, J. E., and Groves, D. J. (1973a). *J. Biol. Chem.* **248**, 8323–8328.

Martensen, T. M., Brotherton, J. E., and Groves, D. J. (1973b). *J. Biol. Chem.* **248**, 8329–8336.

Merlevede, W., and Riley, G. A. (1966). *J. Biol. Chem.* **241**, 3517–3524.

Merlevede, W., Defreyn, G., Goris, G., Kalala, L. R., and Roosenmont, J. (1976). *Arch. Int. Physiol. Biochim.* **84**, 359–423.

Mersmann, H. J., and Segal, H. L. (1969). *J. Biol. Chem.* **244**, 1701–1704.

Miller, T. B., Jr., and Larner, J. (1973). *J. Biol. Chem.* **248**, 3483–3488.

Miller, T. B., Jr., Hazen, R., and Larner, J. (1973). *Biochem. Biophys. Res. Commun.* **53**, 466–474.

Nakai, C., and Thomas, J. A. (1974). *J. Biol. Chem.* **249**, 6459–6467.

Nichols, W. K., and Goldberg, N. D. (1972). *Biochim. Biophys. Acta* **279**, 245–259.

Nolan, C., Nova, W. B., Krebs, E. G., and Fischer, E. H. (1964). *Biochemistry* **3**, 542–551.

Nuttall, F. Q., Gannon, M. C., and Larner, J. (1972). *Physiol. Chem. Phys.* **4**, 497–515.

Nuttall, F. Q., Gannon, M. C., Corbett, V. A., and Wheeler, M. P. (1976). *J. Biol. Chem.* **251**, 6724–6729.

Olivier, J. R., Long, K., Wagle, S. R., and Allen, D. O. (1976). *Proc. Soc. Exp. Biol. Med.* **153**, 367–369.

Patton, G. S., Ipp, E., Dobbs, R., Orci, L., Vale, W., and Unger, R. H. (1976). *Life Sci.* **19**, 1957–1959.

Ray, K. P., and England, P. J. (1976). *Biochem. J.* **157**, 369–380.

Riley, G. A., and Haynes, R. C., Jr. (1963). *J. Biol. Chem.* **238**, 1563–1570.

Roach, P. J., and Larner, J. (1977). *Mol. Cell. Biochem.* **15**, 179–200.

Rubin, C. S., and Rosen, O. M. (1975). *Annu. Rev. Biochem.* **44**, 831–887.

Schauder, P., McIntosh, C., Arends, J., Arnold, R., Frerichs, H., and Creutzfeldt, W. (1976). *FEBS Lett.* **68**, 225–227.

Schender, K. K., Wei, S. H., and Villar-Palasi, C. (1969). *Biochim. Biophys. Acta* **191**, 272–278.

Segal, H. L. (1973). *Science* **180**, 25–32.

Shimazu, T., and Amakawa, A. (1975). *Biochim. Biophys. Acta* **385**, 242–265.

Soskin, S. (1940). *Endocrinology* **26**, 297–308.

Soskin, S., Levine, R., and Taubenhaus, M. (1939). *Proc. Soc. Exp. Biol. Med.* **42**, 689–692.

Stalmans, W. (1976). *Curr. Top. Cell. Regul.* **11**, 56–97.

Stalmans, W., and Hers, H. G. (1975). *Eur. J. Biochem.* **54**, 341–350.

Stalmans, W., DeWulf, H., and Hers, H. G. (1971). *Eur. J. Biochem.* **18**, 582–597.

Stalmans, W., Laloux, M., and Hers, H. G. (1974). *Eur. J. Biochem.* **49**, 415–427.

Sutherland, E. W. (1951). *In* "Phosphorous Metabolism" (W. D. McElroy and B. Glass, eds.) Vol. 1, p. 53. Johns Hopkins Press, Baltimore, Maryland.

Takeda, H., and Tsuiki, S. (1967). *Gann* **58**, 221–224.

Takeda, Y., Brewer, H. B., and Larner, J. (1975). *J. Biol. Chem.* **250**, 8943–8950.

Tan, A. W. H., and Nuttal, F. Q. (1975). *Biochim. Biophys. Acta* **410**, 45–60.

Tan, A. W. H., and Nuttall, F. Q. (1976). *Biochim. Biophys. Acta* **445**, 118–130.

Tan, A. W. H., and Nuttal, F. Q. (1978). *Biochim. Biophys. Acta* **522**, 139–150.

Tao, S., Nakai, C., Huang, F., and Glinsmann, W. (1978). *Proc. FEBS Meet., 11th, 197?* (in press).

Thomas, J. A., and Nakai, C. (1973). *J. Biol. Chem.* **248**, 2208–2213.

Villar-Palasi, C. (1969). *Ann. N.Y. Acad. Sci.* **166**, 719–730.

Villar-Palasi, C., Goldberg, N. D., Bishop, J. S., Nuttal, F. Q., Schender, K. K., and Larner, J. (1970). *In* "Biogenic Amines as Physiologic Regulators" (J. J. Blum, ed.), pp. 161–180.

Villar-Palasi, C., Larner, J., and Shen, L. C. (1971). *Ann. N.Y. Acad. Sci.* **185**, 74–84.

Walsh, D. A., Perkins, J. P., and Krebs, E. G. (1968). *J. Biol. Chem.* **243**, 3763–3765.

Wang, P., Bantle, G., and Sorensen, N. B. (1977). *Biochim. Biophys. Acta* **496**, 436–447.

Woods, H. F., and Krebs, H. A. (1971). *Biochem. J.* **125**, 129–139.

Wosilait, W. D., and Sutherland, E. W. (1956). *J. Biol. Chem.* **218**, 469–481.

Yeaman, S. J., and Cohen, P. (1975). *Eur. J. Biochem.* **51**, 93–104.

Zieve, F. J., and Glinsmann, W. H. (1973). *Biochem. Biophys. Res. Commun.* **50**, 872–878.

CHAPTER 3

Structural Aspects of Steroid Hormones and Carcinogenic Polycyclic Aromatic Hydrocarbons

Jenny P. Glusker

I. STRUCTURES OF STEROIDS

A. INTRODUCTION

The aim of this chapter is to describe the three-dimensional arrangement of atoms found in steroid hormones, and to discuss the extent to which features of these structures may be correlated with the physiological effect of a particular steroid. From these three-dimensional structures, obtained by high resolution X-ray crystallographic studies, some inferences on the modes of interaction of the steroid with biologically relevant macromolecules may be made, presuming that these interactions occur in an approximate "lock-and-key" fashion. X-Ray studies on steroid receptors have not been possible, for they have not yet been obtained as pure compounds. Steroid–nucleic acid interactions will also be discussed, as it is possible that, when the steroid–receptor complex interacts with a nucleic acid, direct steroid–nucleic acid interactions might occur.

This chapter is mainly concerned with structure, and therefore studies on nonsteroidal molecules having steroidlike shapes will also be reviewed. Emphasis is placed on the carcinogenic polycyclic aromatic hydrocarbons, because it was noted as early as 1932 that these had similar shapes and dimensions to those of steroids. Smaller or larger polycyclic aromatic hydrocarbons are less carcinogenic than those which most nearly approximate steroid sizes and shapes. In addition, there is evidence to lead us to suspect that some steroids may be involved in the carcinogenic process; therefore, both biochemical and structural studies that are presently under way in attempts to validate this correlation will be reviewed.

B. NOMENCLATURE

Steroids are defined as a class of organic compounds that contain the perhydrocyclopentanophenanthrene nucleus whose structure is illustrated in the example in Fig. 1. The four-ring steroid structure, designated with rings A, B, C, and D, is found in many naturally occurring compounds of biological interest, such as cholesterol, ergosterol, bile acids, androgens, estrogens, progesterone, adrenocortical hormones, and cardiac glycosides.

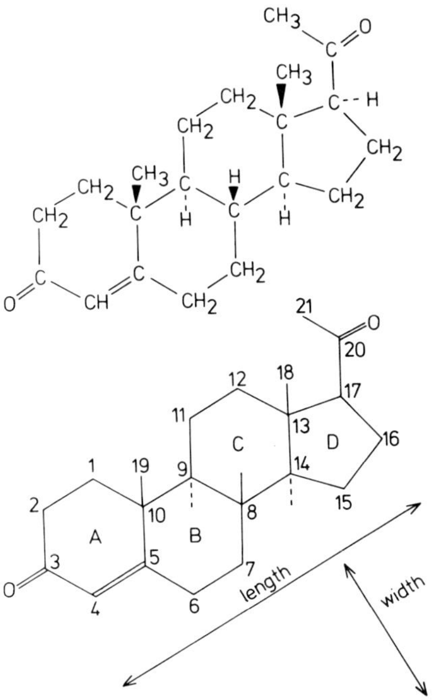

FIG. 1. The arrangement of atoms and numbering of a typical steroid. Progesterone has been chosen as a typical example. The β face is above the plane of the paper, and the α face is below the plane. Heavy black bonds (connecting carbon atoms to H-8, C-18, and C-19 point toward the reader (β side of the molecule), and bonds represented by broken lines (connecting carbon atoms to H-9, H-14, and H-17α) point away from the reader (α side of the molecule).

Steroids generally contain at least some saturated rings (that is, all carbon–carbon bonds in such rings are single bonds). In addition, substitution in the ring system is common. Those steroids containing a hydroxy group (e.g., on C-3) are called sterols; those containing a keto group acquire the suffix, -one; and those containing double bonds between any pairs of carbon atoms have the -ene suffix. The numbering system, from 1 to 17 for carbon atoms, is described in the IUPAC IUB 1971 definitive rules for the nomenclature of steroids (1972) and is shown in Fig. 1. In the conformation in which Fig. 1 is drawn, with the general plane of the molecule in the plane of the paper, the upper face of the steroid (i.e., that above the plane of the paper, with methyl groups C-18 and C-19 pointing toward the reader) is designated β; the lower face (i.e., below the plane of the paper) is designated α. Bonds that point up on the β side of the molecule are drawn with heavy lines, and those on the α side are shown with broken lines.

The main classes of steroid hormones, each defined by their physiological function, are the estrogens, the androgens, the progestogens, the glucocorticoids, the mineralocorticoids, and vitamin D. The estrogens are female sex hormones and are assayed by a test devised by Allen and Doisy (1923) in which characteristic changes in the tissue lining of the vagina of ovariec-tomized rodents are analyzed. The male sex hormones—androgens—may be assayed, for example, by their ability to promote comb growth in capons (Gallagher and Koch, 1929). The progestogens are involved in the preparation for and maintenance of pregnancy, and the glucocorticoids have distinct effects on carbohydrate metabolism and also have antiinflammatory properties. The mineralocorticoids affect ion transport so that sodium is conserved in the cell while potassium is lost. Vitamin D is involved in the regulation of calcium transport. These steroids all contain the four-ring structure, except for vitamin D, which has an opened B ring. The formula of one representative of each class of hormone is given in Fig. 2. Estradiol-17β, an estrogen, has an aromatic A ring, and no methyl group on C-10. Testosterone, an androgen, has a keto group on C-3 and a double bond between C-4 and C-5. Progesterone is similar to testosterone but has an acetyl group on C-17. Cortisol, a glucocorticoid, is similar to progesterone with additional

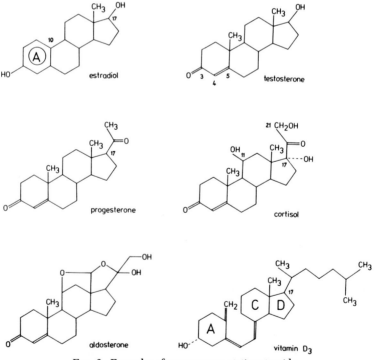

FIG. 2. Formulas of some representative steroids.

hydroxyl groups on C-11, C-17, and C-21. Aldosterone, a mineralocorticoid, can exist as an equilibrium of three forms, two of which have one or two additional rings containing oxygen atoms. The latter form is shown in Fig. 2. Vitamin D, which contains only rings A, C, and D, has a long side chain on C-17.

C. HISTORY: THE DETERMINATION OF THE CHEMICAL FORMULAS OF STEROIDS

Many naturally occurring steroids crystallize readily. For example, cholesterol monohydrate is found in a crystalline state as a major constituent of human gallstones. It was studied extensively by Chevreul (1815), who named it cholesterine (cholesterol) from the Greek *chol* for bile and *stereos* for solid. Since that time, innumerable other steroids have been crystallized. They were studied by the methods of X-ray crystallography at a time when the chemical formulas of steroids were still under investigation. In fact, the establishment of the correct formulas in 1932 involved the simultaneous work of organic chemists and X-ray crystallographers. The story is of historical interest, and furthermore illustrates the various ways in which three types of physical evidence—X-ray diffraction, optical crystallography, and studies of monomolecular films—can complement the studies of organic chemists.

The basic chemical structure of steroids was originally deduced by the researches of Borsche, Diels, Mauthner, Wieland and Windaus to be a four-ring structure (formula I) consisting of two six-membered rings and two

I

five-membered rings (Wieland, 1929; Windaus, 1932). In fact, this basic formula was incorrect; two carbon atoms (designated "obdachlosen" or "homeless" and marked with an asterisk in formula I) could not be adequately accounted for. Other formulas involving one or two seven-membered rings in the structure did not stand the test of further chemical characterization.

The correct arrangement of rings was finally deduced when in 1932, Bernal studied, with Crowfoot and Fankuchen, the X-ray diffraction patterns of crystals of calciferol and related sterols. The unit cell dimensions (the small-est packing unit in the crystal) and the directions of the largest and smallest refractive indices with respect to the edges of the unit cell provided informa-tion on the maximum dimensions within which one steroid molecule could fit. These data suggested that the dimensions of a steroid nucleus such as is found in cholesterol are 17–20 Å long, 7–8 Å wide, and 5 Å thick (as shown in Fig. 3). However, the Wieland and Windaus formula (formula I) was found, by building a model with known carbon–carbon distances of 1.5 Å, to be more bulky, with dimensions of approximately 18.0 Å × 7.0 × 8.5 Å. Such a molecule would be too thick to fit in the unit cell dimensions that are observed experimentally (Bernal, 1932).

Adam obtained similar information, i.e., that the Wieland and Windaus formula was too bulky. He studied molecular cross-section sizes by measur-ing the surface area of a monolayer film of a known amount of steroid (erogo-sterol). The area (width × thickness) occupied by a single molecule could then be calculated using Avogadro's number. These experimental methods for measuring surface films were developed by Langmuir (1916) and Adam (1930). In such a monolayer, the hydroxyl group on C-3 projects into the aqueous layer and the side chains on C-17 pack together and extend toward the steroid–air interface. A molecular cross-section area of 37–44 Å^2 was obtained for ergosterol, in agreement with Bernal's measurements of 7.2 Å × 5.0 Å = 36 Å^2 (Adam and Rosenheim, 1929; Adam, 1930). The Wieland

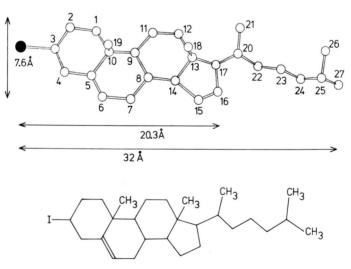

FIG. 3. The general dimensions of a steroid molecule. The structure of cholesteryl iodide is shown. The iodine atom is black, while carbon atoms are white. Hydrogen atoms are not shown. The double bond between C-5 and C-6 is shorter than single bonds.

and Windaus formula could not be packed into an area less than 54Å ^{2} in any orientation, a situation incompatible with the experimental results.

In a publication adjacent to one by Bernal (1932), Rosenheim and King (1932) pointed out that the molecular size could approximate the values obtained by Bernal if the rings were rearranged so that their connectivity resembled that of chrysene (formula II), a compound obtained on dehydrogenation of several steroids. The new formula is shown as III. Wieland and Dane (1933) modified formula III, in view of their experimental data, to include one five-membered ring instead of a six-membered ring, as shown in formula IV. This new formula, IV, has stood the test of time.

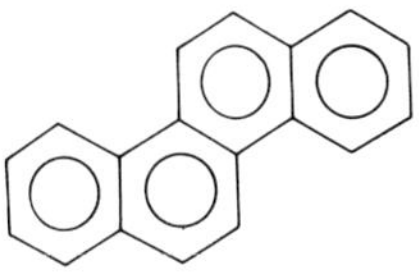

II

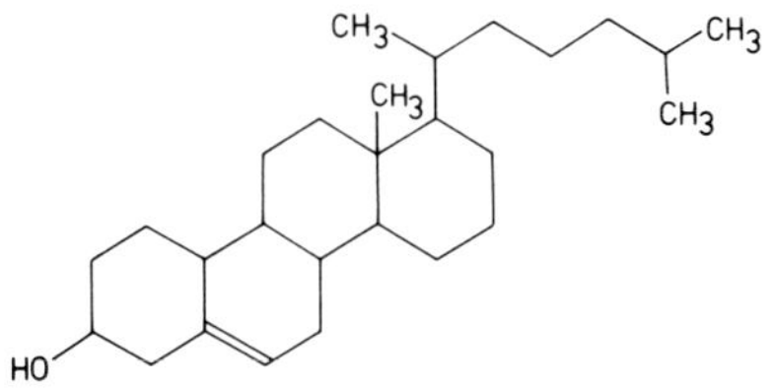

III

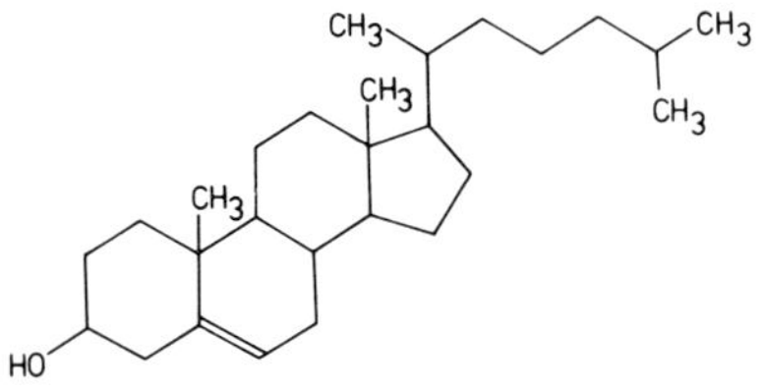

IV

In 1936 and 1940 Bernal, Crowfoot, and Fankuchen published a survey of 105 steroids (Bernal and Crowfoot, 1936; Bernal *et al.*, 1940), mainly those in the cholesterol and ergosterol series. Determinations of cell dimensions and space groups, coupled with optical measurements, indicated that sterols with long side chains, such as ergosterol, when crystallized, formed double layers in which the hydroxyl groups at one end of the molecules ("heads") pack together (head-to-head packing) and the hydrophobic ends of the molecules ("tails") pack together (tail-to-tail packing). However, because the sex hormones did not form such double layers, it was suggested that there are active groups at each end of the molecule, and therefore head-to-tail interactions, by hydrogen bonding, were possible.

The connectivity of atoms in a steroid molecule was finally settled unequivocally when, in 1945, Carlisle and Crowfoot published a paper on the detailed atomic arrangement in cholesteryl iodide (see Fig. 3). The presence of the heavy atom, iodine, facilitated the structure solution. Since that time, the structures of many steroids have been studied; in several cases, such as that of the insect hormone, ecdysone (Huber and Hoppe, 1965), the fact that the molecule was a steroid was first established by X-ray methods.

D. METHODOLOGY

1. Structure Determination

First we must consider how atomic arrangements are determined from a study of the X-ray diffraction of crystals. A crystal is, by definition, a solid that contains a regularly repeating internal arrangement of atoms in three dimensions. As a result of the regular repeating pattern in the crystal (from the packing of many unit cells), diffraction occurs as X-rays are passed through it. It is the measurement of the diffracted beams obtained when X-rays impinge on a crystal that is the basis of the method of structure determination described in this chapter. Diffraction data consist of two measurements for each diffracted beam: (a) the direction in which each beam is diffracted (the angle at which a scintillation counter must be held to detect the beam, or the position of a spot on the photographic film); and (b) the intensity of the diffracted beam (measured as the flux hitting the scintillation counter or as the amount of blackening of photographic film). The *directions* of the diffracted beams give information leading to a measurement of the *dimensions of the unit cell*. The *intensities* of the diffracted beams give information leading to the derivation of the *atomic arrangement* within each unit cell. For a typical steroid, the intensities of 1000 to 5000 diffracted spots (called the "diffraction pattern") are measured.

The derived atomic arrangement (trial structure) is generally obtained by one of two major methods. The first involves interpretation of a Patterson map. This is a three-dimensional map, which may be calculated directly from the diffracted intensities, containing vectors between all atoms. This map can be analyzed readily if one or two heavy atoms are present, as these dominate the X-ray scattering. The second method for structure determination, often very readily completed by computers, is described as a "direct method." It involves the mathematical combination (Fourier synthesis) of the diffracted beams to give an electron density map subject to the condition that this electron density should never be negative.

When a trial structure gives a calculated diffraction pattern that agrees reasonably well with the observed diffraction pattern, refinement of atomic positional and thermal parameters proceeds via least squares methods using a high-speed computer to minimize the differences between calculated and observed diff-action intensities. There are three criteria for a "good" trial structure, i.e., one which is, presumably, the true structure. The first is that observed and calculated diffraction patterns should agree well. The second is that, on refinement, this agreement should improve. Third, the resulting structure should be chemically reasonable; i.e., atoms that should be bonded together do so with bond length values approximating those in other structures. Hydrogen bonds are formed where possible, and no molecule should "bump" into another molecule.

However, it is not the intention of this chapter to give a detailed discourse on X-ray diffraction. For further details the reader is referred to books on the general subject of crystallography by Bunn (1961), Stout and Jensen (1968), and Glusker and Trueblood (1972), to more specialized volumes on space groups (Henry and Lonsdale, 1952) and on protein crystallography (Blundell and Johnson, 1976), and to an article on the application of "direct methods" of X-ray structure analysis to steroids (Karle, 1973). A glossary of selected terms is provided in the Appendix to this chapter.

2. The Absolute Configurations of Steroids

When a molecule contains an asymmetric carbon atom, i.e., a carbon atom with four different substituents, it is not superimposable on its mirror image. Thus two isomers, the original and its mirror image, are possible. The best method for determining which isomer is being scrutinized, that is, its absolute configuration, is to employ X-ray techniques. Use is made of "anomalous dispersion," which is an effect that occurs when the radiation, used in the diffraction experiment, has a wavelength near that for which radiation is strongly absorbed by one or more atoms in the structure. For example, cobalt is a strong absorber and anomalous scatterer of copper $K\alpha$ radiation wavelength 1.54 Å), and rubidium does the same for molybdenum $K\alpha$ radiation (wavelength 0.77 Å) (two commonly used radiations). Such a use of anomalous scattering was made by Bijvoet *et al.* (1951) to establish the first absolute configuration, that of tartaric acid in crystals of its sodium rubidium double salt.

The method has been used successfully for many steroids. The first one studied was a lanostane derivative (Fawcett and Trotter, 1966). The investigation established that the formula, shown in Fig. 1, is the correct absolute configuration for natural steroid hormones. This had also been indicated by chemical correlations (Fieser and Fieser, 1959). Since that time, absolute configurations have been determined for many steroids which have been newly synthesized or isolated from natural sources [e.g., batrachotoxinin A (Gilardi, 1970)].

E. The Detailed Three-Dimensional Structures of Steroids

Because there are seven asymmetric carbon atoms in a saturated steroid nucleus (carbon atoms number 5, 8, 9, 10, 13, 14, 17), then 2^7 or 128 stereoisomers can exist. In fact, the number of naturally occurring isomers of the ring system are found to be very few (four in all). The A/B ring junction may be either *cis* or *trans*; i.e., the substituents or hydrogen atoms on C-5 and C-10 may be on the same (*cis*) or opposite (*trans*) sides of the C-5—C-10 bond to give 5β or 5α compounds, respectively. The B/C ring junction is *trans* in most naturally occurring steroids, while the C/D junction is *trans* in steroids and bile acids and *cis* in cardioactive steroids. Unless otherwise stated, the configuration of a naturally occurring steroid is designated 8β, 9α, 10β, 13β, 14α, and generally 17β [meaning that a hydrogen atom or substituent on the steroid nucleus would point up (β) or down (α) at these carbon atoms]. All ring fusions are *trans* in the steroid represented in Fig. 1.

1. Bond Lengths and Angles

Most carbon–carbon bond lengths in steroids lie near the idealized values, found in other organic compounds, of 1.54 Å for C—C, 1.34 Å for C=C, and 1.39 Å for aromatic bonds. Detailed bond lengths can be found in the original crystallographic articles or in the *Atlas of Steroid Structures* (Duax and Norton, 1975). Substituents in steroid molecules also have typical bond lengths—such as C=O, 1.20 Å and C—OH, 1.42 Å—and they may be either equatorial (roughly in the plane of the steroid nucleus) or axial (with bonds almost perpendicular to the general plane of the steroid molecule). The packing of molecules in the crystalline state is controlled by the van der Waals radii of their atoms: 1.0 Å for H, 1.4 Å for O, 1.7 Å for C, and 1.85 Å for the half-thickness of an aromatic molecule. These radii effectively define a "size" for each atom, so that two nonbonded atoms do not, unless there are additional forces at work, approach closer than the sum of their van der Waals radii.

There is structural strain in steroids. In the structure of diamond, which consists of an infinite three-dimensional network of six-membered rings, every carbon atom is surrounded by four other carbon atoms, so that the bond angles are all 109.5° and the torsion angles are all 60°. In cyclohexane, each carbon atom is surrounded by two carbon atoms and two hydrogen atoms, and values of 111.1° and 55.8° are obtained, respectively, for the bond angles and for the torsion angles involving carbon atoms (Davis and Hassel, 1963). Repulsion between the more bulky carbon atoms has increased the C—C—C bond angle. However, the situation in steroids is further complicated by the strain resulting from the fusion of the five- and six-membered rings at C-13—C-14. It is pointed out in the *Atlas of Steroid Structure* (Duax and Norton, 1975) that, in order to relieve this strain, two angles in steroids are particularly distorted from 109.5°. These are C-8—C-14—C-15, which has an average value of 119.3± 1.9°, andC-14—C-13—C-17, which has an average value of 99.2 ± 2.2°.

2. Conformations of Five- and Six-Membered Rings

There are several conformations of six-membered rings. If no substitution occurs, then the chair form has the lowest energy and therefore is the most stable. However, as a result of substitution in the same or other rings in the molecule, additional conformations, shown in Fig. 4, are possible and are found experimentally. The most important conformations are the chair, the half-chair (four atoms in a plane, and two adjacent atoms above and below the plane, respectively), and the sofa (five atoms in a plane). Similarly, for the five-membered ring there are several possibilities, also shown in Fig. 4. The most important conformations of five-membered rings are the half-chair (three atoms in a plane and two adjacent atoms above and below the plane, respectively) and the envelope (four of the five atoms in a plane). The atoms out of the major plane are labeled to designate the number of the atom, and the side of the plane that it lies on. For example, in the D ring, the 14α

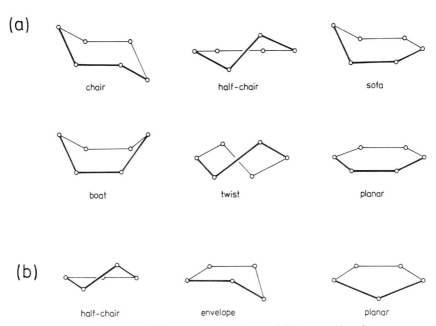

FIG. 4. Conformations of (a) six-membered rings and (b) five-membered rings.

TABLE I

RING CONFORMATIONS IN SOME ESTROGENS AND ANDROGENS, ILLUSTRATING FLEXIBILITY[a]

Name	Reference	Ring A	Ring B	Ring C	Ring D
1 Estradiol hemihydrate	Busetta and Hospital (1972)	Planar	Distorted $7\alpha,8\beta$-half-chair	Chair	13β-Envelope/$13\beta,14\alpha$-half chair[b]
2 Estradiol propand (1:1)	Busetta et al. (1972a)	Planar	Distorted $7\alpha,8\beta$-half-chair	Chair	13β-Envelope/$13\beta,14\alpha$-half-chair
3 Estradiol urea (1:1)	Duax (1972)	Planar	Distorted $7\alpha,8\beta$-half-chair	Chair	13β-Envelope/$13\beta,14\alpha$-half-chair
4 2,4-dibromoestradiol Crystal I	Cody et al. (1971)	Planar	Distorted 8β-sofa	Chair	13β-Envelope/$13\beta,14\alpha$-half-chair
5 Crystal II Molecule 1		Planar	Sofa	Chair	13β-Envelope/$13\beta,14\alpha$-half-chair
6 Molecule 2		Planar	Distorted $7\alpha,8\beta$-half-chair	Chair	13β-Envelope/$13\beta,14\alpha$-half-chair
7 Estrone crystal I	Busetta et al. (1973a)	Planar	$7\alpha,8\beta$-Half-chair	Chair	14α-Envelope/$13\beta,14\alpha$-half-chair
8 Crystal II		Planar	$7\alpha,8\beta$-Half-chair	Chair	14α-Envelope/$13\beta,14\alpha$-half-chair
9 Crystal III Molecule 1		Planar	Distorted 8β-Sofa	Chair	Flat and distorted $13\beta,14\alpha$-half-chair
10 Molecular 2		Planar	$7\alpha,8\beta$-Half-chair	Chair	14α-Envelope
11 Estriol	Cooper et al. (1969a)	Planar	8β-Sofa	Chair	13β-Envelope

		Planar	7α,8β-Half-chair	Chair	13β-Envelope
12 Molecule 2				Chair	13β-Envelope
13 Testosterone Molecule 1	Roberts et al. (1973b)	Distorted 1α-sofa	Chair	Chair	13β-Envelope/13β,14α-half-chair
14 Molecule 2		1α-Sofa	Chair	Chair	Distorted 13β,14α-half-chair
15 Testosterone monohydrate crystal I	Busetta et al. (1972b)	1α,2β-Half-chair	Chair	Chair	13β-Envelope/13β,14α-half-chair
16 Crystal II	Precigoux et al. (1973)	1α-Sofa/1α,2β-half-chair	Chair	Chair	13β-Envelope/13β,14α-half-chair
17 Testosterone mercuric chloride (1:1)	Cooper et al. (1968)	1α-Sofa	Chair	Chair	Distorted 13β,14α-half-chair
18 Testosterone p-bromophenol (1:1)	Cooper et al. (1969b)	1α-Sofa/1α,2β-half-chair	Chair	Chair	13β-Envelope/13β,14α-half-chair
19 Dihydrotestosterone Molecule 1	Courseille et al. (1973a)	Chair	Chair	Chair	Distorted 13β-envelope
20 Molecule 2		Chair	Chair	Chair	Distorted 13β-envelope
21 Dihydrotestosterone monohydrate	Busetta et al. (1972c)	Chair	Chair	Chair	13β-Envelope/13β,14α-half-chair

[a]From Duax and Norton, 1975.

[b]If two conformations are listed (divided by a slash), the observed conformation lies between the two.

envelope has C-14 below (i.e., on the α side of) the plane through the other four atoms in the ring (C-13—C-15—C-16—C-17). In general the detailed conformations of all four rings of a steroid are listed when a structure determination is reported. Conformations of rings in some estrogens and androgens are listed in Table I, together with references.

There have been numerous articles written on the conformations of steroids (Geise *et al.*, 1967; Altona *et al.*, 1968; Romers *et al.*, 1974; Bucourt, 1974; Duax *et al.*, 1975, 1976a); therefore, the subject will not be discussed here in detail.

3. Masking of the β Face

The two bulky methyl groups, C-18 and C-19, mask the β face of a steroid, as does a β side chain at C-17. Thus, as shown in Fig. 5, it is difficult for a reagent to reach C-1, C-5, C-12, C-14, or C-17 from the β side of a steroid that contains both of these methyl groups. It is, of course, possible to attack hydrogen atoms on C-18 and C-19, and also H-6, H-8, and H-11, which point up as shown. Most reactions take place more readily on the α side of a naturally occurring steroid. For example, when steroids are treated with peracids, epoxides are formed but these are generally α-epoxides; e.g., sub-situation is 1α, 2α; 2α, 3α; 9α, 11α; or 11α, 12α.

4. Bowing of the Molecule

Steroid hormone molecules are flat in the sense that a ball-and-stick model of fused cyclohexane rings in a chair conformation may be laid flat on a table, as shown in Fig. 6. Thermodynamically, this is the most stable situation with all ring fusions *trans*. However, those steroids that have two bulky axial

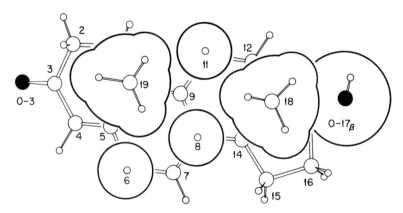

FIG. 5. Masking of the β face of a steroid (androsterone). Van der Waals radii are drawn around each atom that points up on the β face. Oxygen atoms are black and hydrogen atoms are represented by smaller circles than are carbon atoms.

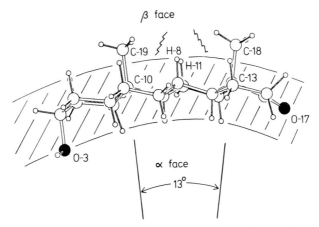

FIG. 6. Bowing of the molecule (androsterone) to the α side. The overall arc shape of the molecule is indicated by shading. Interactions between hydrogen atoms (i.e., H-8 and H-11 with methyl hydrogen atoms), leading to the bowing, are marked by jagged lines. Atom representations as in Fig. 5.

methyl groups (C-18 and C-19) are slightly bowed, so that the molecule is concave on the α side of the molecule. For example, in androsterone (High and Kraut, 1966), illustrated in Fig. 6, the axial bonds C-10—C-19 and C-13—C-18 are not parallel, but lie at an angle of approximately 13° to each other. The bowing occurs because the methyl groups are sterically hindered by the axial hydrogen atoms at C-8 and C-11. In addition, the attachment of the five-membered D ring imposes strain on the system. The α side of the steroid generally contains only less bulky axial hydrogen atoms. However, if there are substituents on the α side, then their interactions with these hydrogen atoms are important, and could even cause the molecule to bow toward the β side.

5. Flexibility Caused by Double Bonds and the Effects of Substitution

If all the six-membered rings of a steroid molecule were fully saturated, the molecule would be fairly rigid and each ring would be shaped like a chair. However, some flexibility is introduced when the molecule contains double bonds in any of its six-membered rings. This is contrary to the usual notion that a double bond is associated with decreased flexibility (because rotation about a double bond is not possible). In addition, a saturated five-membered ring is flexible, and can assume many conformations. This ability is called pseudorotation. Strain at the ring junctions occurs when, as in many steroids, a five-membered ring is fused to a six-membered ring. Because the strain and steric hindrance may be relieved in more than one way, the molecule becomes more flexible.

Steroids often crystallize with two molecules in the asymmetric unit, that is, the initial crystallizing unit contains two molecules. Coordinates of these two molecules are derived independently in the X-ray diffraction analysis, and it is often found that the two molecules have slightly different conformations. Such experimental results, it is believed, give us some measure of the flexibility of the molecule, for it is assumed that these are two conformational isomers with a finite barrier to interconversion. For example, in one crystalline form of estriol the B ring conformation differs in the two molecules in the asymmetric unit, as listed in Table I and illustrated in Fig. 7. This experimental result suggests that these two conformations of ring B, the 8β-sofa and the 7α,8β-half-chair, have similar energies. If ring D is placed in the same position for each molecule, the hydroxyl group oxygen atoms will differ by about 1.7 Å in position, as shown in Fig. 7. There is some steric hindrance in estriol between H-1 and H-11, and therefore, to relieve this strain, twisting about the C-9—C-11 bond occurs. This twist is in opposite directions for the two different molecules in the unit cell as shown in Fig. 7.

In a similar way, as shown in Table I, studies of different crystalline forms of other steroids may give an indication of possible flexibility. For example, in androgens the A ring is flexible, while the B ring is flexible in estrogens. This flexibility of naturally occurring hormones may have very important biological consequences because, as pointed out by Duax and co-workers (1977), a steroid may assume different conformations for optimal binding to

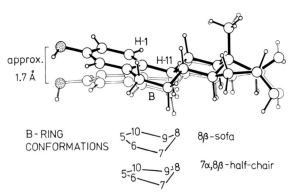

FIG. 7. Flexibility of a steroid. Two conformations of estriol, found in the same crystal, are shown. In the 8β-sofa conformation of ring B (black bonds), atoms 5, 6, 7, 9, and 10 are coplanar. In the 7α,8β-half-chair conformation (white bonds), atoms 5, 6, 9, and 10 are coplanar. Atom 7 lies on the α side and atom 8 on the β side of the steroid.

transport proteins, to metabolizing enzymes, or to steroid receptors. Such flexibility may also facilitate the mechanism by which a steroid comes off a receptor. When, however, a substituent is introduced into a natural steroid, the equilibrium between possible conformations is affected so that one conformation may predominate. For example, binding to a steroid receptor may be enhanced, but all other functions of the natural steroid may be lost.

6. Conformational Transmission

It has been found that changes in the conformation of one ring may affect the conformations of any or all of the other rings, an effect known as "conformational transmission." This is a term originally introduced by Barton and co-workers (1957) to describe the experimental fact that structural changes at one carbon atom in the steroid skeleton may profoundly affect the rate of a specific reaction at some distant carbon atom. The effect arises because each steroid ring shares a common bond with another ring, and the relief of strain at that common bond can easily be transmitted from one ring to the next, and often to other rings as well. For example, the presence of substituents on the B or C rings can strongly influence the conformation of the A rings.

7. Side Chain Conformation

A long side chain at C-17, such as is found in cholesterol, is very flexible, and various conformations, even within the same crystal, may be found. However, torsion angles are usually large ($\sim 180°$), so that the chain is generally fully stretched, or nearly so. For example, both cholesterol (Shieh *et al.*, 1977) and cholesterol monohydrate (Craven, 1976), contain eight molecules in the asymmetric units. Four different side chain conformations are found in each type of crystal.

Side chain orientations are affected by substitution in the D ring. For example, the 17β side chain orientation is influenced by any substitution at the 17α, 20, or 21 positions. In addition, in most steroids studied to date with a keto group in position 20, the C-13—C-17—C-20—O-20 torsion angle lies in the range $80°–115°$ (Duax *et al.*, 1975). This means that the C-20—O-20 bond is almost perpendicular to the plane through C-13—C-17—C-20, as shown in Fig. 8 for progesterone or cortisol.

8. Diagrammatic Representations of Structural Results

The structures of some selected steroid hormones are shown in Fig. 8. Views each of estradiol-17β (Busetta and Hospital, 1972), testosterone (Busetta *et al.*, 1972b), progesterone (Campsteyn *et al.*, 1972a), cortisol (Roberts *et al.*, 1973a), and aldosterone (Duax and Hauptman, 1972) are shown, using atomic positions determined experimentally from X-ray crystallographic studies. Chemical formulas have already been given in Fig. 2.

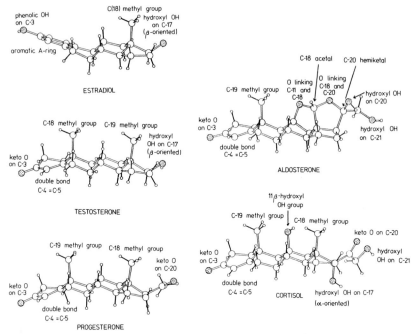

FIG. 8. "Ball-and-stick" representations of the structures of some steroid hormones determined by X-ray crystallographic methods. Details of each structure are labeled. In aldosterone the acetal grouping is $R-CH\overset{OR_1}{\underset{OR_2}{\diagdown}}$ and the hemiketal grouping is $\overset{R_1}{\underset{R_2}{\diagup}}C\overset{OR_3}{\underset{OH}{\diagdown}}$, where R_1, R_2, and R_3 refer to different substituents.

Unless otherwise noted, all "ball-and-stick" diagrams are drawn from coordinates that have been published as a result of X-ray crystallographic studies. It must be remembered, however, that molecules do not look like the diagrams. The ball-and-stick diagram really represents very small nuclei surrounded by electron clouds. Only the spatial arrangement of the centers of the "balls" are correct, but without "sticks" to represent bonds the diagrams would be hard to interpret.

As shown by a single example in Fig. 8, the two main features of the naturally occurring estrogens are the aromatic A ring and the lack of a C-19 methyl group. This aromaticity means that the A ring is planar, while the other rings are buckled. The androgen testosterone, which does not have an aromatic A ring (see Fig. 2 for formula), has a completely different shape from that of estradiol-17β. While estradiol-17β is bowed up to the β side, testosterone is bowed down to the α side. Progesterone and testosterone are very similar in appearance, except that progesterone has a longer side chain on C-17. This means that the O-3······O-(17 or 20) separation is increased from 10.9 Å in both estradiol-17β and testosterone to 11.97 Å in progesterone. Glucocorticoids, such as cortisol, have an axial 11β hydroxyl group as a characteristic structural feature. The mineralocorticoid aldosterone, which controls the flow of sodium ions, has a more complicated structure, with two additional five-membered rings caused by the acetal–hemiketal grouping. These additional rings, which lie approximately perpendicular to the plane through rings A to D, make the molecule very rigid and also cause strain in the C ring.

9. Comparison of Structures in Solution and in the Solid State

The question is continually raised as to whether the structure of a compound found in the crystalline state is the predominant form in solution. The structure determined in the solid is a low-energy state. But several conformations may be found in the crystalline state, sometimes two conformers in the same crystal and sometimes two conformers in two different crystalline forms. If several conformations are found in the crystalline state, these may also all occur in solution.

This problem has been studied by NMR techniques (Havinga, 1973; La Mar and Budd, 1974; Wing *et al.*, 1975). For example, Wing and co-workers studied vitamin D_3 and its analogs by 300 MHz ^{1}H NMR. Their results suggested a dynamic equilibrium between two chair forms of the A ring in an approximately equimolar ratio, as shown in Fig. 9(a). The hydroxyl group on C-3 is equatorial in one form and axial in the other form. These deductions on the equilibrium in solution are in agreement with the X-ray crystallographic results of Dahl and co-workers (Trinh-Toan *et al.*, 1976), shown in Fig. 9(b), in which two molecules crystallize per asymmetric unit with the two conformations predicted from solution studies. Thus, the X-ray results are relevant to the conformations found in solution. This finding, for which many other examples have been found, is true in particular if one takes into account the differences in structure that can be found if the same compound is studied in more than one crystal form.

F. Interactions of Steroids with Other Molecules

1. Interaction of Steroids with Other Molecules in the Crystalline State

Structural results from X-ray studies give information not only on the conformation of the molecule but also on its interactions, if any, with other (similar) molecules in the crystal. There is great variation in the types of packing of steroids in the crystalline state. However, among the multitude of

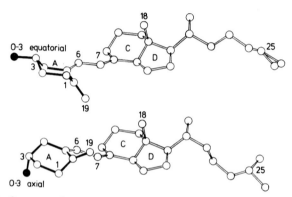

(a) NMR predictions (Wing *et al*, 1975)

0-3 equatorial 50% (19α)   0-3 axial 50% (19β)

(b) X-ray results (Trinh-Toan *et al*, 1976)

0-3 equatorial

0-3 axial

FIG. 9. Conformation of vitamin D_3 predicted from NMR studies and found in one crystal-line form of vitamin D_3. A 50:50 equilibrium mixture of two conformations of the A ring is found in each study. The bonds in the A ring are black, for clarity, and O-3 is black. The location of a 1(S) substituent is indicated by arrows in (a). Note also the differing conformations of the flexible side chains.

packing patterns, there is, specificity in the directionality of certain hydrogen bonds, particularly those involving oxygen atoms on C-3, C-11, and C-17. For example, in the corticosteroids, an 11β hydroxyl group consistently forms hydrogen bonds in a direction *trans* to the C-9—C-11 bond (i.e., the O·····O-11—C-11—C-9 grouping is a planar zigzag). Similarly, a 17α hydroxyl group consistently forms hydrogen bonds in a direction *trans* to the C-13—C-17 bond. These directions of hydrogen bond formation are independent of the nature of the external hydrogen bond acceptor. The directionality of the hydrogen bonding of O-3 is less constant than for the other cases listed above.

The general packing of steroids is determined by the location of the functional groups and by the conformation of the molecule (Bernal *et al.*, 1940). For example, molecules with O-3 (head) and O-17 (tail) both equatorially oriented, as in estradiol and testosterone, pack in infinite head-to-tail chains linked by hydrogen bonds. Other possible types of interactions are face-to-face and side-to-side hydrophobic packing. Molecules with only one functional group, such as cholesterol, pack with their hydrophobic tails in contact, and their hydrophilic O-3 groups usually hydrogen bonded to water (Craven, 1976; Shieh *et al.*, 1977).

Structures of steroids complexed with *p*-bromophenol (Peck *et al.*, 1974; Cooper *et al.*, 1969b; Duax *et al.*, 1971a,b), urea (Duax, 1972), or adenine (Weeks *et al.*, 1975a) have also been determined. They give information on

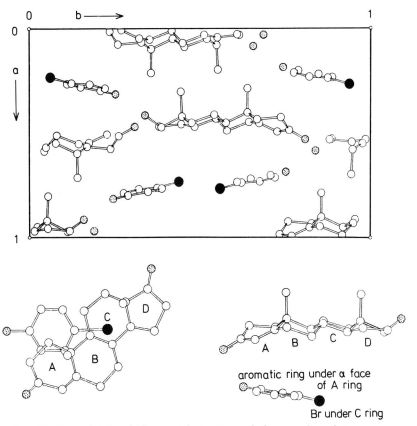

FIG. 10. Some details of the crystal structure of the complex of testosterone and *p*-bromophenol. In the upper portion of the diagram the contents of one unit cell are shown, viewed along the *c* axis. Atoms which are not bonded when they might be expected to be are at very different heights. Part of one molecule is at the top of the unit cell and part is at the bottom. Repetition of unit cells results in fully bonded molecules. In the lower half of the figure, two views (onto and along the aromatic ring), illustrating the interaction between the steroid and *p*-bromophenol are shown. The black circles are bromine atoms.

the interactions of a steroid with a flat molecule such as an aromatic side chain in a protein. The interactions between *p*-bromophenol and testosterone (Cooper *et al.*, 1969b) are illustrated in Fig. 10, which shows the general crystal structure of the complex and views of the interactions involved. A major interaction seems to occur between the bromine atom and the C ring of the steroid. The aromatic ring of *p*-bromophenol lies partially under the A ring of testosterone. Steroid–adenine interactions may be relevant to steroid–nucleic acid complexes, and will be discussed later.

2. *Choleic Acids*

A very interesting example of the interaction between steroids and other types of molecules is the group of complexes collectively described as choleic acids. In 1916 Wieland and Sorge noticed that fatty acids are tenaciously retained when bile acids are purified. They showed (Wieland and Sorge, 1916) that the so-called "choleic acids" that had been isolated from bile consisted of about 92% deoxycholic acid, complexed with about 8% of stearic acid or of palmitic acid. Since that time, a large number of such "choleic acids," consisting of deoxycholic acid complexed with hydrocarbons (such as naphthalene), ketones (such as camphor), phenols, alcohols, and fatty acids have been studied. The physiological importance of these complexes comes from the fact that their alkali salts are water soluble. Therefore, many water-insoluble substances can be solubilized by formation of choleic acids. This allows for membrane permeation, for example, in the intestine, or, possibly for excretion.

When these compounds were examined by X-rays in the early 1930's, it was found that the powder photographs of the various choleic acids were almost identical. In the series of choleic acids involving stearic, palmitic, lauric, caprylic, heptoic, butyric, and propionic acids, the cell dimensions are $a = 13.45$–$13.57\ \text{Å}$, $b = 7.21$–$7.23\ \text{Å}$, and $c = 25.75$–$25.90\ \text{Å}$ in an orthorhombic unit cell. However, the number of fatty acid molecules per molecule of deoxycholic acid lies in the range of 3–8. It was concluded that a framework of deoxycholic acid is formed with channels running parallel to the *b* axis. The fatty acids were then assumed to extend through several unit cells (Giacomello and Kratky, 1936; Herndon, 1967).

Since the 1930's, the detailed structures of some choleic acids, such as one with phenanthrene (De Sanctis *et al.*, 1972), have been reported. The channels are formed by hydrogen bonding between different deoxycholic acid molecules (Friedman *et al.*, 1975).

3. *X-Ray Studies of Proteins That Interact with Steroids*

In addition to the determination of the structures of crystalline steroids, it is possible to study the proteins with which they interact, if these can be obtained in a crystalline form. To date, the only enzyme being studied in detail is the Δ^5-3-ketosteroid isomerase from the bacterium *Pseudomonas testosteroni* (EC 5.3.3.1), which has been described by Westbrook and co-workers. The enzyme exists as a dimer in solution. It was purified by Talalay and Benson, and the amino acid sequence has been determined (Benson *et al.*, 1971) for each subunit of molecular weight 13,394. Two crystalline forms of the enzyme have been reported but, unfortunately, both types of crystals are fragile and their study has been difficult. One crystalline form (Westbrook *et al.*, 1976) exists as platelets, and is monoclinic with six dimers per asymmetric unit (two asymmetric units per unit cell). A second form, which consists of pyramidal crystals, is hexagonal with two dimers per asymmetric unit (12 asymmetric units per unit cell) (Westbrook, 1976). The detailed structure of the hexagonal form of Δ^5-3-ketosteroid isomerase is now being determined by Westbrook. Diffraction data have been collected to 2.7 Å resolution on the enzyme itself, and the ultimate study of the enzyme will be at that resolution (E. M. Westbrook, private communication, 1977). A 4-mercury estradiol and a 21-iodo-21-dehydroxycortisol derivative of the enzyme are being investigated, at present only to 6 Å resolution.

The aim of this structural study is to determine not only the three-dimensional structure of the enzyme, but the structure of its complexes with inhibitors and weak substrates, in order to elucidate the mechanism of action of the enzyme. Some other proteins that interact with steroids have also been crystallized, for example, human placental estradiol 17β-dehydrogenase (Chin *et al.*, 1976), but no X-ray studies have been reported yet. Unfortunately, steroid receptors have not yet been purified sufficiently, nor have they been obtained in large enough quantities to allow for such crystallization studies.

G. OTHER STEROIDS OF INTEREST

1. *Cardiac Glycosides*

The naturally occurring cardiac glycosides, which are cardiotonic agents used for the treatment of patients with heart failure, contain a steroid residue linked to a sugar. Digitalis, prepared from the dried seeds and leaves of the purple foxglove, contains as active components the glycosides digitoxigenin, digoxigenin and gitoxigenin. Most known active cardiac glycosides are derivatives of steroids which contain a hydroxyl group at C-14, an unsaturated lactone ring substituted on the β side of C-17, a *cis* C/D ring fusion, and a hydroxyl or sugar group at C-3. However, other nonsteroidal compounds with similar properties, such as the alkaloid cassaine, do not have all these features. The receptor of these cardiac glycosides is believed, but not proved, to be the membrane sodium potassium adenosinetriphosphatase; this normally pumps sodium out of the cell and potassium into it (Akera, 1977).

The structure of the aglycone digitoxigenin (Karle and Karle, 1969a) is shown in Fig. 11. This shows the effect of the *cis* C/D ring fusion (rather than *trans* as in the steroid hormones). The structure of Δ -8,14-anhydrodigitoxigenin (Gilardi and Karle, 1970), a dehydration product of digitoxigenin that lacks the hydroxyl group on C-14, the *cis* C/D ring junction and lacks any cardioactive properties, is also shown, and compared with that of the cardioactive steroid strophanthidin (Gilardi and Flippen, 1973). The arrangement of the lactone ring is similar in digitoxigenin and strophanthidin but not in the Δ -8,14-anhydro compound. The distances from the hydroxyl oxygen on ring A to the oxygen atom of the lactone ring are 13.21 Å for digitoxigenin and 13.36 Å for the anhydro derivative. The lengths of the steroid, defined as the C-3····C-16 distance, are 7.25 Å in digitoxigenin and 8.44 Å in the anhydro derivative. Because of the *cis* C/D ring fusion, this distance is shorter than the value of 9.1 ± 0.2 Å found in average all-*trans* steroids.

Batrachotoxinin A, a very potent cardiotoxin from the Colombian arrow poison frog, is also a steroid (Karle and Karle, 1969b). A view of the *O*-*p*-bromobenzoate is given in Fig. 11. The relative spatial arrangement of the B, C, and D rings and of the oxygen atom on C-14 is similar to that in strophanthidin and digitoxigenin.

An analysis of the conformations of such cardioactive agents (cardenolides) has been made by Rohrer and Fullerton (1978). Variation in conformations of structures determined crystallographically involve rotation about the C-17—C-20 bond. The lactone carbonyl group and C-20 are believed to be involved in binding. Rohrer and Fullerton conclude that the optimal conformation for binding is one with the lactone carbonyl group pointing toward the back (C-13 rather than C-14) side of the molecule (as shown in the formulas in Fig. 11). They also suggest that any interaction of receptor with C-20 takes place from the C-16 side of the molecule (as shown by arrows in Fig. 11).

2. Vitamin D

The work of Kodicek (1974), Norman *et al.* (1975), and DeLuca (1976) has shown that 1(*S*),25-dihydroxycholecalciferol (called 1α,25-DHCC) is a steroid hormone. It is produced in the kidney and transported (together with the polypeptide parathyroid hormone) to the intestines, bones, and muscles, which are target tissues, and it acts to regulate the normal plasma concentration of calcium and phosphate ions. Thus it stimulates intestinal calcium and phosphate transport, and bone-mineral mobilization. The present point of view is that cholecalciferol (vitamin D_3), when taken internally, must be metabolized to 25-hydroxycholecalciferol (25-HCC) in the liver and then to

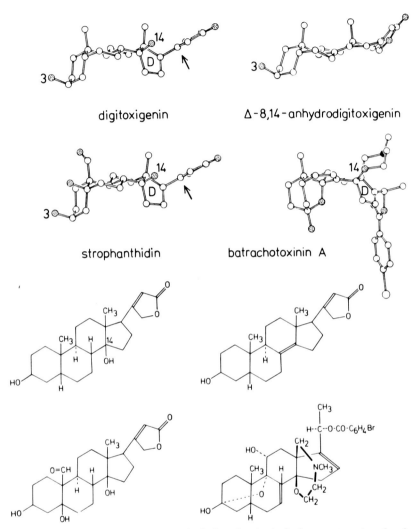

FIG. 11. Cardioactive steroids. Note the hydroxyl at C-14, the lactone ring viewed end-on, and the *cis* C/D ring fusion in the active steroids (digitoxigenin and strophanthidin). The arrows indicate the direction of interaction of a receptor with C-20.

$1\alpha,25$-DHCC in the kidney (see Fig. 9 for numbering system). This compound specifically causes the increased synthesis of a calcium-transporting protein (for a review, see Georghiou, 1977). In some cases metabolism gives the 24,25-DHCC, but the function of this is not clear (Madhok *et al.*, 1977).

As shown in Fig. 9, vitamin D_3 has an opened B ring and exists with two conformations of the A ring, one with O-3 equatorial and the other with O-3 axial (called α and β forms, respectively, where α and β refer to the fact that the 19-methylene group is, respectively, below or above the mean A ring plane). The conformational equilibrium seems to be unaffected by the nature of the side chain, but addition of a 1(S)-hydroxy group [indicated by arrows in Fig. 9(a)] shifts it to favor the β form with the 1(S)-hydroxyl group equatorial (Okamura *et al.*, 1974). Therefore, it was suggested by these workers that the conformers that are biologically active must have the substituent on C-1 in the equatorial position.

3. Cholesterol

Cholesterol is an essential component of mammalian cell membranes and generally occurs as a 1:1 mixture with phospholipid. It is suggested (Demel and de Kruyff, 1976) that a function that cholesterol serves in these cases is to exert a condensing effect on lipids in the liquid crystalline state, and a liquefying effect on lipids on the crystalline state. These effects lead to the same intermediate gel state. In this way membrane function may be controlled. Because cholesterol is mainly hydrophobic, but contains a hydrophilic C-3 hydroxyl group, it can lie at polar–nonpolar interfaces and is found in bile micelles.

When the cholesterol levels in the body are extremely high, it may separate out. In atherosclerosis a large quantity of esterified cholesterol accumulates in plaques, that is, in thickened areas in an arterial wall, and heart disease results. Cholesterol is transported in the body by low-density lipoprotein (LDL) which is recognized by a specific cell receptor. In this way cholesterol is obtained for membrane synthesis but its supply is controlled so that overaccumulation is normally prevented (Goldstein and Brown, 1977). When this process breaks down, plaques may be formed.

In some cases, such as the formation of gallstones in bile, crystalline cholesterol monohydrate may be formed. Cholesterol monohydrate crystals have been studied by Craven (1976) and shown to contain, like anhydrous cholesterol (Shieh *et al.*, 1977), eight molecules in the asymmetric unit. The overall structure consists of stacked bilayers. Interestingly, Craven (1976) points out relationships between the crystallization of cholesterol monohydrate and hydroxyapatite. A comparison of the crystal structures of these two compounds led Craven to suggest that a microcrystal of either may serve as a nucleus for the growth of the other, a condition known as epitaxy. This observation is of interest because both crystalline hydroxyapatite and crystalline cholesterol monohydrate have been implicated in atherosclerosis.

Crystals of cholesteryl nonanoate (Guerina and Craven, 1977a) contain two molecules in the asymmetric unit. The long axes of these two molecules are nearly parallel, but the cholesteryl ring systems lie almost at right angles to each other. One molecule in the asymmetric unit packs as do cholesteryl iodide (Carlisle and Crowfoot, 1945), cholesteryl octanoate, and cholesteryl oleate (Guerina and Craven, 1977b), with steroid nuclei packing with each other and side chains packing with each other. However, in the other molecule in the asymmetric unit of cholesterol nonanoate the steroid nucleus is surrounded by nonanoate chains, and provides an excellent model for the association of cholesterol with fatty acid chains within biomembranes.

II. BIOCHEMICAL MECHANISMS INVOLVING STEROIDS THAT HAVE BEEN STUDIED BY CRYSTALLOGRAPHIC TECHNIQUES

A. Mechanisms Related to Steroid Biosynthesis

Steroids are synthesized *in vivo*, as shown in Scheme 1, from acetate via cholesterol to progesterone. From this, estradiol, testosterone, cortisol, corticosterone, and aldosterone are then synthesized. These biosyntheses are mediated by the appropriate enzymes, some of which are also listed in Scheme 1. In the conversion of cholesterol to estradiol, some of the significant steps involve the removal of the long side chain on C-17 of cholesterol, the oxidation of the hydroxy group on C-3 to a keto group, the movement of the double bond from the 5,6-position in cholesterol to the 4,5-position so that it is conjugated with the keto group on C-3, and, finally, the aromatization of the A ring to make it phenolic in character. Some aspects of the enzymology of these processes have been examined, from the point of view of substrates, by X-ray crystallographic methods. Two examples are given below.

1. Movement of the Double Bond from the 5,6- to the 4,5-Position

The very important conversion of Δ^5-steroids (such as cholesterol) to Δ^4-steroids (such as progesterone or testosterone), which involves a transposition of the double bond, is effected by the enzyme Δ^5-3-ketosteroid isomerase, which is found in most tissues. The enzyme from the bacterium *Pseudomonas testosteroni* has been characterized by Talalay and Benson (1972), and the catalytic mechanism and specificity of this enzyme have been studied in some detail (Batzold *et al.*, 1976). It is one of the more rapid enzymatic transfers of a hydrogen atom that is known to occur. The enzyme catalyzes the removal of a hydrogen atom from C-4 (formula V) and the transfer of the same hydrogen atom to C-6 (formula VI) (see Scheme 2). The equilibrium favors the steroid with the hydrogen atom on C-6 (i.e., the steroid with the double bond in the 4,5-position).

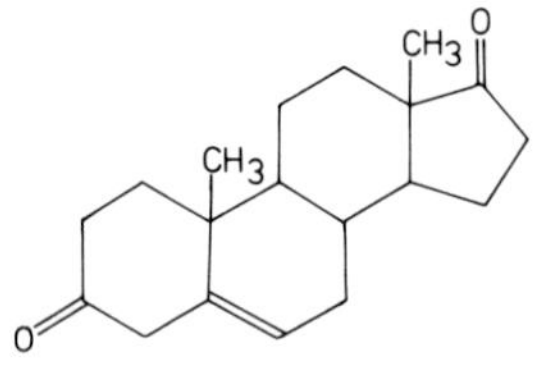

V

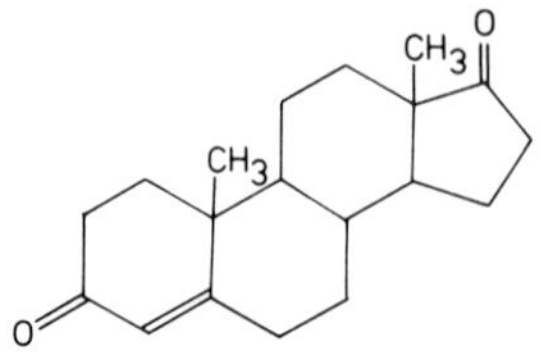

VI

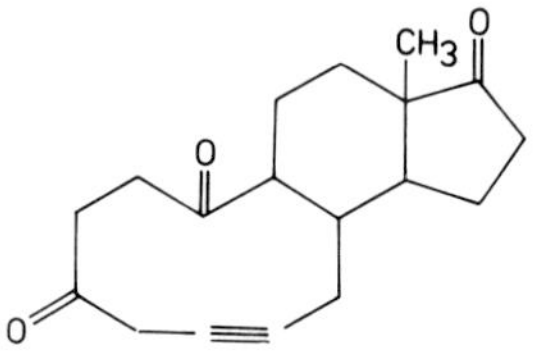

VII

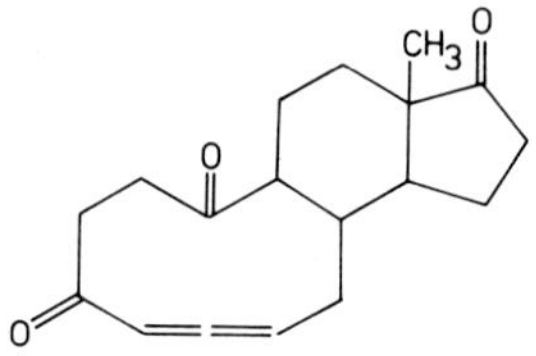

VIII

   In order to investigate this reaction, two compounds lacking the C-5—C-10 bond (secosteroids) and containing, respectively, an acetylenic group —C-4≡C-5—C-6— (formula VII) and an allenic group C-4=C-5=C-6— (formula VIII) were synthesized and were shown to cause irreversible inhibition of the enzyme (Batzold and Robinson, 1975, 1976; Covey and Robinson, 1976). Crystallographic studies of two substrates [a Δ^5-ketosteroid (Carrell *et al.*, 1978) and a Δ^4-ketosteroid (Busetta *et al.*, 1972d)] and of these two secosteroids by Carrell and co-workers (1977) led to a hypothesis on the mode of action of the enzyme. The results of the structure determination of the enzyme itself by E. M. Westbrook (private communication, 1977) will test this hypothesis. The crystal structures of the four compounds, with the C and D rings in a fixed orientation, are shown in Fig. 12.

   Carrell and co-workers (1977) suggest that the substrates are positioned in the active site of the enzyme by the C and D rings. A side chain in the active site is presumed to interact with O-3, controlling the height of O-3 with respect to the general molecular plane. This side chain interaction will ensure the correct conformation of the A and B rings so that the hydrogen atom in the 4β position may be abstracted by a group, possibly a carboxyl group, that is part of the active site of the enzyme. Once the proton is abstracted, a conformational change occurs in the steroid when a conjugated dienol is formed as an intermediate. This conformational change, aided by the active site side chain hydrogen bonded to O-3, will then dictate addition of a proton at C-6 rather than at C-4, as shown in Fig. 12. Effectively, the active site side chain of the enzyme pulls O-3 up or down with respect to the molecular

STEROID BIOSYNTHESIS

acetate

↓

cholesterol

20α-hydroxylase
20,22-desmolase
↓

Δ^5-pregnenolone

3β-hydroxysteroid dehydrogenase
Δ^5-3-ketosteroid isomerase
↓

progesterone

17α-hydroxylase ↙   ↘ 21-hydroxylase

17α-hydroxyprogesterone   11-deoxycorticosterone

↓ 17-desmolase   ↘ 21-hydroxylase   ↓ 11β-hydroxylase

testosterone   11-deoxycortisol   corticosterone

↓ aromatase   ↓ 11β-hydroxylase   ↓ 18-hydroxylase
                                                            18-dehydrogenase

estradiol   cortisol   aldosterone

ANDROGENS AND   GLUCOCORTICOIDS   MINERALOCORTICOIDS
ESTROGENS

SCHEME 1. Steroid biosynthesis.

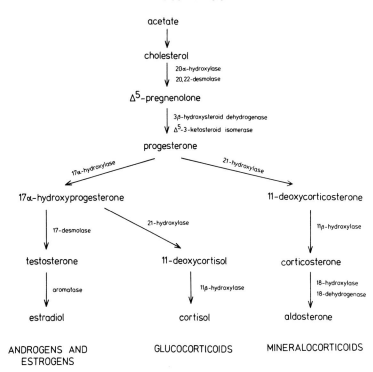

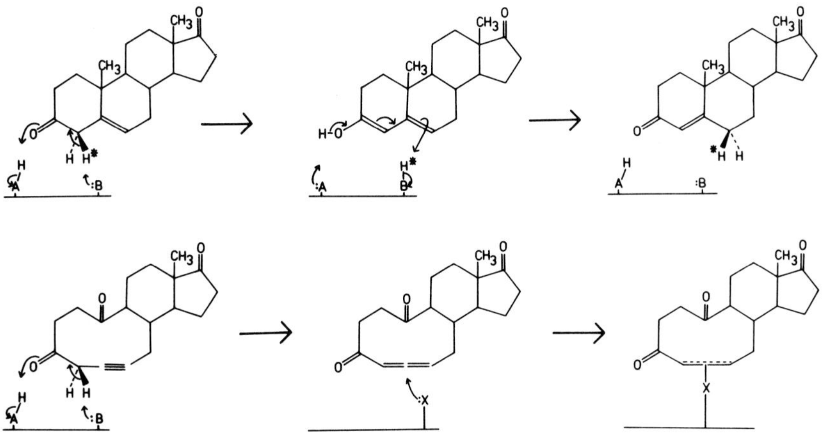

SCHEME 2. Mechanism of Δ^5-3-ketosteroid isomerase.

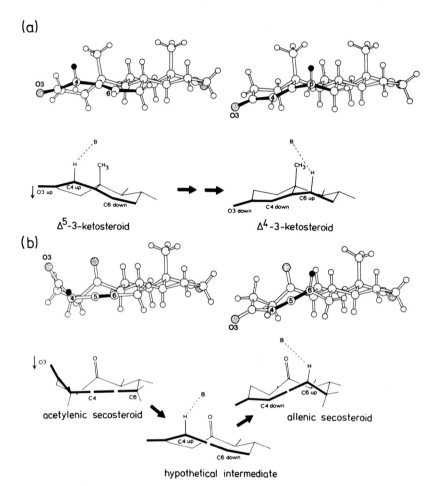

FIG. 12. Mechanism of Δ^5-3-ketosteroid isomerase. All steroids are viewed along the best plane through the C and D rings. Bonds on the near side of the A and B rings in (a) are black. Double and triple bonds are black in (b). The hydrogen atom that is abstracted by the enzyme is black.

plane, and thus controls the direction of the reaction (O-3 up for Δ^5-3-ketosteroid and O-3 down for Δ^4-3-ketosteroid). The hydrophobic 19-methyl group may guide the abstracted hydrogen atom during this protonation.

It is also suggested that the synthetic acetylenic steroid binds in a manner similar to that of the Δ^5-ketosteroid, and is converted, presumably by an analogous mechanism, to an allenic secosteroid (also illustrated in Fig. 12). Subsequent alkylation of the enzyme by the electrophilic allenic compound (i.e., a suicide substrate) then takes place.

2. *Aromatization of the A Ring*

The female sex hormones are biosynthesized from androgens (like Eve from Adam's rib). This aromatization reaction involves expulsion of the angular C-19 methyl group, and the stereospecific loss of the 1β and 2β hydrogen atoms from the androgen to give an aromatic A ring. A microsomal enzyme, "aromatase," is believed to be responsible for the aromatization which occurs in three steps at a single catalytic site (Kelly *et al.*, 1977). The first two steps involve hydroxylations of the C-19 methyl group and the third involves hydroxylation of C-2, as shown in Fig. 13. The 19-hydroxy derivative has been isolated and is an intermediate in the reaction. The dihydroxy derivative is a hypothetical unstable intermediate which is spontaneously transformed into the aldehyde. The latter has been shown to be a substrate of the enzyme.

Crystal structure analyses have been of great importance in the establishment of the conformations of intermediates. The (19S)-hydroxy-19-methyl isomer, a methyl analog of the product of the first hydroxylation step, was studied crystallographically, and the hydroxyl group was shown to lie over the A ring, and the bulky methyl group over the B ring (Osawa *et al.*, 1975; Rohrer *et al.*, 1976) (Fig. 13). It was therefore suggested that the product of the first hydroxylation of C-19 of testosterone has a similar conformation, so that the 19-*pro R* hydrogen atom does not lie over a ring. This conformation presumably occurs as a result of rotation about the C-10—C-19 bond. In the second step, also shown in Fig. 13, this 19-*pro R* hydrogen atom is stereospecifically replaced by another hydroxyl group. These two steps are visualized (Osawa, 1974; Duax *et al.*, 1975) to occur by β-face approach of the substrate to the active site of the enzyme aromatase. In each case the hydrogen atom on C-19 that is hydroxylated is the one that does not lie over a ring. After the second hydroxylation, an aldehyde is formed spontaneously with the experimentally observed conformation shown in Fig. 13 (Weeks *et al.*, 1975b).

The final loss of the 1β and 2β hydrogen atoms is believed to occur enzymatically via the 2β-hydroxy derivative (the third hydroxylation, involving the axial 2β-hydrogen atom), which then loses the elements of water nonenzymatically. A model for this last step is the observed nonenzymatic conversion of 2β-hydroxy-19-oxo-4-androstene-3,17-dione to estrone in the presence of water at neutral pH (Hosoda and Fishman, 1974). Because the 2β position of an androgen is near the C-19 position, these three hydroxylations (19, 19, and 1β) could well occur, as suggested by the results of Kelly *et al.* (1977), at the same site in aromatase. When elements of water are lost, fission of the C-10—C-19 bond also occurs and an aromatic A ring results. As suggested for the isomerization of ketosteroids, this step may be aided by movement of an enzymatic active site group hydrogen bonded to O-3, for the

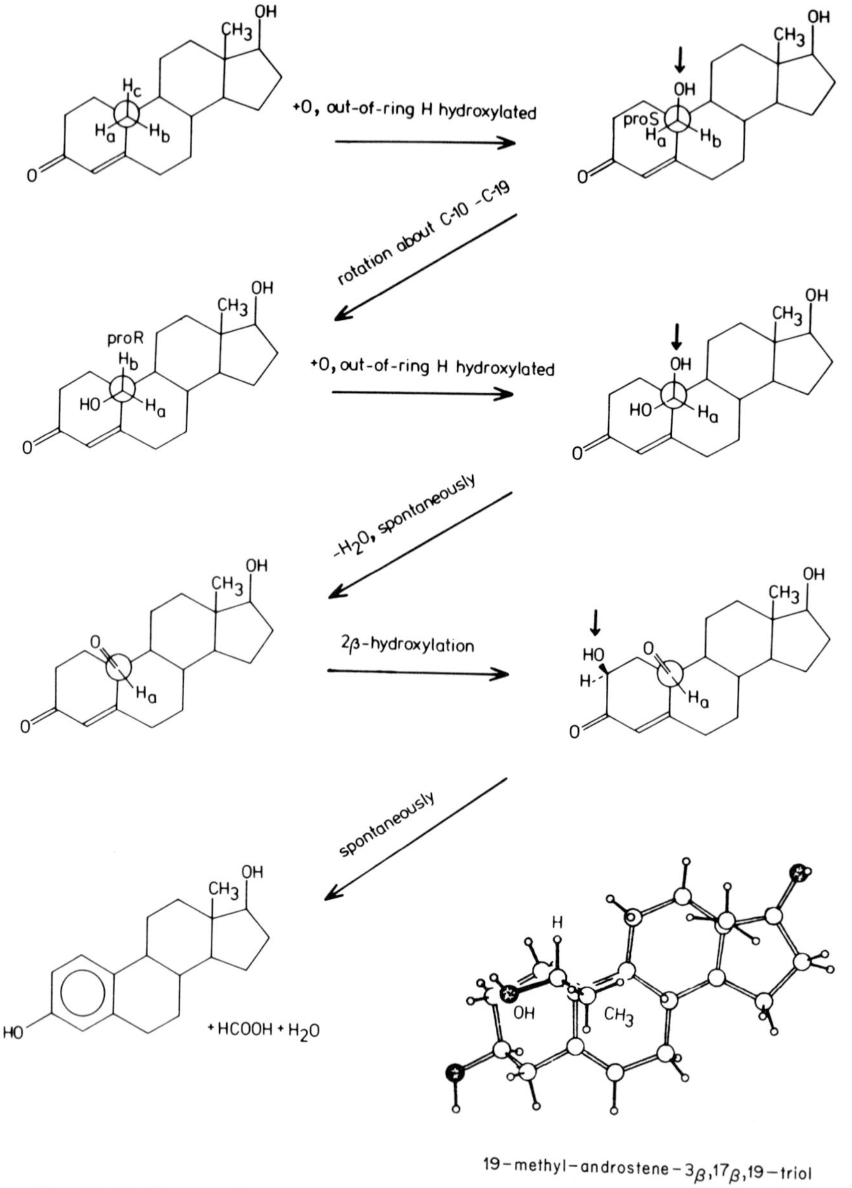

19−methyl−androstene−3β,17β,19−triol

FIG. 13. Mechanism of aromatase. The crystal structure of the analog with H_a replaced by a methyl group as shown in the bottom right-hand side of the figure.

latter would move considerably when an androgen is converted to an estrogen (see Fig. 8).

B. INTERACTIONS OF STEROIDS WITH BIOLOGICAL RECEPTORS

It is not clear how any of the steroid hormones act to effect their biological activity, but it is believed that a major result of their activity *in vivo* is the production of messenger RNA's and hence of new proteins. Steroids, by virtue of their solubility in lipids, can readily enter the cell via the cell membrane. In order to act on a gene, they must enter the nucleus, and this entry must be mediated by another molecule, such as a protein receptor. It is considered, at the present time, that the same protein, referred to as the "steroid receptor," both carries a given steroid into the nucleus and interacts with chromosomes to cause a physiological effect. Alternate models cannot, however, be discounted (Sheridan, 1975). There are also proteins, other than the receptor, that can interact with steroids. Some interact very specifically and, for example, transport the steroid in the blood. Because the structures of steroid hormones are similar, one steroid may bind, although with low affinity, to the protein that has a high-affinity site for a different steroid.

Binding to the steroid receptor is generally assumed to be directly related to the biological activity of a steroid, and there is much evidence to support this idea. However, other compounds (e.g., antiestrogens) may also bind to the steroid receptor and prevent the specific steroid from displaying its physiological effect. This means that the molecular events that occur within the nucleus, rather than simply those in the cytoplasm, such as receptor binding, are extremely important to the definition of the activity of a given hormone. The information that has been obtained from X-ray studies on the manner in which steroids interact with their receptors is scant but will be reviewed here. Because the receptors have not yet been crystallized (and hence have not been studied by X-ray techniques), the only such information we have comes from a merging of structural data on steroids and their analogs, coupled with data on the potencies of their biological effects and the extents of their binding.

1. Estrogen Receptors

The most widely studied receptors are the estrogen receptors, and a general picture of how estrogens interact with them is emerging from biological and biochemical studies. Each uterine cell contains several thousand high-affinity, specific protein receptors for estrogens. An estrogen can only enter the nucleus after it has become bound to its receptor and has undergone a modification process called "activation." The subsequent transfer of the activated hormone–receptor complex to the nucleus is called "translocation." These two processes occur within minutes of the introduction of estrogen into the cell. After translocation to the nucleus, the activated hormone–receptor complex is believed to bind to chromatin at "acceptor sites." Specifically induced proteins, e.g., ovalbumin in the chick oviduct (Comstock *et al.*, 1972) or uterine peroxidase in the rat (Lyttle and DeSombre, 1977), are then synthesized.

The estrogen receptor is a polypeptide, molecular weight 80,000 (for general reviews, see King and Mainwaring, 1974; Edelman, 1975; Leake, 1976), which is highly specific for estrogens. It has a low affinity for estradiol-17α but binds diethylstilbestrol, a potent synthetic estrogen, very strongly. Binding of an estrogenic hormone to the receptor leads to the addition of a second polypeptide subunit of molecular weight 50,000 (Notides and Nielsen, 1974) to give a complex of molecular weight approximately 130,000.

Much effort has been expended in an attempt to obtain information on exactly how an estrogen binds to a receptor, and to define those features of a substituted steroid that make it estrogenic. Particular attention has been paid to the fact that estradiol-17β, a naturally occurring steroid, and diethylstilbestrol, a synthetic stilbene derivative, are each extremely potent estrogens although their formulas are very different. Because estrogenic activity may be correlated with specific binding to its receptor, it was felt that a detailed study of the structures of estrogens might throw light on the geometric factors necessary for binding to the estrogen receptor. As will be shown below, this approach has not clarified the problem.

The general characteristics of steroidal estrogens are a phenolic A ring and a 17β-hydroxyl group. Because these two oxygen atoms, O-3 and O-17, at opposite ends of the molecule, can both form hydrogen bonds, it seemed reasonable to consider the possibility that they are the major points of attachment of estradiol to the high-affinity receptor. In order to investigate this, the surroundings of some estrogens were compared in the crystalline state, for, it was reasoned, this might suggest a common geometry for the receptor. It was found, as illustrated for estradiol in Fig. 14, that O-3 forms two or three hydrogen bonds (two in the case shown in Fig. 14), and O-17 forms two hydrogen bonds.

However, the idea that the estrogen receptor is simply a protein that can bind two oxygen atoms, O-3 and O-17β, at a distance of 11.00 ± 0.05 Å is too simple. If either one of the hydroxyl groups of estradiol-17β is removed, activity is decreased but not lost entirely (Chernayaev *et al.*, 1975). Both hydroxyl groups must be removed to cause complete loss of binding and of estrogenic activity. The optical isomer of estradiol-17β has a very low affinity for the receptor (although the same O-3 $\cdots\cdots$ O-17β distance). 8-Azaestradiol, which was shown (Brown and Trefonas, 1972) to have similar parameters to

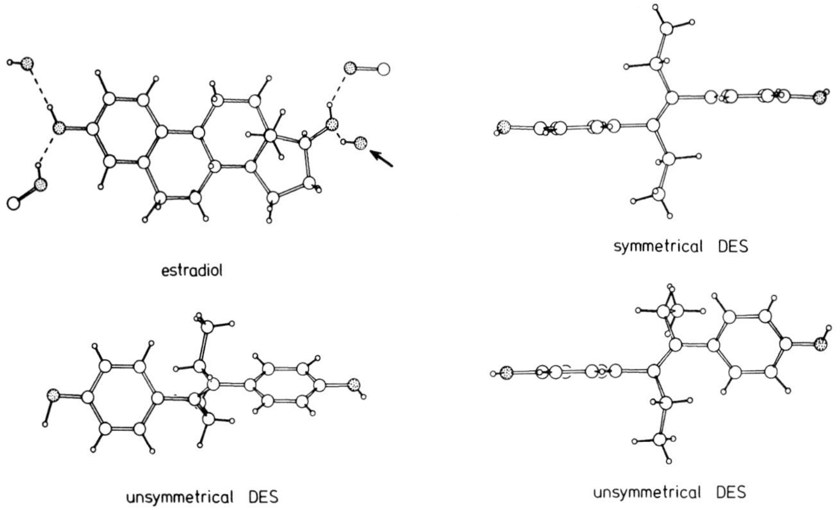

FIG. 14. Comparison of estradiol and symmetrical and unsymmetrical DES. The surroundings of one molecule of estradiol are indicated. The arrow points to the oxygen atom of the water molecule that is hydrogen-bonded to O-17 and has been suggested to be part of the unit that binds to receptor. If this is so, O····O distances for estradiol and DES are both 12.1 Å.

those of estradiol except that C-8 is replaced by a nitrogen atom has also a very low affinity for the receptor. Possibly, in this case, protonation of the nitrogen atom, resulting in a positive charge in an area of the molecule which is normally hydrophobic in an estrogen, causes lack of activity. Thus it may be concluded that other features than the disposition of oxygen atoms, such as hydrophobic interactions, are also important in the binding of estradiol-17β to its receptor.

trans-Diethylstilbestrol (DES), a very potent synthetic estrogen, competitively inhibits the binding of the natural hormone, 17β-estradiol, to the protein receptor of uterine cells, suggesting that it binds to the same receptor site. In unsolvated crystals grown from nonpolar solvents, the molecule of DES is centrosymmetrical (Fig. 14), with the aromatic rings parallel to each other (Weeks, 1970). In solvated crystals grown from polar solvents (Busetta *et al.*, 1973b), the molecule of DES is noncentrosymmetric and the planes of the two rings are not parallel, but inclined at 65° to each other (Fig. 14). This indicates that there is considerable flexibility in the molecule. Hospital and co-workers (1972, 1975) consider that the unsymmetrical form of DES is the one with biological activity.

However, the O-3····O-17 distances are 12.1 Å in DES and 10.9 Å in estradiol. No matter how closely one compares the two estrogens estradiol-17β and DES, there is a difference of 1.2 Å in the overall length, and it is difficult to see how they could both be binding to the same to locations of a single receptor. In order to account for this discrepancy, Hospital and co-workers (Hospital *et al.*, 1975; Busetta *et al.*, 1977) suggest that the part of the molecule which is important for binding to the receptor is the ring D of estradiol. The receptor site is presumed to be loose so that differences of 1.2 Å can be tolerated. The part of the molecule responsible for the estrogenic activity, they suggest, is represented by phenolic ring A of estradiol, and this presumably protrudes from the receptor and interacts with another biological macromolecule with precise orientation. An alternative suggestion (Duax *et al.*, 1977) is that the O·····O distance in DES is equivalent to the O·····O distance in estradiol hydrate (i.e., a value of 12.1 Å, which involves a water molecule, indicated by an arrow in Fig. 14, hydrogen bonded to estradiol). This idea that the natural estrogen, estradiol-17β, binds water in order to bind to the receptor is not a satisfactory resolution of the problem, because one might expect nature to design a receptor which is optimally suited to its natural substrate.

The 11β-methoxy derivative of estradiol is nearly as good an estrogen as estradiol. If the phenolic A rings of 11β-methoxyestradiol and DES are superposed, the methoxy group in the former and the ethyl group in DES lie in similar locations (Courseille *et al.*, 1973b). Courseille and co-workers suggest that the relationship between O-3 and the oxygen atom on C-11 of 11β-methoxyestradiol may be the important feature for estrogenic activity. However, it should be noted that the introduction of an 11β-hydroxy (rather than methoxy) group into estradiol greatly diminishes its activity.

Weber and Galantay (1972) investigated some stereochemical features of the binding of estrogens to their receptor. An 8α derivative of estradiol, 17β-bromoacetoxy-3-methoxy-8α-methyl-1,3,5(10),6-estratetraene   (IX),

IX

which has estrogenic activity, was found to have a very different structure from that of a (normal) 8β derivative. There is, in the 8α compound, a *cis* fusion of the B and C rings (see Fig. 15) so that the shape in this area of the molecule is quite different from that of estradiol, and the O-3·····O-17β distance is reduced to 10.31 Å. In contrast, 8β-methylestradiol has no estrogenic activity, even though the O·····O separation is about 10.8 Å

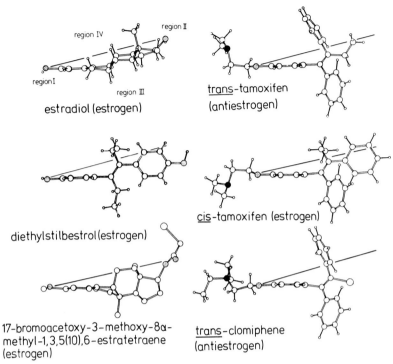

FIG. 15. Some estrogens and antiestrogens. In estradiol, O-3 and O-17 are connected by a line which is repeated in all other compounds illustrated. Regions I–IV are defined by Weeks *et al.* (1977). Note that phenyl groups project into region IV in the two antiestrogens. *Cis*-tamoxifen: $R_1 = C_2H_5$; $R_2 = R_4 = C_6H_5$; $R_3 = (C_6H_4)O(CH_2)_2N(CH_3)_2$. *Trans*-tamoxifen: $R_1 = R_4 = C_6H_5$; $R_2 = C_2H_5$; $R_3 = (C_6H_4)O(CH_2)_2N(CH_3)_2$. *Trans*-clomiphene: $R_1 = R_4 = C_6H_5$; $R_2 = Cl$; $R_3 = (C_6H_4)O(CH_2)_2N(C_2H_5)_2$.

and the backbone is similar to that of estradiol. Weber and Galantay suggested that one important feature of productive binding to the estrogen receptor is that there should be a plane through O-3 and and O-17β such that the steroidal backbone lies entirely on one side of this plane. They visualized that the estrogen is attached to the receptor by hydrogen bonds. Any groups or parts of the estrogen backbone considerably above (i.e., on the β side of) this plane, such as an 8β-methyl group in the inactive isomer mentioned above, would prevent the steroid from approaching the receptor surface closely enough. A 13β-methyl group (C-18) and an 11β-methoxy group are exceptions, as these groups allow for estrogenic activity. They may be important in aligning the molecule on the receptor. These postulated features of the estrogen receptor may be visualized by an inspection of Fig. 15, in which lines are drawn to indicate the plane through O-3 and O-17 for the estrogens that are illustrated.

Weeks *et al.* (1977) also investigated the stereochemical requirements of the estrogen receptor. They made a comparative analysis of the structure of the natural estrogen estradiol, the synthetic estrogen *cis*-tamoxifen (Kilbourn and Owston, 1970), and the antiestrogen *trans*-tamoxifen (Weeks *et al.*, 1977). Antiestrogens are a class of compounds that prevent estrogens from expressing their normal effects on their target tissues; they may compete with estrogens for tight-binding sites, and, if they are transported into the nucleus, they may prevent the receptor complex from binding to nucleic acid and therefore make the receptor unavailable to other steroid molecules. Rochefort and Capony (1977) consider that uncomplexed receptor is sensitive to antiestrogen binding but that estradiol converts the receptor to a form less sensitive to antiestrogens.

In their comparison, Weeks and co-workers divided the structure of each molecule into four regions (shown in Fig. 15). The first, equivalent to the phenol ring of estradiol, is considered to be the initial site for binding to the receptor. At the other end of the molecule, the second region, there is either a hydrogen-bonding group (estradiol O-17β) or a bulky group (*cis*-tamoxifen). The third region (on the α side of estradiol) can accommodate a bulky group. The presence of a bulky group in the fourth region (on the β side of estradiol), such as is found in the antiestrogen *trans*-tamoxifen, is not compatible with estrogenic activity but allows for antiestrogenic activity. These results on estrogen activity are consistent with the ideas of Weber and Galantay (mentioned earlier). Clomiphene B hydrochloride (Ernst and Hite, 1976) and clomiphene A hydriodide (Cantrell, 1977) have been studied crystallographically. It was found that the antiestrogenic B isomer has *trans* stereochemistry (not *cis* stereochemistry, as had been thought) and that, as shown in Fig. 15, there is bulkiness in the fourth region. However, the fact that a bulky group in the fourth region allows for antiestrogenic activity may imply that binding of steroid to receptor is not affected by bulkiness but that some later process, presumably in the nucleus, is affected. A comparison of the structures of estrogens and antiestrogens thus contains clues to the mechanism of action of the receptor.

In summary, it seems fair to remark that the structural features of the binding site of the estrogen receptor are not presently obvious from structural studies of estrogens. Several sites on the estrogen must be important for activity. Different hypotheses have implicated the A ring, the D ring, or the entire estrogen molecule hydrogen bonded to water, as the areas that bind to receptor. Thus, one group (Hospital and co-workers) claims that the D ring is involved in binding and that the A ring is responsible for biological activity, while another group (Duax and co-workers) says that the A ring is involved in binding and that activity resides in the D ring. Another group (Weber and Galantay) holds that the β face should be unsubstituted but that the 11β-methoxy derivative is very active. Thus there is much controversy among the structural workers in this field. One problem is that the property of binding to the estrogenic receptor should be separated, if possible, from that of the manifestation of estrogenic activity (which implies a more complicated process). Only when these various steps in the action of estrogens are separated out can the meaning of the structural experimental results be evaluated.

2. Androgen Receptors

Androgen receptors have been studied by Liao (1975), who suggests that the androgen is probably enveloped by its receptor (Liao *et al.*, 1973; Castañeda and Liao, 1975). This implies that the high-affinity, long-term binding to androgen receptors must involve a site deep in the receptor molecule. This is probably true for all receptors, which not only move steroids to the nucleus but seem also to protect them in the process. In contrast, in the cases of the various steroid-metabolizing enzymes and steroid-transporting proteins (e.g., testosterone-binding globulin) found in the blood, Liao suggested that these proteins, which do not enter the nucleus, interact with only a portion of the steroid molecule, for example, one face of the steroid. This binding must only occur near the surface of the protein.

Testosterone, in the testes, should really be considered a prehormone because it is reduced metabolically, by the enzyme Δ^4-3-ketosteroid-5α-oxidoreductase, to dihydrotestosterone. Structures of these two androgens are shown in Fig. 16. The *in vivo* metabolism to dihydrotestosterone that occurs for testosterone may also occur for all the androgens illustrated in Fig. 16, but this possibility has not yet been established as a fact. The question is, does each of these androgens have its own intrinsic activity, or are the activities dependent on the facility with which dihydrotestosterone (or perhaps testosterone) is made *in vivo?* Again, until the answer to this question is found, the precise meaning of each structural result to be considered below eludes us.

Structure–activity relationships for some androgens will now be described (see Fig. 16). It has been found that 5α-reduced steroids are more active as androgens than are analogs with a $\Delta^{4,5}$ double bond; i.e., 5α-dihydrotestosterone is more active than testosterone. It is also found that the 17-hydroxyl group should be β-oriented, and that the presence of a 3-keto group is probably important for androgenic activity. The β face, apart from the angular methyl groups C-18 and C-19, should be free of other substituents. Epitestosterone with O-17 α-axial (Isaacs *et al.*, 1972) (as opposed

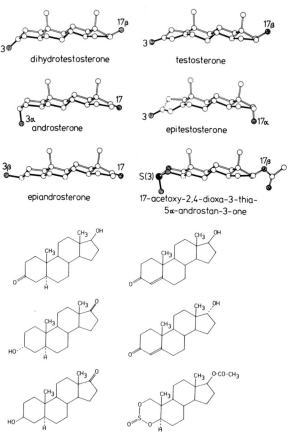

FIG. 16. Comparison of some androgens. Hydrogen atoms have been omitted and the near-side bonds are black.

to β-equatorial in testosterone) is about 25 times less active than testosterone. In androsterone (High and Kraut, 1966), O-3 is in an α-axial position (2.32 Å from the plane through atoms C-5 to C-17). Epiandrosterone (Weeks *et al.*, 1971) has a much flatter structure, with an equatorial O-3 hydroxyl group. These two compounds are, respectively, seven and 50 times less active than testosterone.

A compound with a sulfur atom in place of C-3 and oxygen atoms in place of C-2 and C-4 has similar androgenic activity to that of testosterone. The conformation is shown in Fig. 16. The oxygen atom on S-3 is α-axial (Duax *et al.*, 1976b), like O-3 in androsterone. Therefore, Duax and co-workers (1976b) suggest that the 3-keto group orientation in testosterone and dihydrotestosterone (equatorial in both cases) is not important for androgenic activity. An alternative explanation, as mentioned earlier, is that the conformation at C-3 is changed enzymatically *in vivo*.

A detailed comparison of the structures of testosterone and dihydrotestosterone is given in Fig. 17. The loss of the C-4═C-5 double bond does not have much effect on the deviation of O-3 from the molecular plane (calculated through C-5 to C-17). Listed deviations of O-3 from this plane are 1.61–1.96 Å for dihydrotestosterone (2 structures) and 1.44–1.86 Å for testosterone (6 structures). Thus the idea that dihydrotestosterone is flatter than testosterone (Liao, 1976) is not borne out by the X-ray data, although the A ring conformation differs greatly.

19-Nortestosterone is a more flexible molecule than testosterone. In the crystal structure studied (Precigoux *et al.*, 1975), there are two molecules in the asymmetric unit. The location of O-3 differs in the two forms, but again, the molecule is not flatter than that of testosterone. Thus the important feature of 19-norsteroids is greater flexibility. One of the two molecules in

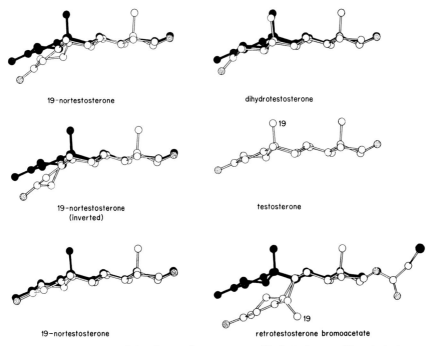

19-nortestosterone   dihydrotestosterone

19-nortestosterone
(inverted)   testosterone

19-nortestosterone   retrotestosterone bromoacetate

FIG. 17. Comparison of the shapes of testosterone, dihydrotesterone, 19-nortestosterone, and retrotestosterone. Note that in retrotestosterone C-19 is on the α side of the molecule. In the case of 19-nortestosterone, there are two molecules in the asymmetric unit and one of these is disordered (hence three representations). Testosterone is drawn in black for comparison for each molecule.

the asymmetric unit is disordered, that is, it can be represented by two structures. In one of these, as shown in Fig. 17, C-2 lies farther below (on the α side of) the plane of C-5 to C-17 than does C-3. This is referred to as an "inverted A ring" because normally C-2 lies nearer to the plane than does C-3. This may alternatively be described (Duax *et al.*, 1978) by noting that C-1 and C-2 have shifted to the opposite side of the Δ^4-3-one plane from that normally occupied. In the inverted A ring, the 2β-hydrogen atom becomes equatorial (instead of axial as found normally), and the area C-2 to C-5 of the molecule becomes flatter. However, O-3 does not change (see Fig. 17).

Antiandrogens antagonize the effects of 5α-dihydrotestosterone either by competing for the androgen binding sites on receptors or by inhibiting the formation of androgens. Cyproterone acetate (Chandross and Bordner, 1974), shown in Fig. 18, is a potent antiandrogen containing a cyclopropane group in the A ring (marked in Fig. 18 with an arrow); it is, interestingly, also a progestogen. It may be compared with chlormadinone acetate (Chandross and Bordner, 1975), which is similar in formula and structure (Fig. 18) but lacks the cyclopropane ring; this has no antiandrogenic activity but has pro-gestational activity. The bulkiness in the cyclopropane ring on the α side thus seems important for antiandrogenic activity, but not for androgenic activity. This situation is reminiscent of the effect of bulkiness in antiestrogen *trans*-tamoxifen. Several nonsteroidal antiandrogens, such as flutamide (X), which

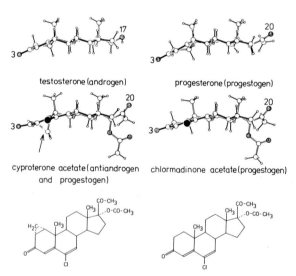

FIG. 18. Comparison of an androgen, an antiandrogen, and some progestogens. The cyclo-propane ring of cyproterone is indicated by an arrow.

bears little resemblance to testosterone, have been found, but to date, all known androgens are steroids.

X

3. Progesterone Receptors

Chick oviduct progesterone receptor has been investigated in considerable detail and has been found to consist of two components (designated A and B, molecular weights 110,000 and 117,000, respectively), both with hormone binding sites (Sherman *et al.*, 1974; Schrader *et al.*, 1977). Component A binds to DNA, while component B binds only to chromatin, for example, possibly to an acidic nuclear protein. This information answers some questions on how the receptor interacts with DNA. It is suggested that the chromatin-binding B protein would specify regions in the chromatin adjacent to hormonally regulated genes. In this way, component A would be directed to its site of action, where it would bind to DNA and thus modify transcription by RNA polymerases. It is implied that progesterone has two distinct binding sites, one on each component (A and B). The net effect of progesterone administration in the chick is the production of new species of RNA (O'Malley *et al.*, 1972). One of these species codes for avidin. Interestingly, Moudgil and Toft (1976, 1977) found that the progesterone receptor from avian oviduct has enzymatic activity and can catalyze the splitting of ATP to give an AMP–enzyme complex and pyrophosphate in a hormone-independent process. The significance of this is not yet clear.

Progesterone (Campsteyn *et al.*, 1972a,b; Dideberg *et al.*, 1975) has a greater distance, 11.97 Å, between oxygen atoms than is found in natural estrogens and androgens (10.8–11.0 Å), because of the presence of the additional carbon atom C-20. The 3-keto group and the $\Delta^{4,5}$ double bond in ring A are essential for activity, as is found for androgens. As shown in Fig. 8, the carbonyl oxygen atom, O-20, points to the front (represented by C-7 and C-15) of progesterone. Many synthetic progestogens have been prepared, such as *d*-norgestrel (DeAngelis *et al.*, 1975), which has nine times the progestational activity of progesterone and contains an ethynyl group ($-C\equiv C-H$) which points in an α-axial manner from C-17.

Mornon *et al.* (1977) analyzed structural results on progestogens. Because synthetic 17α-ethynyl derivatives are such good progestogens, some interaction between the protein receptor site and the 17α-ethynyl group may be envisioned to occur. The A ring conformation is identical in most progestogens, suggesting that the geometry of binding of this ring is similar for both the natural and synthetic progestogens, presumably by hydrogen bonding involving O-3. Four features are listed as important in the binding of progestogens to their receptors. These are the orientation and hydrogen bonding of the 17β-hydroxyl group, the interactions with 17α-ethynyl groups, the hydrogen bonding to O-3, and the general shape of the ring system. In their comparison of progestogens, Mornon *et al.* (1977) used the D ring as the area of reference. Variations of 4 Å in the position of O-3 are then found (in a series of 38 compounds). This compared with a variation of 0.9 Å between testosterone and progesterone in their different crystalline forms.

The importance of hydrophobic binding in the interaction of steroids with their receptors has already been mentioned. The energy change on binding of progesterone is −12 kcal/mole, and is mainly an enthalpy change. Half of this may be accounted for (Kontula *et al.*, 1975) by binding of the two carbonyl groups, C-21 and the C-4═C-5 double bond. Of remaining interactions with the hydrocarbon skeleton, three contacts with —CH_2— groups could account for the rest of the energy. A detailed analysis of 55 androst-4-en-3-one derivatives (Lee *et al.*, 1977) indicates that C-6, C-11, C-16, and C-17α constitute hydrophobic pockets, probably very significant in receptor binding.

The methyl group, C-19, in progesterone is considered to be detrimental (because of its steric bulkiness) to progestational activity and therefore two classes of modified progesterones—19-nor steroids and retrosteroids—have been prepared synthetically, in an effort to increase activity. 19-nor steroids have already been discussed. The retrosteroids have the configurations at C-9 and C-10 inverted, so that the 10-methyl group, i.e., C-19, lies on the α side of the L-shaped molecule which has rings A and B bent to the α side (Oberhänsli and Robertson, 1967) (Fig. 17). Surprisingly, it was found that retroprogesterone was more active than progesterone. Thus it seemed that the general shape of the steroid was unimportant for progestational activity; the important parameters were distances between crucial functional groups. Bucourt (1974) suggested, however, that if conformational changes occurred in rings B and C so that they changed from the chair form to flexible forms, then an overall planar configuration of retroprogesterone could be achieved. This amount of flexibility has not been found yet crystallographically.

Duax *et al.* (1978) suggest that the fit of hormone to protein is loose or nonspecific along the α and β faces of the B, C, and D rings. Only the A ring conformation, they suggest, is important (in contrast to the views of Mornon *et al.*, 1977), and substituents have significance only if they alter the A ring conformation by conformational transmission. They propose from an analysis of many structures that the A ring is primarily responsible for high-affinity binding, and that binding is to an "inverted" A ring. It is possible that our views of a "lock-and-key" fit, obtained from a study of enzyme–substrate interactions (cf. Δ^5-3-ketosteroid isomerase) should be altered when we consider hormone–receptor interactions. Much work in this area remains to be done.

4. Corticosteroid Receptors

A large variety of steroids are secreted by the adrenal glands, and these exhibit several types of biological activity. Those steroids which promote deposition of glycogen in the liver are termed glucocorticoids; those which control the electrolyte balance of body fluids are called mineralocorticoids. They will be considered in turn.

a. Characteristics of Glucocorticoids and Their Receptors. Adrenal glucocorticoids stimulate glyconeogenesis, that is, formation of glycogen from amino acid and carbohydrate precursors, in the liver (Cake and Litwack, 1975). They stimulate the syntheses of certain liver enzymes involved in glyconeogenesis, such as phosphorylase phosphatase. They also cause the induction of enzymes that convert the carbon skeletons of amino acids into glucose, such as tryptophan oxygenase, tyrosine aminotransferase, and ornithine decarboxylase (Lin and Knox, 1957, 1958). In the thymus, glucocorticoids cause inhibition of protein synthesis.

Glucocorticoids are generally characterized by an axial 11β-hydroxyl group, shown for cortisol in Fig. 8. 11-Deoxysteroids such as progesterone, and 11-ketosteroids such as cortisone, bind to glucocorticoid receptors but are not biologically active as glucocorticoids. Thus the hydrogen-bonding potential of the 11β-hydroxyl group is important for activity but not for binding. This suggests some significance to the binding of the C ring. The $\Delta^{4,5}$ double bond in the A ring enhances binding and activity, but an 11α-hydroxyl group removes binding ability (Rousseau *et al.*, 1972). No extensive structure–activity study for glucocorticoids, using crystallographic results, has been made. Because the cytosol contains a glucocorticoid-binding protein, called transcortin or corticosteroid-binding α-globulin, all experiments on binding to receptor must be done in the absence of this protein.

The work of Samuels and Tomkins (1970) has given us more information on the receptor, and gives a picture of two forms of the receptor. One form, when complexed with steroid, is translocated to the nucleus, while the other is not. The response of a steroid will be a function of its relative affinity for the two receptor conformations. The glucocorticoids and their analogs can be divided into those that cause induction of tyrosine aminotransferase (inducers, which interact with the active form of the receptor), those that suppress its induction (antiinducers or antiglucocorticoids, which bind to the inactive form of the receptor) and those that are inactive (i.e., do not bind to the receptor). The receptor has been isolated by Litwak *et al.* (1973).

  b. Characteristics of Mineralocorticoids and Their Receptors. Mineralocorticoids promote increased retention of sodium ions and water and the excretion of potassium ions. Aldosterone is the most active mineralocorticoid, but the glucocorticoids cortisol and corticosterone also have activity as mineralocorticoids. Other steroids, such as progesterone, spironolactone (Dideberg and Dupont, 1972), and canrenone (Weeks *et al.*, 1976) are aldosterone antagonists (i.e., antimineralocorticoids). The interesting feature of the aldosterone structure, determined crystallographically and shown in Fig. 19, is the presence of two additional five-membered rings, designated E and F, and referred to as the 18-acetal-20-hemiketal grouping.

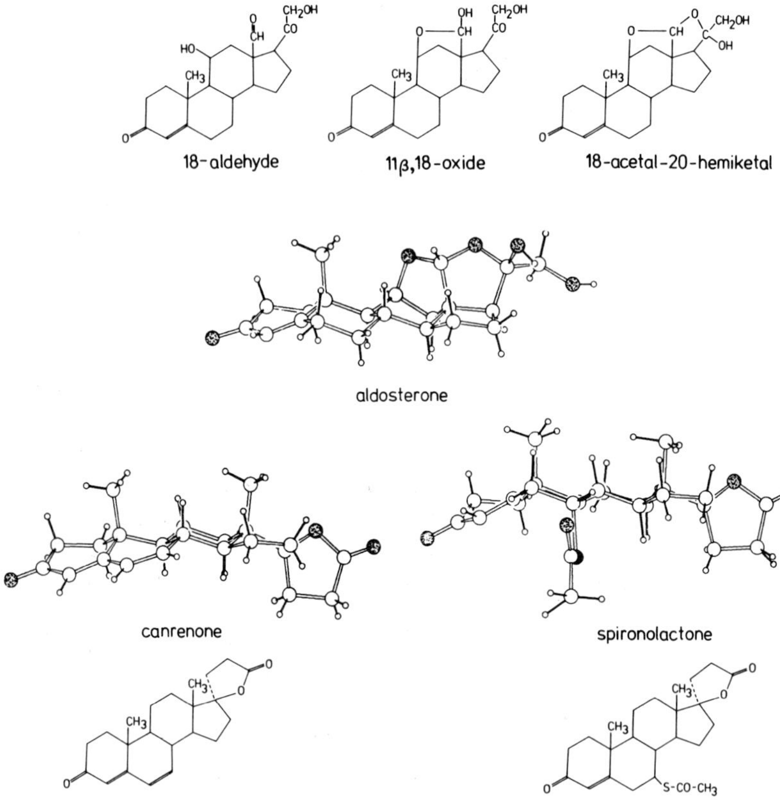

FIG. 19. Aldosterone and two aldosterone antagonists. The three equilibrium forms of aldosterone are shown at the top of the figure. The major component in solution is the $11\beta,18$-oxide which lacks one of the rings found in the crystal structure. In such a form the similarity to canrenone and spironolactone might be more noticeable.

It is possible that one or both of these rings are opened when the molecule is active, and the equilibrium in solution, which favors the structure with only one ring, is shown in Fig. 19. A comparison of aldosterone with the antagonists canrenone and spironolactone shows that their similarity to aldosterone is high at the A ring end of the molecule but low beyond the D ring (Fig. 19).

Dideberg *et al.* (1976) studied the X-ray structures of 20 corticosteroids. They determined the positions of atoms that formed hydrogen bonds to O-3, O-20, and O-21 in the crystal structures of each steroid. One general result is that the distance between the two groups that form hydrogen bonds to O-3 and to O-20 is 16.4 Å. The authors found a similar distance of 16.4 Å between groups that hydrogen bond to O-3 and O-25 (the lactone carbonyl oxygen atom) of spironolactone, and they used this fact to explain the affinity of spironolactone for the mineralocorticoid receptor. It was also suggested that the tighter binding of compounds hydroxylated on C-21 could be explained by assuming that O-3 and O-20 normally form the hydrogen bonds. However, if there is a hydroxyl group on C-21, this, in addition to O-3, is the preferred atom for binding by hydrogen bonding.

c. Antiinflammatory Activity of Corticosteroids. An interesting comparison of the molecular structures of some corticosteroids was made by Weeks *et al.* (1973). The adrenocortical hormone cortisone has been used as an antiinflammatory agent in the treatment of rheumatoid arthritis but, on long-term administration, unpleasant side effects such as excessive sodium retention and potassium excretion, occurred. The introduction of a 9α-fluorine atom, or, to a lesser extent, a 6α-fluorine atom, increases antiinflammatory activity of cortisol, but also increases sodium retention. Sodium retention can be eliminated from the 1,2-dehydrogenated-9α-fluorinated steroid by addition of either a 16α-hydroxyl or a methyl group. Weeks and co-workers were interested in specifying factors that contribute to the antiinflammatory activity. The compounds compared crystallographically in their study were cortisol, 6α-fluorocortisol, 9α-fluorocortisol, 6α-methylprednisolone, cortisone, and 4-chlorocortisone. The conformations of the A ring in these compounds varied significantly, so that, in 9α-fluorocortisol, O-3 is much further from the plane through atoms C-5–C-17 (2.43 Å) than it is in cortisol (1.32 Å), as shown in Fig. 20. This bowing of the A ring to the α side in 9α-fluorocortisol is due, at least in part, to steric hindrance. The situation for other 9α-halocortisols (Weeks and Duax, 1973; Weeks *et al.*, 1973; 1974) is shown in Fig. 20. Weeks and co-workers suggest that A-ring conformation, specifically the deviation of O-3 from the plane through atoms C-5–C-17, must have a significant influence on antiinflammatory activity. The extent of bowing would presumably cause a closer fit of the β face of the A ring to the binding protein. It is assumed that the fact that

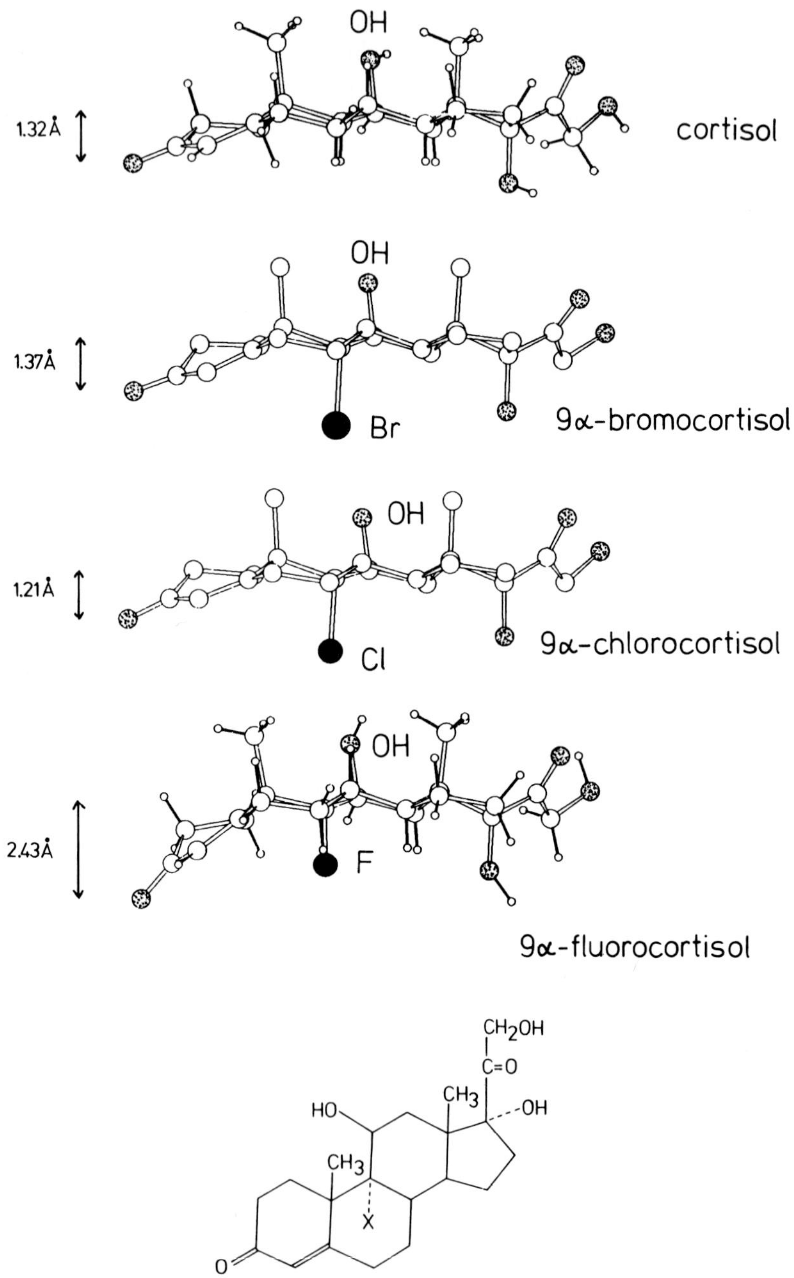

Jenny P. Glusker

FIG. 20. Comparison of the structures of 9α-halocorticoids (X = H, Br, Cl, and F).

9α-substitution can occur means that binding is to the β rather than the α face. However, it was found that cortisone, with half the antiinflammatory activity of cortisol, has O-3 at 2.48 Å from the C-5–C-17 plane, so that it is bowed to the same extent as 9α-fluorocortisol. Presumably, other factors account for its decreased activity over 9α-fluorocortisol.

5. Cyclic AMP

Hormones are chemical messengers, secreted by endocrine glands, and are carried by the blood to target organs where they help control the metabolism and physiology of the cell. They carry out their regulatory activity by binding with high affinity and specificity to proteinaceous hormone receptors. This binding causes some intracellular messenger molecule to stimulate or depress the appropriate biochemical activity. In the case of water-soluble hormones, cyclic AMP acts as the intracellular messenger; in the case of steroids, which are more lipid-soluble, the hormone–receptor complex comprises the intracellular messenger.

Cyclic AMP is made by the enzyme adenylate cyclase from ATP in response to an interaction with a peptide hormone. This mode of action means that the hormone need not enter the cell, but that any specificity of its action depends on the presence of membrane-bound adenylate cyclase in the target tissue. Once made, cyclic AMP carries out hormone functions such as the induction of new enzymes, regulation of cell division, and action as a mediator in inflammatory and immune reactions of tissues. Because cyclic AMP carries out many of the functions of steroid hormones, a comparison of

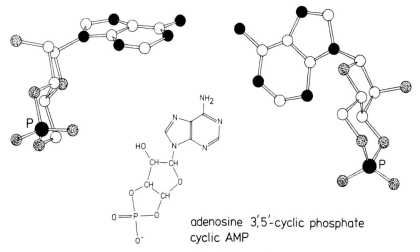

adenosine 3,5'-cyclic phosphate
cyclic AMP

FIG. 21. Cyclic AMP, two views.

their structures is necessary. Two views of cyclic AMP (K. Watenpaugh, private communication, 1977) are shown in Fig. 21. This figure shows that there is no great similarity to the structures of steroid hormones.

6. General Conclusions

Structure–activity relationships among steroids, using the results of three-dimensional analysis by X-ray studies of crystals, have not given us much information on the nature of the steroid-binding site in the biological receptor. Part of the trouble stems from the fact that details of the mechanism whereby the steroid receptor causes its effect are not known. The situation, as noted earlier, is not as simple as that of an enzyme–substrate complex for which the efficacy of various substrates can be measured with comparative ease. A study of the structures of the various steroids has led to two main schools of thought on the location of activity. One claims that the A ring is the important site of activity; the other claims that what happens to the D ring is important. However, it is not known whether "important" means interaction with the receptor or interaction with some other macromolecule (e.g., DNA) while the steroid is still partially enveloped by receptor. Thus, both claims may be partially correct—we can only wait and see.

C. Interactions of Steroids with Nucleic Acids

One of the main effects of steroids, as mentioned earlier, is to induce the formation of new proteins. Such induction, which occurs by translation from nucleic acids, is believed to occur as a result of the binding of the steroid–receptor complex to chromatin or DNA. However, almost nothing is known about the stereochemistry of this interaction, and it should be stressed here that, while both steroids and steroid–receptor complexes can bind to nucleic acids *in vitro*, it is not known at present whether steroid–nucleic acid associations have any biological relevance. It is possible that the steroid is completely enveloped by receptor and that the only function of the steroid is to control the conformation of the protein receptor. Our knowledge on this point *in vivo* is so scant that it can be considered equally possible that some portion of a receptor-bound steroid, or even steroid released from receptor, can bind to nucleic acid. In view of the *in vitro* results, and with the above reservations, the information on steroid–nucleic acid binding will be reviewed.

1. Steroid–Nucleic Acid Interactions

Much biochemical work on the interaction of steroids with nucleic acids has been done by Kidson and co-workers, who have considered the *in vitro*

binding of steroids—particularly estradiol, progesterone, and testosterone—
to native and synthetic nucleic acids. While this is a "test tube" situation,
the results are interesting. A survey of many steroids showed a particularly
high affinity for poly(G) of progesterone, 5α-dihydrotestosterone, and, to a
lesser extent, testosterone. The estrogens bound to poly(G) and also to poly(I)
[2-deaminated poly(G)]. An analysis of the binding of structurally modified
steroids suggests that binding involves the hydroxyl groups at both ends of
these molecules, presumably by hydrogen bonding. Kidson and co-workers
(1971) reported that the steroids only bind to heat-denatured DNA.

However, Arya and Yang (1975) have data to suggest that steroids can
interact with both native (double-stranded) and denatured nucleic acids, and
they found that steroids protect DNA secondary structure against thermal
denaturation. In addition, they found binding of steroids to RNA, poly(A),
and poly(U), and concluded that the affinity for binding depends on the
conformation of the nucleic acid. They suggested that both hydrogen bonding and hydrophobic interactions are involved in the binding, and found that
the oxygen groups on C-3 and C-17 are important, since any modification of
either affects the melting temperature of the nucleic acid–steroid complex.

One X-ray crystallographic study has been done which is important for our
understanding of steroid–nucleic acid interactions. This is the structure of a
complex of a steroid (deoxycorticosterone) and a nucleic acid base (adenine)
(Weeks *et al.*, 1975a,c), which is illustrated in Fig. 22. The very fact that
such a complex can be crystallized is interesting. The two oxygen atoms of
the side chain of deoxycorticosterone form hydrogen bonds to N-1 and N-6 of
adenine. This means that the steroid side chain has recognized the base-
pairing location of adenine that would normally be occupied by thymine or
uracil. Therefore, the observed hydrogen-bonding mode is only relevant to
single-stranded, not base-paired nucleic acid, because the adenine atoms
involved are those that normally take part in Watson–Crick base pairing. The
ketone oxygen O-3 of the steroid does not interact directly with adenine, but
forms a hydrogen bond to water of crystallization; this water molecule is also
hydrogen bonded to N-7 and N-9 of two different adenine molecules. In
addition, adenine rings lie above the A ring of the steroid. The planar conjugated system O-3=C-3—C-4=C-5 of the steroid lies about 3.5 Å from the
plane of the adenine ring; the plane of these four atoms of the steroid is
inclined at an angle of 16° to the plane of the adenine. Thus two kinds of
interaction, the hydrogen bonding via the side chain of the steroid and an
interaction between the steroid A ring and the ring system of adenine, are
observed in this complex, as illustrated in Fig. 22.

Kidson and co-workers (1971) suggested a model of steroid–nucleic acid
interaction that involves a trinucleotide portion of a single-stranded nucleic
acid with the sequence guanine–purine–guanine [from the data on binding
to poly(G)]. The C-3 and C-20 carbonyl groups of progesterone are en-

(a)

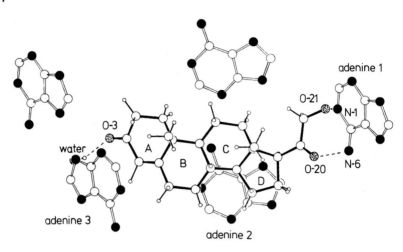

(b)

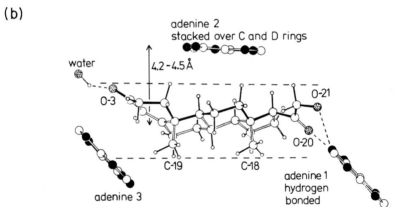

(c)

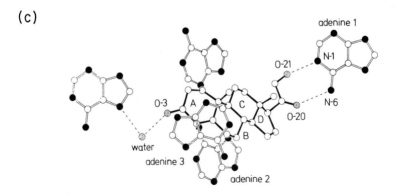

visioned to form hydrogen bonds to the 2-amino groups of the two outer guanine residues, meaning that the steroid is presumed to span the three nucleic acid bases. Similarly, for testosterone the C-3 carbonyl group can form a hydrogen bond with the 2-amino group of an outer guanine residue, while the C-17 hydroxyl group forms a hydrogen bond with N-3 or the amino nitrogen of the other outer guanine residue. However, in this case, from model building, it seems that the second guanine could be replaced by any of the other bases, i.e., that testosterone binding is not as specific. In both cases the α face of the progestogen or androgen is oriented toward the nucleic acid. In the case of estradiol, the β face is probably oriented toward the nucleic acid. No reason for base specificity can be seen.

However, steroids rarely bind to nucleic acids. The number of steroid binding sites *in vitro* corresponding to maximum binding constants is less than 1/10,000 nucleotide residues in poly(G) or denatured DNA. It can be shown that this does not represent binding to the termini of the nucleic acids, for steroids can bind to closed circular DNA (ϕX174 and M13). The binding constants for progesterone and testosterone, but not of estradiol, were increased with increasing salt concentration, a condition under which the extent of base stacking is enhanced. When poly(G) is methylated at N-7, introducing a positive charge into the polymer, only estradiol, not testosterone or progesterone, binds.

The binding of steroids to transfer RNA has also been considered (Chin and Kidson, 1971; Dvorak *et al.*, 1976). Steroids do not bind to tRNA itself, only to the aminoacyl form of tRNA (the tRNA "primed" with an amino acid). The extent of binding depends on both the steroid and the tRNA. As steroids only bind to aminoacyl tRNA, they may affect aminoacyl transfer, and this might provide a mechanism for rate regulation of protein synthesis by sex steroids. No X-ray structural work on steroid–nucleic acid interactions has been done so far (S. H. Kim, private communication, 1977), but a model of the proposed binding, to guanines number 18, 19, and 20 (Dvorak *et al.*, 1976), may be made using X-ray crystallographic coordinates derived for transfer RNA (Kim *et al.*, 1973, 1974; Robertus *et al.*, 1974; Quigley *et al.*, 1975).

FIG. 22. Adenine–deoxycorticosterone (DOC) complex. (a) View onto the best plane through the steroid ring system. Adenine 1 is hydrogen bonded to the side chain of DOC. Adenine 2 lies over (α side in this case) the C and D rings. Adenine 3 lies under (β side) the conjugated portion of the A ring. (b) View along the best plane through the steroid ring system. (c) View onto the planes of adenines 1 and 3. The overlap of the A ring is shown more clearly, but the steroid ring system is not parallel to the plane of adenines 1 and 3. Note that the crystal contains a 1:1 complex. Every adenine shown in the diagram is related in the crystal to another by space group symmetry.

2. Binding of Flat Polycyclic Molecules to Nucleic Acids

There are several ways in which a flat polycyclic molecule can interact with a nucleic acid, and several models have been studied crystallographically, particularly those involving intercalation. Double-stranded DNA contains two grooves, one wide (the major groove) and one narrow (the minor groove), between the phosphate groups. In RNA, the difference between the groove sizes has decreased considerably. In the center of the double helix are hydrogen-bonded nucleic acid bases, which provide a hydrophobic environment for any aromatic molecule. The exterior of the nucleic acid consists of highly polar negatively charged phosphate groups which are hydrophilic.

If a polycyclic molecule such as acridine is flat, it can intercalate between the bases of the nucleic acid (Lerman, 1964). This is a hydrophobic interaction, involving the π-electron systems of the planar molecules, and it has been shown (Craig and Isenberg, 1970a,b) that the criterion for an interaction of this kind is that the molecular size be such that it can be completely enveloped between the hydrophobic nucleic acid bases. A conformational change (stretching and/or unwinding) of the phosphodiester backbone of the nucleic acid will cause the distance between the bases to be increased from 3.4 to 6.8 Å. A flat molecule, thickness 3.5 Å, can then "slip" between the bases. Several models for this have been demonstrated crystallographically, including dinucleotide phosphate complexes with acridine mutagens (Sobell *et al.*, 1976; Neidle *et al.*, 1977).

Steroids are not flat molecules, apart from the aromatic A ring of estrogens and the conjugated C-4═C-5 double bond of some other steroids, and they do not have a π-electron system that can interact with the nucleic acid bases. As shown in Fig. 22, steroids are 5–6 Å thick (compared with a thickness of 3.5 Å for an acridine mutagen), so if they intercalated between the bases, nucleic acid backbone extension would have to increase the interbase spacing from 3.5 to 8.5–9.5 Å. This distance could probably not be found in a linear polymer stretch of nucleic acid (Dearing and Rollett, 1977), but it could possibly be found in areas of local disorder of the nucleic acid. Thus complete intercalation of a steroid is not likely, and it has not been observed in crystallographic studies to date, as may be seen from an examination of Figs. 10 and 22.

A second mode of interaction of polycyclic molecules with DNA could involve recognition of the base-pairing system as local "breathing" of DNA occurs. This is the model that was found in the deoxycorticosterone–adenine complex and involved hydrogen bonding between the side chain on C-17 of deoxycorticosterone and the adenine molecule (Fig. 22). Not all steroids have two or more functional groups on the side chain that could form two or more such hydrogen bonds.

A third mode of interaction would allow the polycyclic molecule (steroid or polycyclic aromatic hydrocarbon) to lie in one of the grooves of DNA, probably (for spatial reasons) the major groove. Some of the $O \cdots O$ distances across the major groove between two strands of DNA are about 16–17 Å. This is a distance that would accommodate a steroid with hydrogen-bond donors attached to C-3 and C-17. Such a model for a steroid has been built (C. M. Weeks, personal communication, 1975). It is interesting to note that in a complex of adenine and cytosine (Shefter, 1968) the two types of molecules lie in planes perpendicular to each other, again an example of this third model. Sobell and co-workers (1978) have proposed that a steroidlike molecule such as irediamine interacts with DNA in a groove at the position of a "kink" or bend.

A fourth model would be one with the steroid interacting with the phosphate groups of DNA and projecting out into the surrounding medium. This might be a less likely model if the part pointing out from the double helix is a very hydrophobic group, but this part could be enveloped by the steroid receptor or by the proteins that pack around the DNA. These proteins would include histones, nonhistone proteins, and the DNA polymerases.

3. Binding of the Steroid–Receptor Complex to Nucleic Acids

So far, only the binding of steroids to nucleic acids has been considered here. However, the binding of steroid–receptor complexes, as opposed to steroids alone, to nucleic acids is another story. For example, as described above, the A component of the progesterone receptor binds to nucleic acid (Schrader *et al.*, 1977). Also, Toft (1973) has shown that the estradiol–receptor complex binds to DNA *in vitro*. The conformation of DNA necessary for binding may be probed by flat molecules using the principles listed above. For example, André *et al.* (1976) showed that if double-stranded DNA is treated with the intercalating drugs ethidium bromide or 9-hydroxyellipticine, the binding of the estradiol–receptor complex to nucleic acid is inhibited. This suggests that double-stranded helical DNA is the target for the hormone–receptor complex in the nucleus, and that the normal helicity, rather than simply the charges on the phosphate groups, is important, i.e., the backbone conformation or the nature of the grooves in DNA is being recognized. "Stretched" or "unwound" DNA's are not recognized by the hormone–receptor complex.

In a similar manner, Edelman (1975) studied the effects of the compounds ethidium bromide, proflavine sulfate, actinomycin D, and netropsin on steroid–receptor–nucleic acid binding. Ethidium bromide and proflavine sulfate are assumed to bind so that portions, such as the phenyl group of the former, protrude into the major groove of the DNA helix. Actinomycin D intercalates between two guanine and cytosine base pairs with peptide lying in the minor groove of the DNA, and netropsin lies primarily in the minor groove of DNA. Both ethidium bromide and proflavine sulfate greatly reduced the steroid–receptor–nucleic acid interactions, while the other compounds did not. Therefore, Edelman suggested that the major groove of DNA is important in the high-affinity binding of steroid–receptor complexes. Alternatively, regulatory proteins in the major groove may be involved in steroid–receptor–nucleic acid binding. However, as polymerases act on local single-stranded areas of DNA, the question of which groove the receptor binds to has no relevance to polymerase activity (L. A. Loeb, private communication, 1977).

4. Summary

Steroids have been found to bind to nucleic acids *in vitro*, although it is not clear whether they bind to single-stranded or double-stranded nucleic acids or to both. The steroid–receptor complex binds to DNA *in vitro* and *in vivo*, but it is not known whether, in the steroid–receptor–DNA complex, there are any steroid–nucleic acid interactions. Several models of these interactions have been proposed. Such model building is speculative at this stage, and more studies of the steroid–receptor–nucleic acid interactions must be conducted, using many techniques, before the results of X-ray studies on steroids will be of use in describing, on a three-dimensional molecular scale, how steroids exert their biochemical action.

III. CARCINOGENIC POLYCYCLIC AROMATIC HYDROCARBONS AND THEIR STRUCTURAL SIMILARITIES TO STEROIDS

When the chemical formulas of steroids were first determined in the early 1930's, it became evident that a whole series of compounds with no apparent physiological connection had a phenanthrene ring (saturated or unsaturated) in common. The compounds listed (Rosenheim and King, 1934) included the naturally occurring estrogenic hormones, calciferol, cardiac glycosides, and also some carcinogenic polycyclic aromatic hydrocarbons that are found as constituents of coal tar. It was further noted by Cook and Dodds (1933) that some carcinogenic substances from coal tar, such as benzo[a]pyrene, had a noticeable estrogenic activity. Because the early stages of malignant growth were, in some aspects, reminiscent of the cell proliferation that is characteristic of the estrous state, they wondered if the reverse was true, i.e., if some estrogens might not be carcinogenic.

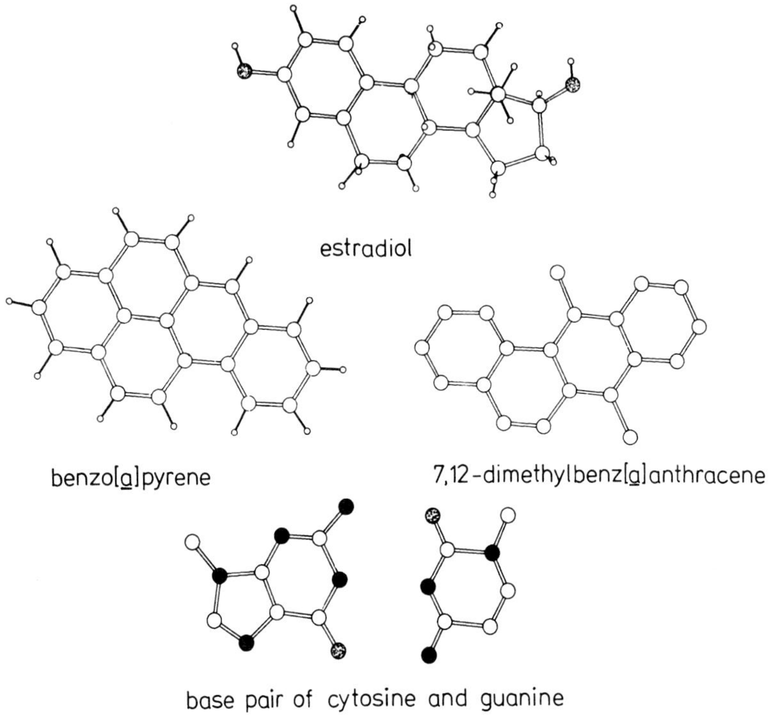

estradiol

benzo[*a*]pyrene

7,12-dimethylbenz[*a*]anthracene

base pair of cytosine and guanine

FIG. 23. Views onto the planes of estradiol. benzo[*a*]pyrene, DMBA, and a cytosine–guanine hydrogen-bonded base pair. Note the size similarities. Hydrogen atoms are not shown for the last two molecules.

The relationship between steroids and carcinogenic polycyclic aromatic hydrocarbons has been considered in more detail from a structural point of view. It was noted that there is a similarity in size (width and length), but not in thickness, between steroids and carcinogenic polycyclic aromatic hydrocarbons (Yang *et al.*, 1961; Huggins and Yang, 1962) and base pairs of nucleic acids (Haddow, 1957). This is illustrated by a comparison of estradiol-17β (Busetta and Hospital, 1972); benzo[*a*]pyrene (Iball *et al.*, 1976); 7,12-dimethylbenz[*a*]anthracene (DMBA) (Iball, 1964; Sayre and Friedlander, 1960); and a base pair involving cytosine and guanine (Neidle *et al.*, 1977) in Fig. 23, which shows views onto the planes of the ring systems. The views from above the planes of the rings show some remarkable similarities, but the side views are not so similar. While base pairs have a van der Waals thickness of 3.5 Å, steroids have a thickness of 5–6 Å, and carcinogenic aromatic hydrocarbons may have intermediate thicknesses.

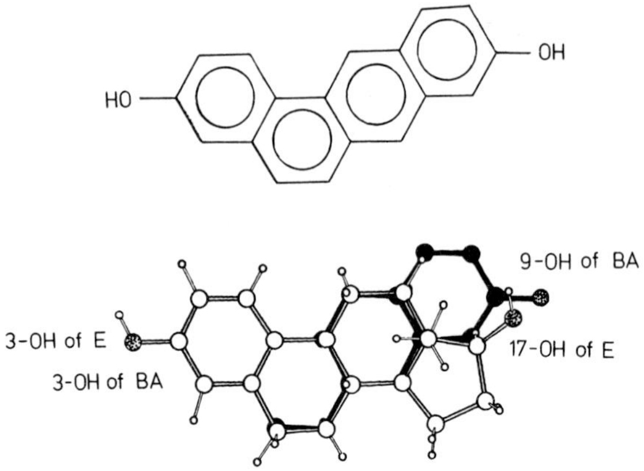

FIG. 24. Comparison of estradiol (E, white bonds) and 3,9-dihydroxybenz-[a]anthracene (BA, black bonds). Because the crystal structure of the latter has not been determined, the structure has been drawn from structural data on benzo[a]pyrene and some phenols. The hydroxyl groups on O-3 of both compounds have been aligned. Note the proximity of the other hydroxy groups in each compound.

A. ESTROGENIC PROPERTIES OF SOME POLYCYLIC AROMATIC HYDROCARBONS

The estrogenic properties of compounds such as 3,9-dihydroxybenz[a]-anthracene have been reported (Schneider *et al.*, 1976). This is, presumably, a flat molecule for which the X-ray structure has not been determined, but approximate, estimated dimensions are shown in Fig. 24 {using ben-zo[a]pyrene parameters and known phenolic C—O bond lengths}. The shape is compared with that of estradiol-17β, with which 3,9-dihydroxybenz[a]-anthracene competes for binding to the receptor. The 3,9-dihydroxy compound is a possible, but not yet isolated, metabolite of benz[a]anthracene, a much less powerful carcinogen than DMBA. Thus, the fact that the derivative of a moderate carcinogen has estrogenic properties may simply be a reflection of the sites of hydroxylation of the hydrocarbon and the general characteristics of its carbon skeleton.

B. POSSIBLE CARCINOGENIC PROPERTIES OF SOME STEROIDS

1. Cholesterol and Bile Acids

Kennaway and Cook (1932) suggested that carcinogenic compounds might be derived from cholesterol or the bile acids in the body. Such dehydrogenations of sterols to give compounds containing many aromatic rings have, of course, been done chemically, and remind one of the enzymes such as aromatase described earlier. Wieland and Dane (1933) found that they could synthesize the carcinogen 3-methylcholanthrene by pyrolysis of deoxycholic acid and then dehydrogenation of the product. Cholesterol and bile acids have recently been investigated as possible precursors of carcinogens in the colon. For example, animal experiments have shown that bile acids such as lithocholic acid and deoxycholic acid, which are formed in more abundance if the diet is fatty, are colon tumor promoters (Narisawa *et al.*, 1974; Reddy *et al.*, 1976). Wynder and co-workers (Reddy *et al.*, 1977) found that the fecal excretion of cholesterol, coprostanol, and cholestane-$3\beta,5\alpha,6\beta$-triol is higher in patients with ulcerative colitis, a disease conferring a risk of development of carcinoma of the colon. Cholestane-$3\beta,5\alpha,6\beta$-triol is formed from the oxidation of cholesterol to a 5,6-epoxide, which is then hydrolyzed. Presumably, the triol represents the end product in a series of reactions for which an intermediate, e.g., an epoxide, is carcinogenic. These studies, therefore, suggest that sterols and bile acids may be implicated in tumor formation, although these data do not envision polyaromatization of a steroid. However, steroids have been unequivocally implicated in the promotion of tumor growth.

2. Estradiol-17β and Diethylstilbestrol

Estradiol can, under certain conditions (such as when unopposed by progesterone or when given in a conjugated form), have a carcinogenic effect (Marx, 1976). However, it is not at all clear whether this is because the molecule of estradiol itself is a carcinogen, or because of some other effect of estradiol, e.g., promotion. Lacassagne (1932) gave estradiol to male mice of a strain with a high incidence of cancer in breeding females but which were free of spontaneous mammary cancer in males. The result of this estrogen administration was mammary cancer in the male mice. This was one of the first demonstrations that the administration of estrogens can lead to cancer in animals.

Diethylstilbestrol (DES) is a well-documented example of an estrogen that has a carcinogenic effect. It can cause a vaginal cancer (clear cell carcinoma) in adolescent daughters of mothers who had taken the drug while pregnant. One hundred fifty cases have been reported in 1,000,000 exposures. Cells which normally do not persist until adulthood are affected.

There must be some role for estrogen in bringing about breast cancer, but it is not clear what it is. Jensen, however, points out (Hertz, 1976) that estrogens are not carcinogens in the way some polycyclic aromatic hydrocarbons or amines are. He suggests that estrogens do not *cause* cancer but are implicated in some way in the etiology of many cancers; i.e., they are "permissive" rather than "causative." It is possible that they are carcinogenic simply because they help maintain mammary and uterine tissue in a functioning state, i.e., a state susceptible to a neoplastic stimulus. It seems (Segaloff, 1975) that women are very resistant to the carcinogenic effect of estrogen, even after very long periods of administration, because there seems to be no increase in the number of malignancies in women using oral contraceptives [although this is a controversial subject (see Lingeman, 1976)]. The polypeptide prolactin may also (or alternatively) play an important indirect role in mammary carcinogenesis (Costlow *et al.*, 1976); i.e., the role of estrogen may be related to the prolactin it produces.

Natural estrogens have been shown to become covalently bound to DNA by rat liver microsomal preparations (Blackburn *et al.*, 1977). It is known that estrogens are metabolized *in vitro* by hydroxylation at positions 2, 6, 7, and 16 (Hamberg *et al.*, 1974). The binding of estrogens to DNA as a result of metabolism apparently involves a loss of hydrogen from positions 2 or 4, not 6 or 7. The similarity of the regiospecificity (see Fig. 25) of this reaction with the activation of benzo[*a*]pyrene led the authors (Hamberg *et al.*, 1974)

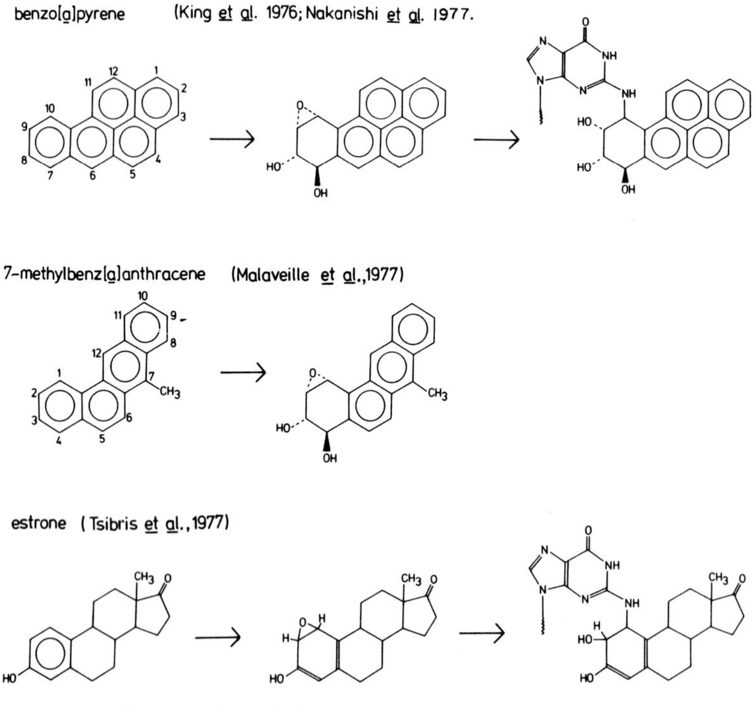

FIG. 25. Proposed course of metabolism and binding to DNA of carcinogens and estrone. The situation for estrone is hypothetical (Tsibris and McGuire, 1977), and the proposed binding to DNA is drawn by analogy to the formula for a benzo[*a*]pyrene–DNA adduct.

to suggest that the hydroxylating system in rat liver microsomes that normally acts on steroids may also affect some polycyclic aromatic hydrocarbons. These ideas have been extended by Tsibris and McGuire (1977). However, there is no real evidence to indicate whether or not covalent binding is necessary for carcinogenicity. L. A. Loeb (private communication, 1977) found that steroids affect the fidelity of DNA polymerase, i.e., the ability to copy a polynucleotide faithfully. These experiments were done under conditions in which covalent bond formation is unlikely, although the steroid concentration used was very high.

DES has been shown to bind covalently to native or denatured DNA by photochemical or oxidative means (Blackburn *et al.*, 1974, 1976). One molecule of DES is bound per 1000 bases, with a preference for purines rather than for pyrimidines. The formation of the covalent linkage is promoted by iodine, which may be correlated with the fact that diiododiethylstilbestrol is more carcinogenic than is DES. The *in vivo* metabolism of DES involves epoxidation of the ethylenic double bond and hydroxylation of phenolic rings (Metzler, 1975). DES is, however, a stilbene derivative, and the fact that it is also an estrogen may not be relevant here. DES may act as a carcinogen in an entirely different manner from that of estrogens, although the site of its effect is the target tissue for estrogens.

C. MODES OF ACTION OF CARCINOGENIC POLYCYCLIC AROMATIC HYDROCARBONS

The mechanism of action of carcinogenic hydrocarbons is still under investigation from three points of view. The first is a structure–activity analysis, that is, the search for a common chemical portion of a molecule that confers carcinogenicity on it; the second is a study of the metabolic products of such hydrocarbons; and the third is a study of their interaction with DNA and the polymerases.

1. Structure–Activity Analysis of Carcinogenic Hydrocarbons

The structures of some of the more potent carcinogenic polycyclic aromatic hydrocarbons are shown in Fig. 26. It is possible that the grouping (marked in heavy black line) that is found in all is important (assuming they all have a common mechanism of action). Some of these hydrocarbons, such as benzo[*a*]pyrene, are planar; others, such as DMBA, are markedly nonplanar as a result of steric hindrance between the 12-methyl group and a hydrogen atom across the so-called "bay region" (illustrated by a zigzag line in Fig. 26). This steric hindrance is caused by the fact that if the molecule of DMBA were flat, the hydrogen atom on C-1 would lie almost on top of one of

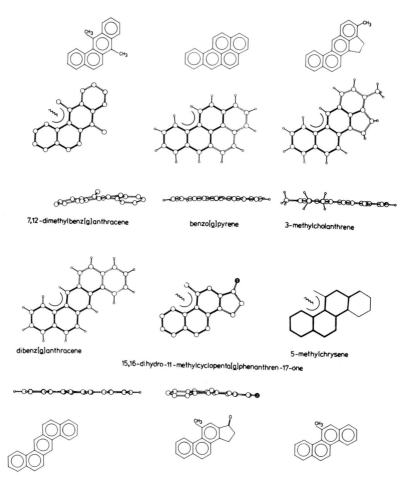

FIG. 26. Structures of some carcinogenic polycyclic aromatic hydrocarbons. Hydrogen atoms are included if their positions have been determined. Note the variation in the nonplanarity or planarity of the ring systems. The "bay region" is indicated by a half-circle and steric hindrance by a jagged line. The structure of 5-methylchrysene has not yet been determined. Bonds that are common to all the structures are drawn in a heavy black line.

the hydrogen atoms of the 12-methyl group. Because atoms repel each other to van der Waals distances (2.0 Å between hydrogen atoms), the rest of the molecule must twist to accommodate the two hydrogen atoms.

2. *Metabolism of Polycyclic Aromatic Hydrocarbons*

Recent theories of chemical carcinogenesis by polycyclic aromatic hydrocarbons contain the assumption that the polycycle is metabolized by so-called "mixed-function oxidases" in cells to an active form, possibly a diol epoxide with alkylating ability (Booth and Sims, 1974; Malaveille *et al.*, 1977). This oxidation solubilizes the hydrocarbon so that it may be excreted, but in some cases a carcinogenic product is made. The site of epoxidation and/or hydroxylation is not clear in all hydrocarbons, but some possibilities are indicated in Fig. 25. In a related way hepato aminoazo dyes such as N,N-dimethylaminoazobenzene undergo N-hydroxylation by mixed-function oxidases and then esterification, principally to sulfate by cytoplasmic sulfotransferases (King and Phillips, 1968; DeBaun *et al.*, 1970). Similarly, N-2-fluorenylacetamide is activated, principally to N-sulfate.

In the case of benzo[a]pyrene, the nature of the diol epoxide that is believed to be the intermediate in chemical carcinogenesis has been investigated in detail. Of the oxides of benzo[a]pyrene, the 7,8-oxide is moderately carcinogenic, the 4,5-oxide is weakly carcinogenic (Levin *et al.*, 1976) and the 9,10- and 11,12-oxides are not carcinogenic. Presumably, the hydrocarbon is oxidized to the 7,8-oxide, which is then hydrated to the *trans*-7,8-dihydrodiol by epoxide hydratase (Fig. 25). The adjacent olefinic double bond is then epoxidized to give benzo[a]pyrene-7,8-dihydro-7,8-diol-9,10-epoxide, for which there are two diastereomers. One dihydrodiol epoxide has the 7-hydroxyl group *cis* to the 9,10-epoxide, while the other has the 7-hydroxyl group *trans* to the 9,10-epoxide. The (−) enantiomer of the 7,8-dihydrodiol of benzo[a]pyrene has been shown spectroscopically to have the 7R,8R absolute configuration (Levin *et al.*, 1977) (Fig. 25). The 7-hydroxy group lies on the β side and the 8-hydroxy group on the α side of the molecule. It is 5- to 10-fold more potent than is the (+) enantiomer as a tumor initiator, and also more active than benzo[a]pyrene itself (Levin *et al.*, 1977). In Fig. 25, the 7-hydroxy group lies on the β side and the 8-hydroxy group lies on the α side of the molecule. Studies *in vitro* of the binding of benzo[a]pyrene to DNA in cell culture led to the conclusion that most of the bound metabolite is derived from the enantiomer with the 7-hydroxy group *trans* to the epoxy ring (King *et al.*, 1976; Yang *et al.*, 1976). However, the fate of the 9,10-epoxide ring in the ultimate carcinogen is still not clear. It is believed that the role of the 7,8,9,10-dihydrodiol epoxide is to generate a carbonium ion at C-10, and the conformation and structure of an alkylation product of the diol epoxide and a guanine base in DNA have been inferred (King *et al.*, 1976; Nakanishi *et al.*, 1977) (see Fig. 25).

In a similar way (Malaveille *et al.*, 1977), it has been suggested that the active metabolite of 7-methylbenz[a]anthracene is the 1,2-epoxy-3,4-diol-1,2,3,4-tetrahydrobenzo[a]pyrene. This is shown in Fig. 25 in the same orientation as the diol epoxide of benzo[a]pyrene. Presumably, the diol epoxide conformation is the same. In both cases the phenanthrenic bay region is involved, and any methyl group in this area must surely have an effect on the product. If DMBA forms an analogous diol epoxide to that of 7-methylbenz[a]anthracene, then, in the active isomer, the 12-methyl group should lie on the opposite side of the molecule from the NH group formed on alkylation so that this methyl group will not interfere with product formation.

Phenols have also been suggested to be active metabolites. Of the various phenols derived from benzo[a]pyrene, 2-hydroxybenzo[a]pyrene is carcinogenic (in the mouse skin system), while 11-hydroxybenzo[a]pyrene is weakly carcinogenic (Wislocki *et al.*, 1977). None of the other monophenols is carcinogenic. 6-Hydroxybenzo[a]pyrene can give rise to a highly reactive phenoxy radical on autooxidation (Lorentzen *et al.*, 1975; Lesko *et al.*, 1975). This compound can induce fibrosarcomas in rats, but it is less active than benzo[a]pyrene (Nagata *et al.*, 1974).

D. X-Ray Crystallographic Studies of Polycyclic Aromatic Hydrocarbons

1. *Structures of Polycyclic Aromatic Hydrocarbons*

Views of the results of X-ray studies of the carcinogens 7,12-dimethylbenz[a]anthracene (DMBA) (Iball, 1964; Sayre and Friedlander, 1960); benzo[a]pyrene (Iball and Young, 1956; Iball *et al.*, 1976); 3-methylcholanthrene (Iball and MacDonald, 1960; Iball and Scrimgeour, 1975); dibenz[a]anthracene (Iball *et al.*, 1975); and 15,16-dihydro-11-methyl-cyclopenta[a]phenanthren-17-one (Coombs *et al.*, 1976a; E. M. McPartlin and A. F. D. Clayton, private communication, 1977) are shown in Fig. 26. The last-named compound is of particular interest because, viewed onto the best plane through the ring system, it resembles a steroid. The 11-methyl derivative, shown in Fig. 26, is carcinogenic, while other monomethyl derivatives are not (Coombs *et al.*, 1976b).

In a similar way, 5-methylchrysene, for which X-ray studies are in progress (D. E. Zacharias, J. P. Glusker, R. G. Harvey, and P. P. Fu, private communication, 1977), is the most carcinogenic of the monomethyl chrysenes (Hoffmann *et al.*, 1974), while chrysene, the parent compound, is not carcinogenic. This effect parallels the greater carcinogenicity of DMBA over 7-methylbenz[a]anthracene. These methyl groups lie in the so-called "bay regions" of phenanthrene derivatives, shown in black in Fig. 26. They cause buckling of the ring system because of steric hindrance of the methyl group and hydrogen atoms across the bay region (illustrated by a zigzag line in Fig. 26). In order to study the geometry of the bay region, Jones and Sowden (1976) have determined the structures of both the carcinogenic 12-methylbenz[a]-anthracene and the noncarcinogenic 1,12-dimethylbenz[a]anthracene. Both are buckled, but presumably the latter compound is not carcinogenic because a metabolite, essential to the carcinogenic process, cannot be formed. In contrast, because benzo[*a*]pyrene and dibenz[*a*]anthracene are found crystallographically to be essentially planar, the steric hindrance between two hydrogen atoms in the bay region can be considered small or negligible.

2. Structures of Metabolites of Polycyclic Aromatic Hydrocarbons

Unfortunately, it has not to date been possible to crystallize a diol epoxide of a carcinogenic polycyclic aromatic hydrocarbon. However, some diols and some arene oxides, i.e. possible metabolic products, have been studied. To date, the K-region oxides of DMBA and benzo[*a*]pyrene have been studied crystallographically, and others are under investigation (D. E. Zacharias, J. P. Glusker, R. G. Harvey, and P. P. Fu, private communication, 1977). The K-region oxide of DMBA (Glusker *et al.*, 1974) shows even more extensive buckling than that found in the hydrocarbon (35° compared with 23°, respectively, between the planes of the A and D rings). The epoxide C—O distances are not equal indicating that cleavage of the C—O bond to C-6 is more likely. The K-region oxide of benzo[*a*]pyrene is flat, apart from the epoxide ring (Glusker *et al.*, 1976b). Zacharias and co-workers (1977), from a study of a *cis*-diol, consider that in DMBA derivatives the methyl substitution will determine the conformation (axial or equatorial) of an introduced adjacent hydroxyl group. However, this gives us no information on the conformation of an atom equivalent to O-3. Recently, the 1,2-*trans*-diol and the 10,11-*trans*-diol of benz[*a*]anthracene have been studied (D. E. Zacharias, J. P. Glusker, R. G. Harvey, and P. P. Fu, private communication, 1977). The hydroxyl groups are, respectively, axial and equatorial in these two compounds, probably for steric reasons. Obviously, more structural studies are required in these systems.

3. Comparisons of Structures of Steroids and Aromatic Hydrocarbons

The structural data from crystallographic studies may be used to compare the shapes of certain polycyclic aromatic hydrocarbons (and their metabolites) with those of steroids. Such a comparison was made by Glusker and co-workers (1974), who compared the K-region oxide of DMBA with progesterone, as shown in Fig. 27(a). As expected, the views onto the planes of the molecules showed great similarities. The side views showed a bowing of each molecule, but the thicknesses are quite different [Fig. 27(a)]. The hydroxyl group of the diol epoxide of benzo[*a*]pyrene that is in the position which would be equivalent to the 3-position of a steroid, is α-oriented. This is similar to the situation found in many steroids, e.g., androsterone. There is, however, no oxygen function on the other end of the diol epoxide, i.e., equivalent to the 17β position.

A particularly interesting comparison [Fig. 27(b)] may be made between

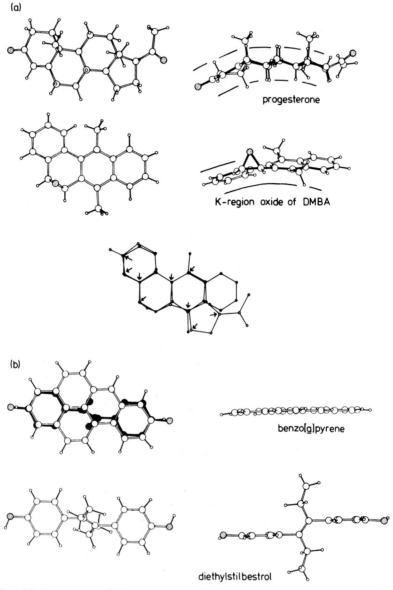

(a)

progesterone

K-region oxide of DMBA

(b)

benzo[g]pyrene

diethylstilbestrol

FIG. 27. Comparisons of (a) progesterone and the K-region oxide of DMBA with arrows indicating points of similar height in the diagram (open circles for progesterone, closed circles for the oxide). The near sides of the molecules are drawn in a heavy black line. (b) DES (symmetrical vs. benzo[a]pyrene.

the carcinogenic synthetic estrogen DES and benzo[*a*]pyrene, which has mild estrogenic activity. The structural comparison in Fig. 27 points out the possibility that the reason that DES is carcinogenic is because it resembles a carcinogenic hydrocarbon. Thus these two compounds, DES and benzo[*a*]pyrene, share estrogenic and carcinogenic activities, and considerable structural similarities.

One further set of comparisons, not involving a hydrocarbon, may also be significant. Aflatoxin B_1, an extremely potent hepatocarcinogen found, for example, in spoiled peanuts, has been shown crystallographically (van Soest and Peerdeman, 1970a,b) to be planar except for the ring which is believed to undergo epoxidation by metabolic activation. Comparisons of its structure with those of benzo[*a*]pyrene, DMBA, and estradiol are shown in Fig. 28. The presumed site of epoxide formation in each isindicated by arrows.

E. Interactions of Steroids and Polycyclic Aromatic Hydrocarbons with Membranes

Because the sterols, such as cholesterol, are common components of membranes (see earlier), and because changes in the permeability of membranes occur in tumors, it is pertinent to question whether carcinogens replace steroids in membranes and, in so doing, cause or promote carcinogenesis. For example, Williams and Rabin (1971) consider that such carcinogens disrupt the hormone-dependent association of membranes with polysomes by occupying or destroying a site in the membrane that is meant for steroid hormones. They showed by enzyme assay that the effect of a variety of carcinogens is the degranulation of the endoplasmic reticulum. It has been found that steroid hormones are involved in the operation of membrane–ribosomal binding sites (Sunshine *et al.*, 1971). Low concentrations of estradiol promote the binding of male polysomes to smooth surface male membranes; similarly, testosterone serves the same function in female tissue (Williams and Rabin, 1971). It is possible that carcinogens which are similar in shape and hydrophobicity or hydrophilicity to these steroids may replace them with damaging effects to the cell membrane (see Section III,B,1).

F. Transport of Carcinogens and Steroids

One of the present theories of carcinogenesis is that some modification of nuclear DNA need occur. This requires that the carcinogen, activated in the cytoplasm, must be able to enter the nucleus in order to cause this modifica-

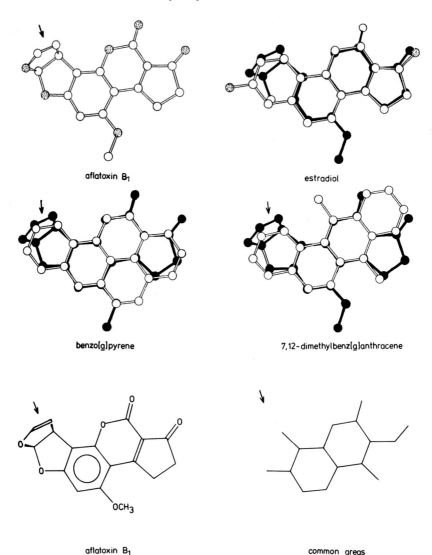

aflatoxin B₁

estradiol

benzo[g]pyrene

7,12-dimethylbenz[g]anthracene

aflatoxin B₁

common areas

FIG. 28. Comparison of aflatoxin B₁ with benzo[*a*]pyrene, DMBA, and estradiol. Locations of presumed epoxide ring formation to give intermediates in carcinogenesis are indicated by arrows. A molecular grouping that is common to aflatoxin B₁, benzo[*a*]pyrene, and DMBA is indicated beside the formula of the aflatoxin.

tion. Such a hydrophobic molecule might either diffuse through the nuclear membrane or be transported by a carrier protein. It is possible that it is carried by a protein that mistakes it for a steroid (i.e., the shape of the carcinogen is helpful to this process).

There is no evidence that carcinogens are transported into the nucleus by estrogen receptors. Heizmann and Wyss (1974) found that the cytoplasmic receptors for DMBA and estradiol, which transport them, respectively, into the nucleus, are not the same. Toft and Spelsberg (1972) reported that estradiol and 3-methylcholanthrene do not bind to the same receptors. Okey and co-workers (Keightley and Okey, 1973) found that DMBA *in vitro* does not compete for estrogen-receptor sites in mammary or uterine cytosol. They found that the effects of DMBA on estrogen binding seem to be rather complicated *in vivo*. At present, it appears that DMBA alters estrogen metabolism, possibly through induction of microsomal enzyme systems, and that it is this change in steroid metabolism which tends to increase the *available* number of cytosol binding sites for steroid, while decreasing the amount of hormone "bound" after a single estradiol injection *in vivo* (A. B. Okey, private communication, 1977).

There are other proteins known to interact with both polycyclic carcinogenic hydrocarbons and steroids. However, these are not proteins that cause transport into the nucleus. For example, one role of the glutathione S-transferases, a group of soluble liver proteins, is the detoxification of compounds that can become electrophilic in character (such as compounds that can form carbonium ions). This detoxification is effected by forming conjugates with glutathione and is a mechanism for preventing such compounds from entering the nucleus. One of these proteins, named ligandin (glutathione S-transferase B) (Litwack *et al.*, 1973), interacts with aminoazo dyes and hydrocarbon carcinogens and some of their metabolites *in vivo*, and has been suggested (Smith *et al.*, 1977; Tipping *et al.*, 1976) to protect against such carcinogens. Smith and co-workers (1977) proposed that ligandin may be involved in the detoxification and excretion of both chemical carcinogens and steroid hormones. For example, glutathione derivatives of DMBA have been found in liver homogenates (Booth *et al.*, 1973). Another, glutathione S-transferase E, may act primarily with epoxides of hydrocarbons. Interestingly, while the Δ^5-3-ketosteroid isomerase from *Pseudomonas testosteroni*, mentioned earlier, has no glutathione S-transferase activity, the activity of Δ^5-3-ketosteroid isomerase from rat liver is associated principally with ligandin (Benson *et al.*, 1977). Although the mechanism of the mammalian enzyme has not been studied, the fact that a steroid isomerase can bind polycyclic aromatic hydrocarbons is of interest.

The protective properties of a protein that envelops a steroid or a carcinogen have been demonstrated by Mainigi and Sorof (1977), who provide evidence for a receptor protein that can transport an activated azocarcinogen into the nucleus. The protein is envisioned as enveloping the azocarcinogen in a hydrophobic groove of the protein which protects the activated azocarcinogen from cellular nucleophiles. The carcinogen is transported into the nucleus, where it can act specifically with a target macromolecule. This protection-transport model may also apply to other carcinogens, and is similar to the model of certain steroid receptors which carry the steroid in a protected state into the nucleus.

G. Interactions with DNA and DNA-Associated Proteins

The information that has been obtained on the nature of the interaction of carcinogenic hydrocarbons and of steroids with nucleic acids will be described briefly. In both cases it is not clear what happens. Our knowledge to date does not indicate that these two classes of compounds act in a similar manner.

1. Polycyclic Hydrocarbons

As described earlier, there are several ways in which a polycyclic molecule may interact with nucleic acids. A model for intercalation of a polycyclic hydrocarbon in DNA has been provided by the study of a crystalline complex of benzo[a]pyrene with tetramethyluric acid (Damiani *et al.*, 1965). While intercalation is possible for a flat molecule such as benzo[a]pyrene, it is less likely for several carcinogenic polycyclic aromatic hydrocarbons, e.g., DMBA, that are not planar. This nonplanarity is, as mentioned earlier, the result of steric hindrance between the 12-methyl group and the hydrogen atom on C-1. In a crystallographic study of two carcinogenic alkylating derivatives of DMBA, both with chloromethyl groups in the 7-position and one lacking the methyl group, Glusker and co-workers (1976a) pointed out that the more carcinogenic compound is less planar. This, they suggested, indicates that intercalation is not a likely mechanism of carcinogenesis. Otherwise, the flatter molecule would be more carcinogenic. In addition, if such molecules alkylate a nucleic acid base, they cannot, for steric reasons, also intercalate between the bases. Therefore, it is more likely that the carcinogenic polycyclic molecule, after alkylating a base, lies in a groove of DNA.

The compounds that alkylate DNA on interaction with benzo[a]pyrene are the benzo[a]pyrene-7,8-dihydrodiol-9,10-epoxides. These have been shown to cause nicking of DNA after covalent binding to it (Gamper *et al.*,

1977). Alkylation of a molecule of viral ϕX174 DNA by a single molecule of benzo[*a*]pyrene diol epoxide will make the DNA noninfectious. Thus, DNA polymerization is believed to be blocked by the benzo[*a*]pyrene groups covalently bound to it, and the newly formed complementary chains are therefore incomplete (Hsu *et al.*, 1977). This *in vitro* experimental result, that DNA copying is blocked for templates modified by polycyclic aromatic hydrocarbons, suggests that *in vivo* some additional process, e.g., excision and repair (sometimes misrepair) or else binding of the hydrocarbons to some other macromolecule, might occur. In line with this idea, Loeb and co-workers (L. A. Loeb, private communication, 1977) found that high concentrations of steroids decreased the fidelity of DNA polymerase leading to copied polynucleotides with errors in them.

2. Steroid–Receptor Complex

The steroid–receptor complex is believed to wrap itself around the nucleic acid and act as a biological switch. In so doing the steroid receptor can, owing to its size, cause high specificity in its interaction with DNA, a specificity that may be less operative in steroids themselves. In addition, it can control the effect of steroids in the nucleus. The steroid may either keep the receptor protein in the correct conformation for interaction with nucleic acid, or else all or part of the steroid may interact directly with nucleic acid (see earlier). Because it is not at present known which possibility pertains *in vivo*, it is premature to speculate on the interaction of the steroid–receptor complex with nucleic acids.

IV. SUMMARY

At present, the mechanisms by which hormones effect their biological action, by which polycyclic aromatic hydrocarbons cause cancer, and by which hormones may be involved in cancer are unclear. Much more experimental work, including structural studies when the components of the system have been highly purified, is required. In this chapter an attempt has been made to explain the state of the art from a detailed structural point of view, and in so doing, to reveal how much more we need to know. The review has shown that we now have much detailed structural information on a large variety of synthetic and naturally occurring steroids. This information has been useful for an investigation of structure–activity relationships and for studying mechanisms of enzymatic reactions involving steroids. However, steroid receptors have not been purified and, while their modes of action on steroids and on target tissue are being investigated, only portions of the story are known at this time. Structural studies of steroids have reinforced the idea that the steroid–receptor interaction may be more complicated than an enzyme–substrate interaction.

The structural similarities and differences between steroids and carcinogenic polycyclic aromatic hydrocarbons, shown in detail from X-ray work, are intriguing, and attempts to determine the significance of these comparisons have proved frustrating so far. The only obvious similarities are an ability to bridge approximately 16 Å if there are functional groups at both ends of the molecule, and a hydrophobic central portion of the molecule which might allow it, by virtue of its dimensions, to lie in a groove of DNA. Alternative possibilities involving proteins, i.e., polymerases and receptor proteins, have been discussed.

No one field of science can give all the answers to such problems, but it is to be expected that the X-ray crystallographer may contribute substantially in the future to the structural portion of these descriptions of how steroids work, whether or not they cause cancer, and if so how. The present is beset by the problems of obtaining purified components (such as steroid receptors) and complexes (such as steroid–receptor–polynucleotide complexes) in amounts large enough to obtain crystals that can be used for X-ray crystallographic investigations. Any reader of this article who obtains a purified sample of a steroid receptor should immediately contact his nearest crystallographer (Abrahams, 1977).

ACKNOWLEDGMENTS

The author wishes to thank Drs. W. L. Duax, C. H. Robinson, S. Sorof, and E. C. Travaglini for much assistance in the writing of this chapter, and Drs. M. M. Coombs, C. Kidson, E. M. McPartlin, C. E. Nordman, A. B. Okey, H. S. Shieh, K. Watenpaugh, and C. M. Weeks for unpublished data and information. The ball-and-stick diagrams were made with the program VIEW, written by Dr. H. L. Carrell of the Institute for Cancer Research, Philadelphia, Pa. and were computed by Miss Kathy Korff. I also wish to thank Miss Pat Bateman who patiently typed the manuscript.

This research was supported by grants CA-10925, CA-06927 and RR-05539 from the National Institutes of Health, U.S. Public Health Service, BC-242 from the American Cancer Society, AG-370 from the National Science Foundation, and an appropriation from the Commonwealth of Pennsylvania.

APPENDIX

A. A Retrieval of Steroid Structure Data

The reader may now ask how information on any structure that has been determined can be located. There is so much information on steroids that it is hard to wade through all of it. Fortunately, others have perceived the problem and have gathered together much of the data. Several sources of information, most notably the data files and reference listings of Kennard and co-workers (Kennard *et al.*, 1975; Kennard and Watson, 1970–1977), and the *Atlas of Steroid Structure* (Duax and Norton, 1975), are available. Both sets of references have been invaluable in the preparation of this chapter.

The data collected by Kennard and co-workers, which includes literature references and atomic parameters and dimensions, may be accessed by computer. This involves searching for some specific chemical grouping (such as a steroid, a five-membered ring fused to a six-membered ring, a 3-keto steroid, etc.) or searching for the name of the compound of interest. Literature references are also available in a yearly volume published by the same group (Kennard and Watson, 1970–1977).

The *Atlas of Steroid Structures*, Volume 1, contains information on estranes, androstanes, and pregnanes. The format of the *Atlas* is as follows: After a short introduction on X-ray crystallography and on conformational analysis, it describes graphically and numerically the detailed structure of each steroid for which a crystal structure has been determined. Three pictorial views are given. All three-dimensional coordinates, pertinent bond lengths, interbond angles, and torsion angles are listed. In addition, the planarity of the ring system as a whole, and of each ring individually, is given, together with the configurations of ring junctions, functional group orientations, and the interatomic distances between functional groups. Finally, the molecular packing is shown by projections down each axis of the unit cell. This is an invaluable catalog for those interested in comparing structures of related steroids.

The second volume of the *Atlas* is expected to be published in 1978 (W. L. Duax, private communication, 1977). It will cover an additional 100 or so estranes, androstanes, and pregnanes, including some synthetic estrogens. The formats have been altered to expedite rapid location of conformational details and to increase the emphasis on hydrogen positions and bonding. The third volume will cover all other classes of steroids and it is planned that it should follow in another year or so (W. L. Duax, private communication, 1977).

Coordinate Errors

In order to compute diagrams for this chapter, the following coordinate changes were guessed at in order to obtain reasonable geometry:

a. Cholesteryl iodide: C-15, x changed from 0.685 to 0.585 (Carlisle and Crowfoot, 1945).

b. DMBA: C-7, z changed from -3.1752 Å to -3.2752 Å (Iball, 1964).

B. A Glossary of Crystallographic Terms

Absolute configuration The spatial arrangement of an enantiomorph (one isomer of a compound) that is independent of any axial system, so that a model can be made directly. The absolute configuration of one enantiomorph cannot be superimposed on that of its mirror image.

Ångstrom unit 1 Å $= 10^{-8}$ cm $= 0.1$ nm.

Anomalous dispersion An anomalous effect on scattering of radiation at wavelengths near those for which this radiation is strongly absorbed. As a result of phase changes so caused, diffracted beams which normally have identical intensities are caused to have differing intensities. These differences may be used to determine the absolute configuration of the compound under study.

Asymmetric unit The unique portion of a crystal structure. The space-group symmetry operations, acting on the asymmetric unit, generate the contents of the entire unit cell, and thus of the whole crystal.

Axis A vector (with magnitude and direction) representing one edge of the unit cell of a crystal. The three independent vectors in a unit cell are called **a, b,** and **c.**

Centrosymmetric Symmetric with respect to a center. A center of symmetry converts any point x,y,z to a point $-x, -y, -z$. The symmetry operation, called inversion, is analogous to turning a glove inside out; it converts a right hand into a left hand and vice versa.

Configuration The absolute arrangement in space of atoms in a structure. The term is often used to imply that the absolute configurations (q.v.) of all asymmetric atoms are known.

Conformation The overall shape of a molecule which is found experimentally. It may represent one of several conformers if free rotation about bonds is possible.

Coordinates A set of numbers which specify the position of each atom of a molecule with respect to the sides of the unit cell. Coordinates are generally expressed as fractions of cell edges but are sometimes converted to orthogonal (all angles between **a, b** and **c** are 90°) coordinates in Å.

Crystal A solid having a regularly repeating internal arrangement of its atoms.

Diffraction When radiation passes by the edges of an opaque object or through a narrow slit, the waves appear to be deflected and to produce fringes of parallel light and dark bands. This effect may best be explained by considering the edges of the object or slit as secondary sources scattering the incident wave in all directions. These secondary waves interfere with one another, and the intensity of the beam in a given direction may be determined by superposing all the wavelets in that direction. When light passes through a narrow slit the waves will all be in phase in the forward direction. In any other direction, each secondary wave traveling in a given direction will be slightly out of phase with its neighbors by an amount that depends on the wavelength of the light and the angle of deviation from the direct beam. The shorter the wavelength or the larger the angle, the more a wave is out of phase with its neighbor. The reduction in intensity at a given angle will depend on the angle of observation, the wavelength of the radiation, and the width of the slit. In X-ray crystallography, the radiation is X-rays and the slit is replaced by the electron clouds of atoms in a crystal.

Direct methods A method of deriving relative phases of diffracted beams by consideration of the stronger beams. Relationships between phases come from the conditions that the structure is composed of atoms and that the electron density should be positive everywhere. Only certain values for the phases are consistent with these conditions. This method is used with high-speed computers.

Electron density map A contoured representation of electron density at various points in a structure. Electron density is expressed in electrons per cubic Å and is highest near atomic centers.

Epitaxy The oriented growth of one crystalline material on a different crystalline substance. The unit cells of the two substances should be similar but need not be identical.

Fourier series A function which is periodic may be represented by a Fourier series. The Fourier theorem states that any periodic function may be resolved into cosine and sine terms involving known constants. Because a crystal has a periodically repeating internal structure, this can be represented, in a mathematically useful way, by a three-dimensional Fourier series.

Fourier synthesis The summation of sine and cosine waves to give a periodic function (for example, the computation of an electron density map from waves of known amplitude, phase, and frequency).

Hexagonal A unit cell is hexagonal if the lengths **a** and **b** are identical and the angle between **a** and **b** is 120°. The other angles between **a** and **c** and between **b** and **c** are 90°.

Least-squares calculations A statistical method of obtaining the best fit of a large number of observations to a given equation. This is done by minimizing the sum of the squares of the deviation of each experimentally observed point from the calculated value. In the case of X-ray crystal analyses, coordinates and thermal parameters may be fit in this way to the observed intensities of the diffracted beam. Ideally, there are at least 10 measurements for each parameter to be determined.

Monoclinic A unit cell is monoclinic if there are no restrictions on the lengths of the unit cell edges, but the angles between **b** and **c** and between **b** and **a** must be 90°. The angle between **a** and **c** may have any value.

Orthorhombic A unit cell is orthorhombic if there are no restrictions on the lengths of the unit cell edges, but all angles between the unit cell edges are 90°.

Patterson map A plot made from the summation of a Fourier series that has the squares of the structure factor amplitudes as coefficients. Because these values can be calculated directly from the intensities, the map can be computed directly. Ideally, the positions of the maxima in the map represent the end points of vectors between atoms, all referred to a common origin.

Phase The difference in position between the crests of two waves of the same wavelength traveling in the same, or nearly the same, direction.

Phase problem The problem of determining the phases to be associated with each diffracted beam, so that the electron density map may be calculated using amplitudes and phases of diffracted beams. The measured intensities of diffracted beams give only the squares of the amplitudes; the phases cannot normally be determined experimentally. They may, however, be calculated for any postulated structure and combined with the experimentally determined amplitudes to give an electron density map.

Resolution The process of distinguishing individual parts of an object when their distances apart are of the order of magnitude of the wavelength of the light used. Most X-ray structures reported in this chapter are determined to 0.5–0.8 Å resolution. At this resolution, each atom is clearly distinct except, possibly, the lightest atom, hydrogen. Protein structures which are calculated at lower resolution, e.g., 3.0 Å, give electron density maps from which individual atoms may not be distinguished. However, the general shape of the molecule and the connectivity of atoms is revealed.

Space group A group of operations which give an infinitely extended regularly repeating pattern, i.e., a group of operations that can convert one molecule into a crystal. There are 230 possible space groups, and information on them is obtained from the diffraction pattern.

Steric hindrance Hindrance between atoms in a molecule resulting in a deformation of the molecule.

Torsion angles The torsion angle (or the angle of twist) about the bond B—C in a series of bonded atoms A—B—C—D is defined as the angle of rotation needed to make the projection of the line B-A coincide with the projection of the line C-D, when viewed along the B-C direction. The positive sense is clockwise.

Unit cell The fundamental portion of a crystal structure that can be repeated infinitely in three dimensions, i.e., the basic building block of the crystal. It is characterized by three vectors, **a, b,** and **c,** which form the edges of a parallelepiped.

van der Waals radii Van der Waals forces are the weak attractive forces between molecules that occur because of the electric polarization induced in each by the presence of the other molecule. Therefore, van der Waals distances between atoms are the closest approaches of these atoms if they are in separate molecules. An analysis of such distances allows a van der Waals radius to be assigned to any atom (roughly twice its covalent radius), so that the van der Waals distance between any two atoms is the sum of their van der Waals radii.

X-ray Electromagnetic radiation of wavelength 0.1–100 Å, produced by bombarding a target (usually metallic) with fast electrons. As a result, electrons from the innermost K shell may be ejected from atoms in the target material. When an electron from an outer shell then moves in to the K shell, energy is emitted in the form of X-rays. The spectrum of this radiation emitted has, therefore, a maximum intensity at a few wavelengths characteristic of the target material. X-Rays can penetrate through various thicknesses of solids and liquids, cause ionization and secondary radiations from any material through which they pass, and produce images on photographic film and fluorescent screens. Their diffraction by atoms arranged regularly in crystals leads to the patterns discussed here.

REFERENCES

Abrahams, S.C. (1977). "World Directory of Crystallographers and of Other Scientists Employing Crystallographic Methods." Polycrystal Book Service, Pittsburgh, Pennsylvania.

Adam, N.K. (1930). "The Physics and Chemistry of Surfaces." Oxford Univ. Press, London and New York.

Adam, N.K., and Rosenheim, O. (1929). *Proc. R. Soc. London, Ser. A* **126,** 25.

Akera, T. (1977). *Science* **198,** 569.

Allen, E., and Doisy, E.A. (1923). *J. Am. Med. Assoc.* **81,** 819.

Altona, C., Geise, H.J., and Romers, C. (1968). *Tetrahedron* **24,** 13.

André, J., Pfeiffer, A., and Rochefort, H. (1976). *Biochemistry* **15,** 2964.

Arya, S.K., and Yang, J.T. (1975). *Biochemistry* **14,** 963.

Barton, D.H.R., Head, A.J., and May, P.J. (1957). *J. Chem. Soc.* p. 935.

Batzold, F.H., and Robinson, C.H. (1975). *J. Am. Chem. Soc.* **97**, 2576.

Batzold, F.H., and Robinson, C.H. (1976). *J. Org. Chem.* **41**, 313.

Batzold, F.H., Benson, A.M., Covey, D.F., Robinson, C.H., and Talalay, P. (1976). *Adv. Enzyme Regul.* **14**, 234.

Benson, A.M., Jarabak, R., and Talalay, P. (1971). *J. Biol. Chem.* **246**, 7514.

Benson, A.M., Talalay, P., Keen, J.H., and Jakoby, W.B. (1977). *Proc. Natl. Acad. Sci. U.S.A.* **74**, 158.

Bernal, J.D. (1932). *Chem. Ind. (London)* **51**, 466.

Bernal, J.D., and Crowfoot, D. (1936). *Z. Kristallogr.*, A **93**, 464.

Bernal, J.D., Crowfoot, D., and Fankuchen, I. (1940). *Philos. Trans. R. Soc. London, Ser. A* **239**, 135.

Bijvoet, J.M., Peerdeman, A.F., and van Bommel, A.J. (1951). *Nature (London)* **168**, 271.

Blackburn, G.M., Flavell, A.J., and Thompson, M.H. (1974). *Cancer Res.* **34**, 2015.

Blackburn, G.M., Thompson, M.H., and King, H.W.S. (1976). *Biochem. J.* **158**, 643.

Blackburn, G.M., Orgee, L., and Williams, G.M. (1977). *J. Chem. Soc., Chem. Commun.* p. 386.

Blundell, T.L., and Johnson, L.N. (1976). "Protein Crystallography." Academic Press, New York.

Booth, J., and Sims, P. (1974). *FEBS Lett.* **47**, 30.

Booth, J., Keysell, G.R., and Sims, P. (1973). *Biochem. Pharmacol.* **22**, 1781.

Brown, J.N., and Trefonas, L.M. (1972). *J. Am. Chem. Soc.* **94**, 4311.

Bucourt, R. (1974). *Top. Stereochem.* **8**, 159.

Bunn, C.W. (1961). "Chemical Crystallography. An Introduction to Optical and X-Ray Methods." Oxford Univ. Press, London and New York.

Busetta, B., and Hospital, M. (1972). *Acta Crystallogr., Sect. B* **28**, 560.

Busetta, B., Courseille, C., Geoffre, S., and Hospital, M. (1972a). *Acta Crystallogr., Sect. B* **28**, 1349.

Busetta, B., Courseille, C., Leroy, F., and Hospital, M. (1972b). *Acta Crystallogr., Sect. B* **28**, 3293.

Busetta, B., Courseille, C., Fornies-Marquina, J.M., and Hospital, M. (1972c). *Cryst. Struct. Commun.* **1**, 43.

Busetta, B., Comberton, G., Courseille, C., and Hospital, M. (1972d). *Cryst. Struct. Commun.* **1**, 129.

Busetta, B., Courseille, C., and Hospital, M. (1973a). *Acta Crystallogr., Sect. B* **29**, 298.

Busetta, B., Courseille, C., and Hospital, M. (1973b). *Acta Crystallogr., Sec. B* **29**, 2456.

Busetta, B., Courseille, C., Precigoux, G., and Hospital, M. (1977). *J. Steroid Biochem.* **8**, 63.

Cake, M.H., and Litwack, G. (1975). *Biochem. Actions Horm.* **3**, 317.

Campsteyn, H., Dupont, L., and Dideberg, O. (1972a). *Acta Crystallogr., Sect. B* **28**, 3032.

Campsteyn, H., Dupont, L., and Dideberg, O. (1972b). *Cryst. Struct. Commun.* **1**, 219.

Cantrell, J.S. (1977). *Am. Crystallogr. Assoc. Summer Meet., Michigan State Univ.* Paper 12.

Carlisle, C.H., and Crowfoot, D. (1945). *Proc. R. Soc. London, Ser. A* **184**, 64.

Carrell, H.L., Glusker, J.P., Covey, D.F., Batzold, F.H., and Robinson, C.H. (1978). *J. Am. Chem. Soc.* **100**, 4282.

Castañeda, E., and Liao, S. (1975). *J. Biol. Chem.* **250**, 883.

Chandross, R.J., and Bordner, J. (1974). *Acta Crystallogr., Sect. B* **30**, 1581.

Chandross, R.J., and Bordner, J. (1975). *Acta Crystallogr., Sect. B* **31**, 928.

Chernayaev, G.A., Barkova, T.I., Egorova, V.V., Sorokina, I.B., Ananchenko, S.N., Mataradze, G.D., Sokolova, N.A., and Rozen, V.B. (1975). *J. Steroid Biochem.* **6**, 1483.

Chevreul, M. (1815). *Justus Liebigs Ann. Chem.* **98**, 5.

Chin. C.-C., Dence, J.B., and Warren, J.C. (1976). *J. Biol. Chem.* **251**, 3700.

Chin, R.-C., and Kidson, C. (1971). *Proc. Natl. Acad. Sci. U.S.A.* **68**, 2448.

Cody, V., DeJarnette, F., Duax, W.L., and Norton, D.A. (1971). *Acta Crystallogr.*, *Sect. B* **27**, 2458.

Comstock, J.P., Rosenfeld, G.C., O'Malley, B.W., and Means, A.R. (1972). *Proc. Natl. Acad. Sci. U.S.A.* **69**, 2377.

Cook, J.W., and Dodds, E.C. (1933). *Nature (London)* **131**, 205.

Coombs, M.M., McPartlin, E.M., and Clayton, A.F.D. (1976a). Imperial Cancer Research Fund. Scientific Report to the Council by the Director of Research for the year 1976.

Coombs, M.M., Kissonerghis, A.M., and Allen, J.A. (1976b). *Cancer Res.* **36**, 4387.

Cooper, A., Gopalakrishna, E.M., and Norton, D.A. (1968). *Acta Crystallogr.*, *Sect. B* **24**, 935.

Cooper, A., Norton, D.A., and Hauptman, H. (1969a). *Acta Crystallogr.*, *Sect. B* **25**, 814.

Cooper, A., Kartha, G., Gopalakrishna, E.M., and Norton, D.A. (1969b). *Acta Crystallogr.*, *Sect. B* **25**, 2409.

Costlow, M.E., Buschow, R.A., McGuire, W.L. (1976). *Cancer Res.* **36**, 3324.

Courseille, C., Precigoux, G., Leroy, F., and Busetta, B. (1973a). *Cryst. Struct. Commun.* **2**, 441.

Courseille, C., Busetta, B., Precigoux, G., and Hospital, M. (1973b). *Acta Crystallogr.*, *Sect. B* **29**, 2462.

Covey, D.F., and Robinson, C.H. (1976). *J. Am. Chem. Soc.* **98**, 5038.

Craig, A.M., and Isenberg, I. (1970a). *Biopolymers* **9**, 689.

Craig, A.M., and Isenberg, I. (1970b). *Proc. Natl. Acad. Sci. U.S.A.* **67**, 1337.

Craven, B.M. (1976). *Nature (London)* **260**, 727.

Damiani, A., De Santis, P., Giglio, E., Liquori, A.M., Puliti, R., and Ripamonti, A. (1965). *Acta Crystallogr.* **19**, 340.

Davis, M., and Hassel, O. (1963). *Acta Chem. Scand.* **17**, 1181.

DeAngelis, N.J., Doyne, T.H., and Grob, R.L. (1975). *Acta Crystallogr.*, *Sect. B* **31**, 2040.

Dearing, A., and Rollett, J.S. (1977). *Eur. Crystallogr. Meet.*, *4th, 1977* Paper S3.3.

DeBaun, J.R., Miller, E.C., and Miller, J.A. (1970). *Cancer Res.* **30**, 577.

DeLuca, H.F. (1976). *J. Lab. Clin. Med.* **87**, 7.

Demel, R.A., and de Kruyff, B. (1976). *Biochim. Biophys. Acta* **457**, 109.

De Sanctis, S.C., Giglio, E., Pavel, V., and Quagliata, C. (1972). *Acta Crystallogr.*, *Sect. B* **28**, 3656.

Dideberg, O., and Dupont, L. (1972). *Acta Crystallogr.*, *Sect. B* **28**, 3014.

Dideberg, O., Dupont, L., and Campsteyn, H. (1975). *Acta Crystallogr.*, *Sect. B* **31**, 637.

Dideberg, O., Dupont, L., and Campsteyn, H. (1976). *J. Steroid Biochem.* **7**, 757.

Duax, W.L. (1972). *Acta Crystallogr.*, *Sect. B* **28**, 1864.

Duax, W.L., and Hauptman, H. (1972). *J. Am. Chem. Soc.* **94**, 5467.

Duax, W.L., and Norton, D.A., eds. (1975). "Atlas of Steroid Structure," Vol. 1. Plenum, New York.

Duax, W.L., Eger, C., Pokrywiecki, S., and Osawa, Y. (1971a). *J. Med. Chem.* **14**, 295.

Duax, W.L., Norton, D.A., Pokrywiecki, S., and Eger, C. (1971b). *Steroids* **18**, 525.

Duax, W.L., Weeks, C.M., and Rohrer, D.C. (1975). *Top. Stereochem.* **9**, 271.

Duax, W.L., Weeks, C.M., and Rohrer, D.C. (1976a). *Recent Prog. Horm. Res.* **32**, 81.

Duax, W.L., Griffin, J.F., and Wolff, M.E. (1976b). *Cryst. Struct. Commun.* **5**, 279.

Duax, W.L., Weeks, C.M., Rohrer, D.C., and Griffin, J.F. (1977). *In* "Identification, Functional Analysis, and Drug Design" (V.H.T. James, ed.), Vol. 2, p. 565. Excerpta Med. Found., Amsterdam.

Duax, W.L., Cody, V., Griffin, J.F., Rohrer, D.C., and Weeks, C.M. (1978). *J. Toxicol. Environ. Health* **4**, 205.

Dvorak, D.J., Kidson, C., and Chin, R.-C. (1976). *J. Biol. Chem.* **251**, 6730.

Edelman, I.S. (1975). *J. Steroid Biochem.* **6**, 147.

Ernst, S., and Hite, G. (1976). *Acta Crystallogr., Sect. B* **32**, 291.

Fawcett, J.K., and Trotter, J. (1966). *J. Chem. Soc. B* p. 174.

Fieser, L.F., and Fieser, M. (1959). "Steroids." Van Nostrand-Reinhold, Princeton, New Jersey.

Friedman, N., Lahav, M., Leiserowitz, L., Popovitz-Biro, R., Tang, C.-P., and Zaretzkii, Z. (1975). *J. Chem. Soc., Chem. Commun.* p. 864.

Gallagher, T.F., and Koch, F.C. (1929). *J. Biol. Chem.* **84**, 495.

Gamper, H.B., Tung, A.S.-C., Straub, K., Bartholomew, J.C., and Calvin, M. (1977). *Science* **197**, 671.

Geise, H.J., Altona, C., and Romers, C. (1967). *Tetrahedron* **23**, 439.

Georghiou, P.E. (1977). *Chem. Soc. Rev.* **6**, 83.

Giacomello, G., and Kratky, O. (1936). *Z. Kristallogr., A* **95**, 459.

Gilardi, R.D. (1970). *Acta Crystallogr., Sect. B* **26**, 440.

Gilardi, R.D., and Flippen, J.L. (1973). *Acta Crystallogr., Sect. B* **29**, 1842.

Gilardi, R.D., and Karle, I.L. (1970). *Acta Crystallogr., Sect. B* **26**, 207.

Glusker, J.P., and Trueblood, K.N. (1972). "Crystal Structure Analysis: a Primer." Oxford Univ. Press, London and New York.

Glusker, J.P., Carrell, H.L., Zacharias, D.E., and Harvey, R.G. (1974). *Cancer Biochem. Biophys.* **1**, 43.

Glusker, J.P., Zacharias, D.E., and Carrell, H.L. (1976a). *Cancer Res.* **36**, 2428.

Glusker, J.P., Zacharias, D.E., Carrell, H.L., Fu, P.P., and Harvey, R.G. (1976b). *Cancer Res.* **36**, 3951.

Goldstein, J.L., and Brown, M.S. (1977). *Annu. Rev. Biochem.* **46**, 897.

Guerina, N.G., and Craven, B.M. (1977a). *Am. Crystallogr. Assoc. Winter Meet., Asilomar, California* Paper KA10.

Guerina, N.G., and Craven, B.M. (1977b). *Am. Crystallogr. Assoc. Summer Meet., Mich. State Univ.* Paper N6.

Haddow, A. (1957). *Proc. Can. Cancer Res. Conf.* **2**, 361.

Hamberg, M., Samuelsson, B., Björkhem, I., and Danielson, H. (1974). In "Molecular Mechanisms of Oxygen Activation" (O. Hayaishi, ed.), p. 29. Academic Press, New York.

Havinga, E. (1973). *Experientia* **29**, 1181.

Heizmann, C.W., and Wyss, H.I. (1974). *Arch. Gynaekol.* **216**, 51.

Henry, N.F.M., and Lonsdale, K., eds. (1952). "International Tables for X-Ray Crystallography," Vol. 1. Kynoch Press, Birmingham, England.

Herndon, W.C. (1967). *J. Chem. Educ.* **44**, 724.

Hertz, R. (1976). *Cancer* **38**, 534.

High, D.F., and Kraut, J. (1966). *Acta Crystallogr.* **21**, 88.

Hoffmann, D., Bondinell, W.E., and Wynder, E.L. (1974). *Science* **183**, 215.

Hosoda, H., and Fishman, J. (1974). *J. Am. Chem. Soc.* **96**, 7325.

Hospital, M., Busetta, M., Bucourt, R., Weintraub, H., and Baulieu, E.-E. (1972). *Mol. Pharmacol.* **8**, 438.

Hospital, M., Busetta, M., Courseille, C., and Precigoux, G. (1975). *J. Steroid Chem.* **6**, 221.

Hsu, W.-T., Lin, E.J.S., Harvey, R.G., and Weiss, S.B. (1977). *Proc. Natl. Acad. Sci. U.S.A.* **74**, 3335.

Huber, R., and Hoppe, W. (1965). *Chem. Ber.* **98**, 2403.

Huggins, C., and Yang, N.C. (1962). *Science* **137**, 257.

Iball, J. (1964). *Nature (London)* **201**, 916.

Iball, J., and MacDonald, S.G.G. (1960). *Z. Kristallogr.* **114**, 439.

Iball, J., and Scrimgeour, S.N. (1975). *Acta Crystallogr., Sect. B* **31**, 2517.

Iball, J., and Young, D.W. (1956). *Nature (London)* **177**, 985.

Iball, J., Morgan, C.H., and Zacharias, D.E. (1975). *J. Chem. Soc., Perkin Trans. 2* p. 1271.

Iball, J., Scrimgeour, S.N., and Young, D.W. (1976). *Acta Crystallogr., Sect. B* **32**, 328.

Isaacs, N.W., Motherwell, W.D.S., Coppola, J.C., and Kennard, O. (1972). *J. Chem. Soc., Perkin Trans. 2* p. 2335.

IUPAC-IUB (1972). *Pure Appl. Chem.* **31**, 285.

Jones, D.W., and Sowden, J.M. (1976). *Cancer Biochem. Biophys.* **1**, 281.

Karle, I.L., and Karle, J. (1969a). *Acta Crystallogr., Sect. B* **25**, 434.

Karle, I.L., and Karle, J. (1969b). *Acta Crystallogr., Sect. B* **25**, 428.

Karle, J. (1973). *In* "Modern Methods of Steroid Analysis" (E. Heftmann, ed.), p. 293. Academic Press, New York.

Keightley, D.D., and Okey, A.B. (1973). *Cancer Res.* **33**, 2637.

Kelly, W.G., Judd, D., and Stolee, A. (1977). *Biochemistry* **16**, 140.

Kennard, O., and Watson, D.G., eds. (1970–1977). "Molecular Structures and Dimensions," Vols. 1–8. N.V.A. Oosthoek's Uitgevers Mij Utrecht (1970, 1970, 1971, 1973, 1974, 1975, 1976, 1977 resp.).

Kennard, O., Watson, D.G., Allen, F.H., Motherwell, W.D.S., Town, W.G., and Rogers, J.R. (1975). *Chem. Br.* **11**, 213.

Kennaway, E.L., and Cook, J.W. (1932). *Chem. Ind. (London)* **51**, 521.

Kidson, C., Cohen, P., and Chin, R.-C. (1971). *In* "The Sex Steroids. Molecular Mechanisms" (K.W. McKerns, ed.), p. 421. Meredith Corporation, New York.

Kilbourn, B.T., and Owston, P.G. (1970). *J. Chem. Soc.* B p. 1.

Kim, S.H., Quigley, G.J., Suddath, F.L., McPherson, A., Snedden, D., Kim, J.J., Weinzierl, J., and Rich, A. (1973). *Science* **179**, 285.

Kim, S.H., Suddath, F.L., Quigley, G.J., McPherson, A., Sussman, J.L., Wang, A.H.J., Seeman, N.C., and Rich, A. (1974). *Science* **185**, 435.

King, C.M., and Phillips, B. (1968). *Science* **159**, 1351.

King, H.W.S., Osborne, M.R., Beland, F.A., Harvey, R.G., and Brooks, P. (1976). *Proc. Natl. Acad. Sci. U.S.A.* **73**, 2679.

King, R.J.B., and Mainwaring, W.I.P. (1974). "Steroid-cell Interactions." Univ. Park Press, Baltimore, Maryland.

Kodicek, E. (1974). *Lancet* **1**, 325.

Kontula, K., Janne, O., Vihko, R., De Jager, E., De Visser, J., and Zeelen, F. (1975). *Acta Endocrinol. (Copenhagen)* **78**, 574.

Lacassagne, A. (1932). *C. R. Hebd. Seances Acad. Sci., Ser. B* **195**, 630.

La Mar, G., and Budd, D.L. (1974). *J. Am. Chem. Soc.* **96**, 7317.

Langmuir, I. (1916). *J. Am. Chem. Soc.* **38**, 2221.

Leake, R. (1976). *Trends Biochem. Sci.* **1**, 137.

Lee, D.L., Kollman, P.A., Marsh, F.J., and Wolff, M.E. (1977). *J. Med. Chem.* **20**, 1139.

Lerman, L.S. (1964). *J. Cell. Comp. Physiol.* **64**, Suppl. 1, 1.

Lesko, S., Caspary, W., Lorentzen, R., and Ts'o, P.O.P. (1975). *Biochemistry* **14**, 3978.

Levin, W., Wood, A.W., Jagi, H., Dansette, P.M., Jerina, D.M., and Conney, A.H. (1976). *Proc. Natl. Acad. Sci. U.S.A.* **73**, 243.

Levin, W., Wood, A.W., Chang, R.L., Slaga, T.J., Yaji, H., Jerina, D.M., and Conney, A.H. (1977). *Cancer Res.* **37**, 2721.

Liao, S. (1975). *Int. Rev. Cytol.* **41**, 87.

Liao, S. (1976). *In* "Receptors and Mechanism of Action of Steroid Hormones" (J.R. Pasqualini, ed.), Part I, Chapter 5, p. 159. Dekker, New York.

Liao, S., Liang, T., Fang, S., Castañeda, E., and Shao, T.-C. (1973). *J. Biol. Chem.* **248**, 6154.

Lin, E.C.C., and Knox, W.E. (1957). *Proc. Soc. Exp. Biol. Med.* **96**, 501.

Lin, E.C.C., and Knox, W.E. (1958). *J. Biol. Chem.* **233**, 1186.

Lingeman, C.H. (1976). *J. Am. Med. Assoc.* **236**, 1690.

Litwack, G., Filler, R., Rosenfield, S., Lichtash, N., Wishman, C.A., and Singer, S. (1973). *J. Biol. Chem.* **248**, 7481.

Lorentzen, R.J., Caspary, W.J., Lesko, S.A., and Ts'o, P.O.P. (1975). *Biochemistry* **14**, 3970.

Lyttle, C.R., and DeSombre, E.R. (1977). *Proc. Natl. Acad. Sci. U.S.A.* **74**, 3162.

Madhok, T.C., Schnoes, H.K., and DeLuca, H.F. (1977). *Biochemistry* **16**, 2142.

Mainigi, K.D. and Sorof, S. (1977). *Proc. Natl. Acad. Sci. U.S.A.* **74**, 2293.

Malaveille, C., Tierney, B., Grover, P.L., Sims, P., and Bartsch, H. (1977). *Biochem. Biophys. Res. Commun.* **75**, 427.

Marx, J.L. (1976). *Science* **191**, 838.

Metzler, M. (1975). *Biochem. Pharmacol.* **24**, 1449.

Mornon, J.-P., Delettré, J., Lepicard, G., Bally, R., Surcouf, E., and Bondot, P. (1977). *J. Steroid Biochem.* **8**, 51.

Moudgil, V.K., and Toft, D.O. (1976). *Proc. Natl. Acad. Sci. U.S.A.* **73**, 3443.

Moudgil, V.K., and Toft, D.O. (1977). *Biochim. Biophys. Acta* **490**, 477.

Nagata, C., Yusaka, T., and Kodema, M. (1974). *In* "Chemical Carcinogenesis" (P.O.P. Ts'o and J.A. Di Paolo, eds.), Part A, p. 87. Dekker, New York.

Nakanishi, K., Kasai, H., Cho, H., Harvey, R.G., Jeffrey, A.M., Jennette, K.W., and Weinstein, I.B. (1977). *J. Am. Chem. Soc.* **99**, 258.

Narisawa, T., Magadia, N.E., Weisburger, J.H., and Wynder, E.L. (1974). *J. Natl. Cancer Inst.* **55**, 1093.

Neidle, S., Achari, A., Taylor, G.L., Berman, H.M., Carrell, H.L., Glusker, J.P., and Stallings, W.C., Jr. (1977). *Nature (London)* **269**, 304.

Norman, A.W., Procsal, D.A., Okamura, W.K., and Wing, R.M. (1975). *J. Steroid Biochem.* **6**, 461.

Notides, A.C., and Nielsen, S. (1974). *J. Biol. Chem.* **249**, 1866.

Oberhänsli, von W.E., and Robertson, J.M. (1967). *Helv. Chim. Acta* **50**, 53.

Okamura, W.H., Norman, A.W., and Wing, R.M. (1974). *Proc. Natl. Acad. Sci. U.S.A.* **71**, 4194.

O'Malley, B.W., Rosenfeld, G.C., Comstock, J.P., and Means, A.R. (1972). *Nature (London), New Biol.* **240**, 45.

Osawa, Y. (1973). *Endocrinol., Proc. Int. Congr., 4th, 1972* p. 814.

Osawa, Y., Shibata, K., Rohrer, D., Weeks, C., and Duax, W.L. (1975). *J. Am. Chem. Soc.* **97**, 4400.

Peck, D., Langs, D.A., Eger, C., and Duax, W.L. (1974). *Cryst. Struct. Commun.* **3**, 573.

Precigoux, G., Hospital, M., and Van den Bosche, G. (1973). *Cryst. Struct. Commun.* **2**, 435.

Precigoux, G., Busetta, B., Courseille, C., and Hospital, M. (1975). *Acta Crystallogr., Sect. B* **31**, 1527.

Quigley, G.J., Wang, A.H. J., Seeman, N.C., Suddath, F.L., Rich, A., Sussman, J.L., and Kim, S.H. (1975). *Proc. Natl. Acad. Sci. U.S.A.* **72**, 4866.

Reddy, B.S., Narisawa, T., and Weisburger, J.H. (1976). *J. Natl. Cancer Inst.* **56**, 441.

Reddy, B.S., Martin, C.W., and Wynder, E.L. (1977). *Cancer Res.* **37**, 1697.

Roberts, P.J., Coppola, J.C., Isaacs, N.W., and Kennard, O. (1973a). *J. Chem. Soc., Perkin Trans.* 2 p. 774.

Roberts, P.J., Pettersen, R.C., Sheldrick, G.M., Isaacs, N.W., and Kennard, O. (1973b). *J. Chem. Soc., Perkin Trans.* 2 p. 1978.

Robertus, J.D., Ladner, J.E., Finch, J.T., Rhodes, D., Brown, R.S., Clark, B.F.C., and Klug, A. (1974). *Nature (London)* **250**, 546.

Rochefort, H. and Capony, F. (1977). *Biochem. Biophys. Res. Commun.* **75**, 277.

Rohrer, D.C., and Fullerton, D.S. (1978). *Am. Crystallogr. Assoc. Winter Meet.*, *Univ. Okla.* Paper J1.

Rohrer, D.C., Duax, W.L., and Osawa, Y. (1976). *Acta Crystallogr.*, *Sect. B* **32**, 2410.

Romers, C., Altona, C., Jacobs, H.J.C., and de Graaf, R.A.G. (1974). *Terpenoids Steroids* **4**, 531.

Rosenheim, O., and King, H. (1932). *Chem. Ind. (London)* **51**, 464.

Rosenheim, O., and King, H. (1934). *Annu. Rev. Biochem.* **3**, 87.

Rousseau, G., Baxter, J. and Tomkins, G. (1972). *J. Mol. Biol.* **67**, 99.

Samuels, H.H., and Tomkins, G.M. (1970). *J. Mol. Biol.* **52**, 57.

Sayre, D., and Friedlander, P.H. (1960). *Nature (London)* **187**, 139.

Schneider, S.L., Alks, V., Morreal, C.E., Sinha, D.K., and Dao, T.L. (1976). *J. Natl. Cancer Inst.* **57**, 1351.

Schrader, W.T., Coty, W.A., Smith, R.G., and O'Malley, B.W. (1977). *Ann. N.Y. Acad. Sci.* **286**, 64.

Segaloff, A. (1975). *J. Steroid Biochem.* **6**, 171.

Shefter, E. (1968). *Science* **169**, 1351.

Sheridan, P.J. (1975). *Life Sci.* **17**, 497.

Sherman, M.R., Atienza, S.B.P., Shansky, J.R., and Hoffman, L.M. (1974). *J. Biol. Chem.* **249**, 5351.

Shieh, H.S., Hoard, L.G., and Nordman, C.E. (1977). *Nature (London)* **267**, 287.

Smith, G.J., Ohl, V.S., and Litwack, G. (1977). *Cancer Res.* **37**, 8.

Sobell, H.M., Tsai, C.-C., Gilbert, S.G., Jain, S.C., and Sakore, T.D. (1976). *Proc. Natl. Acad. Sci. U.S.A.* **73**, 3068.

Sobell, H.M., Jain, S.C., Reddy, B.S., Sakore, T.D., Bhandary, K.K., Seshadri, T.P., and Tsai, C.-C. (1978). *Am. Crystallogr. Assoc. Winter Meet.*, *Univ. Oklahoma* Paper F4.

Stout, G.H., and Jensen, L.H. (1968). "X-ray Structure Determination. A Practical Guide." Macmillan, New York.

Sunshine, G.H., Rabin, B.R., and Williams, D.J. (1971). *Nature (London)* **230**, 133.

Talalay, P., and Benson, A.M. (1972). In "The Enzymes" (P.D. Boyer, ed.), 3rd ed., Vol. 6, p. 591. Academic Press, New York.

Tipping, E., Ketterer, B., Christodoulides, L., and Enderby, G. (1976). *Eur. J. Biochem.* **67**, 583.

Toft, D. O. (1973). *Obstet. Gynecol. Annu.* **2**, 405.

Toft, D.O., and Spelsberg, T.C. (1972). *Cancer Res.* **32**, 2743.

Trinh-Toan, DeLuca, H.F., and Dahl, L.F. (1976). *J. Org. Chem.* **41**, 3476.

Tsibris, J.C.M. and McGuire, P.M. (1977). *Biochem. Biophys. Res. Commun.* **78**, 411.

van Soest, T.C., and Peerdeman, A.F. (1970a). *Acta Crystallogr.*, *Sect. B* **26**, 1940.

van Soest, T.C., and Peerdeman, A.F. (1970b). *Acta Crystallogr.*, *Sect. B* **26**, 1947.

Weber, H.P., and Galantay, E. (1972). *Helv. Chim. Acta* **55**, 544.

Weeks, C.M. (1970). *Acta Crystallogr.*, *Sect. B* **26**, 429–433.

Weeks, C.M., and Duax, W.L. (1973). *Acta Crystallogr.*, *Sect. B* **29**, 2210.

Weeks, C.M., Cooper, A., Norton, D.A., Hauptman, H., and Fisher, J. (1971). *Acta Crystallogr.*, *Sect. B* **27**, 1562.

Weeks, C.M., Duax, W.L., and Wolff, M.E. (1973). *J. Am. Chem. Soc.* **95**, 2865.

Weeks, C.M., Duax, W.L., and Wolff, M.E. (1974). *Acta Crystallogr.*, *Sect. B* **30**, 2516.

Weeks, C.M., Rohrer, D.C., and Duax, W.L. (1975a). *Science* **190**, 1096.

Weeks, C.M., Rohrer, D.C., Duax, W.L., Osawa, Y., and Soriano, M. (1975b). *Acta Crystallogr.*, *Sect. B* **31**, 2525.

Weeks, C.M., Erman, M.G., and Duax, W.L. (1975c). *Cryst. Struct. Commun.* **4**, 637.

Weeks, C.M. Hazel, J.P., and Duax, W.L. (1976). *Cryst. Struct. Commun.* **5**, 271.

Weeks, C.M., Griffin, J.F., and Duax, W.L. (1977). *Am. Crystallogr. Assoc. Summer Meet.*, *Mich. State Univ.* Paper PB6.

Westbrook, E.M. (1976). *J. Mol. Biol.* **103**, 659.

Westbrook, E.M., Sigler, P.B., Berman, H., Glusker, J.P., Bunick, G., Benson, A.M., and Talalay, P. (1976). *J. Mol. Biol.* **103**, 665.

Wieland, H. (1929). *Z. Angew. Chem.* **42**, 421.

Wieland, H., and Dane, E. (1933). *Hoppe-Seyler's Z. Physiol. Chem.* **216**, 91.

Wieland, H., and Sorge, H. (1916). *Hoppe-Seyler's Z. Physiol. Chem.* **96**, 1.

Williams, D.J., and Rabin, B.R. (1971). *Nature (London)* **232**, 102.

Windaus, A. (1932). *Annu. Rev. Biochem.* **1**, 109.

Wing, R.M., Okamura, W.H., Rego, A., Pirio, M.R., and Norman, A.W. (1975). *J. Am. Chem. Soc.* **97**, 4980.

Wislocki, P.G., Chang, R.L., Woods, A.W., Levin, W., Yagi, H., Hernandez, O., Mah, H.D., Dansette, P.M., Jerina, D.M., and Conney, A.H. (1977). *Cancer Res.* **37**, 2608.

Yang, N.C., Castro, A.J., Lewis, M., and Wong, T.-W. (1961). *Science* **134**, 386.

Yang, S.K., McCourt, D.W., Roller, P.P., and Gelboin, H.V. (1976). *Proc. Natl. Acad. Sci. U.S.A.* **73**, 2594.

Zacharias, D.E., Glusker, J.P., Harvey, R.G., and Fu, P.P. (1977). *Cancer Res.* **37**, 775.

CHAPTER 4

Modulation of Chemical Carcinogenesis by Hormones

Russell Hilf

I. INTRODUCTION

The purpose of this chapter will be to review those data that implicate a role of hormones in the neoplastic transformation of cells and organs. It should be indicated at the outset that in so doing, certain limitations are required in defining the term "role" when discussing hormones. In mammals, hormones play a vital role in development, differentiation, homeostasis, survival, and reproduction. Because hormones circulate throughout the body, they can interact with all tissues and cells and not just with those that are usually classified as "target cells." Such hormone–cell interactions may be important for maintenance of cells' well-being or, conversely, they may result in an altered state, making the cell more susceptible to neoplastic transformation by other agents. Whether hormones per se are carcinogenic is a critical question, and the literature is replete with papers claiming or disclaiming the carcinogenic potential of certain estrogens, as just one example. It will not be the purpose here to enter into this discussion directly but only as it may serve as a background when considering hormonal actions at the cellular level. The reader interested in the carcinogenic potential of sex hormones is directed to an IARC monograph (World Health Organization, 1974), which is an excellent overview of data at the time that the monograph was compiled.

Berenblum (1974), in his book on carcinogenesis, treats hormones primarily as "modifying or permissive influences," for they may act at the level of the action of the carcinogen or on the host. A further distinction is needed, as hormones may alter the target prior to neoplastic transformation or may enhance (or inhibit) the growth of the neoplasm after transformation. Examples of these effects are readily realized in the role of estrogens in the induction and growth of mammary tumors induced by administration of the polycyclic hydrocarbons such as 3-methylcholanthrene or 7,12-dimethylbenz[a]anthracene, data that will be presented below. Because many hormones exert trophic effects on target tissues, their presence may be essential for the preservation of a sufficiently constituted target organ to respond to neoplastic transformation. Such a case may be exemplified by the difference in incidence of breast cancer in men and women, the former being about 1% of the latter (Silverberg, 1977). If one eliminates the possibility that the hormones are carcinogenic in themselves, one can reason that the difference in susceptibility for cancer of the breast is a result of the normal physiological role of ovarian hormones in stimulating and maintaining the breast while awaiting its function in lactation. Thus, many endocrine target tissues can be termed "dependent," and dependence may reside at more than one level of the overall hormone network; i.e., thyroid function and control is dependent on thyrotrophin-stimulating hormone (TSH) and thyrotrophin-releasing hormone (TRH) as primary and secondary stimulators. Most hormonal secretion is regulated by feedback control mechanisms (although feed-forward interactions are also known); one must therefore keep in mind the potential alteration in hormonal milieu that arises on perturbation of the homeostatic situation. While many of these concerns have been and will be expressed when dealing with carcinogenesis regarding the breast, these factors should be kept in mind for other target tissues of carcinogens.

II. MAMMARY GLAND

Cancer of the breast leads all other sites of cancer in this country; females have the highest probability for developing breast cancer and are more likely eventually to die of this disease than of cancer of any other organ (Silverberg, 1977). There has therefore been a major scientific effort to elucidate the causes, course, diagnosis, and therapy of this disease. Experimental scientists have also found that certain strains of mice had a very high incidence of the disease and further, that mammary cancer in the rat could occur spontaneously, as well as by exposure to certain agents. It would appear that chemical carcinogens, X-irradiation, viruses, and perhaps hormones themselves, along with unknown genetic factors, can be identified as agents in the etiology of the disease, depending on the experimental setting; all must be considered as potential carcinogens for the human. One must also consider that the biological aspects of the disease may be different in different physiological settings—e.g., in premenopausal vs. postmenopausal women—and that the same etiological agent may give rise to different morphological entities.

A. NORMAL MAMMARY GLAND

Before discussing the influence of hormones on tumorigenesis, it is advisable to review briefly the hormonal and functional aspects of the normal breast. The mammary gland undergoes striking morphological and biochemical changes as a result of hormonal stimulation, the best known being those during pregnancy and postparturition. Fetal development of the gland, studied primarily in the mouse (Raynaud, 1961, 1971), gives rise to similar mammary buds in female and male. In the female, the ectoderm grows and forms a primary mammary cord, which is the precursor of the duct system; in the male, this is suppressed by androgens, and sensitivity to androgens was found to occur at 13–15 days of gestation (Kratochwil, 1971). At puberty, mammary gland growth accelerates in concert with ovarian cyclicity, with growth of duct systems seen in rats and mice; estrogen, glucocorticoids, and growth hormone are required. The bulk of the human mammary gland at puberty and postpuberty is adipose tissue. During pregnancy, proliferation of the lobulo-alveolar system occurs; in the rat, estrogen, progesterone, glucocorticoids, growth hormone, and prolactin all appear to be necessary (Lyons *et al.*, 1958). During pregnancy, placental hormones such as chorionic somatomammotrophin also influence mammary growth. Thus, prior to parturition, the gland presents as one which has undergone considerable epithelial cell multiplication at the expense of reduced adipose tissue.

At parturition, with the onset of lactogenesis, striking biochemical alterations occur, as measured by the marked increases in certain enzymes and in
the metabolic components directed toward the production of milk. Hormonal requirements for lactation vary depending on the species examined.
In rabbits, only prolactin is necessary; in mice and rats, prolactin and
glucocorticoids are needed; and in goats, prolactin, glucocorticoids, and
growth hormone are required. Milk contains several unique components,
and study of these and their control by hormones has provided valuable
information on the function of the normal gland. The major milk proteins—
casein(s), β-lactoglobulin, and α-lactalbumin—are actively synthesized in
the rough endoplasmic reticulum (RER), formed into protein granules in the
Golgi apparatus, and discharged into the lumen by exocytosis. Fatty acids
are synthesized from glucose in rats and probably in man, but ruminants
utilize acetate and β-hydroxybutyrate. The high proportion of short and
medium-chain (C_4-C_{12}) fatty acids in milk is another unique biochemical
marker; esterification of the fatty acids with glycerol also occurs in the RER,
and fat droplets are secreted into the lumen by an apocrinelike process. The
reader is directed for further details to several recent books on lactation
(Cowie and Tindal, 1971; Falconer, 1971; Josimovich *et al.*, 1974; Kretchmer
and Rossi, 1974; Larson and Smith, 1974).

Another unique product in milk is lactose, and its synthesis and the role of
hormones thereon have been recently elucidated. The final step in lactose
synthesis is controlled by the enzyme lactose synthetase, which catalyzes the
reaction of UDP-galactose plus glucose to yield lactose plus UDP. Lactose
synthetase was found to be composed of two proteins: An A protein, which is
a galactosyl transferase and found throughout the body, and a B protein,
which is α-lactalbumin. Through the pioneering studies of Ebner and his
co-workers, the following sequence has been elucidated: The catalytic unit
(A protein), galactosyl transferase, usually catalyzes the transfer of galactose
from UDP-galactose to N-acetylglucosamine to form N-acetyllactosamine.
However, in the presence of α-lactalbumin (B protein or specifier protein),
the substrate affinity is altered, such that galactose from UDP-galactose is
transferred to glucose, yielding the milk sugar, lactose. Data have been
obtained to indicate that progesterone can inhibit the induction of
α-lactalbumin synthesis and as such, prevent the formation of lactose (Turkington and Hill, 1969).

Because the highest progesterone levels occur during the last trimester of
pregnancy, lactose synthesis is suppressed. The drop in progesterone prior
to parturition and the further decrease during postparturition, along with the
enhanced secretion of prolactin immediately postpartum, may allow release
of the inhibition of α-lactalbumin synthesis, resulting in the synthesis of
lactose. Thus, a rather unique control mechanism exists in the mammary
gland for the production of lactose.

Another hormonal factor not yet considered is oxytocin, an octapeptide of the posterior pituitary (actually synthesized in the paraventricular nucleus). This hormone acts primarily on the myoepithelial cells, causing them to contract; this response has been called "milk let-down." Stimuli for oxytocin release are neural, with suckling the major stimulus, but it is well known that oxytocin secretion and milk ejection can arise in nursing women at the sight and sound of their baby. After weaning, either by cessation of suckling or by hormonal inhibition of lactation, the biochemical activity of the lactating breast undergoes profound involution, with a return to the quiescent state prior to pregnancy. Once again, epithelial cells become a minor constituent in a gland largely composed of adipose tissue.

B. INDUCTION OF CARCINOMA IN THE BREAST

For the purpose of this review, I will consider chemical and X-irradiation as two different etiological carcinogenic agents. A third agent, viruses, will not be reviewed here, as there exists a most extensive literature on that subject. The fourth, hormones, as a distinct subgroup of chemical carcinogens, will not be discussed; they represent an area of research and dispute that deserves a separate discussion.

Polycyclic Hydrocarbons

Probably the first clear demonstration of chemical induction of breast carcinoma in the rat was the report by Shay *et al.* (1949). These investigators were attempting to induce gastric carcinoma by administration of 3-methylcholanthrene (MC) by gavage to Wistar rats. In a delightfully candid paper, they admit their complete failure to produce a single carcinoma in the stomach or intestine but, to their credit, go on to describe the high incidence (50–70%) of breast adenocarcinoma that arose in noncastrate female animals. That ovarian function is critical to the induction of breast carcinoma by MC was shown by the cancer incidence of 2/19 in intact male rats and 1/20 in castrate male rats and in castrate female animals. They conclude by referring to the importance of the ovaries in the tumorigenic process: "Whether this secretion is important only as it contributes to the adequate development of the breast or whether it serves as a cocarcinogen cannot be stated at the present time." Thus, in one sentence, Shay *et al.* (1949) set the stage for a continuing active scientific effort.

This first report by Shay *et al.* (1949) was followed by another study exploring the effect of various hormones on tumorigenesis by MC. In this latter paper (Shay *et al.*, 1952), the authors conclude that both the incidence and the type of tumor resulting from exposure to MC was influenced by hormones; glandular tumors predominated in female rats or males given estradiol, spindle-cell and collagenous tumors predominated in male rats or females given testosterone, and fibroadenomas predominated in animals "in which the sex hormone effects were experimentally counterbalanced." A careful reinvestigation of induction of mammary tumors in rats was performed by Huggins *et al.* (1959a). Using Sprague–Dawley rats, they identified optimum conditions, based on dosage, timing of administration, and hormonal status, that yielded tumors in 100% of the animals in 60 days or less. They also demonstrated that a majority of the established tumors were hormone-dependent, for tumor mass diminished after ovariectomy, hypophysectomy, or androgen treatment. Some tumors continued to grow after ovariectomy; these were classified as hormone-independent. Of great interest (particularly relevant to the clinical disease) was the observation that the tumor cell population was not always uniform in its response to hormonal alteration of the host; some tumor cells underwent atrophy while adjacent tumor cells in the same lesion continued to grow. Thus, although it had been demonstrated earlier in mice that MC could induce mammary tumors by direct application (Maisin and Coolen, 1936), by oral administration (Prohaska *et al.*, 1949), or by intranasal administration (Orr, 1943), the studies by Shay *et al.* (1949) and the improvements made by Huggins *et al.* (1959a) in the techniques to assure rapid and efficient tumor induction in rats provided the stimulus for extensive investigations on mammary gland carcinogenesis.

A major contribution to the study of carcinogen-induced mammary carcinomas was made by Huggins and his colleagues. In their continuing efforts to simplify the process of administration of carcinogens, they turned to investigation of the effects of a single dose of carcinogen on tumor production and compared the carcinogen potency of MC, 7,12-dimethylbenz[a]anthracene (DMBA), and acetylaminofluorene (AAF) under identical conditions (Huggins *et al.*, 1961). In this report, they demonstrated that a single dose of any of the carcinogens could produce mammary tumors, but that the most effective agent was DMBA; that production of tumors was related directly to dose of carcinogen administered; that the age of the recipient animal was critical for success, with animals around 50 days old proving to be the most susceptible to MC and animals 100 days or older being essentially resistant; and that tumor appearance could be suppressed by hormonal therapy initiated 15 days after gastric instillation of MC. Sydnor *et al.* (1962) demonstrated that, unlike Sprague–Dawley rats, Long–Evans strain rats had a low incidence of mammary tumors when DMBA was administered in a single dose under similar conditions. A genetic difference in susceptibility was apparent, as shown by the response in F_1 hybrids. The ability of a single intragastric dose of DMBA to induce mammary tumors in rats was confirmed by Dao (1962), who also demonstrated the requirement of ovarian function for tumor induction for up to 7 days beyond the time of administration of the carcinogen.

It should be noted, however, that earlier studies by Geyer *et al.* (1950) demonstrated the efficacy of DMBA to induce mammary tumors in rats after multiple injections of the carcinogen. These investigators also reported (Geyer *et al.*, 1953) that an emulsion of DMBA, administered three times for one week and repeated in the same manner three weeks later, resulted in an incidence of mammary tumors of 80%. Somewhat later, Huggins *et al.* (1965) demonstrated that a single intravenous injection of a lipid emulsion of DMBA was equally effective as a single dose given by gastric instillation, and they cited the advantage of the intravenous technique as more convenient, less hazardous, and less costly, because smaller doses were required. Thus, investigators could select either the oral or the intravenous route of administration for DMBA to produce a high yield of mammary carcinomas.

It would be improper to leave the impression that MC and DMBA are the only carcinogens that produce mammary tumors. Indeed, the earlier literature clearly demonstrates that 2-acetylaminofluorene (2-AAF) is a mammary gland carcinogen (Weisburger and Weisburger, 1958). Miller *et al.* (1961) demonstrated that the N-hydroxy metabolite of 2-AAF (N-HO-AAF) was more active in producing tumors of the mammary gland than the parent amide. Equimolar doses injected intraperitoneally to immature rats (50–70 g) thrice weekly for 4 weeks gave the following results: at 23 weeks, 2/10 rats had mammary tumors induced by 2-AAF, whereas 10/12 rats had mammary tumors after receiving N-HO-AAF; at 27 weeks, the incidences were 4/10 and 11/12 in animals given 2-AAF and N-HO-AAF, respectively. In a second experiment, at 23 weeks, the mammary tumor incidence was as follows: 2-AAF, 3/16; N-HO-AAF, 16/16; and 1-HO-AAF (another metabolite of 2-AAF), 0/16.

Malejka-Giganti *et al.* (1973) showed that a single topical application of 0.02 nmole of N-HO-AAF to the left thoracic mammary gland of Sprague–Dawley rats resulted in a 70% tumor incidence by 6 months, whereas the same technique yielded a tumor incidence of only 30% when 2-AAF was used. Topical application of N-HO-3-AAF or 3-AAF was said to give tumor yields similar to the 2-isomers, although in this report, 3-AAF induced no tumors and 2-AAF induced tumors in 2/6 rats. In their most recent publication, they did demonstrate that 2-AAF and 3-AAF gave similar tumor yields; 3/18 and 2/18 (tumors/number of rats), respectively (Malejka-Giganti *et al.*, 1977). They confirmed their earlier finding that the N-hydroxy derivatives of 2-AAF were much more potent carcinogens, and extended their study by showing that the N-acetoxy derivatives of 2-AAF and 3-AAF were also carcinogenic. Neither N-HO-AAF nor N-HO-3-AAF produced tumors in ovariectomized rats.

In a recent report, Gullino *et al.* (1975) described their experiments with N-nitrosomethylurea (NMU) as a carcinogenic agent for the induction of mammary tumors. They achieved high incidences of carcinomas in Buffalo, Sprague-Dawley or Fischer rats with a modest latent period (77–94 days) and negligible mortality. Interestingly, they observed metastases to bone marrow and spleen, which continued to grow after surgical removal of the primary lesion. Another interesting demonstration was their finding that almost all the tumors were transplantable to intact or ovariectomized–adrenalectomized hosts; the transplanted tumors also demonstrated the ability to metastasize. Castration of the female host prior to NMU administration yielded a negligible incidence of tumors, whereas removal of ovaries 1 day after the last injection of NMU did not alter tumor incidence, although the appearance of tumors was delayed and the average number of lesions per animal was reduced. Ovarian dependence of the majority of established tumors was demonstrated on the basis of regression or arrest of growth subsequent to ovariectomy, adrenalectomy, or both surgical ablative procedures.

C. Uptake by Mammary Gland of Carcinogens

Since the finding of high incidences of mammary tumors after administration of the carcinogens, several investigators logically turned their attention to ascertaining the uptake of the carcinogen by the target tissue. Initial experiments involved the estimation of the amount of carcinogen present in the mammary gland after a fixed or several time periods.

1. 3-Methylcholanthrene

Shortly after their initial report on the ability of MC to induce breast cancer, Shay et al. (1950) examined mammary glands of lactating rats treated with daily doses of MC (8 mg/day for 10 days). Using a spectrophotometric assay, they found that MC was excreted through the milk and could be recovered from the stomachs of the nursing pups. Recovery of carcinogen was higher when MC was administered intravenously vs. orally, suggesting that there was a loss of carcinogen via the feces.

Dao et al. (1959) developed a quantitative spectrofluorometric assay for MC and analyzed the tissue distribution and time course of MC after a single feeding of MC. From the former experiment, they concluded that the carcinogen concentrated in the breast and fat of virgin female rats, and that the level of MC in other tissues was either low or not measurable. They also demonstrated that MC persisted in the breast for at least 8 days after it was administered, although it was there in low levels (about 1/10 that found at the highest level seen 1 day after feeding the carcinogen).

Shortly thereafter, Flesher and Sydnor (1960) synthesized tritiated MC with a high radiospecific activity, administered it by gastric intubation (19 mg), and examined the distribution of labeled carcinogen 24 hours after administration. They found less than 2% of the radioactivity in the tissues analyzed, with 60–90% of the radioactivity in gastric and intestinal contents and in feces and 4–5% in the urine. Approximately 0.1% of the administered MC was found in the breast, and this was calculated to represent about 5–7 μg MC per gm mammary tissue. Following the animals for a longer period, they reported that significant quantities of tritium-labeled material appeared in the urine for 13–17 days and in feces for 7–11 days after administration of the carcinogen.

Bock and Dao (1961) observed that the concentrations of MC in mammary tissue after one feeding (30 mg) were not notably different than after 10 daily doses of 10 mg MC. The levels of MC in breast tissue were lower in pregnant animals, whereas, compared to intact animals, the levels in mammary tissue from castrate or hypophysectomized rats were higher. There was little difference between male and female animals. They suggested that the mammary fat pad may act as a lipid trap, retaining the carcinogen and then releasing it slowly. Wieder *et al.* (1967) confirmed the findings of Bock and Dao (1961) that repeated daily doses of MC did not show a higher uptake of carcinogen in mammary glands than a single dose of MC, but Wieder *et al.* (1967) did report that levels of MC in mammary fat pads were higher in female vs. male rats. They concluded that no simple relationship existed between carcinogen levels and carcinogenic response.

2. 7,12-Dimethylbenz[a]anthracene

With the report of the carcinogenic efficacy of a single dose of DMBA, attention was given to the study of distribution of DMBA. Lo (1964) administered [^{14}C]DMBA intravenously (2–3 mg per dose) to 4 month old female rats and found little accumulation in the mammary gland; three doses gave the same result. Furthermore, ovariectomy or pregnancy did not influence the distribution of DMBA in the organs studied. High initial accumulation of labeled DMBA was observed in ovaries, adrenals, liver, kidney, and spleen at 1 hour after administration of the carcinogen, and this was followed by a gradual decrease. In a study comparing DMBA with MC, Wieder *et al.* (1967) used fluorescence techniques to measure uptake and retention of the two carcinogens. After a single intragastric dose, DMBA levels reached a peak at 16 hours in axillary and inguinal mammary fat pads, declining thereafter to 25% of the peak value at 1 week. The peak value for DMBA was lower than that seen for MC, and DMBA was eliminated faster from these tissues than MC. Thus, there appeared to be an inverse relationship between carcinogenic potential and tissue uptake and retention.

Using tritium-labeled DMBA, Flesher (1967) found that the carcinogen accumulated in perirenal fat and mammary gland after a single oral dose. Pretreatment of animals with estradiol and progesterone altered the suscep-

tibility of the gland to tumor formation but did not have any effect on the
amount of radioactivity present in the gland or on the degree of binding of
the labeled carcinogen to nucleic acids and proteins. These results are in
general agreement with those of Gammal *et al.* (1965) and of Hamilton and
Jacobson (1965), in which there was seen a rapid peak of radioactivity in
plasma, reaching a peak at 8–12 hours, followed by retention of radioactivity
in the mammary gland for at least 3 days.

Daniel *et al.* (1967) examined the absorption, distribution, and excretion
of radioactive DMBA, MC, dibenz[*a-h*]anthracene, and dibenz[*a-c*]anthra-
cene, the latter compound not a carcinogen. The general picture was similar for all four hydrocarbons, with the first stage being absorption into
the lymphatics. The adrenals and ovaries took up relatively large quantities
of the labeled compounds, and elimination from these organs was slow relative to other tissues. The mammary glands did not show any appreciable
concentration of radioactive material, but because they are embedded in fat,
the storage of carcinogen in the adjacent fat may be important.

Janss and Moon (1970) recognized that one problem facing the investigation of carcinogen distribution in the mammary gland was the cellular composition of the gland, particularly the large proportion of adipose tissue in
the virgin animal. To resolve this problem, a technique was devised to
separate parenchymal cells from adipose tissue (Moon *et al.*, 1969) by enzymatic dissociation. Using this technique, they (Janss and Moon, 1970)
examined the distribution of labeled DMBA after a single oral feeding of 20
mg to 50 day old virgin rats. They found that maximal specific activity was
reached at 6 hours in the parenchymal cell but at 16 hours in all other tissue
fractions. They concluded that the presence of adipose tissue obscured the
concentration of the carcinogen in the parenchymal cells. Furthermore, the
differences in uptake patterns appeared to be independent of one another,
and this suggested that the uptake of the carcinogen by the adipose tissue
was of minor importance to the uptake of carcinogen by the parenchymal
cell. Thus, the earlier proposal (Dao, 1969b) that the mammary gland
adipose tissue acted as a reservoir for slow release of carcinogen to the
parenchymal cell was not supported by these studies.

In subsequent experiments, Janss *et al.* (1972) examined the binding of
labeled DMBA to protein and DNA of mammary parenchymal cells after
gastric administration of 20 mg of the carcinogen. Parenchymal cells were
isolated, proteins and DNA were extracted and purified, and DMBA bound
to the macromolecules was assessed. Approximately 45–50 pmoles of DMBA
were bound per mg DNA at 16 hours after administration of the carcinogen;
at 14 days, the amount of DMBA/mg DNA was about 50% of that found at
the 16-hour time point; and at 42 days, about 1/3 of the amount of the DMBA
measured at 16 hours was still detectable. Overall, the levels of DMBA
bound to parenchymal cell protein were less than 50% of that bound to DNA

at each time examined. These data indicate a persistent binding of the carcinogen to DNA. It is interesting that in tissues that are less susceptible to transformation by DMBA—i.e., liver, spleen, kidney—the amount of DMBA bound to protein exceeded that bound to DNA (Marquardt *et al.*, 1971; Prodi *et al.*, 1970). However, Brookes and Lawley (1964) have presented evidence to demonstrate a positive correlation between binding of various polycyclic hydrocarbons to mouse skin DNA and their carcinogenic potency. It would appear that the primary macromolecule receptor for DMBA in mammary gland parenchyma may be DNA, but additional investigation is certainly warranted.

Evidence for metabolic alteration of the administered carcinogen is required to identify the ultimate carcinogen, and this should lead to a better understanding of the chemical process of neoplastic transformation. In the case of DMBA, direct exposure of the gland *in vitro* has resulted in the induction of cancer (Brennan *et al.*, 1966; Dao and Sinha, 1972). These results suggest either that metabolism of DMBA takes place in the mammary gland or that no metabolism of DMBA was required to cause transformation.

To explore these findings, Tamulski *et al.* (1973) examined the metabolism of labeled DMBA by preparations of liver and mammary gland (100g supernatant preparations of tissue homogenates). They found that the preparations of mammary gland from 55–60 day old rats were able to metabolize DMBA to 7-hydroxymethyl-12-methylbenz[*a*]anthracene and 12-hydroxymethyl-7-methylbenz[*a*]anthracene, but no 7,12-dihydroxymethylbenz[*a*]anthracene was found, a metabolite identified when liver preparations were used. While it is not known whether the carcinogenic action of DMBA may be attributable to these derivatives, the data imply that metabolic conversion of DMBA can occur in the mammary gland. It will be of interest to learn if these metabolites are carcinogenic.

3. Acetylaminofluorene

Investigation of tissue uptake of labeled 2-AAF has been accomplished. In a study in which uptake and retention of labeled 2-AAF and its N-hydroxy metabolite was examined, Janss and Irving (1972) reported that the tissue levels were higher after injection of 2-AAF than after administration of the N-hydroxy metabolite. When the time course of retention was assessed, there was approximately twice the amount of specific radioactivity in parenchymal mammary gland cells from animals that received N-hydroxy-AAF-9-^{14}C than in comparable cell preparations of animals that received AAF-9-[14]C. Animals receiving AAF-9-^{14}C in the diet showed an early increase (peak at 2 weeks) in the amount of carcinogen bound to DNA of parenchymal cells. During the course of 8 weeks of feeding, the amount of labeled carcinogen bound to DNA did not increase beyond that seen at 2 weeks, whereas the amount of AAF bound to protein gradually rose throughout the time period and exceeded that bound to DNA at 8 weeks. It would appear that binding of the carciogen to cellular macromolecules is essential for carcinogenesis, but which macromolecule target is the most critical is still open to question.

Because 2-AAF is carcinogenic to the mammary gland, the question arose as to what was the ultimate form of the carcinogen in the breast. It had been shown that conjugates of the N-hydroxy metabolites of 2-AAF were reactive in the liver (Irving, 1970). One such candidate for the ultimate carcinogen is the O-sulfonate of N-hydroxy-2-AAF, a metabolite formed by action of a sulfotransferase. Studies by Irving *et al.* (1971) were performed to examine the potential formation of the O-sulfonate derivative of N-hydroxy-2-AAF. Incubation of mammary gland parenchymal cells from immature female rats, or whole gland preparations, with N-hydroxy-2-AAF yielded no detectable sulfonate derivative; this was further supported by data showing that the mammary gland did not possess sulfotransferase activity for the metabolic conversion of N-HO-AAF to the O-sulfonate. As they ruled out the presence in the mammary gland of an endogenous inhibitor of the enzyme or an unusually rapid tissue clearance, they concluded that the O-sulfonate derivative was not the ultimate carcinogen in the mammary gland. These data clearly point out the need for investigation of carcinogen distribution and metabolism at the target organ and caution against generalizations of the carcinogenic process.

D. Influence of Hormones on Mammary Tumorigenesis

Although some aspects of this area have already been alluded to above, a more careful examination is required. In the sections that follow, I will not make a distinction between the types of carcinogens used, knowing full well that this is naive as viewed from metabolic aspects; the influence that different hormones may have on metabolism of chemically diverse carcinogens needs to be considered.

1. Age of Host

Because the mammary gland undergoes development during pubescence, one can consider that the hormonal milieu is quite different in the prepubertal state vs. adulthood. In their earlier paper, Huggins *et al.* (1961) treated Sprague–Dawley rats of various ages with a single dose (66.6 mg/100 gm body weight) of MC and studied the incidence of mammary tumors that arose during an observation period of 150 days. The results obtained were as follows (age at carcinogen feeding, rats with tumors/total rats treated): 23

days, 6/10; 30 days, 8/10; 40 days, 9/10; 50, 55, and 65 days, 10/10; 100 days, 1/10; and 365 days, 1/10. Clearly, the more adult rat was less susceptible to this dose of MC than the younger animal, particularly the animal shortly after the onset of ovarian function (approximately 35–40 days of age). Comparable results were obtained by Dao (1969a) with DMBA (3 mg/100 gm body weight administered intravenously) in Wistar rats studied for 6 months: 56 days, 8/10; 70 days, 7/10; 90 days, 5/10; 120 days, 2/10; 150 days, 0/10; and 175 days, 1/10.

Meranze *et al.* (1969) examined the effects of a single intragastric dose of DMBA on tumor incidence in Wistar rats for a 16 month period. In 50 immature rats (2 weeks old) treated with 0.5–1.0 mg DMBA, 4 carcinomas and 32 fibroadenomas and fibromas were observed; in 25 rats 5–8 weeks of age at the time of DMBA (15 mg) administration, 14 carcinomas and 9 benign lesions were obtained; and in 26 rats, who were 26 weeks old when 15 mg DMBA was given, 4 carcinomas and 5 benign lesions were observed. In an earlier report, these investigators (Gruenstein *et al.*, 1966) had compared the effects of DMBA in Wistar and Sprague–Dawley rats at two ages; 60–80 gm vs. 130–150 gm, the former receiving 15 mg DMBA and the latter 20 mg DMBA. In Wistar rats, 63–65% of the animals had carcinomas and in Sprague–Dawley rats 72–87% had carcinomas, the differences being rather slight in the incidences observed between these two strains of rats. Thus, all the experiments would suggest that the older rat is less susceptible to carcinoma induction by DMBA, and there appears to be a definite time (age) at which the best yield of tumors could be obtained, that time being a few weeks after puberty.

There is a need to examine the basis for the apparent greater sensitivity to carcinogenic transformation of the early postpubertal mammary gland: Does the hormonal environment of the host at that time present some unique condition of ovarian–pituitary balance favoring susceptibility to transformation? Is the biochemistry of the mammary gland peculiar at this time during development of the gland? An investigation of the latter was performed by Nagasawa and Yanai (1974), who examined [³H]thymidine incorporation into DNA of the mammary glands of virgin Sprague–Dawley rats. They reported that a peak in thymidine incorporation was observed in 50 day old rats, and this was significantly higher than that seen in glands from 70, 90, or 110 day old animals. It should be noted that similar values for thymidine incorporation were found in 30 day old animals, animals that do not yield as many DMBA-induced tumors as seen with 50 day old rats.

In a subsequent study, Nagasawa *et al.* (1976) found that thymidine incorporation into DNA was higher on the day of proestrus than on the second day of diestrus in 50 day old rats; tumor number, weight, and growth rate were higher in animals that were in procstrus at the time of administration of

DMBA. Studies of this type will need to be performed in the older rat, i.e., 70 and 90+ day old rat, because the level of thymidine incorporation observed in the 50 day old rats in diestrus was comparable to that reported earlier by these investigators for 70 day old animals, and this does not explain the differences in tumor yield. Thus, additional investigation directed toward elucidation of the biochemistry of the target gland should afford useful insights into the differences in susceptibility to carcinogenic transformation.

2. *Effect of Pregnancy and Lactation*

Several classical studies were done by Dao and his colleagues to investigate the susceptibility of the differentiated mammary gland to chemical carcinogens (Dao and Sunderland, 1959; Dao et al., 1960). Using MC, they found that the tumor yield was significantly reduced when the carcinogen was administered to pregnant or lactating rats; animals exposed to MC prior to mating and pregnancy showed a promotion of tumor growth and a reduction in the time for appearance of tumors. Following parturition tumor regression occurred, but rapid tumor growth was seen again during a subsequent pregnancy. Lactation per se was not required for the postpartum regression of tumor mass. Clearance of MC from the mammary gland was significantly accelerated in pregnant and lactating rats such that at 7 days after administration of MC, there was no detectable level of the carcinogen in glands from pregnant or lactating rats, whereas MC was still retained in significant quantities in the gland of the virgin animal of the same age. MC was recovered in the milk from the lactating animal, a result confirming the earlier finding of Shay et al. (1950). From these studies, Dao et al. (1960) concluded that the initial carcinogenic event (initiation or induction) occurred early in the virgin gland, and that the enhancement or promotion of carcinogenesis resulted from the hormonal milieu; the hormonal milieu of pregnancy promoted tumor growth, but the hormonal milieu of lactation resulted in tumor regression. It was concluded that the hormonal milieu of pregnancy or lactation inhibited the initiation of carcinogenesis; one could also state that the well-differentiated or functional mammary gland is much less susceptible to carcinogenic insult.

The question as to a critical concentration and/or retention of the carcinogen in the mammary gland required for transformation is at present difficult to answer; the data by Dao and his colleagues suggest that the refractoriness of the gland in pregnant or lactating animals may be due to reduction in level and retention time of the carcinogen. However, in light of the results from experiments in which exposure of mammary glands to DMBA for only 20 minutes *in vitro*, followed by extensive washing, led to carcinomas in 19/21 exposed glands that had been transplanted autologously (Brennan et al., 1966), the possibility exists that the time of exposure of the gland to MC was indeed sufficient but that the differentiated gland was altered in such a way as to no longer present susceptibility to the carcinogen. It would seem appropriate that further experiments of carcinogen effects on pregnant or lactating tissue, followed by transplantation *in vivo* or culture *in vitro*, be conducted.

McCormick and Moon (1965) also reported that the hormonal changes attendant with pregnancy accelerated tumor development in rats given 15 mg DMBA and mated 15 days later. A most interesting observation was made by Moon (1969) regarding the induction of tumors by DMBA and the previous reproductive history of the recipient animal. Animals that had two preceding pregnancies, with or without lactation, demonstrated a significant reduction in incidence of mammary carcinomas (3/23 and 5/32, respectively) when compared to virgin rats of the same age (10/26 rats had tumors). This result is quite different from that seen in mice, where there are several reports of increased tumor incidence in breeders as compared to virgins (Mühlbock, 1956; Heston, 1958). Of particular relevance in this report by Moon (1969) are the data which demonstrate that subsequent risk for breast cancer in women is reduced in women who have had early full-term pregnancy (MacMahon *et al.*, 1970). Studies of the biochemical characteristics of the mammary gland of parous vs. virgin rats need to be performed to gain understanding of differences in susceptibility of the gland to chemical carcinogens.

3. Effects of Estrogen and Progesterone on Induction and Growth of Mammary Tumors

These will be discussed together primarily because of the early studies on the effects of ovariectomy, which removes both hormones simultaneously. Administration of one or the other hormone to ovariectomized animals does not achieve complete hormonal replacement, and interpretation of results from such experiments should keep this point in mind.

a. Ovariectomy. In the earlier paper by Shay *et al.* (1952), ovariectomy of prepubertal rats resulted in a reduced incidence and delayed appearance of mammary tumors after administration of MC. Huggins *et al.* (1959b) reported that ovariectomy of rats at 42 days of age, one week prior to initiation of exposure to MC, resulted in a lowered incidence of mammary tumors, 68.5% vs. 100% in the intact host. This result was confirmed by Sydnor and Cockrell (1963), who found that ovariectomy one week prior to carcinogen feeding at 50 days of age reduced tumor incidence to 63% of the animals. Dao (1962) provided results on the role of ovaries for induction of tumors with DMBA. Because DMBA is effective as a single dose, it was possible to demonstrate that removal of the ovaries immediately or up to 7 days after administration of the carcinogen reduced the incidence of tumor formation compared to intact animals. Each group had 10 rats, and the results were as follows: intact control (rats with tumors/total tumors, percent of animals with tumors), 10/40, 100%; ovariectomy day 1, 1/2, 10%; ovariectomy day 3, 3/3, 30%; ovariectomy day 7, 4/5, 40%; ovariectomy day 15, 4/5, 40%; and ovariectomy day 20, 5/6, 50%. Transplantation of ovaries back to the castrate host at 40 or 50 days after feeding of DMBA resulted in a greater incidence in tumors, from 50 to 100% of the animals with the ovarian grafts. Similar results were also seen for MC, in which a single suboptimal dose of MC was employed. Administration of DMBA after castration of the host yielded very few tumors: 1/20 rats had tumors when castrated one week before carcinogen treatment, and 0/20 had tumors if castrated 15 days before DMBA was given. Thus, ovarian function significantly influenced carcinogenic induction of mammary tumors.

Once tumors were established, removal of ovaries caused regression of a large proportion of the lesions (Huggins *et al.*, 1959a), although it is important to carefully assess the extent of tumor regression. In MC-induced lesions, Daniel and Prichard (1964) observed that ovariectomy, performed when the tumors had reached 1–3 cm in diameter, caused complete regression in 6 rats, partial (including less than 50%) remission in 4 rats, and no regression in 3 rats. Teller *et al.* (1966a), in a careful evaluation of DMBA-induced tumors, found that, when ovariectomy was performed on rats with lesions of 1 cm in average diameter, 57% of the rats (40/70) demonstrated complete remission, 9% (6/70) showed partial remission, and 34% (24/70) were classified as nonresponders, showing less than a 25% reduction in mass. A somewhat greater response to ovariectomy, performed at 3 months after DMBA treatment, was obtained by Griswold *et al.* (1966); 11 rats with a total of 22 tumors at the time of ovariectomy showed a total of 3 tumors by 8 months after carcinogen intubation. However, by one month later, 9 tumors were observed in these animals. They also did not find any marked difference in the response to ovariectomy of large (1 gm or larger) vs. small (500 mg or less) lesions. It is particularly important to evaluate each lesion after hormonal alteration of the host; rarely does one observe complete regression of all tumors. However, these data do support the original proposal that a majority of MC- or DMBA-induced tumors are ovarian-dependent.

b. Administration of Estrogens.   Huggins and his collaborators (1959b, 1961, 1962) demonstrated that higher doses of estradiol-17β reduced the incidence of MC- and DMBA-induced tumors, the dose that was effective being 10 to 20 μg/day; lower doses of estradiol-17β were ineffective. Furthermore, a low dose of estradiol-17β (0.01 μg) did not influence tumor induction with MC in intact animals but did decrease the incidence in ovariectomized animals given MC (Sydnor and Cockrell, 1963). Castrate male rats fed MC and supplemented with a pellet containing 25 mg estradiol showed a higher and earlier incidence of mammary tumors than intact male rats or intact male rats with an implanted estradiol pellet (Shay *et al.*, 1952). It has been concluded that estrogens have a biphasic role in the initiation of mammary tumors by MC in ovariectomized hosts; large amounts or very small amounts inhibit tumor formation, but at certain intermediate levels (1 μg/day), mammary cancer was observed (Huggins *et al.*, 1961).

The well-known clinical paradox that removal of estrogens (ovariectomy) or administration of pharmacological doses of estrogen can cause remission of disease can also be observed with carcinogen-induced mammary tumors of rats. Administration of diethylstilbestrol (Griswold *et al.*, 1966), estradiol-17β or 17α-thioestradiol (Teller *et al.*, 1966b), or estradiol valerate (Hilf *et al.*, 1969) produced regression of DMBA-induced tumors, and estradiol benzoate was effective against MC-induced carcinomas (Gropper and Shimkin, 1967). A most interesting finding was first reported by Rees and Huggins (1960) in MC-induced tumors: Administration of estrogen induced striking secretory changes in the tumors, and these morphological changes were accompanied by numerous biochemical responses. This has also been noted for DMBA-induced tumors after treatment with estrogens, indicating that these carcinogen-induced neoplasms are hormone-responsive. A summary of estrogen-induced responses has been presented earlier (Hilf, 1973; Hilf *et al.*, 1976).

It has therefore been difficult to clearly assess the role of estrogen in tumorigenesis, for it is necessary to separate the initial steps of neoplastic transformation from those involved in maintenance or inhibition of tumor growth. As will be discussed below, consideration of estrogens without concomitant consideration of prolactin is no longer possible, and this situation adds further complexity to identification of the role of hormones in breast cancer.

c. Progesterone. The role of progesterone in mammary cancer has been somewhat overshadowed by the greater publicity given to estrogens; this may be due, at least in part, to the biological activities that progesterone possesses, which are often to augment or supplement the effects of estrogen on the accessory sex organs. However, ovariectomy does remove the major source of progesterone, and it must be considered as an important factor in the development and differentiation of the breast. The changes in progesterone levels during pregnancy, a state that accelerates growth of carcinogen-induced tumors, may be a reflection of the ability of progesterone to enhance tumor growth. Administration of progesterone (4 days mg/day) to intact animals, starting 15 days after intubation of DMBA, enhanced the number of tumors observed and shortened the mean time of appearance (Huggins *et al.*, (1962). Similar results were reported by these investigators for progesterone and 9α-bromo-11-ketoprogesterone to enhance tumorigenesis after feeding MC (Huggins *et al.*, 1959b). Thus, Huggins and his colleagues confirmed and extended the earlier findings of Cantarow *et al.* (194), who observed the ability of progesterone to enhance the carcinogenic actions of 2-AAF. Subsequent confirmation of these effects of progesterone on mammary tumorigenesis has appeared, either with administration of progesterone alone (Jabara, 1967) or due to stimulation of endogenous progesterone levels by pregnancy (McCormick and Moon, 1965). Administration of equine gonadotrophin (Huggins *et al.*, 1959b, 1962) also enhanced the appearance of mammary tumors, but it is not clear (in the absence of measurement of plasma estrogen and progesterone levels) if this was due solely to enhanced secretion of progesterone. Progesterone administered to animals ovariectomized 7 days prior to DMBA treatment enabled tumors to develop in 25% of the animals, whereas no tumors arose in the ovariectomized animals fed the carcinogen (Jabara and Hartcourt, 1970).

In a latter study, Jabara *et al.* (1972) showed enhancement of DNA synthesis in the mammary gland after treatment with progesterone, but DMBA, administered alone or with progesterone did not alter DNA synthesis, as measured by autoradiographic techniques. They concluded from this and additional studies (Jabara *et al.*, 1974) that the ability of progesterone to enhance mammary tumorigenesis was not due to enhanced DNA synthesis. It would seem that there is general agreement that progesterone may enhance carcinogen-induced tumorigenesis, although the mechanism for this effect is not clear.

d. Estrogen Plus Progesterone. The widespread use of oral contraceptive preparations, predominantly composed of synthetic estrogens combined with synthetic progestagens, has fostered a continuing discourse regarding the potential effect of such hormones on the incidence of breast cancer. No final statements can be made at this time. However, studies were performed using such hormone combinations, and their effect on mammary cancer induction by chemical carcinogens was observed. In these studies, Huggins and his colleagues obtained data indicating that treatment with combinations of estrogen and progesterone prevented mammary tumor formation by MC (Huggins *et al.*, 1959b) or DMBA (Huggins *et al.*, 1962).

Gruenstein *et al.* (1964) administered the contraceptive preparation Enovid (norethynodrel plus mestranol) after completion of MC intubations; no cancers arose in animals receiving Enovid alone, and mammary carcinogenesis was neither enhanced nor retarded. J. H. Weisburger *et al.* (1968) found that Enovid reduced tumorigenesis by DMBA, when Enovid treatment was initiated 10 days prior to intubation of DMBA; similar results were reported by McCarthy (1965). Stern and Mickey (1969) administered Enovid in a cyclical dose schedule to stimulate the regimen used in women;

intubation of DMBA 10 days after initiation of the hormone therapy resulted in a delayed appearance and slower growth of mammary tumors.

All these results should not be interpreted as suggesting that combination estrogen plus progestagen contraceptive preparations prevent breast cancer induction in humans, nor do these studies rule out a stimulatory role on mammary tumors that are subclinical at the time such preparations are used. However, it is quite possible that these preparations may not be detrimental on the basis of their ability to stimulate the mammary glands to a more differentiated state, perhaps somewhat like that seen during pregnancy or pseudo-pregnancy, and that they may thereby render the gland less susceptible to carcinogen-induced transformation. The apparent reduction in risk for breast cancer associated in women with an early full-term pregnancy may be a reflection of the differentiated state of the gland during a potentially susceptible time.

4. Adrenal Glands

There appears to be good agreement that adrenalectomy does not affect the induction of mammary tumors by MC (Huggins *et al.*, 1959b; Shay *et al.*, 1960; Kim and Furth, 1960; Daniel and Prichard, 1967). Daniel and Prichard (1967) reported that adrenalectomy performed after tumors were present did not decrease tumor growth and may have stimulated growth of tumors present at the time of adrenalectomy. A reinvestigation of the effect of adrenalectomy on DMBA-induced tumors was published recently (Chen *et al.*, 1976). It was found that adrenalectomy, performed after each rat had at least one tumor, significantly increased mammary tumor size and number compared to intact controls. Although treatment with hydrocortisone acetate did not affect tumor growth, administration of the glucocorticoid to adrenalectomized rats prevented the increase in tumor size. These studies indicated that the effects of adrenalectomy were due to elevation of prolactin release (see Section II,D,6).

Administration of adrenal steroids may prevent tumors resulting from intubation of DMBA; 4 mg of 11-deoxycorticosterone, given 4 times per day for 5 days, starting at 24 hours prior to DMBA, reduced the incidence of mammary tumors from 90% in controls to 15% in the treated rats (Jull, 1961). In a later report, Jull (1966) demonstrated that administration of metapirone, an inhibitor of 11-hydroxylation, also reduced the incidence of mammary tumors arising after DMBA administration. He concluded that either metapirone or 11-deoxycorticosterone would act via similar mechanisms, both agents producing elevated circulating levels of 11-deoxycorticosterone. Although glucocorticoids have been used clinically in the therapy of advanced breast cancer in women, there seems to be little in the literature regarding a systematic examination of effects of glucocorticoids, either alone or in relationship to other hormones, on induction and/or growth of carcinogen-induced mammary tumors.

5. *Thyroid*

Administration of MC to rats thyroidectomized 3 weeks prior to initiation of carcinogen feeding resulted in a decrease in tumor formation (7/12 vs. 10/10 for controls) and a delay in appearance of palpable tumors. Thyroidectomized rats, receiving 0.5 mg/day of L-thyroxine, showed tumor incidence (10/10) equal to intact control animals, whereas thyroidectomized animals receiving 1.0 mg/day of L-thyroxine showed a reduced tumor incidence (4/11). It was concluded that the reduced caloric intake caused by thyroidectomy may have affected the genesis of tumors, but this explanation did not apply to the rats receiving thyroxine at the 1 mg/day dose (Jull and Huggins, 1960).

Helfenstein *et al.* (1962) induced hypothyroidism by daily administration of propylthiouracil, starting on the same day as intubation of DMBA. Tumor incidence was as follows: intact rats, 10/24 at 60 days, 16/22 at 80 days, and 20/20 at 100 days; hypothyroid rats, 1/22 at 60 days, 4/21 at 80 days, and 7/14 at 100 days. They concluded, in agreement with the results of Jull and Huggins (1960) that a reduction of mammary carcinogenesis resulted from hypothyroidism.

Several years later, Eskin *et al.* (1968) demonstrated that in rats placed on an iodine-deficient diet or treated with propylthiouracil starting 4 days prior to intubation of DMBA, there was no effect on the total number of tumors produced, but rather that these animals showed an earlier appearance of tumors than did intact control animals. They concluded that iodine deficiency and hypothyroidism accelerate the rate of tumor appearance, results quite different from those cited above (Helfenstein *et al.*, 1962). Almost simultaneously, Newman and Moon (1968) reported that administration of L-thyroxine (2.5 μg/100 gm body weight daily for 7 months) had little or no effect on the carcinogenic effect of MC, whereas treatment with propylthiouracil significantly inhibited mammary cancer induction. Rats, initially made hypothyroid by propylthiouracil treatment but then treated with thyroxine (2.5 μg/100 gm body weight) beginning 10 days after cessation of MC feedings, demonstrated the same tumor incidence as control intact rats. Although they concluded that body growth reduction by thyroid inactivity may have played a role, they proposed that the effects of thyroid hormone or its lack was on growth of established neoplastic cells rather than on the process of neoplastic transformation. Earlier, they had reported (Newman and Moon, 1966) that MC feeding had marginal effects on thyroid function of rats, and that the reduced protein-bound iodine levels in serum were probably due to reduced food consumption; these effects apparently did not interfere with mammary tumor production.

Eskin (1970) summarized his earlier findings and extended them by examining uptake of ^{125}I into breast tissues of iodine-deficient or propylthiouracil-treated rats. He claimed that breast dysplasia was related to iodine deficiency and that carcinogenesis occurred earlier in the dysplastic breast.

Recent attention to the potential role of thyroid function and mammary glands has led to a proposal that the mammary glands may be more sensitive to prolactin as a result of thyroidectomy (Mittra, 1974). Earlier, Shellabarger (1969) had reported that propylthiouracil treatment, prior to intubation of DMBA, enhanced the mammary tumor yield, but that continued hypothyroidism inhibited the subsequent growth or carcinogenesis. With the growing knowledge that TRH can cause prolactin release, a relationship between thyroid function and prolactin has potential importance in the etiology of breast cancer. Mittra *et al.* (1974; Mittra and Hayward, 1974) examined the thyroid–prolactin axis in women with breast cancer and demonstrated that these women had a lower level of thyroid function but that there were no differences in circulating levels of prolactin. They propose that the lower levels of circulating thyroid hormones may lead to greater sensitivity of the mammary epithelial cells to prolactin stimulation, a process that could lead to dysplasia and eventual neoplasia. While these results are provocative, further careful studies in animals and humans will be required to establish with certainty the role of the thyroid gland in the etiology of breast cancer.

A role for thyroid hormones in the hormonal response of the mammary gland, measured by α-lactalbumin activity as an indicator of differentiated function, has been reported by Vonderhaar (1977). She reported that addition of triiodothyronine to explant cultures of mouse mammary glands caused a 3- to 5-fold increase in α-lactalbumin activity above that obtained in the presence of insulin, hydrocortisone, and prolactin. This effect of triiodothyronine was not blocked by progesterone but was prevented by addition of actinomycin D or cycloheximide, suggesting that the response in the gland to thyroid hormone was due to increased synthesis of α-lactalbumin. Data were also obtained that suggested that thyroid hormone may act by enhancing the sensitivity of the gland to prolactin, for it (the mammary gland) appeared to require 10-fold greater concentration of prolactin in the absence of thyroid hormone than in its presence to achieve the same level of α-lactalbumin activity. At least one possible explanation offered for these results was a consideration of differences in prolactin receptors in the mammary gland, as it has been noted that thyroid hormone may regulate prolactin binding to the liver (Gelato *et al.*, 1975). It would appear that these results are opposite to those of Mittra *et al.* (1974), who propose that the mammary gland is more sensitive to prolactin in the hypothyroid state. Perhaps it will be necessary to consider the interaction of prolactin and thyroid hormones on mammary gland growth separately from the effects of these hormones on differentiated function of the mammary gland. The reduced tumor incidence reported in animals receiving a high dose of L-thyroxine and MC may be somewhat analogous to the effects of high doses of estrogen or prolactin; a milieu that enhances differentiation of the mammary gland seems to prevent neoplastic transformation.

6. *Prolactin*

There has always been considerable interest in defining the role of prolactin in breast cancer, because its hormonal actions are primarily directed toward the mammary gland in mammals. Several recent advances, such as the ability to measure prolactin by sensitive radioimmunoassay techniques and the availability of experimental drugs that either inhibit or stimulate prolactin release, have fostered a proliferation of reports in the literature. Fortunately, two very fine reviews have recently appeared that address the questions of prolactin and carcinogenesis. The first of these, by Kim and Furth (1976) presents an excellent overview of the history of the role of prolactin in the development of mammary neoplasia. The second review, by Welsch and Nagasawa (1977), is a most thorough summary of the role of prolactin in murine mammary tumorigenesis resulting from administration of chemical carcinogens. Therefore, the information presented in this section represents only a brief summary of these studies, and the reader is advised to consult these up-to-date reviews for detailed information.

The majority of experimental evidence has clearly demonstrated that both MC- and DMBA-induced mammary tumors in rats are very sensitive to alterations in prolactin levels. Thus, any procedure that caused a hyperprolactin state, such as pregnancy (Dao and Sunderland, 1959; McCormick and Moon, 1965), pituitary homografts (Welsch *et al.*, 1968), implantation of prolactin-secreting pituitary tumors (Kim and Furth, 1960), lesions of the hypothalamus (Welsch *et al.*, 1969; Klaiber *et al.*, 1969; Sinha *et al.*, 1973), or administration of such drugs as perphenazine (Pearson *et al.*, 1969) or reserpine (Welsch and Meites, 1970), resulted in enhanced tumor growth. Procedures that remove prolactin or produce significant reduction in prolactin secretion, such as hypophysectomy (Huggins *et al.*, 1959b; Daniel and Prichard, 1963; Sterental *et al.*, 1963), antirat prolactin serum (Butler and Pearson, 1971), certain ergot alkaloids (Cassell *et al.*, 1971; Nagasawa and Meites, 1970; Welsch *et al.*, 1973) or ergoline derivatives (Sweeney *et al.*, 1975), and other drugs capable of suppressing prolactin release, result in significant reduction of growth of established mammary tumors. Specific binding sites for prolactin have been described (Costlow *et al.*, 1974; Kelly *et al.*, 1974; Turkington, 1974; Smith *et al.*, 1976), but no obvious relationship has been observed between prolactin binding and tumor growth response to treatments that alter prolactin concentrations (DeSombre *et al.*, 1976; Smith, *et al.*, 1976). Thus, these carcinogen-induced tumors can be classified as prolactin-dependent, but the molecular mechanism whereby prolactin or its absence alters tumor growth remains to be elucidated.

As with the earlier-described effects of estrogen, tumorigenesis can be inhibited by excess prolactin at the time of or prior to administration of MC or DMBA. The same procedures that are indicated above, which enhance the prolactin milieu of the host—e.g., pregnancy, pituitary homografts, hypothalamic lesions, etc.—will significantly depress the induction of mammary carcinomas. This effect is probably due to the stimulation of the mammary gland by elevated prolactin levels, and it has been postulated by Welsch and Nagasawa (1977) that the extensive lobulo-alveolar development may render the gland refractory to the carcinogen. A similar situation may attain for the lactational stage of the gland, another state of differentiation that is relatively refractory to chemical carcinogenesis. The question of a relationship between DNA synthesis and susceptibility to chemical carcinogen transformation can be raised again, as DNA synthesis during active lactation is rather low except during the middle to late stages of pregnancy. A less satisfactory explanation is simply to state that the mammary gland is most susceptible at some intermediate stage of differentiation; endocrine-induced differentiation provides a degree of protection against neoplastic transformation. Studies directed toward defining the biochemical characteristics that make a cell most vulnerable to these chemical carcinogens are sorely needed.

7. Prolactin–Ovarian Interations

It becomes increasingly difficult to dissect *in vivo* the effects of prolactin and ovarian steroids, although it is well accepted that both ovarian and pituitary hormones are very important in chemical carcinogensis of the mammary gland. Elevation of prolactin levels in ovariectomized animals did not increase incidence of tumors compared to ovariectomized animals (Welsch *et al.*, 1968), and mammary tumorigenesis was not apparent in the absence of pituitary hormones, although Young (1961) did report that MC was capable of inducing tumors in hypophysectomized rats treated with estrogen, progesterone, and growth hormone (prolactin contamination?).

Once tumors had appeared, however, a somewhat different situation was observed. Ovariectomy caused a large number of the lesions to regress, although a significant number (5–10%) of tumors continued to grow; if followed in time, some of the lesions that showed initial regression to ovariectomy resumed growth at a later time (Leung *et al.*, 1975). Leung *et al.* (1975) have concluded that estrogen plays a predominant role in DMBA-induced tumor growth. In contrast, Pearson and his colleagues (Pearson *et al.*, 1969; Sterental *et al.*, 1963; Manni *et al.*, 1977) have suggested from their studies that prolactin plays the major role in supporting tumor growth. Their most recent report (Manni *et al.*, 1977) indicated that stimulation of endogenous prolactin secretion with perphenazine caused a stimulation of tumor growth, whether or not the antiestrogen Tamoxifen was present. Because this was observed in ovariectomized animals and in intact animals during continued treatment with the antiestrogen, they concluded that prolactin supported tumor growth and that estrogen (receptors) was not required under these conditions; estrogen treatment could not reactivate tumor growth when prolactin secretion was inhibited.

The question of whether either prolactin or estrogen alone can continue to support tumor growth is certainly critical, particularly as it relates to therapy of human breast cancer. Elucidation of such an important hormonal interrelationship will require a continuing effort, and such investigations will need to include examination of several mammary tumor models to assess the application of such findings.

8. Insulin

Although insulin is usually not considered as a primary hormone involved in mammary cancer, there are data in the literature that suggest a role for insulin in mammary tumor growth (see review by Hilf *et al.*, 1976). Of direct pertinence to this review were the findings of Heuson and his colleagues, who initially demonstrated that insulin stimulated cell proliferation of organ cultures of DMBA-induced tumors *in vitro;* 5/12 tumors showed a marked increase in thymidine incorporation into DNA (Heuson *et al.*, 1967). They also reported that this stimulation of thymidine incorporation was not accompanied by a major effect on glucose utilization (Heuson and Legros, 1968). Applying these findings *in vitro* to tumor growth *in vivo*, Heuson and Legros (1970) showed that induction of diabetes at 146 days after DMBA was administered resulted in regression of 90% of the 57 tumors present at the onset of diabetes. Furthermore, large doses of insulin and/or glucose supplements in the drinking water stimulated growth of these carcinogen-induced tumors.

In a more extensive publication, Heuson and Legros (1972) affirmed these findings and also demonstrated that administration of estradiol benzoate failed to prevent tumor regression produced by alloxan diabetes. It is certainly of relevance that when diabetes was induced 3–4 weeks after DMBA treatment, no mammary tumors arose, results that suggest a role for insulin in carcinogenesis. As before, tumors regressing in diabetic rats were usually dependent on insulin *in vitro*, whereas those tumors that continued to grow in diabetic hosts (about 10%) were not insulin-dependent *in vitro*. Unfortunately, considerable weight loss accompanied the induction of diabetes with alloxan, and regression of tumors does occur under food restriction conditions that produce body weight loss.

In a series of experiments from our laboratory (Cohen and Hilf, 1974, 1975; Matusik and Hilf, 1976), streptozotocin-induced diabetes induced regression (>20% decrease in lesion size) in 50/89 tumors, caused stasis (less than 20% change in size) in 19/89 lesions, and did not alter growth of 20/89 tumors. Because no weight loss was observed in the diabetic rats (body weight was comparable to intact tumor-bearing rats), we concluded that a majority of DMBA-induced lesions were insulin-dependent but that a significant number of lesions were independent of endogenous insulin for growth. We also observed that tumors regressing in diabetic rats demonstrated reduced glucose utilization *in vitro* (Cohen and Hilf, 1974); reduced activities of glucose-6-phosphate dehydrogenase, 6-phosphogluconate dehydrogenase, pyruvate kinase, and phosphofructokinase (Cohen and Hilf, 1974); reduced glucose transport (Harmon and Hilf, 1976b); an increase in the level of cAMP but no change in cGMP (Matusik and Hilf, 1976); and a decrease in the level of specific estrogen-binding capacity (Gibson and Hilf, 1976). This latter finding of decreased estrogen receptor content in regressing tumors in diabetic animals may explain, at least in part, the failure that Heuson and Legros (1972) reported of estrogen to stimulate tumor growth in animals deprived of insulin. Thus, studies of the influence of one hormone on the regulation of receptors for other hormones can help elucidate the biochemical basis for response, or lack of response, of tumor growth.

In a recent study, Pasteels *et al.* (1976) extended their earlier findings on the effects of hormones on DNA synthesis in DMBA-induced tumors *in vitro* and found that lesions that were insulin-independent were essentially unresponsive to other hormones, such as estradiol-17β, progesterone, and prolactin. A majority of tumors that were insulin-dependent were responsive to the combination of prolactin and progesterone, and about 50% of the tumors responded to insulin plus prolactin with an induction of secretory changes. As with the estrogen receptors, insulin may play an important role in control of prolactin receptors, for R. D. Smith *et al.* (1972a,b) have demonstrated significant reductions in prolactin receptors in a transplantable mammary tumor as well as in DMBA-induced tumors after induction of diabetes with streptozotocin. This further reinforces the need to explore the interrelations of several hormones and their effects on carcinogen-induced tumor growth and biochemistry. Because we have recently ascertained the existence of insulin receptors in DMBA-induced tumors (S. Shafie, S. L. Gibson, and R.

Hilf, unpublished observations), as well as in transplantable mammary tumors (Harmon and Hilf, 1976a), a role for insulin in tumor growth and possibly in tumorigenesis is indicated. Thus, hormones that may play a permissive role may be critical to the overall outcome of tumorigenesis (initiation) or tumor maintenance (acceleration) and may be important to achieving the best results of hormonal therapy by their ability to influence the levels of hormone receptors.

E. Ionizing Radiation

Any one of several types of ionizing radiation produces mammary tumors. This response is related to strain of rats (Shellabarger, 1972) and dose of radiation exposure (Shellabarger, 1976) but not to age of the rat at the time of exposure (Shellabarger, 1976). An interesting observation is the suggestion of a possible relationship between X-irradiation and MC in causing mammary tumors; an additive effect was seen over a short time period when both treatments were given (Shellabarger, 1967). Further studies will be needed to clarify the respective roles of each agent in carcinogenesis, particularly with regard to dose, time of exposure, age of host, etc.

Effects of Hormones

In what appears to be the first report of its kind, Segaloff and Maxfield (1971) showed that continuous administration of diethylstilbestrol plus exposure to a total dose of 800 R yielded many more mammary carcinomas in A×C rats than were observed in animals exposed to either treatment alone. The results were interpreted as a demonstration of a substantial synergism between these two modalities for induction of carcinoma. Shellabarger (1976) confirmed these results using neutrons and diethylstilbestrol in A×C rats, but a similar result was not seen in Sprague–Dawley rats. The difference in response among the two strains of rats may have been due to the development of pituitary tumors in A×C, but not in Sprague–Dawley, rats, and these pituitary tumors were judged to be secreting prolactin. Because it had been shown many years ago that prolactin might synergize with X-irradiation to produce mammary cancers (Yokoro and Furth, 1961), it is possible that the effects of estrogen administration may be due, at least in part, to the anticipated enhanced release of prolactin by the estrogen treatment. However, this would not clearly explain the strain differences reported by Shellabarger (1976). This aspect of possible hormonal synergism with other carcinogens, such as X-irradiation, is of utmost importance for further investigation, for the common use in young women of contraceptive preparations containing estrogen and progesterone could alter the sensitivity of the breast to radiation.

III. OVARY

The ovary has been used as a model for studying tumorigenesis. Agents such as irradiation or certain chemicals produce effects on the ovary that lead to tumor formation. A fine review of this subject was written by Jull (1973), and the reader should consult this for a more detailed description than presented here. Tumors of the ovaries in mice have been induced by DMBA when administered by any one of the following techniques: repeated applications to the skin (Marchant *et al.*, 1954; Howell *et al.*, 1954); gastric instillation (Biancifori *et al.*, 1961; Jull *et al.*, 1966); intraperitoneal injection (Krarup, 1967); intravenous administration (Kuwahara, 1967); subcutaneous administration (Shisa and Nishizuka, 1968); or direct application to the ovary *in situ* (Krarup, 1969). It is important, however, to keep in mind that a variety of tumors arise, and there is a need to classify the neoplasms on a morphological basis, such as tubular adenomas, luteomas, and granulosa/thecal tumors. Although the distribution among these tumor types appears to be influenced by strain differences, the most common neoplasms arising were granulosa/thecal tumors (Jull, 1973).

A. EFFECTS OF HORMONES ON OVARIAN TUMOR DEVELOPMENT

As with normal breast tissue discussed above, normal development of ovarian tissue is dependent on pituitary hormones. Marchant (1961) demonstrated that pituitary hormones were required for DMBA-induced ovarian tumorigenesis by experiments in which ovaries from intact mice were exposed to DMBA and then transplanted into hypophysectomized mice; no tumors developed. In contrast, ovaries from hypophysectomized mice given DMBA and transplanted to ovariectomized mice developed a significant number of granulosa cell tumors. Similar conclusions were reached earlier by Mühlbock (1953), using parabiotic mice, in which one of the mice had been exposed to X-irradiation prior to performing the parabiotic union to a castrated partner; the frequency of ovarian tumors was greater in the irradiated animal paired with a castrate partner, a situation that gives rise to elevated gonadotrophins in the intact animal. Unfortunately, the individual roles of FSH and LH have not been identified and may be very difficult to clarify for one hormone is ineffective in the total absence of the other.

IV. LIVER

The liver has been extensively studied as a target organ for chemical carcinogens. These investigations have led to considerable elucidation of metabolic alterations of the administered compounds and to the now well-accepted findings that metabolic conversion from less to more potent (ultimate carcinogen) carcinogens does occur *in vivo*. A concerted effort to identify and characterize the "preneoplastic" lesion in the liver is under way (see review of Farber, 1973). There have been many reports of sex differences in response to carcinogen administration, and it is appropriate to briefly review these in view of the fact that sex hormones, as well as other hormones, probably play an important permissive role in the induction of hepatocarcinomas.

A. SEX STEROIDS

As pointed out in the review of Toh (1973), the incidence of hepatic cancer is higher in men than in women, and this difference cannot simply be related to dietary differences. This sex difference has been found in rats fed 2-AAF (Bielschowsky, 1961; Firminger and Reuber, 1961; Toh, 1972), certain azo dyes (Rumsfield *et al.*, 1951; Baba and Takayama, 1961), or alfatoxin B_1 (Butler, 1964), in which hepatoma formation was higher in males, was reduced in castrate males, and was elevated in castrate males treated with testosterone (Firminger and Reuber, 1961; Rumsfield *et al.*, 1951; Morris and Firminger, 1956). Similar findings have also been reported in mice (Leathem, 1951; Kirschbaum, 1957; Heston and Vlahakis, 1968; Biancifori, 1970). Because the incidence of liver tumors was lower in female rats and mice, Reuber and Firminger (1962) examined the effects of administration of diethylstilbestrol to intact male rats receiving carcinogens and found a decrease in tumor incidence; castrate male rats treated with diethylstilbestrol showed more resistance to induction of carcinomas (Reuber and Firminger, 1962). Progesterone appeared to increase the incidence of hepatic carcinoma in either intact or castrate male or female rats, but not in intact female rats (Reuber and Firminger, 1962). Administration of testosterone to neonatal rats resulted in an increased tumor incidence in female rats, whereas estradiol treatment of male rats at birth resulted in a decreased tumor incidence (E. K. Weisburger *et al.*, 1968).

B. PITUITARY HORMONES

Hypophysectomy of rats exposed to chemical carcinogens results in complete prevention of liver tumors (Griffin *et al.*, 1953; Goodall and Butler, 1969; Lee and Goodall, 1968; Weisburger, 1968). Furthermore, removal of the pituitary at 14 weeks, but not at 23 weeks, prevented the appearance of hepatic carcinomas by 2-AAF (Skoryna, 1955; Reuber, 1969). However, removal of the pituitary not only removes the hormones of the pituitary but also causes a cessation of function of thyroid, adrenals, and gonads. Thus, because adrenalectomy (Perry, 1961; Reuber, 1965) or thyroidectomy (Bielschowsky and Hall, 1953; Goodall, 1965) has been shown to prevent hepatic carcinogenesis, it is quite possible that the effects of hypophysectomy were due indirectly to cessation of function of other endocrine organs. It therefore becomes quite difficult to demonstrate direct effects of hormones on the subsequent metabolic alterations induced by the feeding of hepatocarcinogens.

Replacement of a single hormone in the hypophysectomized rat is a classical approach and can yield useful information, and it was reported that administration of growth hormone to hypophysectomized rats restored the ability of azo dyes to cause hepatic tumors (Robertson *et al.*, 1954; Griffin *et al.*, 1955). In view of our increasing biochemical sophistication at the molecular level, it would appear most appropriate that additional investigation is needed to define the role of pituitary hormones, such as growth hormone and prolactin, in the response of the liver to chemical carcinogens. Several studies along these lines are reviewed by Toh (1973).

C. Hormones and Metabolic Characteristics

The differences in response to carcinogens between male and female animals could be due to differences in metabolism of the carcinogens, rather than to a difference in the target organ per se, e.g., mammary gland in females vs. males. It was found by Weisburger *et al.* (1964) that adult male rats excreted less of a dose of labeled N-HO-AAF than did adult female rats. The urine of male rats contained greater quantities of the sulfate conjugates than of the glucuronic acid conjugates (Miller *et al.*, 1970). Castration of adult male rats resulted in an increased excretion of the N-hydroxy derivative of AAF, and administration of testosterone to the castrate prevented the rise in N-HO-AAF excretion (Lotlikar *et al.*, 1964).

As it is believed that the ultimate carcinogen for AAF is the sulfate ester of N-HO-AAF, it is of interest that the sulfotransferase activity in the liver of male rats was about five times that found in female rats (DeBaun *et al.*, 1968, 1970). Curiously, castration of the male rat had no effect on sulfotransferase activity, nor did administration of testosterone to the castrate male rat alter the activity of this enzyme. Because the former procedure reduced tumor formation compared to intact male rats and the latter procedure returned tumor production to that seen in the intact animal, a simple correlation between sulfotransferase activity and tumorigenesis was not apparent.

Hypophysectomy or thyroidectomy reduced sulfotransferase activity, and this hormonal alteration completely prevented carcinogenesis, but adrenalectomy was just as effective in preventing carcinogenesis and had no effect on sulfotransferase activity. Additionally, administration of estradiol reduced sulfotransferase activity in normal and gonadectomized male rats and these animals showed a lower carcinogenic response.

These resuts suggest that other factors may be involved in the final steps of neoplastic transformation. For example, glucuronide synthesis in the liver of male rats was found to be higher than in female or castrate male rats, but urinary excretion of the glucuronic acid ester of N-HO-AAF was lower in male rats. These data point out the difficulty in attempting to correlate enzymatic capability with overall metabolism *in vivo*. Sex differences in drug-metabolizing enzymes have been reported, although the role of these enzymes in metabolism of hepatocarcinogens is not known (Toh, 1973).

Another factor that may be influenced by hormones and may thereby contribute to differences in carcinogenic response is the effect of hormones on macromolecular synthesis. It is now well accepted that chemical carcinogens interact with cellular macromolecules, and that the targets most likely attacked are DNA and proteins. As pointed out by Miller and Miller (1973), the metabolism of polycyclic hydrocarbons leads to stronger electrophilic products, which are capable of interacting with a variety of cellular nucleophiles present in proteins or nucleic acids. Because many hormone-induced responses in target tissues are expressed via effects on nucleic acids and proteins, a role for hormones can be indirectly attributed to the availability of susceptible macromolecular targets. For example, androgens are generally anabolic hormones, inducing positive nitrogen balance and stimulation of protein synthesis. Growth hormone and thyroid hormones also exert effects in a positive manner on metabolism. These effects of hormones could contribute to the reported enhancement or maintenance of hepatocarcinogenic potency of chemical carcinogens. The higher incidence of liver tumors in male rats, on one hand, and the decrease in incidence of tumor formation in animals deprived of growth hormone or thyroid hormones on the other hand, could be due, at least in part, to an increase or a reduction, respectively, in cellular nucleic acids and protein targets of the carcinogen.

Irving and Veazey (1971) found significantly higher amounts of labeled AAF and N-HO-AAF bound to tRNA and rRNA in livers of male rats compared to female rats, although no sex differences were seen for binding to DNA. There were also overall metabolic differences, with a greater amount of retention of the N-acetyl group in male rats. The studies of Weinstein and his colleagues (Fink *et al.*, 1970; Agarwal and Weinstein, 1970; Grünberger and Weinstein, 1971) indicated that both structural and functional changes in RNA occur as a result of covalent binding of AAF. Thus, the effect of testosterone to increase synthesis of mRNA (Kidson and Kirby, 1964), the effect of androgens to maintain the activity of DNA-dependent RNA polymerase (Widnell and Tata, 1966), the ability of testosterone in neonatal female rats to increase the uptake of ^{32}P into liver nuclear RNA (Toh, 1971), and the effects of growth hormone on protein and nucleic acid synthesis (Korner, 1965), may explain in part the enhanced effects of these hormones on neoplastic transformation in the liver.

V. RELATIONSHIP OF BINDING PROTEINS (ENZYMES) AND CARCINOGENESIS

Although it is probable that DNA is the critical macromolecule with which chemical carcinogens react, binding of carcinogens to cellular proteins has been demonstrated by several investigators (Baldwin *et al.*, 1968; Filler *et al.*, 1974; Ketterer *et al.*, 1967; Sorof and Young, 1973). In a recent review, G. J. Smith *et al.* (1977) have offered the provocative thesis that some of the binding of carcinogens is to proteins that are involved in cellular detoxification of electrophilic carcinogens. Thus, data point to the strong possibility that ligandin and other glutathione S-transferases in the liver bind a variety of chemical carcinogens and thereby reduce the hepatocarcinogenic potential of aminoazo dyes, polycyclic hydrocarbons and aromatic amines.

Evidence was presented to suggest that there was a correlation between an increased level of ligandin or ligandin-binding activity, resulting from altered physiological states, and a decreased susceptibility of the liver to carcinogenesis. Most pertinent to the discussion here is the ability of these binding proteins to bind steroid hormones. Unfortunately, there appears to be little or no data on the presence of these glutathione S-transferases in mammary gland, where one should expect that the critical interaction between carcinogen and macromolecule must take place prior to transformation of the gland. Considering that hormonal manipulation may alter the susceptibility of the mammary gland to chemical carcinogens, it would seem logical that studies of the protein-binding capacity of the gland are needed. If one assumes that the interaction of a carcinogen with cellular protein molecules is critical to neoplastic transformation and that hormones act primarily to promote or facilitate the expression of this initial interaction, then it is crucial that the presence of such proteins be established and their characteristics be defined. On the other hand, hormones may act to compete with carcinogens for these putative binding proteins, and if these binding proteins are necessary for detoxification, one can envision higher levels of such carcinogens remaining in the circulation and potentially interacting with cellular proteins outside the liver.

Another system for metabolism of hydrocarbon carcinogens involves conversion to oxides, and such reactions are catalyzed by mixed function oxidases, one of which is termed aryl hydrocarbon hydroxylase (AHH) (Heidelberger, 1975). It is known that this oxidase is present in various tissues in a variety of species, and it has been shown to be induced by numerous agents, such as polycyclic hydrocarbons and steroids (Nebert and Gelboin, 1969; Bürki *et al.*, 1973). Interestingly, little attention has been paid to the presence of AHH or its inducibility in the mammary gland of rodents susceptible to mammary tumorigenesis by polycyclic hydrocarbons.

In an attempt to relate AHH activity and susceptibility to mammary cancer, Chuang and Bresnick (1976) examined AHH activity in six different mouse strains demonstrating a broad spectrum of susceptibility or resistance to mammary tumorigenesis. They found essentially no correlation between susceptibility to tumor induction by MC and AHH activity (basal or induced), and they ruled out, in at least two strains of mice, the possibility that the lack of response was due to the inability of the mice to absorb and transport MC to the mammary gland. Although these results are initially disappointing, it is obvious that additional investigation is needed to further elucidate the potential role of AHH in the mammary gland. Further study of the rat model is needed, perhaps at those ages when the greatest sensitivity to polycyclic hydrocarbon carcinogens is apparent, i.e., 50–60 day old Sprague–Dawley female rats. Another approach would be to investigate the effects of steroid hormones on AHH activity in the mammary gland. It is clear that an understanding of carcinogen metabolism at the target cell, such as the mammary gland, will be needed if we are to properly place in perspective the susceptibility or resistance of a cell to neoplastic transformation.

VI. CONCLUSIONS

In attempting to restrict this review to hormones and carcinogens, we obviously placed most of the emphasis on the mammary gland as the target tissue. This was done with the purpose of demonstrating the complexity of the problem, because hormones act to alter that target tissue, which has a very high susceptibility of neoplastic transformation by a variety of carcinogenic agents. One must consider not only synergistic interactions among the hormones, but also the fact that synergism among the carcinogens can take place. This is of great concern to the female population, and constantly comes to the forefront of discussion when the etiology of the disease is addressed. A good example of such a discussion arose recently regarding the potential effects of X-ray mammography as a screening device in asymptomatic young women.

There is still no explanation for the apparent paradox regarding susceptibility of the mammary gland to chemical carcinogens; the highly differentiated gland (lactating) is not transformed, nor is the atrophic (prepubertal) gland as susceptible to carcinogenic insult. It appears that the state of differentiation of the mammary gland may be critical for the initial interaction of carcinogen with its target(s). If one assumes that a potential target is DNA, then it follows that less of this target molecule would be available for interaction with the carcinogen (or its metabolites) at the time that the cell is engaged in its differentiated function, i.e., milk production. It is also possible that the enhanced protein synthesis and increased protein content of the mammary cell during lactation presents to the carcinogen a larger array of targets for attack; should these be proteins that are lost via secretion, the overall result would be to decrease and remove the carcinogen from the cell. Still another possibility is that through hormonal stimulation, the cell is reprogramed for its functional purpose, and in the process, areas of the genome that are usually repressed are now derepressed while areas that are usually derepressed are now repressed; it would be the latter areas that might be most susceptible for the carcinogen to attack in the nondifferentiated state.

Unfortunately, the above suggestions do not apply fully to the prepubertal gland. Perhaps this situation is a result of fewer susceptible macromolecules for carcinogens to attack, as well as fewer epithelial cells in the organ. The onset of puberty and the resultant changes in the hormonal milieu as a result of ovarian function and cyclicity may enhance the number of macromolecular targets available for carcinogen interaction.

It is therefore possible that the reported reduction in risk for subsequent breast cancer in women who have experienced an early full-term pregnancy, or in animals treated with estrogen or exposed to high levels of prolactin prior to administration of chemical carcinogens, may be due to a decreased time interval of heightened susceptibility for carcinogenic transformation. Any hormonal intervention that reduces the period of time between prepubescence and full differentiation apparently reduces the risk of neoplastic transformation. It should be noted that little is known regarding the biochemistry of the mammary gland during this period of heightened susceptibility, and investigations of this aspect are necessary.

In keeping with such studies, there is a need to establish the role of the target tissue in metabolism of the carcinogen. While most efforts have been directed toward the liver and its metabolic activities, the information obtained regarding carcinogen metabolism in the mammary gland has clearly lagged behind other aspects of studies of breast cancer. It will be important to learn of the metabolism of carcinogens at the mammary gland site, particularly in terms of hormonal modification of the target tissue. Investigation of carcinogen metabolism in the liver is also pertinent, because hormonal perturbation of the host would of necessity require consideration of the effects that such perturbations would have on the metabolic activity of the liver, such as induction of mixed function oxidases.

Of major concern is the elucidation of the role of hormones in the etiology of cancer in humans. The high incidence of cancer in accessory sex organs, which are markedly influenced by endogenous and exogenous hormones, mandates extensive investigation of relationships of hormones to the initiation and growth of cancer of the breast, uterus, prostate, ovaries, etc.

In choosing to discuss hormones and their roles in modifying carcinogenic transformation of the mammary gland, we found it necessary to present information pertinent to tumor induction as well as to tumor growth, for it is clear that hormones play a role in both aspects of cancer of the breast. Regarding the role of hormones in the initial interaction of chemical carcinogen with the mammary gland, it was proposed that a certain hormonal milieu, which maintains the target tissue at some state of differentiation, caused the gland to be most susceptible to transformation. The possibility that hormones could interfere with the interaction of carcinogens and target macromolecules has not been ruled out, particularly in light of the recent work on glutathione S-transferases and the ability of steroids to bind to these proteins. However, a more probable role of hormones in the initial interaction between carcinogen and macromolecule is an indirect one, such as maintenance of the target tissue. The data by Dao (1962) clearly indicate the need for ovarian contributions during the first seven days after administration of DMBA to achieve the anticipated high yield of tumors; likewise, the low yield of tumors in the male rat supports the role of ovarian hormones in the process of transformation. However, until the critical macromolecule(s) is identified, it will not be possible to establish with certainty the role of hormones in the primary step of carcinogen interaction.

There is little doubt, however, that hormones provide a fertile soil for growth of neoplasms of the breast. Alteration of growth, measured by tumor size or tumor appearance, clearly is regulated by a variety of hormones. The most intriguing and puzzling aspect is the dual action that certain hormones demonstrate, as best exemplified by estrogens. The endogenous levels of estrogen (and progesterone) are required for induction of mammary tumors by DMBA or MC, and removal of ovaries will cause prompt cessation of growth and regression of tumor mass in a majority of the chemical carcinogen-induced carcinomas. A similar response can be obtained after administration of pharmacological doses of estrogens. Although it is clear that these tumors also require prolactin for growth and that estrogen influences prolactin secretion, the exact mechanism whereby high doses of estrogens produce the same type of response in the tumors as removal of estrogen has not been elucidated. Because there is a parallel situation in the clinical disease, this is a most important area for investigation.

Some of the apparent confusion on hormones and carcinogenic transformation of the breast results from the multihormonal control of the mammary gland. As the highly differentiated gland has a reduced susceptibility to tumor induction, any one or any combination of hormones that interferes with gland development can play an apparent role in the process of neoplasia. Unfortunately, we are essentially discussing data at the phenomenological level rather than at the more desired, molecular level. For example, does the mammary cell of the 50–60 day old female Sprague–Dawley rat present to the carcinogen a greater quantity of critical macromolecule targets for interaction, or does it present some class of macromolecules that are no longer seen after the cell has differentiated fully? Is one hormone or a combination of hormones responsible for the availability of target cell macromolecules, or do hormones act only as promoters of the initial event?

The majority of the evidence, in my opinion, points to a role for hormones as promoters, or as deterrents, after the initial critical event has occurred; knowledge of the latter aspect of hormone action is used daily in the treatment of the clinical disease. Study of the former, by trying to identify a particular hormonal milieu that would lead to a higher risk of breast cancer, is an essential approach to identification of susceptibility. However, the number of potential important hormonal factors is large, and this, combined with a changing hormonal milieu during the years prior to puberty and through menopause, presents an extremely complex picture. Adding to this complexity is the well-documented pulsatile release of hormones, a situation that requires frequent sampling during a 24-hour period. It would appear to me that if a subgroup of women can be identified on the basis of high-risk factors—e.g., obesity, genetic background, nulliparous, etc.—then a thorough study of their hormonal milieu would be a valuable contribution to furthering our knowledge regarding those hormonal factors that might play a role in the predisposition to cancer.

ACKNOWLEDGMENT

The studies from the author's laboratory have been supported by USPHS Grants CA16660, CA12836 and CA11198 (University of Rochester Cancer Center). I wish to thank Ms. K. Scheuermann for her help with the bibliography and for overcoming the burden of my handwriting when typing the manuscript.

ADDENDUM

A review of endocrine aspects of carcinogenesis was recently written by Jull (1977). In this paper, Jull described those neoplastic lesions that arise from endogenous and exogenous exposure to the protein hormones of the anterior pituitary and the steroid hormones produced by the ovary, testis, and adrenal glands. Thus, he summarized the ability of exogenous estrogen administration to induce in rats and mice pituitary tumors, adrenal tumors, tumors of the testis, renal tumors, and tumors of the female genital tract. In addition, Jull discussed breast cancer by considering the agents that can induce neoplasms in this organ—virus, chemical, x-irradiation, and hormones. He concluded that the hormonal environment may constitute a major modifying parameter and suggested four possible mechanisms whereby hormones might be involved in the carcinogenic process: (1) direct carcinogenic action has not been demonstrated but hormones can be responsible for maintaining tumor growth, (2) hormones may stimulate secretion of a second endocrine factor which may be directly or indirectly involved in carcinogenesis, (3) hormones are essential for tumor induction in certain tissues by maintaining the cells of that tissue on which the carcinogens act, and (4) hormones may modify the metabolism of chemical carcinogens to yield higher levels of proximate or ultimate carcinogens. The conclusions that were independently reached in this chapter (see Section V) are essentially in good agreement with those summarized by Jull.

An interesting series of papers (Noble *et al.*, 1975; Noble and Hoover, 1976; Noble, 1976) has appeared in the last few years dealing with a wide spectrum of tumors arising in the Nb rat after prolonged estrogenization (implantation of pellets containing estrone). From these studies, Noble (1977) has proposed a working theory of hormonal carcinogenesis. It is postulated that all normal cells are in a continuous state of progression; progression is defined as a tendency for the cell to escape from its inherent limited capacity for proliferation. Accordingly, estrogen treatment of the normal animal would cause hyperplasia, such as in the mammary gland, and as such, would make available a larger population of normal cells available for a malignant transformation. Estrogens, therefore, would not be considered as carcinogenic agents but rather as agents that accelerate the growth of cells that are exhibiting the natural process of progression. Additionally, Noble proposed that progression independent of growth may also be affected by hormones and that a fluctuating hormonal milieu (or an abrupt change in hormonal status) may act as a selection process for hormonal autonomy. While this proposal also considers estrogens as promoters rather than as direct carcinogens, it remains difficult to reconcile it with the observation of refractoriness of the mammary gland to chemical carcinogens when these chemical agents are administered during pregnancy (see Section I,D,2) or exogenous estrogen treatment (see Section I,D,3b).

REFERENCES

Agarwal, M.L., and Weinstein, I.B. (1970). *Biochemistry* **9**, 503–508.

Baba, T., and Takayama, S. (1961), *Gann* **52**, 73–82.

Baldwin, R.W., Baker, C.R., and Moore, M. (1968). *Br. J. Cancer* **22**, 776–786.

Berenblum, I. (1974). "Carcinogenesis as a Biological Problem." Am. Elsevier, New York.

Biancifori, C. (1970). *J. Natl. Cancer Inst.* **44**, 943–953.

Biancifori, C., Bonser, G.M., and Cashera, F. (1961). *Br. J. Cancer* **15**, 270–283.

Bielschowsky, F. (1961). *Acta Unio Int. Cancrum* **17**, 121–130.

Bielschowsky, F., and Hall, W.H. (1953). *Br. J. Cancer* **7**, 358–366.

Bock, F.G., and Dao, T.L. (1961). *Cancer Res.* **21**, 1024–1029.

Brennan, M.J., Grau, W.H., and Singley, J.A. (1966). *Proc. Am. Assoc. Cancer Res.* **7**, 9.

Brookes, P., and Lawley, P.D. (1964). *Nature (London)* **202**, 781–784.

Bürki, K., Liebelt, A.G., and Bresnick, E. (1973). *J. Natl. Cancer Inst.* **50**, 369–380.

Butler, T.P., and Pearson, O.H. (1971). *Cancer Res.* **31**, 817–820.

Butler, W.H. (1964). *Br. J. Cancer* **18**, 756–762.

Cantarow, A., Stasney, J., and Paschkis, K.E. (1948). *Cancer Res.* **8**, 412–418.

Cassell, E.E., Meites, J., and Welsch, C.W. (1971). *Cancer Res.* **31**, 1051–1053.

Chen, H.J., Bradley, C.J., and Meites, J. (1976). *Cancer Res.* **36**, 1414–1417.

Chuang, A.H.L., and Bresnick, E. (1976). *Cancer Res.* **36**, 4125–4129.

Cohen, N.D., and Hilf, R. (1974). *Cancer Res.* **34**, 3245–3252.

Cohen, N.D., and Hilf, R. (1975). *Proc. Soc. Exp. Biol. Med.* **148**, 339–343.

Costlow, M.E., Buschow, R.A., and McGuire, W.C. (1974). *Science* **184**, 85–86.

Cowie, A.T., and Tindal, J.S. (1971). "The Physiology of Lactation." Arnold, London.

Daniel, P.M., and Prichard, M.M.C. (1963). *Br. J. Cancer* **17**, 446–453.

Daniel, P.M., and Prichard, M.M.C. (1964). *Br. J. Cancer* **17**, 687–690.

Daniel, P.M., and Prichard, M.M.C. (1967). *Int. J. Cancer* **2**, 619–627.

Daniel, P.M., Pratt, O.E., and Prichard, M.M.C. (1967). *Nature (London)* **215**, 1142–1146.

Dao, T.L. (1962). *Cancer Res.* **22**, 973–981.

Dao, T.L. (1969a). *Science* **165**, 810–811.

Dao, T.L. (1969b). *Prog. Exp. Tumor Res.* **11**, 235–261.

Dao, T.L., and Sinha, D.K. (1972). *J. Natl. Cancer Inst.* **49**, 591–593.

Dao, T.L., and Sunderland, H. (1959). *J. Natl. Cancer Inst.* **23**, 567–585.

Dao, T.L., Bock, F.G., and Crouch, S. (1959). *Proc. Soc. Exp. Biol. Med.* **102**, 635–638.

Dao, T.L., Bock, F.G., and Greiner, M.J. (1960). *J. Natl. Cancer Inst.* **25**, 991–1003.

DeBaun, J.R., Miller, E.C., and Miller, M.A. (1970). *Cancer Res.* **30**, 577–595.

DeBaun, J.R., Rowley, J.Y., Miller, E.C., and Miller, J.A. (1968). *Proc. Soc. Exp. Biol. Med.* **129**, 268–273.

DeSombre, E.R., Kledzik, G., Marshall, S., and Meites, J. (1976). *Cancer Res.* **36**, 354–358.

Eskin, B.A. (1970). *Trans. N.Y. Acad. Sci.* [2] **32**, 911–947.

Eskin, B.A., Murphey, S.A., and Dunn, M.A. (1968). *Nature (London)* **218**, 1162.

Falconer, I.R. (1971). "Lactation." Buterworth, London.

Farber, E. (1973). *Cancer Res.* **33**, 2537–2550.

Filler, R., Morey, K.S., and Litwack, G. (1974). *Biochem. Biophys. Res. Commun.* **60**, 431–439.

Fink, M.L., Nishimura, S., and Weinstein, I.B. (1970). *Biochemistry* 9, 496–502.
Firminger, H.I., and Reuber, M.D. (1961). *J. Natl. Cancer Inst.* 27, 559–595.
Flesher, J.W. (1967). *Biochem. Pharmacol.* 16, 1821–1831.
Flesher, J.W., and Sydnor, K.L. (1960). *Proc. Soc. Exp. Biol. Med.* 104, 776–779.
Gammal, E.B., Carroll, K.K., Mühlstock, B.H., and Plunkett, E.R. (1965). *Proc. Soc. Exp. Biol. Med.* 119, 1086–1089.
Gelato, M., Marshall, S., Boudreau, M., Bruni, I.J., Campbell, G.A., and Meites, J. (1975). *Endocrinology* 96, 1292–1296.
Geyer, R.P., Bleisch, V.R., Bryant, J.E., Robbins, A.N., Saslaw, I.M., and Stare, F.J. (1950). *Cancer Res.* 11, 474–478.
Geyer, R.P., Bryant, J.E., Bleisch, V.R., Pierce, E.M., and Stare, F.J. (1953). *Cancer Res.* 13, 503–506.
Gibson, S.L., and Hilf, R. (1976). *Cancer Res.* 36, 3736–3741.
Goodall, C.M. (1965). *Endocrinology* 76, 1027–1032.
Goodall, C.M., and Butler, W.H. (1969). *Int. J. Cancer* 4, 422–429.
Griffin, A.C., Rinfret, A.P., and Corsigilia, V.F. (1953). *Cancer Res.* 13, 77–79.
Griffin, A.C., Richardson, H.L., Robertson, C.H., O'Neal, M.A., and Spain, J.D. (1955). *J. Natl. Cancer Inst.* 15, 1623–1628.
Griswold, D.P., Skipper, H.E., Laster, W.R., Jr., Wilcox, W.S., and Schabel, F.M., Jr. (1966). *Cancer Res.* 26, 2169–2180.
Gropper, L., and Shimkin, M.B. (1967). *Cancer Res.* 27, 26–32.
Gruenstein, M., Shay, H., and Shimkin, M.B. (1964). *Cancer Res.* 24, 1656–1658.
Gruenstein, M., Meranze, D.R., Thatcher, D., and Shimkin, M.B. (1966). *J. Natl. Cancer Inst.* 36, 483–502.
Grünberger, D., and Weinstein, I.B. (1971). *J. Biol. Chem.* 246, 1123–1128.
Gullino, P.M., Pettigrew, H.M., and Grantham, F.H. (1975). *J. Natl. Cancer Inst.* 54, 401–414.
Hamilton, T., and Jacobson, H.I. (1965). *Proc. Soc. Exp. Biol. Med.* 118, 827–829.
Harmon, J.T., and Hilf, R. (1976a). *Cancer Res.* 36, 3993–4000.
Harmon, J.T., and Hilf, R. (1976b). *Eur. J. Cancer* 12, 933–934.
Heidelberger, C. (1975). *Annu. Rev. Biochem.* 44, 79–121.
Helfenstein, J.E., Young, S., and Currie, A.R. (1962). *Nature (London)* 196, 1108.
Heston, W.E. (1958). *Ann. N.Y. Acad. Sci.* 71, 931–942.
Heston, W.E., and Vlahakis, G. (1968). *J. Natl. Cancer Inst.* 40, 1161–1166.
Heuson, J.C., and Legros, N. (1968). *Eur. J. Cancer* 4, 1–7.
Heuson, J.C., and Legros, N. (1970). *Eur. J. Cancer* 6, 349–351.
Heuson, J.C., and Legros, N. (1972). *Cancer Res.* 32, 226–232.
Heuson, J.C., Coune, A., and Heimann, R. (1967). *Exp. Cell Res.* 45, 351–360.
Hilf, R. (1973). *Methods Cancer Res.* 7, 55–114.
Hilf, R., Goldenberg, H., Michel, I., Carrington, M.J., Bell, C., Gruenstein, M., Meranze, D.R., and Shimkin, M.B. (1969). *Cancer Res.* 29, 977–988.
Hilf, R., Harmon, J.T., Matusik, R.J., and Ringler, M.B. (1976). *In* "Control Mechanisms in Cancer" (W.E. Criss, T. Ono, and J.R. Sabine, eds.), pp. 1–24. Raven, New York.
Howell, J.S., Marchant, J., and Orr, J.W. (1954). *Br. J. Cancer* 8, 635–646.
Huggins, C., Briziarelli, G., and Sutton, H., Jr. (1959a). *J. Exp. Med.* 109, 25–42.
Huggins, C., Grand, L.C., and Brillantes, F.P. (1959b). *Proc. Natl. Acad. Sci. U.S.A.* 45, 1294–1300.
Huggins, C., Grand, L.C., and Brillantes, F.P. (1961). *Nature (London)* 189, 204–207.
Huggins, C., Moon, R.C., and Morii, S. (1962). *Proc. Natl. Acad. Sci. U.S.A.* 48, 379–386.
Huggins, C., Ford, E., and Jensen, E.V. (1965). *Science* 147, 1153–1154.
Irving, C.C. (1970). *Metab. Conjugation Metab. Hydrolysis* I, 53–119.

Irving, C.C., and Veazey, R.A. (1971). *Cancer Res.* 31, 19–22.
Irving, C.C., Janss, D.H., and Russell, L.T. (1971). *Cancer Res.* 31, 387–391.
Jabara, A.G. (1967). *Br. J. Cancer* 21, 418–429.
Jabara, A.G. and Hartcourt, A.G. (1970). *Pathology* 2, 115–123.
Jabara, A.G., Toyne, P.H., and Fisher, R.J. (1972). *Br. J. Cancer* 26, 265–273.
Jabara, A.G., Wilson, F.C., and Fisher, R.J. (1974). *J. Pathol.* 113, 235–240.
Janss, D.H., and Irving, C.C. (1972). *J. Natl. Cancer Inst.* 49, 765–771.
Janss, D.H., and Moon, R.C. (1970). *Cancer Res.* 30, 473–479.
Janss, D.H., Moon, R.C., and Irving, C.C. (1972). *Cancer Res.* 32, 254–258.
Josimovich, J.B., Reynolds, M., and Cobo, E. (1974). "Lactogenic Hormones, Fetal Nutrition and Lactation." Wiley, New York.
Jull, J.W. (1961). *Proc. Can. Cancer Res. Conf.* 4, 109–123.
Jull, J.W. (1966). *Cancer Res.* 26, 2368–2373.
Jull, J.W. (1973). *Adv. Cancer Res.* 7, 131–186.
Jull, J.W. (1977). *In* "Chemical Carcinogens" (C.E. Searle, ed.), ACS Monograph 173, pp. 52–81. American Chemical Society, Washington, D.C.
Jull, J.W., and Huggins, C. (1960). *Nature (London)* 188, 73.
Jull, J.W., Streeter, D.J., and Sutherland, L. (1966). *J. Natl. Cancer Inst.* 37, 409–420.
Kawahara, I. (1967). *Gann* 58, 253–266.
Kelly, P.A., Bradley, C., Shiu, R.P.C., Meites, J., and Friesen, H.G. (1974). *Proc. Soc. Exp. Biol. Med.* 146, 816–819.
Ketterer, B., Ross-Mansell, P., and Whitehead, J.K. (1967). *Biochem. J.* 103, 316–324.
Kidson, C., and Kirby, K.S. (1964). *Nature (London)* 203, 599–603.
Kim, U., and Furth, J. (1960). *Proc. Soc. Exp. Biol. Med.* 103, 643–645.
Kim, U., and Furth, J. (1976). *Vitam. Horm. (N.Y.)* 34, 107–136.
Kirschbaum, A. (1957). *Cancer Res.* 17, 432–453.
Klaiber, M.S., Gruenstein, M., Meranze, D.R., and Shimkin, M.B. (1969). *Cancer Res.* 29, 999–1001.
Korner, A. (1965). *Recent Prog. Horm. Res.* 21, 205–240.
Krarup, T. (1967). *Acta Pathol. Microbiol. Scand.* 70, 241–248.
Krarup, T. (1969). *Int. J. Cancer* 4, 61–75.
Kratochwil, K. (1971). *J. Embryol. Exp. Morphol.* 25, 141–153.
Kretchmer, N., and Rossi, E. (1974). "Milk and Lactation." Karger, Basel.
Larson, B.L., and Smith, V.R. (1974). "Lactation: A Comprehensive Treatise." Academic Press, New York.
Leathem, J.H. (1951). *Cancer Res.* 11, 266.
Lee, K.Y., and Goodall, C.M. (1968). *Biochem. J.* 106, 767–768.
Leung, B.S., Sasaki, G.H., and Keung, J.S. (1975). *Cancer Res.* 35, 621–627.
Lo, S.M. (1964). *Vopr. Onkol.* 10, 41–47.
Lotlikar, P.D., Enomoto, M., Miller, E.C., and Miller, J.A. (1964). *Cancer Res.* 24, 1835–1844.
Lyons, W.R., Li, C.H., and Johnson, R.E. *Recent Prog. Horm. Res.* 14, (1958). 219–248.
McCarthy, J.D. (1965). *Am. J. Surg.* 110, 720–723.
McCormick, G.M., and Moon, R.C. (1965). *Br. J. Cancer* 19, 160–166.
MacMahon, B., Cole, P., Len, T.M., Lowe, C.R., Mirra, A.P., Raunihar, B., Salber, E.J., Valaoses, V.G., and Yuasa, S. (1970). *Bull. W.H.O.* 43, 209–221.
Maisin, J., and Coolen, M.L. (1936). *C. R. Seances Soc. Biol. Ses Fil.* 123, 159–160.
Malejka-Giganti, D., Gutmann, H.R., and Rydell, R.E. (1973). *Cancer Res.* 33, 2489–2497.
Malejka-Giganti, D., Rydell, R.E., and Gutmann, H.R. (1977). *Cancer Res.* 37, 111–117.
Manni, A., Trujillo, J.E., and Pearson, O.H. (1977). *Cancer Res.* 37, 1216–1219.
Marchant, J. (1961). *Br. J. Cancer* 15, 821–827.

Marchant, J., Orr, J.W., and Woodhouse, D.L. (1954). *Nature (London)* **173**, 307.
Marquardt, H., Bendich, A., Philips, F.S., and Hoffmann, D. (1971). *Chem.-Biol. Interact.* **3**, 1–11.
Matusik, R.J. and Hilf, R. (1976). *J. Natl. Cancer Inst.* **56**, 659–661.
Meranze, D.R., Gruenstein, M., and Shimkin, M.B. (1969). *Int. J. Cancer* **4**, 480–486.
Miller, E.C., and Miller, J.A. (1973). *In* "The Molecular Biology of Cancer" (H. Busch, ed.), pp. 377–402. Academic Press, New York.
Miller, E.C., Miller, J.A., and Hartmann, A.A. (1961). *Cancer Res.* **21**, 815–824.
Miller, E.C., Smith, J.Y., and Miller, J.A. (1970). *Proc. Am. Assoc. Cancer Res.* **11**, 56.
Mittra, I. (1974). *Nature (London)* **248**, 525–526.
Mittra, I., and Hayward, J.L. (1974). *Lancet* **1**, 885–888.
Mittra, I., Hayward, J.L., and McNeilly, A.S. (1974). *Lancet* **1**, 889–891.
Moon, R.C. (1969). *Int. J. Cancer* **4**, 312–317.
Moon, R.C., Janss, D.H., and Young, S. (1969). *J. Histochem. Cytochem.* **17**, 182–186.
Morris, H.P., and Firminger, H.I. (1956). *J. Natl. Cancer Inst.* **16**, 927–949.
Mühlbock, O. (1953). *Acta Endocrinol. (Copenhagen)* **12**, 105–114.
Mühlbock, O. (1956). *Adv. Cancer Res.* **4**, 371–391.
Nagasawa, H., and Meites, J. (1970). *Proc. Soc. Exp. Biol. Med.* **135**, 469–472.
Nagasawa, H., and Yanai, R. (1974). *J. Natl. Cancer Inst.* **52**, 609–610.
Nagasawa, H., Yanai, R., and Tanaguchi, H. (1976). *Cancer Res.* **36**, 2223–2226.
Nebert, D.W., and Gelboin, H.V. (1969). *Arch. Biochem. Biophys.* **134**, 76–89.
Newman, W.C., and Moon, R.C. (1966). *Cancer Res.* **26**, 1938–1942.
Newman, W.C., and Moon, R.C. (1968). *Cancer Res.* **28**, 864–868.
Noble, R.L. (1976). *Ann. Roy. Cell Phys. Surg. Canada* **9**, 169–180.
Noble, R.L. (1977). *Cancer Res.* **37**, 82–94.
Noble, R.L., Hochachka, B.C., and King, D. (1975). *Cancer Res.* **35**, 766–780.
Noble, R.L., and Hoover, L.A. (1975). *Cancer Res.* **35**, 2935–2941.
Orr, J.W. (1943). *J. Pathol. Biol.* **55**, 483–488.
Pasteels, J.L., Heuson, J.C., Heuson-Stiennan, J., and Legros, N. (1976). *Cancer Res.* **36**, 2162–2170.
Pearson, O.H., Llerana, O., Llerana, L., Molina, A., and Butler, T. (1969). *Trans. Assoc. Am. Physicians* **82**, 225–238.
Perry, D.J. (1961). *Br. J. Cancer* **15**, 284–290.
Prodi, G., Rocchi, P., and Grill, S. (1970). *Cancer Res.* **30**, 1020–1023.
Prohaska, J.V., Brunschwig, A., and Wilson, H. (1949). *Arch. Surg. (Chicago)* **38**, 328–333.
Raynaud, A. (1961). *In* "Milk: The Mammary Gland and its Secretion" (S.K. Kon and A.T. Cowie, eds.). Vol. 1, pp. 3–46. Academic Press, New York.
Raynaud, A. (1971). *In* "Lactation" (I.R. Falconer, ed.), pp. 3–29. Butterworth, London.
Rees, E.D., and Huggins, C. (1960). *Cancer Res.* **20**, 963–971.
Reuber, M.D. (1965). *J. Natl. Cancer Inst.* **34**, 587–594.
Reuber, M.D. (1969). *J. Natl. Cancer Inst.* **43**, 445–451.
Reuber, M.D., and Firminger, H.I. (1962). *J. Natl. Cancer Inst.* **29**, 933–943.
Robertson, C.H., O'Neal, M.A., Richardson, H.L., and Griffin, A.C. (1954). *Cancer Res.* **14**, 549–553.
Rumsfield, H.W., Jr., Miller, W.C., Jr., and Baumann, C.A. (1951). *Cancer Res.* **11**, 814–819.
Segaloff, A., and Maxfield, W.S. (1971). *Cancer Res.* **31**, 166–168.
Shay, H., Aegertar, E.A., Gruenstein, M., and Komarov, S.A. (1949). *J. Natl. Cancer Inst.* **10**, 255–266.
Shay, H., Friedmann, B., Gruenstein, M., and Weinhouse, S. (1950). *Cancer Res.* **10**, 797–800.
Shay, H., Harris, C., and Gruenstein, M. (1952). *J. Natl. Cancer Inst.* **13**, 307–331.

Shay, H., Harris, C., and Gruenstein, M. (1960). *Acta Unio Int. Cancrum* **16**, 225–232.

Shellabarger, C.J. (1967). *J. Natl. Cancer Inst.* **38**, 73–77.

Shellabarger, C.J. (1969). *Proc. Am. Assoc. Cancer Res.* **10**, 79.

Shellabarger, C.J. (1972). *Cancer Res.* **32**, 883–885.

Shellabarger, C.J. (1976). *In* "Biology of Radiation Carcinogenesis" (J.M. Yuhas, R.W. Tennant, and J.D. Regan, eds.), pp. 31–43. Raven, New York.

Shisa, H., and Nishizuka, Y. (1968). *Br. J. Cancer* **22**, 70–76.

Silverberg, E. (1977). *Ca* **27**, 26–41.

Sinha, D., Cooper, D., and Dao, T.L. (1973). *Cancer Res.* **33**, 411–414.

Skoryna, S.C. (1955). *Proc. Can. Cancer Res. Conf.* **1**, 107–113.

Smith, G.J., Ohl, V.S., and Litwack, G. (1977). *Cancer Res.* **37**, 8–14.

Smith, R.D., Hilf, R., and Senior, A.E. (1976). *Cancer Res.* **36**, 3726–2731.

Smith, R.D., Hilf, R., and Senior, A.E. (1977a). *Cancer Res.* **37**, 595–598.

Smith, R.D., Hilf, R., and Senior, A.E. (1977b). *Cancer Res.* **37**, 4070–4074.

Sorof, S., and Young, E.M. (1973). *Cancer Res.* **33**, 2010–2013.

Sterental, A., Dominguez, J.M., Weissman, C., and Pearson, O.H. (1963). *Cancer Res.* **23**, 481–484.

Stern, E., and Mickey, M.R. (1969). *Br. J. Cancer* **23**, 391–400.

Sweeney, M.J., Poore, G.A., Kornfeld, A.C., Bach, N.J., Owen, N.V., and Clemens, J.A. (1975). *Cancer Res.* **35**, 106–109.

Sydnor, K.L., and Cockrell, B. (1963). *Endocrinology* **73**, 427–432.

Sydnor, K.L., Butenandt, O., Brillantes, F.P., and Huggins, C. (1962). *J. Natl. Cancer Inst.* **29**, 805–814.

Tamulski, T.S., Morreal, C.E., and Dao, T.L. (1973). *Cancer Res.* **33**, 3117–3122.

Teller, M.N., Stock, C.C., Stohr, G., Merker, P.C., Kaufman, R.J., Escher, G.C., and Bowie, M. (1966a). *Cancer Res.* **26**, 245–252.

Teller, M.N., Stock, C.C. and Bowie, M. (1966b). *Cancer Res.* **26**, 2329–2333.

Toh, Y.C. (1971). *Br. J. Cancer* **25**, 516–519.

Toh, Y.C. (1972). *J. Natl. Cancer Inst.* **48**, 113–118.

Toh, Y.C. (1973). *Adv. Cancer Res.* **18**, 155–209.

Turkington, R.W. (1974). *Cancer Res.* **34**, 758–763.

Turkington, R.W., and Hill, R.L. (1969). *Science* **163**, 1458–1460.

Vonderhaar, B.K. (1977). *Endocrinology* **100**, 1423–1431.

Weisburger, E.K., and Weisburger, J.H. (1958). *Adv. Cancer Res.* **5**, 331–431.

Weisburger, E.K., Grantham, P.H., and Weisburger, J.H. (1964). *Biochemistry* **3**, 808–812.

Weisburger, E.K., Yamamoto, R.S., Glass, R.M., Grantham, P.H., and Weisburger, J.H. (1968). *Endocrinology* **82**, 685–692.

Weisburger, J.H. (1968). *N. Z. J. Med.* **67**, 44–58.

Weisburger, J.H., Weisburger, E.K., Griswold, D.P., Jr., and Casey, A.E. (1968). *Life Sci.* **7**, 259–266.

Welsch, C.W., and Meites, J. (1970). *Experientia* **26**, 1133–1134.

Welsch, C.W., and Nagasawa, H. (1977). *Cancer Res.* **37**, 951–963.

Welsch, C.W., Clemens, J.A., and Meites, J. (1968). *J. Natl. Cancer Inst.* **41**, 465–471.

Welsch, C.W., Clemens, J.A., and Meites, J. (1969). *Cancer Res.* **29**, 1541–1549.

Welsch, C.W., Iturri, G., and Meites, J. (1973). *Int. J. Cancer* **12**, 206–212.

Widnell, C.C., and Tata, J.R. (1966). *Biochem. J.* **98**, 621–629.

Wieder, R., Thatcher, D., and Shimkin, M.B. (1967). *J. Natl. Cancer Inst.* **38**, 959–967.

World Health Organization (1974). *Int. Agency Res. Cancer, Monogr.* **6**, 000–000.

Yokoro, K., and Furth, J. (1961). *Proc. Soc. Exp. Biol. Med.* **107**, 921–924.

Young, S. (1961). *Nature (London)* **190**, 356–357.

CHAPTER 5

How Important Are Steroids in Regulating the Growth of Mammary Tumors?

R.J.B. King

I. GENERAL COMMENTS ON MAMMARY TUMOR GROWTH

There is no doubt that manipulation of the steroidal environment affects mammary tumor growth in many species. The questions to be discussed in this article are how important steroids are in controlling the growth pattern and the physiological mechanisms whereby the steroid effects are mediated. Biochemical and molecular events involved in steroid-mediated cell division will only be considered in a superficial manner. For more detailed views, the reader should consult Bruchovsky and Lesser (1975), King et al. (1976b), King (1978), and Mainwaring (1977). Emphasis will largely be placed on explaining the growth characteristics of human breast tumors, and an extensive review of the rodent literature will not be attempted.

In the human, endocrine therapy very rarely, if ever, achieves extinction of the tumor. Dramatic decreases in tumor size can be achieved in a proportion of tumors by ablative and additive therapy, but these are almost invariably of a temporary nature. The course of the metastatic disease in a woman who exhibits a good response to endocrine therapy (adrenalectomy) is demonstrated in Fig. 1; the patient improves for a variable period, in this case 8 months, then goes into decline and dies. Analogous results are obtained with a range of other endocrine treatments. Thus, hormones can markedly affect mammary tumors but only on a temporary basis; endocrine therapy for the metastatic disease is palliative, not curative.

In rodents, the situation is superficially different. Removal of the endocrine stimulus from tumor-bearing mice produces prompt and apparently complete regression. However, when the stimulus is reapplied, regrowth of the tumor at the same locus is observed (Foulds, 1969).

Thus, endocrine treatment, although having a greater effect in rodents than in the human, does not eliminate the tumor. Hence, mammary tumor growth is responsive to, but not dependent on, endocrine factors. The view that mammary tumor cells are responsive to rather than dependent on steroids is compatible with the growing body of data that, in most cases, steroids are modulating agents rather than switch operators (King, 1976). The same general conclusion can be reached from considerations of cell kinetics; agents (including steroids) that affect proliferation do so by modulating an existing reaction rate rather than by switching cells in and out of cycle

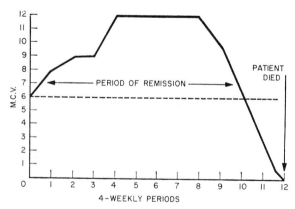

FIG. 1. Response to adrenalectomy of a woman with advanced breast cancer. Reprinted from Hayward (1970). M.C.V. denotes mean clinical value and is an assessment of all measurable lesions. A value of 6 indicates no overall change; a value greater than 6 indicates a decrease in size to a maximum improvement value of 12; a value smaller than 6 indicates disease progressing.

(Smith and Martin, 1974; Armelin, 1975). This topic is important to further considerations of the way in which steroids interact with other factors in determining the size of a tumor and will therefore be discussed in some detail later in this chapter.

Returning to the question of regrowth of human tumors after a period of remission, one can ask the question: What causes the resumption of active growth? The simplest and conventional explanation is that preferential selection of unresponsive cells occurs in the steroid-poor environment. Such selection processes undoubtedly occur both *in vivo* and in cell culture. However, if one accepts that steroids are only growth-modulating agents, an alternative explanation for the regrowth phenomenon can be suggested (Fig. 2). Tumor growth is determined by the balance between increase in cell number caused by proliferation and decrease by cell loss. Both of these processes can be regulated in a positive and negative fashion by many factors; steroids represent only a limited number of those factors, not necessarily the most important ones. Alteration of the hormone environment could then temporarily change the growth equation in favor of decreased tumor size until some of the other factors reset themselves and provoke accelerated growth. The fundamental difference between this model and the more conventional one is that regrowth does not necessarily involve genotypic changes leading to the production of endocrine unresponsive cells. My thoughts were directed to this possibility by two pieces of data. It is a clinical observation that human breast tumors that have responded to ovariectomy and then relapsed, respond to subsequent hormone manipulation (Hayward, 1970). This is hard to reconcile with the preferential selection of unresponsive cells unless one further postulates the selection of altered, but still

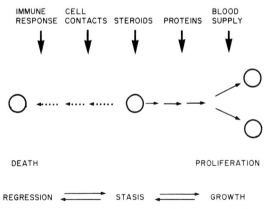

FIG. 2. Regulation of tumor size. The location of the factors printed above the heavy arrows is not meant to indicate where that particular factor is though to act.

endocrine-sensitive, cells. The second piece of data relates to the observed phenotypic changes in human breast tumors: Only about 10% of tumors change their estradiol receptor phenotype over a period of up to 6 years (King *et al.*, 1978). If this phenotypic change is a reflection of the alteration in cell composition of a tumor, it seems intuitively to be too small to explain the frequent recurrence of tumor within months of achieving a good response to endocrine therapy.

Neither of the observations just made proves that cell selection has not occurred, but I think they suggest that alternate models should be considered. The present article discusses various aspects of the nonselection model, but I would like to stress that, while thinking it explains some features of endocrine-related growth of human breast tumors, the conventional cell selection model is also important.

II. GROWTH CHARACTERISTICS OF HUMAN BREAST TUMORS

A number of estimates have put the "doubling time" for tumor volume (T_D) at 3–200 days, about half the estimates giving T_D's of less than 25 days (Sylvestrini *et al.*, 1974; Pearlman, 1976; Meyer and Bauer, 1976). Pearlman (1976) calculated the doubling time from the time between mastectomy and recurrence (of measured size) at the site of the mastectomy scar, and showed a linear relationship between tumor doubling time and survival after mastectomy (Fig. 3). From these data it would appear that a 3-fold increase in doubling time would result in a 3-fold increase in survival time. He further calculated that after mastectomy, patients had a 70% probability of being alive after 30 doublings falling to 10% after 90 doublings. So, for a patient with a tumor doubling time of 1 month, there is a 10% probability of being alive at 90 months. If endocrine therapy slows the doubling time by a factor of three then, at 90 months, only 30 doublings will have occurred, with a 70% probability of being alive at that time.

In practice, the clinical benefits of treatment are not as good as this (Hayward, 1970). Such calculations are very crude and rely on several assumptions but, in terms of the thesis being developed in this article, the above calculations suggest that the effects of endocrine therapy in responsive patients could be explained by only a small change in growth rate of the tumor. Put another way, this means that hormones need only be relatively weak modulating agents to account for their effects on human breast cancer.

Tumor growth can be analyzed in a different way, namely, by measurement of cell cycle parameters. The most common method as applied to human breast tumors is the assessment of DNA synthesis by means of

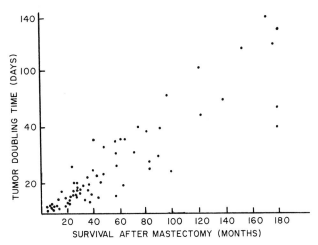

F<small>IG</small>. 3. Relationship of mammary tumor doubling time to duration of survival after mastectomy. From Pearlman (1976).

[³H]thymidine ([³H]TdR] incorporation; from these data, cell cycle parameters can be calculated (Steele, 1977). Estimates of the proportion of human breast cancer cells that are in the DNA synthetic stage of the cell cycle at any one time vary from 1 to 30% (Sylvestrini *et al.*, 1974; Pearlman, 1976; Meyer and Bauer, 1976; Nordenskjöld *et al.*, 1976). This [³H]TdR labeling index decreases with age of the patient, which is compatible with the idea of hormonal regulation of the cell cycle, but such a relationship is not a simple one.

Nordenskjöld and colleagues (1976) carried out a very interesting series of experiments on this point. They obtained [³H]TdR labeling data on serial biopsies of human breast tumors before and after either ovariectomy or treatment with the antiestrogen, Tamoxifen, taking care to remove nonviable cells first. All tumors that regressed showed a fall in labeling index, but the fall was variable with respect to both time and magnitude of response. Maximum depression occurred by 4 weeks posttreatment, with a mean 10-fold fall in labeled cells. After a further 6 weeks when DNA synthesis was still low, tumor size had only decreased to about half the pretreatment value. Representative examples of their results are reproduced in Fig. 4. Some stationary tumors in incomplete remission exhibited quite large increases in [³H]TdR incorporation; in one unresponsive but stationary tumor, approximately 20% of the cells were undergoing DNA synthesis.

It is clear that changes in tumor growth cannot be predicted from labeling indices or other measurements of DNA synthesis. This phenomenon has been well documented for a wide range of tumors (Steele, 1967, 1977) and

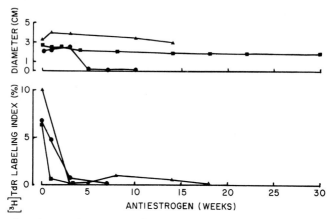

FIG. 4. Effect of Tamoxifen *in vivo* on [³H]TdR labeling index and tumor diameter of human breast tumors. Modified from Nordenskjöld *et al.* (1976). The characteristics of three different tumors are shown, each represented by a different symbol.

has been explained in terms of growth fractions and cell loss. Both these topics will be elaborated on later, but a useful point can be made at this stage about cell loss. Loss can occur either by desquamation or by death and, in tumors, cell loss is extensive (Steele, 1967, 1977), human breast tumors being no exception. Estimates of 35–45% loss of daughter cells in actively growing human breast tumors have been made (Sylvestrini *et al.*, 1974; Tubiana and Malaise, 1976). Theoretically, a 50% loss of daughter cells would result in a static tumor, and anything greater than this value would produce regression. Thus, a small increase in cell loss, provided it was by death rather than metastasis, could have important effects.

The point to be made is that one cannot just think of endocrine effects on tumor size in terms of cell proliferation; changes in cell loss could be just as important. Furthermore, endocrine effects on proliferation and cell loss could be mediated indirectly via other parts of the body as well as directly on the tumor itself. Some of the factors affecting mammary tumor growth and endocrine effects thereon will be considered. In order to simplify presentation of the information, the two components of the growth equation—cell proliferation and loss—will be considered separately.

III. REGULATION OF CELL PROLIFERATION

The most popular model for cell proliferation is that of the classical cell cycle in which the proliferative cycle is divided into a phase of DNA synthesis (S) followed by a gap (G_2) before mitosis (M) and another gap (G_1) before the next S phase (Prescott, 1976; Steele, 1977). Direct application of this model to tumor cell proliferation proved unsatisfactory and the concepts of "growth fraction," G_0, and "cell arrest in G_1" were devised and added to the cell cycle model (Steele, 1977).

However, experimental features such as the frequency of labeled mitoses and the time course of cell entry into S phase were not satisfactorily explained by the modified classical models and, largely as a result of experimentation with androgen-sensitive S115 cells, a probability model was proposed (Smith and Martin, 1973). The basic tenets of the probability model are that the cycle is divided into a B phase of relatively fixed duration and an A state of very variable length. Transition from A state to B phase is a random process that can be mathematically defined by a probability factor P analogous to the half-life factor of a radioisotope. Changes in proliferation rate of cells are largely mediated by changes in P. For further general points about this model the reader is referred to Smith and Martin (1974), Brooks (1977), and Shields and Smith (1977).

The two models are represented in Fig. 5. In the classical model (Fig. 5a), cells can be arrested either in G_1 at restriction point X_1 or a distinct G_0 phase can be suggested, exit from which requires a definite stimulus in order to overcome the block at X_2. The loci of the major control points X_1 and X_2 have been allocated by guesswork and are not meant to represent precise points in the cycle. This caveat also applies to the probability model (Fig. 5b). Transition from A state to B phase occurs by passing through X_3 with a certain probability. X_3 is thought to be at or near the classical G_1/S boundary

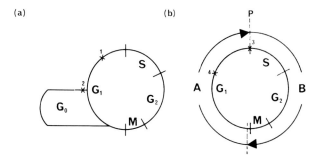

FIG. 5. Cell proliferation models. (a) Classical cell cycle. Cells pass through a cycle made up of G_1, S, G_2, and M phases. Cells progressing around this cycle comprise the "growth fraction" in contradistinction to the cells that have decycled into the G_0 compartment. (b) Probability model (Smith and Martin, 1974). The cell cycle terms have been included to aid comparison between the two models. The proliferation cycle is divided into a B phase of relatively constant duration and an A state of variable length. For any given cell population there is a certain probability of passing from A to B. This probability can be altered by agents such as hormones. Major control points are represented by X. For further details, see text.

(Brooks, 1977). Many agents, including steroid hormones, are known to exhibit a lag of several hours between their addition and the onset of DNA synthesis. For this reason regulation point X_4 has been included in Fig. 5b, although X_4 must be closely linked with X_3. As discussed by Smith and Martin (1974), one of the main distinctions between models a and b is in the kinetics of entry into DNA synthesis/cell division of quiescent cells.

If the proportion of cells that have not divided is plotted against time after adding a proliferative agent, one obtains the theoretical curves shown in Fig. 6. According to the classical model (Fig. 6a–c), there is a lag period representing the time taken to overcome blocks at either X_1 and/or X_2 (Fig. 5a). If such cells were completely synchronous, the results shown in Fig. 6a would be obtained. If the durations of the lag phase of a cell population were normally distributed, curves like 6b and 6c would result. With the probability model, in which the addition of a stimulus raises the probability of overcoming X_3 (Fig. 5b), an exponential curve would be obtained (Fig. 6d), the slope of which is determined by P.

When such calculations are made with the S115 cells stimulated by testosterone (Fig. 7), the results clearly favor the probability model (Robinson et al., 1976). The same conclusion is reached from other studies on proliferation rates of cells in culture (Jimenez de Asua et al., 1977; Shields and Smith, 1977; Smith, 1977).

In practical terms, how does the probability model influence our thinking about the way in which steroids and other regulatory agents affect proliferation? Smith and Martin (1973) have pointed out that the doubling time of

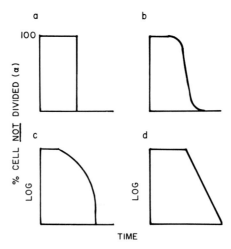

FIG. 6. Theoretical curves for the exit of cells from interphase. From Smith and Martin (1974). Curves a–c denote the classical cell cycle. Curve d represents the probability model.

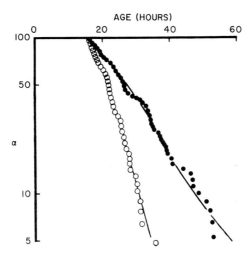

FIG. 7. Time-lapse cinematographic analysis of exit from interphase of S115 mouse mammary tumor cells cultured in the presence (○) and absence (●) of testosterone. Modified from Robinson *et al.* (1976) and reproduced from King (1978). α = % cells not divided.

cells growing with P values in excess of 0.05 is little influenced by changes in P. However, very fine control of growth can be achieved with P values below 0.02. This is illustrated in Fig. 8, in which theoretical P values have been calculated for different doubling times. It was suggested above that a 3-fold change in growth rate induced by steroids could explain many of the features of human breast tumor response to therapy. From Fig. 8 it can be seen that

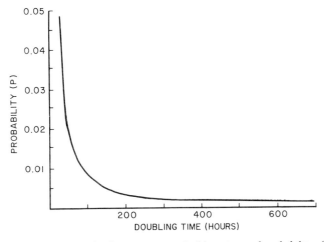

FIG. 8. Theoretical relationship between tumor doubling time and probability of entering B phase. Modified from Smith and Martin (1973).

such a rate change would only require a 2- to 3-fold change in P for tumors with doubling times of greater than 100 hours.

The relevance of this calculation can be appreciated when related to proliferation data on mammary tumors. The doubling times of fast-growing human tumors are in excess of 100 hours (see above). Such calculations overestimate the true cell cycle times, but even so it is clear that mammary tumor proliferation rates *in vivo* would be very sensitive to changes in P. Values of P are difficult to derive from published results but, applying the frequency of labeled mitoses method (Smith and Martin, 1974) to the data on estrone–progesterone-induced growth of GR mouse mammary tumors *in vivo* published by Janik *et al.* (1975), one can calculate that hormone withdrawal alters P from 0.12 to 0.06.

The point was made earlier that steroids were only one of several types of agents that could influence tumor cell proliferation and tumor size. What the probability model predicts is that effects of these agents on P need not be large to achieve the observed changes in mammary tumor growth both in respect to the remission and progression stages of the disease, as illustrated in Fig. 1.

Biochemical studies on mechanisms whereby steroids might regulate proliferation have been confined largely to the regulation of RNA metabolism (Mueller *et al.*, 1972; Katzenellenbogen and Gorski, 1975; Mainwaring, 1977). Detailed discussion of these results will not be attempted here but, in the light of the foregoing discussion, it is noteworthy that early (less than 24 hours) effects of steroids on mRNA production by cells exhibiting a proliferative response are difficult to detect (Frolik and Gorski, 1977; Parker, 1978). This is in marked contrast to the results obtained with cell types induced to make specific proteins (Rosen and O'Malley, 1975; Schimke *et al.*, 1977; Tata, 1978). This anomaly might be due to different response pathways in cells undergoing proliferation as compared with those manufacturing secretory proteins but, from the above discussion, a partial explanation may reside in the small response to be anticipated in the proliferative cells.

IV. CELL LOSS

The preceding section dealt with the proliferative component of the growth equation. Cell loss is an important factor in that equation and will now be discussed in relation to changes in mammary tumor size. Of the two loss components—cell death and shedding of live cells to other parts of the body—the former appears to be quantitatively the most important. Growing MTW9 mouse mammary tumors spill about 3×10^6 cells per g tissue per hour into the blood stream, a figure that is unaltered when regression is induced by removal of the endocrine stimulus (Butler and Gullino, 1975). This rate of loss of viable cells is about two orders of magnitude less than estimates of total cell loss calculated from the discrepancy between tumor doubling times and cell cycle times (Steele, 1967, 1977). Hence it is reasonable to conclude that cell loss is primarily by means of cell death, and attention will be confined to this topic.

CELL DEATH

Two types of death can be defined—a general, nonspecific variety and a more specific type that has been called programed or active cell death and may include apoptosis (Wyllie, 1974; Cooper *et al.*, 1975). Programmed cell death is an important feature of embryological development (Saunders, 1966), but no evidence is available as to whether or not it is a relevant factor in mammary tumors. Apoptosis does occur in human mammary tumors (Wyllie, 1974), but poor biochemical characterization of this phenomenon does not yet allow the conclusion that apoptosis is analogous to programed cell death. The latter term applies to situations in which elevated macromolecular synthesis leads to death, the best documented example of which is the corticoid-induced lysis of lymphoma cells (Thompson and Lippman, 1974; Munck and Leung, 1977). Indirect attempts at distinguishing between general and specific cell death have been made by asking whether specific receptors are required for steroid-induced death of mammary tumor cells in culture. High levels of estradiol (10^{-6} M) result in the death of human MCF-7 mammary tumor cells, known to contain estradiol receptors. However, other receptor-negative cells derived from mammary tumors are also killed by estradiol, and estradiol-17α has the same inhibitory effect as the 17β isomer on MCF-7 cells, suggesting a nonspecific killing mechanism (Lippman, 1976). On the other hand, the androgen-induced death of mouse S115 cells is not mimicked by estradiol or diethylstilbestrol (King *et al.*, 1976a). Obviously, cell culture systems will be useful in studying steroid-medicated death, but the high concentrations of steroid required for this effect means that caution will have to be exerted in interpreting the results so obtained because of nonspecific, toxic effects.

General as opposed to programed death occurs extensively in human mammary tumors, with figures ranging from 70 to 90% of the cell production rate being quoted (Sylvestrini *et al.*, 1974; Meyer and Bauer, 1976; Tubiana and Malaise, 1976; Steele, 1977). Such values have been obtained with actively growing tumors, so the question arises as to whether steroids alter the death rate. No data are available for human mammary tumors and virtually no information is available for mammary tumors of other species.

Janik *et al.* (1975) reported no difference in cell death rate in GR mouse mammary tumors growing under the combined influence of estrone and progesterone as compared with tumors regressing after steroid withdrawal. However, such a conclusion might not be applicable to tumors regressing under the additive influence of high levels of steroids.

There have been several studies on possible mechanisms of hormone-induced regression of mammary tumors (Hilf *et al.*, 1967; Lanzerotti and Gullino, 1972). These publications have been devoted largely to mea-surements of lysosomal enzymes and enzymes related to energy metabolism. Quite large changes have been noted in these experiments regardless of whether regression was induced by hormone withdrawal or addition. How-ever, the changes occur when regression is under way, so it is unlikely that they represent primary loci of actions of the hormones. The enzyme changes are more likely to be consequences than causes of regression. Indeed, if one wanted to generalize from the GR mammary tumor data just mentioned (Janik *et al.*, 1975) that cell death is similar in growing and regressing tumors, then one could say that all the enzyme studies are related to de-creased proliferation, not increased death. This criticism would of course apply to any experiments in which mixed populations of cells were used.

An interesting suggestion has recently been made by Rouleau and Gullino (1977). They noted that total soluble protein from mammary tumors regress-ing because of hormone withdrawal were more susceptible to exogenous proteases than proteins from growing tumors; endogenous proteolytic activ-ity was the same in both types of tumors. These authors suggest that hor-mone withdrawal may lead to increased production of defective proteins.

From the foregoing discussion, there is no doubt that steroids can affect the proliferative component of the equation determining tumor size and they might affect cell loss. I will now proceed to discuss other factors that I think are important in regulating tumor volume.

V. BLOOD SUPPLY

Tumor vasculature may be one of the most important factors determining proliferation and size of tumor. In the very early stages of tumor develop-ment growth occurs in an environment containing a normal vasculature, but the production of an angiotrophic factor by the neoplasm leads to enhanced blood supply and increased tumor growth (Folkman and Cotran, 1976). This process, originally worked out with nonendocrine-related tumors, also applies to mammary tumors. Grimbone and Gullino (1976) measured the ability of normal mammary gland, hyperplastic alveolar nodules (HAN's) and spontaneous mouse mammary tumors to induce a neovascularization response. Only 6% of the normal mammary glands induced a positive response, as compared with 90% of the tumors. Interestingly, the HAN's gave an intermediate value of 30%. As the HAN's can be considered as preneoplastic lesions, the result suggested that tumor development might be associated with the increased production of an angiotrophic factor. This surmise was reinforced by the observation that HAN's producing a high incidence of tumors gave a greater vascularization response than HAN's of low progression incidence. As the two types of HAN had similar morphologies, this result could not be explained on the basis of differing cell numbers introduced into the test system. Supportive data for the production of an angiotrophic factor by rat mammary tumors have also been published (Brem *et al.*, 1977). Thus, changes in angiotrophic factor production could lead to a resumption of neoplastic growth.

The importance of mammary tumor vasculature has also been emphasized by Tannock (1968, 1970). He studied DNA synthesis in a transplantable mouse mammary tumor. These tumor cells grow as cords, 60–120 μm in diameter, surrounding a blood vessel with areas of necrosis in between the cords. The [^{3}H]TdR labeling index decreases from a value of 75% for cells in contact with the blood vessel to 30% for the most remote cells (Fig. 9). He further demonstrated (Tannock, 1970) that extension of the capillary network within the tumor depended mainly on division of endothelial cells within the capillary. According to this thesis, changes in capillary growth would profoundly influence tumor cell viability. Tannock equated the limiting size of the tumor cords with the diffusion distance of oxygen, and went on to suggest that proliferation of the tumor was limited by the oxygen supply. Other

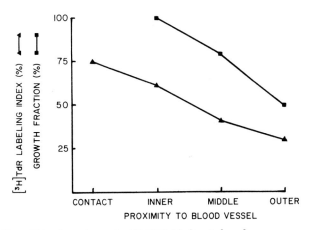

FIG. 9. Effect of blood supply on the [^{3}H]TdR labeling index of a mouse mammary tumor. Taken from Tannock (1968).

blood-borne components could also be important; serum is a known stimulant of cell proliferation, and many growth-regulating factors have been identified therein in addition to the classical protein and steroid hormones known to influence mammary cells (Gospodarowicz and Moran, 1976).

VI. CELL–CELL INTERACTION

The influence of stroma on the development of embryonic epithelium is well established (Karkinen-Jääskeläinen et al., 1977), and mammary epithelium is no exception (Drews and Drews, 1977; Kratochwil, 1978). What has not been clearly defined is how much, if any, of this stromal–epithelial interrelationship is retained in adult life after neoplastic transformation of the epithelial component. Intuitively, one would think that neoplasia would result in loss of regulatory influences but, given the examples of retrodifferentiation occurring in tumors, intuition may be wrong. Two examples can be quoted of the influence of stromal elements on neoplastic mammary growth in the human. Heuson et al. (1975), in studying hormone effects on mammary tumors maintained in organ culture, noticed that tumors with loose stroma were maintained well whereas schirrhous carcinomata survived poorly unless estradiol was added. The poor growth of the schirrhous carcinomata could also be overcome by treatment with collagenase. Thus, collagen seemed to be limiting tumor growth. However, schirrhous carcinomata do not have a better prognosis than other forms of breast cancer, so the significance of the organ culture data is not clear. The prognostic advantage of having large amounts of elastic tissue in the tumor (Shivas and Douglas, 1972; Masters et al., 1978) is probably a better example of the way in which stromal elements can limit tumor development. Thus, although it has not been established in man that stromal cells can influence neoplastic mammary epithelium, that possibility does exist, either by direct cell–cell interaction or via the production of extracellular elements such as collagen or elastica.

Direct communication can also occur between apparently normal human mammary epithelial cells (Fentiman et al., 1976). Again, the relevance of this effect to the neoplastic situation is not clear, as MCF-7 mammary tumor cells will not communicate with any of the cell types tested, including itself. However, the experiments do establish the principle of selective communication among cell types derived from the human mammary gland.

A third type of cell–cell interaction that may be of importance in controlling neoplasia is that between histiocytes and neoplastic mammary epithelium (Friedell et al., 1974; Black et al., 1976a). The presence of histiocytes is a prognostically favorable factor usually explained on the basis of an immunological defense mechanism against the cancer cells.

Finally, potential interaction between normal and neoplastic cells within the tumor must be considered. Nandi (1978) has summarized the available evidence indicating that, in rodents, neoplastic cell development is inhibited by the presence of normal cells. This result should be considered together with the observation that human breast tumors contain appreciable numbers of what look like normal epithelial cells (Hallowes *et al.*, 1977).

VII. IMMUNE RESPONSE TO BREAST TUMORS

The immune response elicited by mammary tumor cells is a complex interplay of enhancing and suppressing factors involving both cellular and humoral components (Lucas, 1976). The current impression is that the immune system does play a part in regulating mammary tumor growth, although the magnitude of the immune effect is debatable. The evidence for changed immune reactions in patients with breast cancer derives mainly from studies on favorable prognosis associated with sinus histiocytosis (Friedell *et al.*, 1974; Black *et al.*, 1976a), *in vitro* cellular hypersensitivity to mouse mammary tumor virus antigens (Black *et al.*, 1976b), and the relative paucity of serum immune complexes (Hoffken *et al.*, 1977). Conversely, disease progression is associated with decreased cellular immunity (Bolton *et al.*, 1975; Black *et al.*, 1976a,b). Fragmentary supportive data are also available from studies with rodent mammary tumors (Lucas, 1976; Immunological Control of Virus-Associated Tumors in Man, 1976).

VIII. CONCLUSIONS

There is no reason to doubt that steroids can regulate the growth of mammary tumors; what can be questioned is the central role that has been allocated to them. This idea of a pivotal role for steroids has evolved from studies in rodents and from the undoubted benefits of endocrine therapy to some women with breast cancer. I hope that the present article has introduced some healthy skepticism into the presently held attitudes. Tumor growth is determined by a large number of interrelating factors, the major ones having been discussed in this article. Steroids, in addition to directly affecting the mammary tumor cell, might also affect blood supply and its constituents, cell–cell interaction and the immune response. Such putative effects might help or hinder tumor growth and have different time courses of response. Given the paucity of data on factors regulating the growth of human breast tumors, I think it is premature to assume that steroids are *the* factors.

ACKNOWLEDGMENTS

I am grateful to J.A. Smith and I. Fentiman for helpful criticisms of the manuscript. I also appreciate permission from the following journals/publishers to reproduce or adapt the following figures: Springer-Verlag, Fig. 1; *Cancer*, Fig. 3; *Acta Cytologica*, Fig. 4; North-Holland, Fig. 5; *Proc. Nat. Acad. Sci. U.S.A.*, Figs. 6 and 8; *Nature (London)*, Fig. 7; *Br J. Cancer*, Fig. 9.

REFERENCES

Armelin, H.A. (1975). *Biochem. Acations Horm.* **3**, 1–21.

Black, M.M., Zachrau, R.E., Shore, B., and Leis, H.P. (1976a). *Cancer Res.* **36**, 769–774.

Black, M.M., Zachrau, R.E., Dion, A.S., Shore, B., Fine, D.L., Leis, H.P., and Williams, C.J. (1976b). *Cancer Res.* **36**, 4137–4142.

Bolton, P.M., Mander, A.M., Davidson, J.M., James, S.L., Newcombe, R.G., and Hughes, L.E. (1975). *Br. Med. J.* **3**, 18–20.

Brem, S.S., Gullino, P.M., and Medina, D. (1977). *Science* **195**, 880–881.

Brooks, R.F. (1977). *Cell* **12**, 311–317.

Bruchovsky, N., and Lesser, B. (1975). *Sex Horm. Res.* **2**, 1–57.

Butler, T.P., and Gullino, P.M. (1975). *Cancer Res.* **35**, 512–516.

Cooper, E.H., Bedford, A.J., and Kenney, T.E. (1975). *Adv. Cancer Res.* **21**, 59–120.

Drews, V., and Drews, V. (1977). *Cell* **10**, 401–404.

Dürnberger, H., Heuberger, B., Schwartz, P., Wasner, G., and Kratochwil, K. (1978). *Cancer Res.* **38**, 4066–4070.

Fentiman, I., Taylor-Papadimitriou, J., and Stoker, M. (1976). *Nature (London)* **264**, 760–762.

Folkman, J., and Cotran, R. (1976). *Int. Rev. Exp. Pathol.* **16**, 207–248.

Foulds, L. (1969). *In* "Neoplastic Development," Vol. 1, pp. 54–56. Academic Press, New York.

Friedell, G.H., Soto, E.A., Kumaoka, S., Abe, O., Hayward, J.L., and Bulbrook, R.D. (1974). *Lancet* **1**, 1228–1229.

Frolik, C.A., and Gorski, J. (1977). *J. Steroid Biochem.* **8**, 713–718.

Gospodarowicz, D., and Moran, J.S. (1976). *Annu. Rev. Biochem.* **45**, 531–558.

Grimbone, M.A., and Gullino, P.M. (1976). *J. Natl. Cancer Inst.* **56**, 305–310.

Hallowes, R.C., Millis, R., Pigott, D., Shearer, M., Stoker, M.G.P., and Taylor-Papadimitriou, J. (1977). *Clin. Oncol.* **3**, 81–90.

Hayward, J. (1970). *Recent Results Cancer Res.* **24**.

Heuseon, J.-C., Pasteels, J.-L., Legros, N., Heuson-Stienon, J., and Leclerq, G. (1975). *Cancer Res.* **35**, 2039–2048.

Hilf, R., Michel, I., and Bell, C. (1967). *Recent Prog. Horm. Res.* **23**, 229–290.

Hoffken, K., Meredith, I.D., Robins, R.A., Baldwin, R.W., Davies, C.J., and Blamey, R.W. (1977). *Br. Med. J.* **2**, 218–220.

Immunological Control of Virus-Associated Tumors in Man (1976). *Cancer Res.* **36**, 728–782.

Janik, P., Briand, P., and Hartmann, N.R. (1975). *Cancer Res.* **35**, 3698–3704.

Jimenez de Asua, L., O'Farrell, M.K., Clingan, D., and Rudland, P.S. (1977). *Proc. Natl. Acad. Sci. U.S.A.* **74**, 3845–3849.

Karkenen-Jääskeläinen, M., Saxén, L., and Weiss, L. (1977). "Cell Interactions in Differentiation." Academic Press, New York.

Katzenellenbogen, B.S., and Gorski, J. (1975). *Biochem. Actions Horm.* 3, 188–245.

King, R.J.B. (1976). *Essays Biochem.* 12, 41–76.

King, R.J.B. (1978). *Horm. Cell Regul.* 2, 15–36.

King, R.J.B., Cambray, G.J., and Robinson, J.H. (1976a). *J. Steroid Biochem.* 7, 869–873.

King, R.J.B., Cambray, G.J., Jagus-Smith, R., Robinson, J.H., and Smith, J.A. (1976b). *In* "Receptors and Mechanism of Action of Steroid Hormones" (J.R. Pasqualini, ed.), pp. 215–216. Dekker, New York.

King, R.J.B., Redgrave, S., Hayward, J.L. Millis, R.R., and Rubens, R.D. (1978). *In* "Methodological and Clinical Aspects of Steroid Receptor Assays in Human Breast Tumours" (R.J.B. King, ed.). pp. 57–75. Alpha Omega Alpha Publ., Cardiff, Wales.

Lanzerotti, R.H., and Gullino, P.M. (1972). *Cancer Res.* 32, 2679–2685.

Lippman, M. (1976). *In* "Breast Cancer: Trends in Research and Treatment" (J.C. Heuson, W.H. Mattheiem, and M. Rozencweig, eds.), pp. 111–139. Raven, New York.

Lucas, Z.J. (1976). *In* "Breast Cancer: Trends in Research and Treatment" (J.C. Heuson, W.H. Mattheiem, and M. Rozencweig, eds.), pp. 59–74. Raven, New York.

Mainwaring, W.I.P. (1977). "The Mechanism of Action of Androgens." Springer-Verlag, Berlin and New York.

Masters, J.R.W., Hawkins, R.A., Sangster, K., Hawkins, W., Smith, I.I., Shivas, A.A., Roberts, M.M., and Forrest, A.P.M. (1978). *Eur. J. Cancer* 14, 303–307.

Meyer, J.S., and Bauer, W.C. (1976). *J. Surg. Oncol.* 8, 165–181.

Mueller, G.C., Vonderhaaer, B., Kim, U.H., and Mahieu, M.L. (1972). *Recent Prog. Horm. Res.* 28, 1–45.

Munck, A., and Leung, K. (1977). *In* "Receptors and Mechanism of Action of Steroid Hormones" (J.R. Pasqualini, ed.), Part II, pp. 311–397. Dekker, New York.

Nandi, S. (1978). *Cancer Res.* 38, 4046–4049.

Nordenskjöld, B., Löwhagen, T., Westerberg, H., and Zajicek, J. (1976). *Acta Cytol.* 20, 137–143.

Parker, M. (1978). *Mol. Cell. Endocrinol.* 10, 119–133.

Pearlman, A.W. (1976). *Cancer* 38, 1826–1833.

Prescott, D.M. (1976). "Reproduction of Eukaryotic Cells." Academic Press, New York.

Robinson, J.H., Smith, J.A., Totty, N.F., and Riddle, P.N. (1976). *Nature (London)* 262, 298–300.

Rosen, J.M., and O'Malley, B.W. (1975). *Biochem. Actions Horm.* 3, 271–315.

Rouleau, M., and Gullino, P.M. (1977). *Cancer Res.* 37, 670–677.

Saunders, J.W. (1966). *Science* 154 604–612.

Schimke, R.T., Pennequin, P., Robins, D., and McKnight, G.S. (1977). *In* "Biochemical Actions of Progesterone and Progestins" (E. Gurpide, ed.), pp. 116–124. N.Y. Acad. Sci., New York.

Shields, R., and Smith, J.A. (1977). *J. Cell. Physiol.* 91, 345–355.

Shivas, A.A., and Douglas, J.G. (1972). *J. R. Coll. Surg. Edinburg* 17, 315–320.

Smith, J.A. (1977). *Cell Biol. Int. Rep.* 1, 283–289.

Smith, J.A., and Martin, L. (1973). *Proc. Natl. Acad. Sci. U.S.A.* 70, 1263–1267.

Smith, J.A., and Martin, L. (1974). *In* "Cell Cycle Controls" (G.M. Padilla, T.L. Cameron, and A. Zimmerman, eds.), pp. 43–60. Academic Press, New York.

Steele, G.G. (1967). *Eur. J. Cancer* 3, 381–387.

Steele, G.G. (1977). "Growth Kinetics of Tumours." Oxford Univ. Press (Clarendon), London and New York.

Sylvestrini, R., Sanfilippo, O., and Tedesco, G. (1974). *Cancer* 34, 1252–1258.

Tannock, I.F. (1968). *Br. J. Cancer* 22, 258–273.

Tannock, I.F. (1970). *Cancer Res.* **30**, 2470–2476.

Tata, J.R. (1978). *Horm. Cell Regul., Proc. INSERM Eur. Symp. Horm. Cell Regnl.*, 2nd, 1977 pp. 37–54.

Thompson, E.B., and Lippman, M.E. (1974). *Metabolism* **23**, 159–201.

Tubiana, M., and Malaise, E.P. (1976). *In* "Scientific Foundations of Oncology" (T. Symington and R.L. Carters, eds.), pp. 126–135. Heinemann, London.

Wyllie, A. H. (1974). *J. Clin. Pathol.* **27**, Suppl. 7, 35–42.

CHAPTER 6

Biochemical Actions of Neurohypophysial Hormones and Neurophysin

Melvyn S. Soloff and A. Frances Pearlmutter

I. INTRODUCTION: PHYSIOLOGICAL ACTIONS OF NEUROHYPOPHYSIAL HORMONES

Nine biologically active vertebrate neurohypophysial peptides have been identified (Table I). In the early 1950's, du Vigneaud (1960) and his co-workers first determined the structures of the three mammalian octapeptides and synthesized them. The structures of the remaining six peptides were established later by Acher (1974) and co-workers; these were also synthesized.

The neurohypophysis of most mammals contains oxytocin and arginine vasopressin, which is also known as antidiuretic hormone. In the pig the arginine in vasopressin is replaced by lysine. Arginine vasotocin, a hybrid of vasopressin and oxytocin, consists of the tripeptide tail of arginine vasopressin attached to the ring of oxytocin. Arginine vasotocin occurs in all non-mammalian vertebrates and may be the ancestor of all other active neurohypophysial peptides (Acher, 1974; Sawyer, 1977). Arginine vasotocin was synthesized by Katsoyannis and du Vigneaud (1958) as part of a study of structure–activity relationships prior to its recognition as a naturally occurring hormone in the pituitary of the chicken (Munsick *et al.*, 1960).

The principal pharmacological actions of the neurohypophysial principles are shown in Table II. Sawyer (1977) has reviewed the possible physiological

TABLE I

THE KNOWN NATURALLY OCCURRING ACTIVE
NEUROHYPOPHYSIAL PEPTIDES[a,b]

Peptide	Amino acid in positions		
	X	Y	Z
Vasopressor peptides			
Arginine–vasopressin	Phe	Gln	Arg
Lysine–vasopressin	Phe	Gln	Lys
Arginine–vasotocin	Ile	Gln	Arg
Oxytocinlike peptides			
Oxytocin	Ile	Gln	Leu
Mesotocin	Ile	Gln	Ile
Isotocin	Ile	Ser	Ile
Glumitocin	Ile	Ser	Gln
Aspartocin	Ile	Asn	Leu
Valitocin	Ile	Gln	Val

[a] Common structure: Cys—Tyr—X—Y—Asn—Cys—Pro—Z—Gly(NH$_2$)
$\qquad\qquad\qquad$ 1 $\quad$ 2 $\quad$ 3 $\quad$ 4 $\quad$ 5 $\quad$ 6 $\quad$ 7 $\quad$ 8 $\quad$ 9

[b] From Sawyer (1977).

TABLE II

RELATIVE POTENCIES OF ARGININE VASOPRESSIN, OXYTOCIN,
AND ARGININE VASOTOCIN[a]

Activity	Arginine vasopressin (%)	Oxytocin (%)	Arginine vasotocin (%)
Antidiuretic (rat)	100	1	56
Pressor (rat)	100	1	63
Oxytocic (rat isolated uterus)	4	100	27
Milk-ejecting (rabbit)	15	100	49
Depressor (chicken)	14	100	67
Hydro-osmotic (toad bladder)	1	4	100
Natriferic (frog)	2	21	100
Antidiuretic (frog)	0	0	100
Oviduct-contracting (hen)	44	6	100

[a] Adapted from Bisset (1976) by permission of the publisher.

roles of neurohypophysial principles in lower vertebrates. In this report we shall confine our discussion to the biochemical actions of the mammalian neurohypophysial hormones, oxytocin and vasopressin.

The neurohypophysial hormones and the neurophysins are synthesized by neuronal cells of the hypothalamus. The hormones and neurophysins are incorporated into neurosecretory granules which are bounded by a membrane. These granules move by axoplasmic transport to the nerve terminals in the posterior pituitary, where they are stored. On depolarization of the cell membranes, neurophysin and the neurohypophysial hormones pass out of the nerve cells and through endothelial cells to enter the bloodstream.

In most mammals, oxytocin plays an essential role in lactation (for a review, see Bisset, 1974). Milk is ejected from the mammary alveoli and smaller ducts by oxytocin-induced contractions of myoepithelial cells (Fig. 1). Oxytocin also elicits the contraction of uterine smooth muscle and possibly plays a role in labor, but the importance of oxytocin in the initiation of labor remains to be clarified. Vasopressin serves the important physiological function of homeostatic control of the extracellular fluid volume (for recent reviews, see Jard and Bockaert, 1975; Dousa and Valtin, 1976). Neurohypophysial peptides stimulate net active transport of Na^+ across the mucosal epithelium of toad bladder and increase the rate of water flow in response to an osmotic pressure difference between the solutions bathing the two sides of the bladder. An increased permeability of the epithelial cell to such

FIG. 1. Arrangement of myoepithelial cells (black) around alveolar and ductal epithelial cells. Left: myoepithelial cells, alveoli full with milk. Right: myoepithelial cells contracted, alveoli emptied, and ducts widened. From Bisset, 1968.

small hydrophilic molecules as urea accompanies the hydro-osmotic effect of vasopressin.

A large body of experimental evidence indicates that the two effects of vasopressin are mediated by cAMP (for reviews, see Orloff and Handler, 1967; Jard and Bockaert, 1975). Stimulation of sodium transport is accomplished primarily by a cAMP-induced increase in the permeability of the luminal membrane of the mucosal cells to Na^+, rather than by a direct action of cAMP on the active transport mechanism that is assumed to be located at the contraluminal surface of the mucosal cells (Civan and Frazier, 1968). Increased water flow in response to a gradient results from an increased permeability of the luminal membrane to water (Dibona *et al.*, 1969). The effects of vasopressin on the permeability of the membrane to sodium and to water can be dissociated, and this suggests that they may be due to separate hormone-activated adenylate cyclases (Petersen and Edelman, 1964; Lipson and Sharp, 1971). One of the major unresolved questions is the nature of the mechanism(s) by which cAMP can produce alterations in membrane permeability to sodium and water. Another unanswered question is how neurohypophysial peptides that are active when exposed only to the contraluminal surface of epithelial cells from toad bladder (Peachey and Rasmussen, 1961; Bentley, 1966; Leaf, 1967; Ganote *et al.*, 1968) and renal collecting tubules (Grantham and Burg, 1966) are able to elicit permeability changes in the luminal surface.

The effects of neurohypophysial hormones on vascular smooth muscle have been reviewed recently (Altura and Altura, 1977) and will not be discussed here.

II. NEUROPHYSINS

Neurophysins are a class of polypeptides found in the posterior pituitary in association with oxytocin and vasopressin [for a recent symposium on this subject, see *Ann. N.Y. Acad. Sci.* **248** (1975)]. Neurophysins, which were characterized originally by van Dyke *et al.* (1942), have been demonstrated in several mammalian species as well as in the codfish (for a review, see Walter and Breslow, 1974) and chicken (Peek and Watkins, 1977). Most mammals have two major and one to three minor forms of neurophysin (Breslow, 1974). One of the major neurophysins is usually found *in vivo* in association with oxytocin, while the other is found in association with vaso-pressin.

A. BIOSYNTHESIS

Sachs and co-workers (Sachs and Takabatake, 1964; Takabatake and Sachs, 1964; Sachs *et al.*, 1969) postulated that neurophysin and the neurohypophysial hormones are derived from the posttranslational cleavage of a common precursor protein. The existence of the presumed precursor has been shown in the rat (Brownstein and Gainer, 1977; Gainer *et al.*, 1977a,b) and dog (Walter *et al.*, 1977b) by pulse-chase labeling studies with [^{35}S]cys-teine. In the dog, combinations of *in vivo*-pulse and *in vitro*-chase as well as *in vivo*-pulse and *in vivo*-chase demonstrated that hypothalamic neurosec-retory cells are simultaneously able to synthesize the precursors of neurophysin and vasopressin, which were subsequently converted to a neurophysinlike protein and vasopressin.

In the rat, [^{35}S]cysteine was injected adjacent to the supraoptic nucleus and the rats were killed at intervals after injection. The radioactivity was incorporated initially into a 20,000 dalton protein which then formed an intermediate of 17,000 daltons. The intermediate was converted into a 12,000 dalton protein 24 hours later. Two distinct precursor molecules were demonstrated in normal rats, whereas only one was seen in the Brattleboro rat, which lacks neurophysin I and vasopressin (Sokol and Valtin, 1967). It was concluded that a precursor was synthesized in the supraoptic nucleus, and was then cleaved to neurophysin and related peptides during axonal transport to the neurohypophysis. Definitive proof of this postulate awaits the purification and identification of the presumed precursor.

Oxytocin and vasopressin are synthesized in the supraoptic and paraven-tricular nuclei and are stored with their corresponding neurophysins in sepa-rate neurosecretory granules. The hormones and neurophysins are secreted simultaneously into the blood from the neurohypophysis. At the pH of the blood, the hormone–neurophysin complex is dissociated.

B. Amino Acid Composition

The neurophysin molecule consists of a single chain of approximately 95 amino acids. The amino acid compositions of neurophysins from various species are summarized in Table III. In the rat, three neurophysins have been identified and their amino acid compositions determined (Watkins, 1972; Burford and Pickering, 1972; Sunde and Sokol, 1975). Rat neurophysin III appears to be formed from rat neurophysin II by a C-terminal cleavage (North *et al.*, 1977; North and Valtin, 1977). *In vivo*, rat neurophysin I was found in association with vasopressin, and rat neurophysins II and III were found in association with oxytocin (Sunde and Sokol, 1975; North *et al.*, 1977; North and Valtin, 1977). The Brattleboro rat, which genetically lacks vasopressin, is deficient in rat neurophysin I (Sokol and Valtin, 1967; Aspeslagh *et al.*, 1976; van Leeuwen and Swaab, 1977). Oxytocin and vasopressin were found in distinct neurons of the paraventricular and the supraoptic nuclei of the hypothalamus (Tasso *et al.*, 1976). The external region of the rat median eminence also contained separate neurophysin-vasopressin and neurophysin–oxytocin fibers (Dierickx *et al.*, 1976). These results support the hypothesis that the synthesis of neurophysin and its corresponding neurohypophysial hormone takes place in one cell.

Two major bovine neurophysins have been identified and their amino acid sequences determined (Chauvet *et al.*, 1976c; Audhya and Walter, 1977; Wuu and Crumm, 1976a; Schlesinger *et al.*, 1974). The sequence of fetal bovine neurophysin II was identical to the adult form (Chauvet *et al.*, 1976a). *In vivo*, bovine neurophysin I was found in association with oxytocin and bovine neurophysin II, with vasopressin (Dean *et al.*, 1968; Zimmerman *et al.*, 1974; Vandesande *et al.*, 1975; de Mey *et al.*, 1975).

Three neurophysins have been identified in the pig, and the amino acid sequences of types I and III have been reported (Wuu *et al.*, 1971; Wuu and Crumm, 1976b; Chauvet *et al.*, 1976b). Porcine neurophysin I, which contains 92 amino acids, has been shown to be a breakdown product of neurophysin III, which contains three additional C-terminal amino acids (Wuu and Crumm, 1976b; Wuu *et al.*, 1971). Two distinct populations of neurosecretory neurons, containing either neurophysin I or neurophysin II, have been demonstrated in the pig (Watkins, 1976). Porcine neurophysin I, which appears in the blood in increased concentrations during hemorrhage, was found to be associated with vasopressin *in vivo* (Watkins and Choy, 1976; Dax *et al.*, 1977). During parturition and lactation porcine neurophy-

TABLE III

Amino Acid Composition of Major Neurophysins from Various Species

Amino acid	Rat[a]			Ox		Human[d]			Sheep[e]		Pig[f]		Horse[i]	Guinea pig[g]	Whale[i]	Cod[h]
	I	II	III	I[b]	II[c]	I	II	III	I	III	I(III)	II				
Asx	5	8	8	7	5	7	5	4	9	4	5	12 (9)	5	7	5	10
Thr	3	3	3	2	2	2	2	2	3	2	2	3 (2)	2	3	2	4
Ser	7	7	6	5	6	4	6	6	8	6	7	9 (6)	6	4	7	11
Glx	13	10	8	10	14	10	13	13	11	13	13	18 (16)	13	12	13	22
Pro	8	10	9	9	8	9	5	8	10	8	7	20 (14)	8	7	8	12
Cys/2	14	14	13	14	14	14	14	14	14	14	14	12 (14)	14	12	14	16
Gly	14	14	14	14	16	12	15	15	16	15	14	18 (16)	15	10	14	21
Ala	9	10	9	8	6	9	8	6	11	6	7 (8)	12 (9)	8	7	8	12
Val	1	1	1	1	4	3	3	3	4	3	2	4 (4)	2	3	1	4
Met	1	1	1	0	1	0	1	1	0	1	1	0 (0)	1	0	2	1
Ile	2	2	2	2	2	1	1	4	2	4	2	3 (2)	2	1	2	3
Leu	7	6	6	6	6	7	6	6	8	6	7	9 (7)	7	6	6	13
Tyr	1	1	1	1	1	1	1	1	1	1	1	2 (1)	1	1	1	1

(continued)

TABLE III (continued)

Amino acid	Rat[a]			Ox		Human[d]			Sheep[e]			Pig[f]		Horse[i]	Guinea pig[g]	Whale[j]	Cod[h]
	I	II	III	I[b]	II[c]	I	II	III	I	II	III	I(III)	II				
Phe	4	3	3	3	3	3	4	3	4	4	3	3	6 (4)	2	3	3	3
His	0	0	0	1	0	1	1	0	1	1	0	0	0 (0)	0	0	0	2
Lys	2	3	3	2	2	3	2	2	2	2	2	2	4 (4)	2	1	2	3
Arg	6	5	5	4	7	4	6	7	6	6	7	5 (7)	6 (6)	7	4	7	5
Associated hormone in vivo	VP[k]	Oxy[k]	Oxy[k]	Oxy[l]	VP[l]	Oxy[m]	VP[m]					VP[n]	Oxy[n]				

[a] North and Valtin (1977) and references therein.

[b] North et al. (1975); R. Walter et al. (1977a), sequence included.

[c] Wuu and Crumm (1976a), sequence included.

[d] Capra et al. (1974) and references therein; partial sequences included. Cheng and Friesen (1972).

[e] Chauvet et al. (1976c), sequence included. Watkins (1973); Audhya and Walter (1977); Schlesinger et al. (1975).

[f] Wuu et al. (1971) sequence included; Wuu and Crumm (1976b), sequence included; Chauvet et al. (1976b), sequence included. Porcine neurophysin I is a C-terminal truncated form of porcine neurophysin III. Uttenthal and Hope (1970), pig neurophysin II; Cheng and Friesen (1972), pig neurophysin II in parenthesis.

[g] Watkins and Ellis (1973).

[h] Pickering (1968).

[i] Chauvet et al. (1978), sequence included.

[j] Chauvet et al. (1977), sequence included.

[k] North et al. (1977); Sunde and Sokol (1975); Burford and Pickering (1972).

[l] Vandesande et al. (1975); de Mey et al. (1975); Legros et al. (1976).

[m] Robinson (1975). Robinson equates the human neurophysin I described by Cheng and Friesen (1972) as estrogen-stimulated neurophysin which is associated presumably with oxytocin secretion in vivo.

[n] Watkins and Choy (1976); Dax et al. (1977); Pickup et al. (1973).

sin II, which is associated *in vivo* with oxytocin, was found in increased concentrations in the blood (Watkins and Choy, 1976; Dax *et al.*, 1977).

Three neurophysins have been found in sheep (Watkins, 1973); however, ovine neurophysins I and II have nearly identical amino acid compositions and probably are derived from a single neurophysin *in vivo*. The amino acid sequence of ovine neurophysin III has been determined, and it is remarkably similar to bovine neurophysin II and porcine neurophysin III (Chauvet *et al.*, 1976c; Schlesinger *et al.*, 1975). The specific neurohypophysial hormone associated with each ovine neurophysin *in vivo* is not known.

Two major neurophysins are found in humans (Legros and Louis, 1973–1974), The amino acid composition and the sequence of the first 54 amino acids have been reported (Foss *et al.*, 1973; Capra *et al.*, 1974). There has been some confusion as to which hormone is associated with each of the human neurophysins *in vivo* because of inconsistencies in nomenclature. Under physiological conditions when oxytocin secretion would be increased, Robinson (1975) found that what presumably is human neurophysin I (Cheng and Friesen 1972) was present in increased concentrations in the blood.

Chauvet *et al.* (1975) postulated that at least two distinct lines of neurophysin exist in mammals. The two lines have been classified according to the amino acid residues in positions 2, 3, 6, and 7. One class has been labeled MSEL neurophysins (Met-Ser-Glu-Leu) and the other, VLDL neurophysins (Val-Leu-Asp-Val). The MSEL neurophysins (bovine neurophysin II, porcine neurophysin I or III) are found *in vivo* in association with vasopressin; the VLDL line (bovine neurophysin I, porcine neurophysin II, and human neurophysin I) is associated with oxytocin (see Table III). These relationships suggest that neurophysin and its neurohypophysial hormone are products of the same gene and are synthesized as part of a larger precursor.

The neurophysins are very similar in amino acid sequence. The positions occupied by the half-cystine residues are the same; therefore, the location of the disulfide bonds should be identical. Greater differences in sequence are found at the ends of the polypeptide chain than in the central region, which is thought to be involved in hormone binding. Tyr-49, which appears to be part of the hormone binding site, is also invariant. All the neurophysins contain a high content of glycine, cystine, glutamic acid, and proline; aromatic amino acids are present in very small amounts.

C. BIOLOGICAL ACTIVITIES

Although the biological activities of the neurohypophysial hormones are well known, there appears to be no demonstrable function of circulating neurophysin. Neurophysins have been credited with lipolytic, ketogenic, hyperglycemic, hypocalcemic, and serum amino acid lowering activities (Trygstad *et al.*, 1975). In all these studies, neurophysin from one species was injected into another. Microgram quantities of neurophysin were required for an observable effect; however, resting plasma levels of neurophysins are in the nanogram range (Breslow, 1974). When 30 μg/kg of a crude human neurophysin preparation was injected into humans, the only significant metabolic effect observed was a decrease in serum amino acids, particularly aspartate and glutamate (Trygstad *et al.*, 1975). It is possible, as pointed out by Trygstad *et al.* (1975), that the effect was due to a contaminant. Injection of a mixture of bovine neurophysin I and II (50 μg) intravenously into hydropenic dogs caused an increase in Na^+ excretion. Highly purified neurophysins I and II, however, had little or no effect (Robinson *et al.*, 1975). It was concluded from these results that the impure mixture contained a natriuretic principle. The natriuretic activity may have been due to contamination by oxytocin and vasopressin, or by some other unidentified peptide(s).

Rudman *et al.* (1975) found that purified bovine neurophysins I and II had no lipolytic or melanotropic activities in rabbit adipose tissue and frog skin, respectively. Reexamining their preparations of porcine and bovine neurophysins, they discovered that the lipolytic property previously attributed to neurophysin I was due to a contaminating smaller peptide. Ponec and Lichardus (1977) found that rat neurophysin had no natriuretic effects on acutely hypophysectomized rats that were saline loaded.

At the present time, the hormonal actions, if any, of the neurophysins are unknown. These polypeptides may exist as part of the precursor of oxytocin and vasopressin, and may act as protective agents when the hormone–neurophysin complexes are stored in the secretory granules, in a fashion analogous, but not identical, to that of proinsulin and the C-peptide.

D. Neurophysin Conformation and Hormone Binding

Studies in this area through 1973 have been reviewed by Breslow (1974). We shall summarize these data and include more recent findings.

Breslow and co-workers have used a variety of experimental techniques to elucidate the conformation of neurophysin and the molecular interactions between neurophysins and the neurohypophysial hormones. Circular dichroism studies have indicated that neurophysin contains very little α-helix, but may contain a significant amount of β-structure (Breslow and Weis, 1972; Breslow, 1974).

All the neurophysins that have been sequenced contained seven disulfide bonds which were very susceptible to reduction in the absence of urea (Menendez-Botet and Breslow, 1975). Reoxidation did not regenerate the original disulfide bonds; this indicates that the disulfides are not present in the most stable or lowest energy conformation. This is indirect evidence that the neurophysins are synthesized as part of a larger precursor molecule.

The hydrogen ion titration curves of bovine neurophysins I and II indicated that all titratable groups were available and had normal intrinsic pK values (Breslow *et al.*, 1971). However, neurophysin that was mononitrated at its single tyrosine exhibited a higher pK than would be expected (Breslow *et al.*, 1971). This observation may reflect the importance of the location of tyrosine-49 and its role in hormone binding. The affinity of bovine nitrotyrosine neurophysin for oxytocin and oxytocin analogs was decreased as the pH was lowered from 6.2 to 1 (Breslow and Gargiulo, 1977). The transition midpoints of mononitrated neurophysins II and I were pH 4.25 and 4.85, respectively. The free energy of salt-bridge formation, -2.4 kcal/mole at $25°$, was calculated from binding data below pH 2.

The binding of hormone to neurophysin appears to be stabilized by the formation of a salt bridge between the protonated amino group of the hormone and a negatively charged glutamic acid of neurophysin (Breslow and Abrash, 1966). Hydrophobic interactions between the neurophysin molecule and positions 2, 3, and 4 of the hormone also appear to play an important role. Thermodynamic studies with small peptide analogs of the first two, three or four amino acid residues of the hormone showed that positions 1 and 2 contribute about half the binding free energy, and that positions 1, 2, and 3 together contribute about two-thirds of the binding free energy (Breslow, 1970, 1975; Breslow *et al.*, 1971, 1973; Breslow and Weis, 1972). Nuclear magnetic resonance studies of the binding reaction have shown the direct participation of positions 1, 2 and 3 of the neurohypophysial hormones in complex formation; there was little or no involvement of positions 7, 8, and 9 in the binding to neurophysin (Balaram *et al.*, 1972, 1973; Cohen *et al.*, 1972; Alazard *et al.*, 1974; Glasel *et al.*, 1973; Blumenstein and Hruby, 1977; Griffin *et al.*, 1977; Convert *et al.*, 1977). These data are summarized in the model of neurophysin–oxytocin interaction shown in Fig. 2.

The neurophysins exist in a monomer–dimer equilibrium and may form oligomers under certain conditions. Meniscus-depletion sedimentation-equilibrium studies of bovine neurophysins I and II indicated dimerization constants of $7.7 \times 10^3 \, M^{-1}$ and $5–5.8 \times 10^3 \, M^{-1}$, respectively (Breslow *et al.*, 1971; Nicolas *et al.*, 1976). Mononitrated neurophysins I and II had dimerization constants that were comparable to the native peptides (Nicolas *et al.*, 1978b). The dimerization of bovine neurophysin I has been examined by relaxation techniques (Pearlmutter, 1978). Bromphenol blue, which

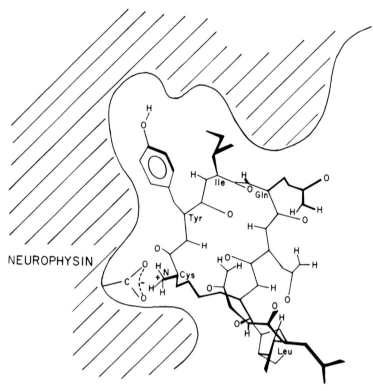

FIG. 2. A model for the binding of oxytocin to the high-affinity site of a monomer subunit of the neurophysin dimer. The overall conformation of oxytocin is that of Urry and Walter (1971). An electrostatic interaction is shown between a negatively charged carboxyl group of the neurophysin and the protonated amino terminus of oxytocin. The side chains of residues 2 and 3 are bound in a hydrophobic area within the neurophysin binding site. The terminal tripeptide residues of oxytocin (-Pro-Leu-Gly-amide) do not interact with neurophysin. From Convert *et al.*, 1977.

binds preferentially to the neurophysin I monomer, was used as an indicator. The rate constants for the dimerization were $k_f = 1 \times 10^5 \, M^{-1} \mathrm{sec}^{-1}$ and $k_r = 8 \, \mathrm{sec}^{-1}$ for the association and dissociation, respectively. The dimerization of neurophysin is two orders of magnitude slower than the theoretical diffusion-controlled rate of encounter and, therefore, represents a sterically restricted process.

The binding of neurohypophysial hormones by neurophysins has been studied in several laboratories under different experimental conditions; this has resulted in a variety of interpretations. Whereas some workers have concluded that there is a single strong binding site on neurophysin for both oxytocin and vasopressin (Breslow and Walter, 1972; Breslow *et al.*, 1973), others have postulated two or more binding sites under specific conditions (Camier *et al.*, 1973; Nicolas *et al.*, 1976, 1978a,b; Lord and Breslow, 1978). Pliska and Sachs (1974) found two classes of binding sites for lysine vasopressin on bovine neurophysins I and II—a high-affinity site on the monomer, and a low-affinity site on the polymeric form of neurophysin. In a study of the binding of oxytocin to bovine neurophysin II, Hope *et al.* (1975) observed sigmoidal binding curves that were attributed to isomerization of the neurophysin. Two explanations for the isomerization were proposed. Either oxytocin was bound preferentially to a preexisting isomeric state of neurophysin, or the binding of oxytocin induced the isomerization. Glasel *et al.* (1976) studied the binding of oxytocin and vasopressin to bovine neurophysins. They proposed that the neurophysins possess multiple sites for hormone binding; the binding constants and the number of hormone binding sites were strongly dependent upon temperature, pH, and neurophysin concentration.

A model for the binding of oxytocin and vasopressin to bovine neurophysins has been proposed by Cohen and co-workers (Camier *et al.*, 1973; Griffin *et al.*, 1973, 1977; Alazard *it al.*, 1974; Nicolas *et al.*, 1976, 1978a,b; Convert *et al.*, 1977). According to this model, both the monomeric and dimeric forms of neurophysin bind the hormones. The dimer, however, has a higher affinity for the hormone than does the monomer. Similar conclusions can be drawn from the work of others (Hope *et al.*, 1975; Breslow and Gargiulo, 1977). At high hormone concentrations, the dimer binds two hormone molecules. The binding of oxytocin to the two sites on the dimer of bovine neurophysin I or II appears to be cooperative (positive) (Nicolas *et al.*, 1978a). The neurophysin protomer can bind two molecules of oxytocin or vasopressin in the presence of 1.4 M LiCl (Nicholas *et al.*, 1976, 1978b). Nitrated neurophysin, however, bound only one molecule of hormone in 1.4 M LiCl (Nicholas *et al.*, 1978b). Electron spin resonance studies of neurophysin and spin-labeled peptides have also suggested the presence on neurophysin of a second weaker binding site, which is uncovered upon the binding of the first hormone molecule (Lord and Breslow, 1978).

The interaction of bovine neurophysins I and II with oxytocin and vasopressin has been studied by temperature-jump relaxation (Pearlmutter and McMains, 1977). The reaction was monitored with the pH indicator phenol red. A mixture of neurophysins I or II with oxytocin or vasopressin showed a single relaxation time in the millisecond range; Fig. 3 shows the results of a relaxation experiment. The relaxation time depended on the concentrations of neurophysin and hormone, and decreased with decreasing pH. The mechanism that fits the relaxation data is as follows:

$$
\begin{array}{ccc}
\text{HNP} & \text{L} & \\
\parallel & + & \\
\text{H}^+ & \text{H}^+ + \text{In}^- \rightleftharpoons \text{HIn} & \\
+ & \parallel & \\
\text{NP}^- + & \text{HL}^+ \overset{k_{1f}}{\underset{k_{1r}}{\rightleftharpoons}} \text{NPHL} & \\
+ & & + \\
\text{NP}^- & & \text{NP}^- \\
\parallel & & \parallel \\
(\text{NP}^-)_2 + & \text{HL}^+ \overset{k_{2f}}{\underset{k_{2r}}{\rightleftharpoons}} (\text{NP})_2\text{HL}
\end{array}
$$

where HNP is neurophysin with protonated carboxyl residues; NP^- is neurophysin with negatively charged carboxyl residues; HL^+ is hormone with a positively charged α-amino group; L is the neutral hormone; NPHL is the neurophysin–hormone monomer complex; $(\text{NP}^-)_2$ is the dimer form of neurophysin; $(\text{NP}^-)_2$ HL is the hormone–neurophysin dimer complex; HIn and In are the protonated and unprotonated forms of phenol red, respectively; and H^+ is the proton. Fast reactions are indicated by equal signs, and the reactions being monitored are shown by arrows. Table IV shows the rate constants for the neurophysin-binding systems that were examined. The dissociation rate constants for the dimer–oxytocin complex have been confirmed by nmr (Blumenstein *et al.*, 1977). These results support the conclusion that the dimer has greater affinity for the hormone than does the

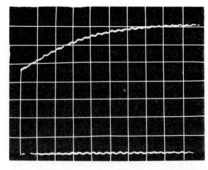

Fɪɢ. 3. A temperature-jump kinetic trace showing the interaction of oxytocin 37.5 μM, with bovine neurophysin I, 25.5 μM. The reaction was monitored at 558 nm, at pH 7.40, in 0.1 M KNO_3 containing 10 μM phenol red. The time scale is 20 milliseconds per division of the x axis; each division of the y axis is 200 mV. A 5 kV discharge through the cuvette resulted in a temperature rise from 9° to 25°. A relaxation time of 58.8 milliseconds was calculated from this tracing.

		k_{1f}	k_{2f}	k_{1r}	k_{2r}
		(mole^{-1} sec^{-1})		(sec^{-1})	
Neurophysin I	Oxy[b]	0.8×10^5	2.8×10^6	2	11
	LVP[b]	3.6×10^5	2.3×10^6	7	15
Neurophysin II	Oxy[b]	0^c	6.0×10^6	0^c	24
	LVP[b]	5.4×10^5	2.4×10^6	11	16

[a] Taken from Pearlmutter and McMains (1977). The rate constants correspond to the mechanism shown in the text.

[b] Oxy = oxytocin; LVP = lysine vasopressin.

[c] Within experimental error.

monomer. The similarity in the relaxation profiles for vasopressin and oxytocin binding to neurophysin suggests that hormone binding sites on neurophysin for vasopressin and oxytocin are identical. The pH dependence of binding indicates that the protonated hormone participates in the formation of an amino-carboxylate electrostatic bond on binding.

III. NEUROHYPOPHYSIAL HORMONE–RECEPTOR INTERACTIONS

Investigations of the interactions between neurohypophysial hormones and receptor sites in target tissues have followed three general approaches: studies of structure–activity relations with analogs of the parent hormones; conformational analysis of oxytocin and vasopressin and their analogs; and studies of the binding of radioactive hormones to putative receptor sites.

A. STRUCTURE–ACTIVITY RELATIONSHIPS

Oxytocin was the first neurohypophysial hormone whose primary structure was proven by chemical synthesis (du Vigneaud, 1960). About 400 analogs of oxytocin and vasopressin have since been made, and there is much information available on the structure–activity relationships of these peptides. Several reviews summarize information in these areas (Berde and Boissonnas, 1968; Sawyer and Manning, 1973; Rudinger *et al.*, 1972).

Among the nine biologically active neurohypophysial peptides found in vertebrates, variations occur in positions 3, 4, and 8 (see Table 1). The remaining positions would appear to be critical for biological activity. An examination of the pharmacological activities of hundreds of synthetic analogs of oxytocin and vasopressin has resulted in some understanding of the general molecular characteristics that are essential for activity.

The reduction of the disulfide bond between the two half-cystines of either oxytocin or vasopressin destroyed biological activity. For example, linear analogs containing alanine in positions 1 and 6 were essentially devoid of activities (Jošt and Rudinger, 1967). Biological activities were retained if one or both sulfur atoms were replaced by selenium or methylene groups, keeping the ring structure intact (Jošt and Šorm, 1971). Thus, an intact pentapeptide ring, but not the disulfide bond itself, is needed for biological activity.

The exact size of the ring, while not absolutely essential for bioactivity, plays an important role. When the 20-membered ring of (1-deamino) oxytocin was enlarged by addition of a methylene group, oxytocic activity was reduced by about 99% (Jarvis *et al.*, 1965). The deletion of one amino acid from the ring also resulted in a 99% reduction in uterotonic activity (Sawyer and Manning, 1973). The addition of two methyl groups to the β-carbon of the half-cystine in the 1 position, as in [1-penicillamine]oxytocin, destroyed the activities characteristic of oxytocin, but the analog competitively inhibited the effects of oxytocin on the rat uterus *in vivo* and *in vitro* (Chan *et al.*, 1967).

The optimum length of the side chain has also been defined, although its exact amino acid composition does not appear to be critical. The amide groups at positions 5 and 9 are essential for activity, while the amide at position 4 is not. The nature of the amino acids in positions 3 and 8 is critical for the manifestation of maximum oxytocinlike and vasopressinlike activities, respectively.

In some instances nature has been improved upon with man-made structural modifications of neurohypophysial peptides that have led to increased activities. For example, removal of the terminal amino group enhanced oxytocic, fowl vasodepressor, and antidiuretic activities of oxytocin and vasopressins, while it reduced vasopressor activities (Chan and du Vigneaud, 1962; Huguenin *et al.*, 1965). Hope and Wälti (1971) reported that substitution of a hydroxyl for the terminal amino group of oxytocin resulted in a peptide with about twice the oxytocic activity of [1-deamino]oxytocin and three times that of oxytocin. Substitution of glutamine by threonine in the 4 position of oxytocin resulted in a peptide with about twice the uteronic activity of oxytocin (Manning *et al.*, 1970).

Recent efforts have been directed toward the design of peptides with selectively enhanced oxytocic and antidiuretic activities. For example, the ratio of oxytocic to antidiuretic activities of [4-threonine,7-glycine]oxytocin was about 270 times greater than that of oxytocin itself (Manning *et al.*,

1977). [1-Deamino,4-valine,8-D-arginine]vasopressin had undetectable vasopressor activity and, consequently, an antidiuretic to pressor activity ratio
approaching infinity (Manning *et al.*, 1977). For a more complete discussion
of studies involving the design of peptides with selected agonist and antagonist properties, see Manning *et al.* (1977).

B. Conformation of Neurohypophysial Hormones in Solution

Along with the synthesis of a large number of analogs for biological testing,
advances in the technology and versatility of magnetic resonance techniques
have led to an examination of the conformation of oxytocin and vasopressin,
as well as many analogs. The most complete model proposed to date for the
biologically active conformation of oxytocin, the "cooperative" model, is
shown in Fig. 4 (Walter, 1977). This model was formulated from nmr studies
in dimethyl sulfoxide (DMSO) and from structure–activity studies. According to the model, oxytocin is an antiparallel β-pleated sheet that is stabilized
by the disulfide bridge, which completes the ring. In DMSO, the solvent in
which most of the original nmr work has been done, the ring is postulated to
contain a ten-membered, hydrogen-bonded, type II β-turn with the sequence Tyr-Ile-Gln-Asn-. The C-terminal sequence, which is composed of
the residues -Cys-Pro-Leu-Gly-amide, is arranged in a type I β-turn. Urry

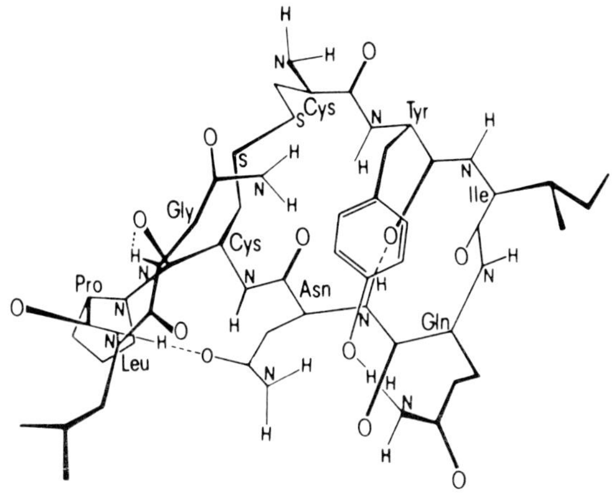

FIG. 4. The "cooperative" model for the biologically active conformation of oxytocin. This
model has been formulated from nuclear magnetic resonance studies in DMSO and from
structure–activity studies. From Walter, 1977.

et al. (1970; Urry and Walter, 1971) suggested that the peptide N—H of Asn-5 is hydrogen bonded to the carbonyl group of Tyr-2. Brewster *et al.* (1973) have suggested two other possible hydrogen-bonded structures. Other possible backbone structures, if they were present, would contribute insignificantly to the average conformation of oxytocin (Glickson, 1975). In aqueous solution, conformational averaging becomes significant. One plane of the ring of the "cooperative" model, referred to as the "hydrophobic surface," appears to be relatively featureless except for the protruding disulfide bond and the peptide N—H of glutamine. The opposite side of the ring, the "hydrophilic surface," contains a cleft which is composed of the hydroxyl group of tyrosine-2 and the carboxamide groups of the glutamine-4, asparagine-5, and glycine residues. This hydrophilic cleft presumably contains the active center. Contributions of individual amino acid residues may be subdivided into two categories: those important for binding to the receptor, and those important for modulating the activity. According to Walter (1977), elements of residues located in the four corners of the β-turns—isoleucine-3, glutamine-4, proline-7, and leucine-8—participate in the binding to the oxytocin receptor. The affinity of the receptor site for oxytocin is enhanced by tyrosine-2.

The correct configuration of tyrosine-2 and the asparagine-5 seems to be important for the initiation of the oxytocic response (Walter, 1977). Oxypressin, in which the tyrosine-2 residue presumably is stabilized away from the 20-membered ring (compare this configuration with that in Fig. 4), had 90% of the intrinsic activity of oxytocin or [3-β-cyclohexylalanine]oxytocin (Walter *et al.*, 1976). Hydrophilic residues in positions 4 and 9 also appear necessary for full activity (Walter, 1977).

Another consideration when relating conformation to agonistic and antagonistic properties is the relative rigidity of the hormone. In a magnetic resonance study of oxytocin and [1-L-penicillamine]oxytocin, a competitive inhibitor of oxytocin, it was shown that the antagonist has a conformation more restricted than oxytocin (Meraldi *et al.*, 1977). It has been proposed that the intrinsic rigidity of [1-L-penicillamine]oxytocin presents an energy barrier that prevents formation of the biologically active form of the receptor required for transduction of the hormone response. Thus, the antagonist binds, but fails to initiate the response.

In DMSO, arginine vasopressin, lysine vasopressin, and oxytocin have similar average conformations (Walter *et al.*, 1972, 1973, 1974). In aqueous solution, lysine vasopressin and oxytocin have similar overall shapes, but the conformation of lysine vasopressin appears to be more extended than that of oxytocin (Craig *et al.*, 1964; Walter *et al.*, 1974). Arginine vasopressin, arginine vasotocin, and lysine vasopressin, like oxytocin, appear to possess a ten-membered hydrogen-bonded β-turn. The backbone N—H of Asn-5 probably is hydrogen bonded to the carbonyl of Tyr-2 (Walter *et al.*, 1974). The backbone of the acyclic tripeptide tail (residues 7–9) of both lysine vasopressin and oxytocin seems to exhibit greater conformational freedom than the ring; the charged tail of lysine vasopressin seems to possess a greater freedom than the uncharged tail of oxytocin (Walter *et al.*, 1974).

C. Cellular and Tissue Binding Sites for Oxytocin and Vasopressin

Over the past 20 years evidence has accumulated to suggest that the binding of peptide hormones to a specific site on the plasma membrane of the cell, known as a receptor site, is the primary event in peptide hormone action. More recently, with the development of methods for preparation of biologically active labeled hormones of high specific activity and of hormonally responsive cells or cell membranes, direct studies of hormone–receptor interactions have become possible (for reviews, see Cuatrecasas, 1974; Kahn, 1976). One of the more recent advances in the area of neurohypophysial hormone action has been the demonstration of specific binding sites for [^{3}H]oxytocin and [^{3}H]vasopressin on their target cells. Radioiodinated derivatives of these hormones generally have lacked binding and biological activities (Thompson *et al.*, 1972; Flouret *et al.*, 1977).

High-affinity binding sites for [^{3}H]oxytocin have been demonstrated in a number of preparations from target tissues and cells (Table V), including the uterus and mammary gland. The apparent dissociation constants are in the range of 0.5–5 nM, except for particulate fractions from frog bladder epithelium and from rat fat cell ghosts, which have K_d values of 250 and 20 nM, respectively.

The concentration of oxytocin causing half-maximal contraction of the rat isolated uterus is 1.2 nM (Follett and Bentley, 1964), which agrees well with the concentration of oxytocin binding to half the receptor sites in uterine particulate preparations, 1.6 nM (Soloff, 1976c) and 1.8 nM (Soloff and Swartz, 1974). Nontarget tissues, such as the ovaries (Soloff, 1975b), seminal vesicles, prostate, vas deferens, and testes of the rat (Soloff, 1976a), do not possess specific binding sites for oxytocin. Within the target tissues for oxytocin, the binding activity was confined specifically to target cells. Radioactivity from [^{3}H]oxytocin was localized by autoradiography in myoepithelial cells of the mammary gland of the lactating rat (Soloff *et al.*, 1975). Little or no radioactivity was present in alveolar or ductal epithelial cells. Oxytocin binding activity has also been localized autoradiographically in smooth muscle cells of the rat oviduct (Soloff *et al.*, 1975). Mammary cells from the lactating rat have been isolated, and [^{3}H]oxytocin-binding activity

TABLE V

SUMMARY OF THE AFFINITY AND CONCENTRATION OF BINDING SITES FOR OXYTOCIN

Site	Apparent K_d (nM)	Concentration of binding sites (fmol/mg protein)	Reference
Broken cell preparations			
Lactating rat mammary	0.76	280	Soloff and Swartz, 1973
Lactating rabbit mammary[a]	2.8	1,700	Markle *et al.*, 1978
Rat uterus,			
Ovariectomized	10	330	Soloff, 1975a
Ovariectomized, treated with estrogen 24 hr earlier	2.4	390	
Intact, treated with estrogen for 2 days	1.8 1.6	180	Soloff, and Swartz, 1974 Soloff, 1976c
Rat myometrium[a]	1.98	128	Crankshaw *et al.*, 1978
Rat oviduct, treated with estrogen for 2 days	1.8	233	Soloff, 1975b
Sow myometrium, last trimester of pregnancy	1.5	150	
Human myometrium, end of first trimester of pregnancy	2.0 2.8	180	Soloff *et al.*, 1974
Sheep myometrium, estrus	0.6	9	Roberts *et al.*, 1976
Sheep endometrium, estrus	0.6	24	
Frog bladder epithelium	250	6,000	Roy *et al.*, 1973
Rat fat cell ghosts	20	500	Bonne and Cohen, 1975
Isolated Cells		(fmoles/10^6 cells)	
Rat mammary gland	5	45	Schroeder *et al.*, 1977
Frog skin epithelium	2.5–5.5	[b]	Bockaert *et al.*, 1972a
Rat fat	5	70–500	Bonne and Cohen, 1975

[a] Purified plasma membranes.
[b] 1–2 pmol/gm of fresh weight.

was concentrated in an enriched myoepithelial cell fraction obtained by density gradient centrifugation (Schroeder *et al.*, 1977). Isolated myoepithelial cells, purified from the mammary gland of the lactating rat (Soloff *et al.*, 1978), contracted in response to the addition of oxytocin to the medium (Fig. 5). The binding of [^{3}H]oxytocin by a crude preparation of mammary cells, isolated from the mammary gland of the lactating rat, was proportional to the concentration of oxytocin; the binding reached a steady state by 40 minutes (Fig. 6). Binding was also proportional to the number of cells under steady-state conditions (Fig. 7). Concentrations of cells greater than 25×10^6 per 250 μl of medium bound less [^{3}H]oxytocin than expected (Fig. 7). These results may be due to a reduction in accessible binding sites because of the increased aggregation of cells when present in higher concentrations.

The binding capacity for [^{3}H]oxytocin of 2.8×10^6 cells per 250 μl was about 0.5 nM oxytocin (Fig. 8), corresponding to about 4.5×10^{-20} mole of

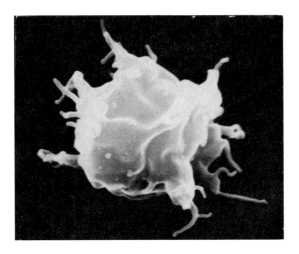

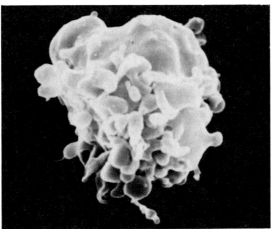

FIG. 5. Scanning electron micrographs of myoepithelial cells in the relaxed state (top) and in the contracted state (bottom) after the addition of oxytocin. The cell processes are shortened and blunted upon contraction, whereas the cell body appears unchanged. Magnification ca. 11,000×. From Soloff *et al.*, 1978a.

oxytocin bound per cell. Scatchard plots (Scatchard, 1949) of oxytocin binding were linear throughout the entire concentration range of oxytocin tested, indicating a single class of independent binding sites (Fig. 8). Oxytocin was bound with an apparent K_d of about 5 nM (Fig. 8), which agrees with the value obtained either by the ratio of the reverse and forward rate constants ($5.8 \times 10^{-4} \text{sec}^{-1}$ and $2.2 \times 10^{5} M^{-1} \text{sec}^{-1}$, respectively) or by varying the concentration of cells (see Fig. 7). The apparent K_d for oxytocin binding to broken cell preparations from the mammary gland of the lactating rat deter-

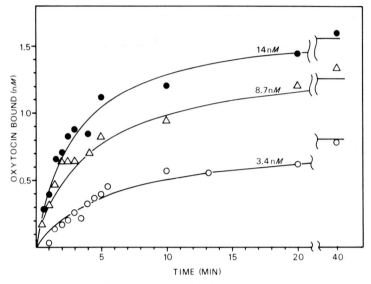

FIG. 6. The binding of [³H]oxytocin to isolated mammary cells. The isolated cells were incubated with 3.4, 8.7, and 14 nM oxytocin at 20°. The lines are theoretical curves based on estimates of forward and reverse rate constants. From Schroeder *et al.*, 1977.

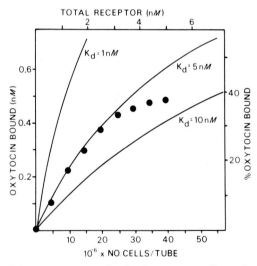

FIG. 7. Effect of the concentration of isolated mammary cells on the specific binding of [³H]Oxytocin, 1.3 nM, was incubated for 1 hour at 20° with increasing concentrations of mammary cells isolated from 5-day lactating rats. The three curves were calculated from apparent dissociation constants of 1, 5, and 10 nM. From Schroeder *et al.*, 1977.

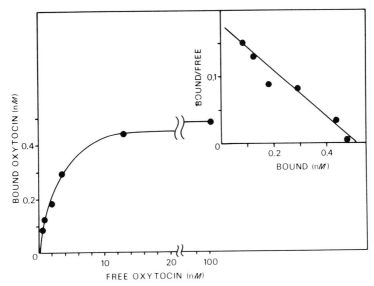

FIG. 8. The specific binding of [³H]oxytocin to isolated mammary cells. The cells, about 2.8 × 10⁶ per 250 μl, were incubated with increasing concentrations of oxytocin for 1 hour at 20°. The data are also expressed as a Scatchard plot (inset). From Schroeder *et al.*, 1977.

mined under steady-state conditions also agreed with the K_d estimated from the ratio of the rate constants (Pearlmutter and Soloff, 1978).

The binding of oxytocin is highly specific with respect to the structure of the ligand. About a dozen synthetic oxytocin analogs, including antagonists and agonists which range in activity from practically zero to about twice the activity of oxytocin, have been examined for the ability to compete with [³H]oxytocin for binding sites in the uterus and mammary gland (Soloff and Swartz, 1973, 1974; Soloff *et al.*, 1974; Soloff, 1976c; Schroeder *et al.*, 1977). The agonists were found to inhibit [³H]oxytocin binding in proportion, generally, to the agonist activities. Several synthetic analogs of oxytocin have been shown to possess partial or negligible agonistic activities and competitively antagonize oxytocin action on the rat uterus. These antagonists, most of which are related to [1-deaminopenicillamine]oxytocin, had affinities for oxytocin-binding sites in proportion to their potencies as antagonists (Soloff, 1976c). Thus, the apparent K_d values calculated from pA₂ values, agreed with the apparent K_d values estimated from inhibition of [³H]oxytocin binding (Table VI). The four antagonists examined appear to be essentially devoid of intrinsic activity, and the antagonist potency was thus a function of the affinity for receptor sites.

Specific binding sites for [³H]oxytocin have been demonstrated in frog skin and bladder epithelial cells (Bockaert *et al.*, 1970, 1972a), and in broken

TABLE VI

COMPARISON OF THE K_d VALUES DERIVED FROM THE BIOASSAY ACTIVITIES OF FOUR COMPETITIVE
ANTAGONISTS OF OXYTOCIN WITH THE K_d VALUES ESTIMATED FROM THE INHIBITION
OF [^{3}H]OXYTOCIN BINDING

	Bioassay		Binding assay	
	pA$_2$	K_d $(10^{-8}$ $M)$	Relative inhibitory potency (%)	K_d $(10^{-8}$ $M)^a$
[N-acetyl,2-O-methyltyrosine]	7.03	9.33	1.6 (1.3→2.0)^b	10 (12 →4.8)^b
Oxytocin			1.5 (1.3→1.8)	11 (12 →8.9)
[1-(β-mercapto-β,β-diethylpro-	7.24	5.75	2.5 (1.5→3.7)	6.4 (11 →4.3)
pionic acid)]Oxytocin			2.5 (1.8→3.3)	6.4 (8.9→4.8)
[1-(β-mercapto-β,β-pentamethyl-	7.43	3.71	4.2 (3.6→5.3)	3.8 (4.4→3.0)
enepropionic acid)]Oxytocin			3.4 (2.6→4.5)	4.7 (6.2→3.6)
[1-(deaminopenicillamine),4-	~7.7	~2.0	6.1 (4.2→8.2)	2.6 (3.8→2.0)
threonine]Oxytocin			5.9 (4.7→7.1)	2.7 (3.4→2.2)

^{a} K_d oxytocin $= 1.6\pm0.04$ nM.

^{b} 95% confidence limits were determined by the method of Finney for parallel line assays. Adapted from
Soloff (1976c).

cell preparations of frog bladder epithelium (Roy *et al.*, 1973). There appears
to be a causal relationship between the binding of [^{3}H]oxytocin to sites on
frog skin epithelium and increases in Na$^+$ and water permeability (Bockaert
et al., 1970, 1972a). For example, the binding preceded the onset of both
biological responses; the affinity of the epithelial cells for oxytocin, as estimated from the binding studies, was similar to estimates derived from the
dose–response relationships for Na$^+$ and water transport; and there were
parallel structural requirements for hormone binding and biological potency,
as determined with analogs of oxytocin.

The binding of [^{3}H]oxytocin to a class of high-affinity sites also corresponded to the activation of adenylate cyclase activity in particulate fractions
from frog bladder epithelial cell homogenates (Roy *et al.*, 1973). The apparent K_m values (ca. 0.25 μM) deduced either from binding data or from
adenylate cyclase activation appeared to be identical. The relative specificities of the binding sites for oxytocin and lysine vasopressin corresponded to the specificities of adenylate cyclase stimulation.

Oxytocin has been shown to bind to fat cells. The hormone exerts an
insulin-like effect on white fat cells, isolated from epididymal fat pads from
male rats, by stimulating glucose oxidation and lipid synthesis (Braun *et al.*,
1969). The mechanisms of oxytocin and insulin action, however, appear to be
different (Braun *et al.*, 1969). For example, the effects of both hormones

were additive at hormone concentrations where maximum stimulation occurred. The maximum effect of oxytocin on either glucose oxidation or lipogenesis was considerably less than the maximum effect of insulin. In addition, about 1000 times more oxytocin than insulin was required to stimulate glucose utilization. An oxytocin analog which antagonized the oxytocin effect on fat cells did not affect the insulin response. Omission of Ca^{2+} from the incubation medium abolished the metabolic effects of oxytocin without affecting insulin activity. Fain and Loken (1969) found that treatment of fat cells with trypsin resulted in a loss of response to insulin but not to oxytocin. Trypsin treatment probably inactivated insulin receptors because the cells lose the ability to bind insulin (Kono *et al.*, 1969). The metabolism of glucose by brown fat cells was stimulated by insulin but not by oxytocin (Fain and Loken, 1969).

Thompson *et al.* (1972) found that iodination of oxytocin reduced the maximum effect of oxytocin on glucose oxidation by 20–25%. [^{125}I]Oxytocin was bound to the isolated fat cells but not to preparations of the uterus, kidney medulla, or toad bladder. The fat cell, then, is unique among oxytocin targets in its ability to bind radioiodinated oxytocin. Unlabeled oxytocin, lysine–vasopressin, and arginine–vasopressin were about equally potent in competing with radioactive oxytocin for binding sites on fat cells (Thompson *et al.*, 1972).

Bonne and Cohen (1975) reported that 5 nM oxytocin stimulated half-maximal glucose oxidation by isolated fat cells. The cells displayed high-affinity sites for [^{3}H]oxytocin with an apparent K_d of 5 nM. About 3×10^4 oxytocin-binding sites were estimated per cell. Insulin, 100 nM, did not compete with [^{3}H]oxytocin; these results support the conclusion that oxytocin interacts with receptors that are separate from insulin receptors. Several oxytocin analogs competed with [^{3}H]oxytocin for binding sites in proportion, generally, to the activation of cellular respiration. Disruption of fat cells resulted in a 4-fold reduction in affinity of the membrane fraction for oxytocin and a 75% reduction in the binding capacity.

[^{3}H]Lysine vasopressin is bound by membrane fractions prepared from pig and rat kidney medulla (Table VII). Binding was reversible and appeared to involve a single population of independent binding sites (Bockaert *et al.*, 1973). The ratio of rate constants for the dissociation and formation of the hormone–receptor complex ($k_r = 5.8 \times 10^{-4} sec^{-1}$, $k_f = 3.8 \times 10^5 M^{-1}sec^{-1}$; $K_d = k_r/k_f = 1.5$ nM) agreed with the apparent K_d value as measured by the concentration of vasopressin leading to 50% saturation of the binding sites in pig membrane fractions (Bockaert *et al.*, 1973).

The binding of vasopressin was shown to be related to adenylate cyclase activation in the pig kidney preparations. For example, the $t_{\frac{1}{2}}$ for hormone binding corresponded to the $t_{\frac{1}{2}}$ of maximum adenylate cyclase stimulation

TABLE VII

SUMMARY OF THE AFFINITY AND CONCENTRATION OF BINDING SITES FOR VASOPRESSIN

Site	Apparent K_d (nM)	Concentration of binding sites (fmoles/mg protein)	Reference
Pig kidney medulla membranes	0.8–8.7	—	Bockaert et al., 1973
Rat kidney medulla particulate fraction	7	400	Rajerison et al., 1974
Rat kidney medulla papillary membranes	14	180	Rajerison et al., 1976

over a range in hormone concentrations (Bockaert et al., 1973). On reduction of the vasopressin concentration in the medium, the reversal of adenylate cyclase activation followed the same time course as the dissociation of [^{3}H]vasopressin from binding sites. The binding sites and adenylate cyclase activation showed comparable specificities toward more than 30 vasopressin (Roy et al., 1975a) and oxytocin (Roy et al., 1975b) analogs.

Despite the correlation between neurohypophysial hormone binding and adenylate cyclase activation in broken cell preparations from both frog bladder epithelial cells and pig kidney medulla, the affinity for the hormone of acellular preparations was considerably less than that of intact cells. For example, the apparent K_m of [^{3}H]oxytocin binding to particulate fractions from frog bladder epithelial cells or of adenylate cyclase activation was 60 times the corresponding values derived from the dose–hydro-osmotic response relationship determined with the intact bladder. This kind of direct comparison is harder to apply to the kidney because of the difficulty in estimating the hormone concentration in the fluid phase in contact with the receptors.

1. The Chemical Nature of Neurohypophysial Hormone Binding Sites

Little is known of the precise chemical identity of the neurohypophysial hormone receptors. [^{3}H]Oxytocin is bound specifically to plasma membrane fractions from rat mammary gland (Soloff, 1976a; Markle et al., 1978) and rat uterus (Soloff, 1976b; Soloff et al., 1977; Crankshaw et al., 1978). The binding site appears to be protein, at least in part, because the binding of [^{3}H]oxytocin was reduced or abolished by treatment of mammary (Soloff and Swartz, 1973) and uterine (Soloff and Swartz, 1974) particulate material with trypsin and certain sulfhydryl reagents. Oxytocin binding to myometrial particles from the sow uterus was inhibited by 1 mM N-ethylmaleimide, possibly accounting for the inhibition of oxytocin-induced contraction of isolated rat uterus by this reagent (Bentley, 1964). No definite conclusions can be drawn as to the phospholipid nature of the receptor site, because the inhibition of oxytocin binding by a crude preparation of phospholipase A could be accounted for by nonenzymatic activity (Soloff and Swartz, 1973, 1974). Purer preparations of phospholipase D had no effect on oxytocin binding to either mammary or myometrial particles (Soloff and Swartz, 1973, 1974). Neuraminidase also had no effect (Soloff and Swartz, 1973, 1974).

Adenylate cyclase and lysine–vasopressin receptor activities have been solubilized from pig kidney medulla membranes with Triton X-100 (Roy *et al.*, 1975c). The solubilized adenylate cyclase was no longer sensitive to vasopressin, and it was activated only slightly by sodium fluoride. Neer (1973a) found that removal of detergent from Lubrol-solubilized adenylate cyclase from rat renal medulla partially restored the responsiveness to vasopressin. The affinity of the solubilized receptor from pig kidney medulla for vasopressin was about 5 times less than that of the membrane-bound receptor. Nevertheless, the positive cooperativity of vasopressin–receptor interaction was preserved, as was the ligand specificity. These findings suggest that no major denaturation of the receptor occurred as a result of detergent treatment (Roy *et al.*, 1975c).

The yield of solubilized receptor was about 30% despite the fact that all the binding activity had disappeared from the residual pellet of the detergent-treated membranes. To reduce the dissociation of hormone, the membrane receptors were occupied before solubilization and then extracted at low temperature. Under these conditions, 65–100% of the hormone-receptor complex was recovered in the soluble fraction. Attempts to purify the vasopressin receptor or to relate the solubilized hormone binding material to adenylate cyclase have not been reported.

2. Neurohypophysial Hormone Action and Metal Ions

Calcium appears to be necessary for the action of all myometrial stimulants, whereas Mg^{2+} is important only for the effects of neurohypophysial hormones and analogs on the uterus. Removal of Mg^{2+} from the bathing medium reduces the stimulatory effects of the hormones. Uterine contractions are potentiated by an increase in the Mg^{2+} concentration over the range 0–1 mM, whereas more than 10 mM depresses the contractions (van Dyke and Hastings, 1928; Clegg *et al.*, 1963; Bentley, 1965; Krejčí and Polacek, 1968). The potentiating action of Mg^{2+} is greater for vasopressin and for analogs of oxytocin modified in positions 3 and 8 than for oxytocin itself (Bentley, 1965; Munsick and Jeronimus, 1965; Krejčí and Polacek, 1968). Because Mg^{2+} caused a parallel shift to the left in dose–response curves of several oxytocin analogs (Bentley, 1965; Krejčí and Polacek, 1968), Mg^{2+}

appeared to increase the affinity of the receptor sites for the analogs. Bentley (1965) found that 0.1 mM Mn^{2+} was generally more effective than 0.5 mM Mg^{2+} in potentiating the potency of several oxytocin analogs. Bentley has suggested that the metal ion may act to alter the steric configuration of the peptide molecule, producing a better fit with receptors. Alternatively, the metal ion may favorably influence the binding of peptides to receptors by modifying the receptor site.

These two modes of potentiation of oxytocic activity are not mutually exclusive. In harmony with Bentley's postulate, Mg^{2+} was found to enhance the binding of [^{3}H]oxytocin to receptors in the mammary gland (Soloff and Swartz, 1973) and sow uterus (Soloff and Swartz, 1974). Other ions can replace Mg^{2+}. The rank order of metal ion effectiveness was Mn^{2+} = Co^{2+} > Mg^{2+} > Zn^{2+} (Soloff and Swartz, 1973, 1974). Ca^{2+} was ineffective in concentrations up to 5 mM (Soloff and Swartz, 1974) or 50 mM (Soloff and Swartz, 1973). The concentrations of Mg^{2+} giving maximal and half-maximal augmentation of oxytocin binding by sow myometrium were 5 and 0.4 mM, respectively (Soloff and Swartz, 1974). The corresponding values with rat mammary particles were approximately 10 and 0.5 mM.

The binding of [^{3}H]oxytocin by rat mammary particles as a function of concentration of several divalent metal ions has been studied (Pearlmutter and Soloff, 1978). Scatchard plots for Co^{2+}, Mn^{2+}, and Mg^{2+} (Fig. 9) indicate that the affinity of the mammary particles for oxytocin was maximal with 5 mM Co^{2+} ($K_a = 9 \times 10^8 M^{-1}$); the order of affinity was Co^{2+} > Mn^{2+} > Ni^{2+} > Mg^{2+} > Zn^{2+}. Specific binding was absent in the presence of Ca^{2+}, Cu^{2+}, and Fe^{2+}. With all the effective metal ions except cobalt, a decrease in metal ion concentration resulted in a decrease in the apparent concentration of receptor sites with no change in binding affinity. The number of available sites remained constant in the presence of 0.1–5.0 mM Co^{2+}, but the affinity decreased as the Co^{2+} concentration was decreased (Fig. 9).

The rate constants for the association and the dissociation of the oxytocin–mammary receptor complex were not significantly modified by increasing concentrations of Mn^{2+} and Mg^{2+} (Table VIII). These results are consistent with the Scatchard analyses, which showed that the metal ions acted to increase the number of available receptor sites, but did not affect the equilibrium constant. In contrast, as the Co^{2+} concentration was raised, the association rate constants increased and the dissociation rate constants decreased (Table VIII). The kinetic effects of Co^{2+} on both on and off rates account for the increase in stability of the hormone–receptor complex as the concentration of Co^{2+} is increased.

All the kinetic data are compatible with a one-step reaction for the binding of hormone to the mammary receptor. Ratios of the forward and reverse rate

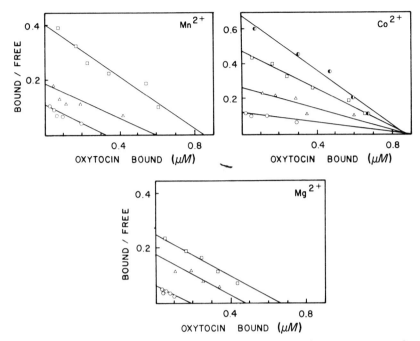

FIG. 9. Specific binding of [^{3}H]oxytocin to a rat mammary particulate preparation as a function of the concentration of Mn^{2+} ($\square$ = 5 μM, $\triangle$ = 1 μM, $\bigcirc$ = 0.5 μM), Co^{2+} ($\mathbb{O}$ = 5 μM, $\square$ = 1 μM, $\triangle$ = 0.5 μM, $\bigcirc$ = 0.1 μM), and Mg^{2+} ($\square$ = 5 μM, $\triangle$ = 1 μM, $\bigcirc$ = 0.5 μM). Each point is the mean of triplicate determinations. The lines were estimated by least-squares analyses. Experimental conditions are given in Pearlmutter and Soloff (1978).

constants were approximately equal to the equilibrium constants, measured independently.

When metal ion was added to a preequilibrated mixture of receptor and oxytocin, the rate of binding was identical to that observed when all three components were added simultaneously (Fig. 10). The dissociation of hormone was accelerated rapidly by the addition of EDTA (Fig. 10). The metal ions appeared to bind to identical sites because combinations of metal ions did not increase the measured association constant.

A tentative model describing the role of metal ions in promoting oxytocin binding to the receptor sites is shown in Figure 11. The receptor, R, contains at least two different regions, A and B, which bind metal ions. Species II (Fig. 11) represents the receptor site when metal ions are bound to the A site(s). This form of the receptor has a relatively low affinity, but is fully available for oxytocin binding. We postulate that the A site(s) has a higher affinity for Co^{2+} than for Mn^{2+} or Mg^{2+}, and species II represents the

TABLE VIII

EFFECT OF VARYING DIVALENT METAL ION CONCENTRATION ON THE
KINETICS OF OXYTOCIN BINDING TO A RAT
MAMMARY RECEPTOR PREPARATION[a]

Metal	Concentration[b] (nM)	$k_f \times 10^{-5}$ (mole^{-1} sec^{-1})	$k_r \times 10^3$ (sec^{-1})
Co^{2+}	0.5(0.22)	2.9	2.0
	1.0(0.45)	2.7	1.8
	5.0(2.30)	3.8	1.2
Mn^{2+}	0.5(0.48)	2.3	0.8
	1.0(0.95)	2.3	0.9
	5.0(4.80)	2.3	0.8
Mg^{2+}	1.0(—)[c]	4.6	2.4
	5.0(—)[c]	3.5	1.9

[a] From Pearlmutter and Soloff (1978).

[b] Numbers in parentheses represent the actual unbound concentration. The amount of metal ion complexed to Tris was calculated using the association constants in Hanlon *et al.* (1966); Hall *et al.* (1962); Bai and Martell (1969).

[c] Binding of Tris to Mg^{2+} is less than or equal to that of Mn^{2+} (Hanlon *et al.*, 1966).

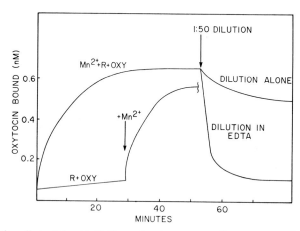

FIG. 10. The effect of 5 mM Mn^{2+} on the time course of association and dissociation of oxytocin–mammary receptor complexes. The metal ion was added either simultaneously with the hormone and receptor or after a delay of 30 minutes. The equilibrated hormone–metal–receptor complex was dissociated by 1:50 dilution either in buffer alone, or in buffer containing 1 mM EDTA. Adapted from Pearlmutter and Soloff (1978).

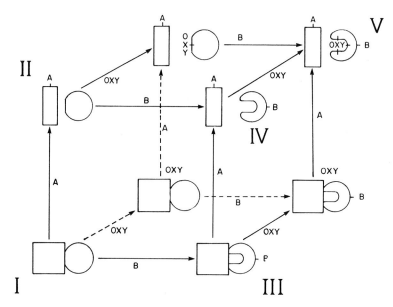

FIG. 11. A model for the role of metal ions in promoting the specific binding of oxytocin to mammary receptor sites. The symbols are discussed in the text. From Pearlmutter and Soloff (1978).

predominant form of the receptor at low Co^{2+} concentrations. At higher concentrations of Co^{2+}, the B site(s) becomes occupied by the metal ion resulting in species IV, which has an increased affinity for oxytocin. The increase in affinity for oxytocin is proportional to the occupancy of the B site(s) by metal ion, II → IV. Species III represents the form of the receptor when metal ions are bound only to the B site(s). This form of the receptor has a potentially high affinity but it cannot bind oxytocin. The B site(s) has a higher affinity for Mn^{2+} and Mg^{2+} than for Co^{2+}, and species III represents the predominant form of the receptor at low Mn^{2+} or Mg^{2+} concentrations. As the concentration of Mn^{2+} or Mg^{2+} is increased, the A site becomes occupied by the metal ion, resulting in the formation of species IV. The increase in the number of binding sites for oxytocin is proportional to the occupancy of the A site by Mn^{2+} or Mg^{2+}, III→IV (Fig. 11).

Because little or no oxytocin binding occurred in the absence of divalent metal ion, the pathways shown as dotted lines would be insignificant.

The model accounts for the Scatchard plots obtained with increasing concentrations of metal ions and for the lack of an increase in the affinity and concentration of receptor sites for oxytocin with combinations of maximal concentrations of metal ions.

Because Ca^{2+} is necessary for the biological responses to oxytocin, but Ca^{2+} had no effect on the binding of [^{3}H]oxytocin to mammary and uterine particles (Soloff and Swartz, 1973, 1974), Ca^{2+} must be involved in molecular events which occur subsequent to the initial oxytocin–receptor interaction. It is possible that Co^{2+}, Mn^{2+}, or Mg^{2+} may also act at some particular site in the sequence linking excitation and contraction beyond the primary binding step. Monovalent cations such as Na^+, K^+, and Li^+ at concentrations of 100 mM did not affect the binding of oxytocin to mammary particles (Soloff and Swartz, 1973).

The potentiating effect of the metal ions on the contractile response of the uterus occurs in K^+-depolarized as well as in normal uteri. Thus, the presence of propagated action potentials is not essential for the metal ion effect (Krejčí and Polacek, 1968).

An increase by 6–8 mM in the concentration of Ca^{2+} in the medium bathing the isolated toad bladder has been shown to inhibit the hydroosmotic response to submaximal concentrations of vasopressin (Bentley, 1959, 1960; Petersen and Edelman, 1964). Active Na^+ transport, however, was not affected by Ca^{2+}. The site of the Ca^{2+} effect on water and urea permeability appeared to be vasopressin-stimulated adenylate cyclase activity, because the inhibitory action of Ca^{2+} was not evident when osmotic water flow, urea permeability, or active Na^+ transport were stimulated by cAMP (Petersen and Edelman, 1964; Argy et al., 1967). Vasopressin-stimulated increases in the permeability of kidney slices of *Necturus* were also inhibited by an increase in the Ca^{2+} concentration of the medium to 10 mM (Whittembury et al., 1960).

More direct evidence has also indicated that these effects of Ca^{2+} on vasopressin action are at the level of vasopressin-stimulated adenylate cyclase activity. For example, Ca^{2+} in concentrations of 0.01–1 mM inhibited vasopressin-stimulated adenylate cyclase activity in homogenates of the bladder from toad (Hynie and Sharp, 1971a) and frog (Bockaert et al., 1972b). The Ca^{2+} effect was specific for vasopressin stimulation because basal and fluoride-stimulated adenylate cyclase activities were not affected by Ca^{2+}. Calcium did not appear to modify the affinity of vasopressin receptors for the hormone because half-maximal stimulation of adenylate cyclase activity occurred with the same concentration of vasopressin in the presence or absence of Ca^{2+} (Bockaert et al., 1972b). In addition, the concentration-dependent binding of [^{3}H]oxytocin by particulate fractions from frog bladder epithelial cells was not affected by 0–1 mM Ca^{2+} (Roy et al., 1973). These observations led Roy et al. (1973) to conclude that the calcium effect is located at the coupling between receptor occupation and adenylate cyclase activation rather than an effect on the accessibility of the receptor sites to hormone. This conclusion seems reasonable because neurohypophysial hormone receptors located on the surface of bladder epithelial cells are exposed to millimolar concentrations of Ca^{2+}.

Other results have not been in total agreement with the findings discussed above. Campbell *et al.* (1972) found that 10 mM Ca^{2+} completely inhibited the binding of [^{3}H]lysine vasopressin to a membrane fraction from pig kidney medulla. However, in harmony with the findings in anuran preparations, lysine vasopressin-sensitive adenylate cyclase activity in the pig medulla preparation was inhibited with concentrations of Ca^{2+} greater than 1 μM (Campbell *et al.*, 1972). Basal and fluoride-stimulated activities were only slightly inhibited with 1 mM Ca^{2+}. In kidney homogenates from the hamster (Marumo and Edelman, 1971) and rat (Jakobs *et al.*, 1972), Ca^{2+} inhibited not only vasopressin sensitive adenylate cyclase activity, but basal and fluoride-stimulated activities. The inhibition occurred under conditions in which PGE_1 inhibited the response of adenylate cyclase to vasopressin but had no effect on basal or fluoride-stimulated activities (Marumo and Edelman, 1971).

The removal of all Ca^{2+} also results in the inhibition of adenylate cyclase activity. When broken epithelial cells from frog bladder were depleted of Ca^{2+} by washing with EGTA and Ca^{2+}-free medium, oxytocin-stimulated adenylate cyclase activity was reduced by 20–100% (Bockaert *et al.*, 1972b). Activity was restored completely by the addition of 1 μM Ca^{2+}. The addition of Ca^{2+} in concentrations greater than 5×10^{-5} M resulted in the inhibition of oxytocin-stimulated adenylate cyclase activity while the apparent K_m for oxytocin was unchanged. EDTA, 1 mM, also inhibited basal and lysine vasopressin-stimulated adenylate cyclase activities in a membrane fraction from pig kidney medulla (Campbell *et al.*, 1972). However, the EDTA effect may be unrelated to Ca^{2+} chelation, because the inhibition of enzyme activity caused by the presence of 1 mM EDTA was reversed by 0.5 mM Ca^{2+}. Under these conditions the concentration of free Ca^{2+} would be about 0.1 nM (Reed and Bygrave, 1975). The inhibition of adenylate cyclase by EDTA might have been due to the chelation of Mg^{2+}. EDTA had no effect on the binding of [^{3}H]lysine vasopressin to the membrane fraction from pig renal medulla (Campbell *et al.*, 1972).

In summary, the exact role of Ca^{2+} in the activation of adenylate cyclase by neurohypophysial hormones is unknown. The observation that Ca^{2+} inhibited the hydro-osmotic response of the toad bladder to vasopressin, but did not affect vasopressin stimulation of active Na^+ transport, suggests that the two responses are mediated by separate adenylate cyclase systems (Petersen and Edelman, 1964).

Mg^{2+} is required for adenylate cyclase activity. An increase in Mg^{2+} concentration from 0.75 to 10 μM gave a linear increase in both basal and vasopressin-stimulated adenylate cyclase activities in particulate fractions from rat renal medulla (Rajerison *et al.*, 1974). Concentrations of Mg^{2+} greater than 10 mM were inhibitory. The ratio of vasopressin-stimulated adenylate cyclase activity to basal levels was maximum at Mg^{2+} concentrations lower than 1.25 mM; the ratio decreased with higher concentrations of Mg^{2+} (Rajerison *et al.*, 1974).

Mn^{2+} was shown to inhibit vasopressin- and oxytocin-stimulated adenylate cyclase activity in the toad bladder (Hynie and Sharp, 1971b). The inhibition was similar to that found with Ca^{2+}. NaCl and KCl produced a biphasic effect on adenylate cyclase activity in the rabbit renal medulla (Dousa, 1972). Concentrations of salt between 50 and 150 mM produced small but significant increases in basal, fluoride-, and vasopressin-stimulated activities. Concentrations of NaCl and KCl greater than 200 mM markedly inhibited these activities. At these concentrations of salt, the dose of vasopressin required for half-maximal stimulation was not altered, but the magnitude of the adenylate cyclase response to all concentrations of vasopressin was reduced. NaCl and KCl, therefore, do not appear to modify the affinity of the receptor site for vasopressin, but are involved either in the coupling of the receptor to adenylate cyclase or in the activity of adenylate cyclase in general. Mixtures of solutes simulating the composition of medullary fluids in antidiuresis inhibited vasopressin-stimulated adenylate cyclase activity, while the mixture simulating a state of water diuresis allowed a normal response to vasopressin. These observations suggested to Dousa (1972) that the composition of renal medullary fluid could regulate the cellular response to vasopressin.

Anions may also be involved in the regulation of adenylate cyclase activity in the renal medulla. Basal activity in a membrane fraction from pig renal medulla was reduced when Cl^- in the incubation medium was replaced by SO_4^{2-} (Roy *et al.*, 1977). Vasopressin-stimulated adenylate cyclase activity was not affected. The ratio of vasopressin-stimulated adenylate cyclase activity to basal activity (activation ratio), therefore, was higher in the presence of SO_4^{2-} than Cl^-. The substitution of anions also induced a shift in adenylate cyclase activity from Michaelis–Menten kinetics with respect to ATP to positive cooperative behavior under both basal and vasopressin-stimulated conditions. The effects of SO_4^{2-} could not be overcome by addition of up to 500 mM Cl^-. The anions also had an effect on the activation by Mg^{2+}. The vasopressin–activation ratio remained almost constant in the presence of 1–100 mM $MgSO_4$ but fell from 10 to 3 when $MgCl_2$ was increased from 1 to 50 mM.

The sites of action of anions and cations on neurohypophysial hormone sensitive adenylate cyclase remain to be clarified.

3. *Effects of Steroids on Neurohypophysial Hormone Action*

    a. Sex Steroids and Myometrial Contractility.   Uterine sensitivity to oxytocin is greatest in proestrus and estrus (for review, see Soloff *et al.*, 1977). Oxytocic activity appears to be negligible in metestrus. The physiological basis for the uterine sensitivity to oxytocin appears to be endogenous estrogen. Estrogen treatment causes uterine muscle to contract spontaneously and regularly. Uterine sensitivity to oxytocin can be raised 13-fold by daily injections of diethylstilbestrol into rats for 3 days (Follett and Bentley, 1964).

The administration of progesterone to ovariectomized rats diminished the spontaneous contractions of the uterus *in vitro* and markedly reduced the response to oxytocin (Berger and Marshall, 1961). The well-known antagonism of estrogen action by progesterone probably accounts for the reduced uterine sensitivity to oxytocin. Estrogens may possibly act at several sites in promoting the sensitivity of the uterus to oxytocin; this will be further discussed in the following paragraphs.

i. The resting membrane potential of myometrial cells. Administration of estrogens to ovariectomized or immature animals of several species led to an increase in the resting membrane potential of the myometrial cell from 35 mV to 40–50 mV (for a review, see Marshall, 1974). Because the excitability of the myometrium to oxytocin and other uterotonic drugs was increased by estrogen pretreatment, estrogens may bring the membrane potential of the myometrial cell into a more favorable range for excitation (Marshall, 1974). Progesterone treatment caused the action potentials to be abolished or to become small, independent, and irregular (Csapo. 1961a).

ii. Receptor sites for oxytocin. The changes in the sensitivity of the rat myometrium to oxytocin during the estrous cycle appear to be a reflection of changes in the affinity and capacity of oxytocin receptor sites. Oxytocin was bound by particulate fractions from the sheep uterus with an apparent K_d of 0.5–0.7 nM throughout the estrous cycle (Roberts *et al.*, 1976). The concentration of binding sites per mg of protein was relatively low 4 days prior to estrus, rose to a peak on the day of estrus, and fell to baseline levels at 5 days after estrus (Fig. 12). The binding of oxytocin to endometrial material paralleled that of myometrial preparations. The amount of oxytocin bound per mg of endometrial protein, however, was about 3 times greater than that of the myometrium on the day of estrus (Fig. 12). The significance of endometrial receptors for oxytocin is discussed in Section VI,A.

The changes in oxytocin binding by the sheep uterus during the estrous cycle may be due to changes in estrogen levels in the blood. For example, the administration of a single dose of 5 μg of diethylstilbestrol to ovariectomized rats increased the affinity of uterine particulate fractions for [^{3}H]oxytocin more than 4-fold 24 hours later (Fig. 13). An increase in affinity was apparent, however, as early as 6 hours after estrogen treatment. The concentration of binding sites per uterus for oxytocin was doubled 24 hours after estrogen treatment.

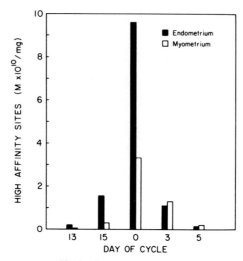

FIG. 12. The concentration of high-affinity sites for oxytocin in endometrial and myometrial particulate fractions from ewe uterus during the estrous cycle. The data are expressed per mg of particulate protein. From Roberts *et al.*, 1976.

iii. The release of activator calcium . The uterotonic action of neurohypophysial hormones is mediated by Ca^{2+} (see Section V,A). Berger and Marshall (1961) found that when uterine horns from ovariectomized rats, treated *in vivo* with either estradiol or progesterone, were washed repeatedly in Ca^{2+}-free Krebs solution, spontaneous contractile activity gradually disappeared. The decline in spontaneous contractions was about 3 times

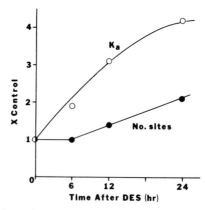

FIG. 13. The effect of a single injection of 5 μg of diethylstilbestrol (DES) on the apparent affinity (K_a) and number of binding sites of the ovariectomized rat uterus for [^{3}H]oxytocin. The control group received no DES. From Soloff, 1975a.

slower in uteri from progesterone-treated than from estrogen-treated animals. These findings suggested that the progesterone-treated uterus bound Ca^{2+} more firmly than did the estrogen-treated muscle. Because of the sequestration of activator Ca^{2+}, the progesterone-dominated uterus would be less susceptible to the stimulatory actions of oxytocin. Comparable conclusions were reached from studies on the rabbit uterus (Torok and Csapo, 1976).

iv. The uterine contractile apparatus. The concentration of contractile elements in the myometrium was increased by estrogen treatment. Actomyosin, ATPase activity, and high-energy phosphates were at the lowest levels after ovariectomy and increased in response to estrogen administration (Csapo, 1950; Needham and Shoenberg, 1967). Progesterone, with or without estrogen pretreatment, had only a slight effect on the contractile components (Michael and Schofield, 1969).

v. Myometrial cAMP. Sim and Chantharaksri (1973) observed that the activities of both adenylate cyclase and cyclic nucleotide phosphodiesterase in the rat uterus were lowest at proestrus and highest during metestrus. These activities indicated that the turnover of cellular cAMP was maximal during metestrus. The dose–response curves of oxytocin-induced uterine contractions were shifted to the right during metestrus. Because cAMP can inhibit the action of oxytocin on the rat uterus (see Section V,B), it is possible that the change in sensitivity to oxytocin during the estrous cycle is mediated by intracellular cAMP.

Perhaps the most important mechanism by which estrogens increase uterine sensitivity to oxytocin involves an increase in oxytocin binding to receptors. The other mechanisms discussed above also may be involved.

b. Adrenal Steroids and Vasopressin Action. The administration of aldosterone to adrenalectomized rats increased the maximal activation by vasopressin of adenylate cyclase activity in kidney medulla membranes (Rajerison *et al.*, 1974). The apparent affinity of the membranes for the hormone, as measured by the concentration of vasopressin giving half-maximal stimulation, was not changed. When the relative increase in adenylate cyclase activation was compared to the relative increase in the binding of [^{3}H]lysine vasopressin to the renal medulla membranes, it became apparent that the aldosterone effect could be accounted for by an increase in receptor concentration. The administration of dexamethasone, on the other hand, led to a more pronounced effect on vasopressin-stimulated adenylate cyclase activity than on vasopressin binding. It appears, therefore, that while aldosterone modified vasopressin action by increasing the concentration of receptor sites, dexamethasone increased the efficiency of receptor–adenylate cyclase coupling. It is notable, however, that the effects of aldosterone and dexamethasone were not additive, as would be expected if they were operating by separate mechanisms. Corticosterone, the major endogenous corticosteroid in the rat, was inactive. Aldosterone and dexamethasone were inactive when added *in vitro*.

D. REGULATION OF RECEPTOR CONCENTRATION

The findings shown in Figs. 12 and 13 indicate that the concentration of oxytocin receptors, like that of any other membrane component, is not fixed. Whether the change in concentration of binding sites reflects continual synthesis and degradation, or whether it reflects modification of existing units, remains to be determined. Over the last several years, studies with a variety of hormones have indicated that changes in receptor concentrations may provide a mechanism for target cell regulation of hormonal sensitivity (for reviews, see Kahn, 1976; Lesniak and Roth, 1976). It is possible that labor in rats is triggered by the appearance of receptor sites for oxytocin in the myometrium.

1. Oxytocin Binding by the Rat Uterus during Pregnancy

There have been conflicting reports on oxytocin levels in the systemic circulation of women in labor (Chard *et al.*, 1971; Kumaresan *et al.*, 1974). Whereas circulating oxytocin levels are elevated in several species during the final stages of labor (Fitzpatrick and Walmsley, 1965), oxytocin has not been detected in the blood at the outset of labor (Caldeyro-Barcia *et al.*, 1971), and many investigators have dismissed oxytocin as the sole physiological agent that initiates parturition. The sensitivity of the myometrium to oxytocin increases markedly prior to labor in rats and rabbits (Fuchs, 1973). Under these circumstances, the myometrial cell may respond to circulating levels of oxytocin (Fuchs, 1973).

Studies of oxytocin binding to rat myometrium as a function of the day of gestation have suggested that the increased sensitivity of the myometrium to oxytocin may result from an increase in oxytocin receptor concentration. The binding of [3H]oxytocin by particulate fractions from rat myometrium was elevated on the first day of pregnancy, which corresponds to estrus (Fig. 14). These results agree with the findings that [3H]oxytocin binding to sheep myometrium was greatest on the day of estrus (Fig. 11). The concentration of binding sites decreased to near baseline levels by the fifth day of pregnancy and remained low until the day of parturition, day 22 (Fig. 14). Binding then increased, reached peak values on the first postpartum day, and fell thereafter to near baseline values. The large variation seen in the concentration of binding sites on day 22 and on the first postpartum day may be due to the variation among rats in the precise time of parturition. It is possible that

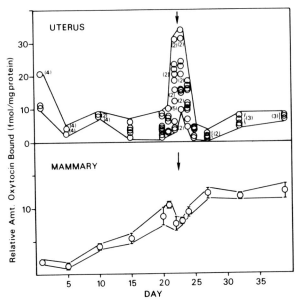

FIG. 14. The relative amount of [³H]oxytocin bound specifically by particulate fractions from the rat myometrium and mammary gland during pregnancy. Parturition occurred between days 22 and 23, as shown by arrow. In some instances uteri were pooled, with the number per group shown in parentheses. For the most part, each point represents a separate myometrial sample. The mammary results are expressed as mean ± S.E. (*n* = 6). From Soloff *et al.*, 1979a

during labor the concentration of oxytocin binding sites far exceeded the values reported in Fig. 14. These results support the observations of Fuchs (1973), who found that exogenous oxytocin could not induce labor in rats earlier than 6 to 8 hours before term.

The binding of [³H]oxytocin to particulate fractions from the rat mammary gland increased steadily throughout pregnancy, except for a transient dip near term, and was maximal during postpartum lactation (see Fig. 14). Like the myometrial cell, the concentration of receptor sites for oxytocin in the mammary gland appears to correspond to the sensitivity of the myoepithelial cell to oxytocin. For example, Sala and Freire (1974) found that mammary strips from the virgin mouse were insensitive to 1000 μU of oxytocin per ml (ca. 2 n*M*) *in vitro*. The threshold response to oxytocin on days 9 and 18 of pregnancy and 1 and 10 of lactation were > 1000, 25, 10, and 10 μU/ml, respectively.

The factors that stimulate the appearance of oxytocin binding sites in the uterus and mammary gland remain to be determined. In view of the differences in oxytocin binding by the mammary gland and uterus during pregnancy, the two targets must be controlled by different effectors. The impor-

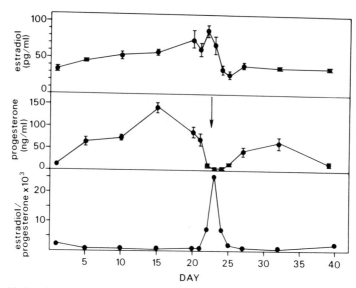

FIG. 15. Levels of estradiol-17β, progesterone, and the estradiol: progesterone ratio in the plasma of rats during pregnancy. Each point is the mean ± S.E. from at least 8 rats. Parturition occurred between days 22 and 23, as shown by arrow. Adapted from Soloff *et al.*, 1979b.

15). The increase in oxytocin binding sites might have been suppressed, however, by the concomitant rise in plasma progesterone (Fig. 15). Progesterone levels declined rapidly from day 21 through term. The sharp decline in blood progesterone preceding labor, with the accompanying maintenance of estrogen levels, gave an estrogen/progesterone ratio which resembled the spike in oxytocin binding (Fig. 15). These results appear to support the "progesterone block" theory for the initiation of parturition (Csapo, 1956). However, in individual animals, the plasma estradiol/progesterone ratios did not correlate with [3H]oxytocin binding activity (Soloff, 1978), suggesting that additional factors are involved in regulation of the oxytocin receptor concentration. One such factor may be prostaglandin. Liggens *et al.* (1972) found that whereas $PGF_{2\alpha}$ itself was not oxytocic in pregnant sheep, $PGF_{2\alpha}$ did enhance the response of the uterus to oxytocin. Prostaglandins released near term, therefore, may stimulate the appearance of receptor sites for oxytocin on the myometrial cell.

Estrogen treatment of ovariectomized mice stimulated changes in mammary myoepithelial cell structure and the ability to respond to oxytocin (Sala tance of estrogens in regulating the concentration of binding sites has been discussed. Circulating estrogen levels rose steadily during pregnancy (Fig.

and Freire, 1974). The administration of progesterone had no effect on the structure or activity of myoepithelial cells. Thus, estrogen may also play some role in stimulating the appearance of receptor sites for oxytocin in the mammary gland.

2. Regulation of Vasopressin Receptors by Vasopressin

Dousa et al. (1975) found that in the Brattleboro rat, which is unable to synthesize vasopressin, basal and vasopressin-sensitive adenylate cyclase activities of the kidney medulla were lower than those of heterozygous rats of the same strain having endogenous vasopressin. The chronic administration of vasopressin to Brattleboro rats increased the sensitivity of renal adenylate cyclase activity to vasopressin *in vitro* but had no effect on the basal activity of the enzyme. These results suggest that the responsiveness of the renal medullary cells to vasopressin is regulated by circulating levels of the hormone.

In accord with the conclusion, Rajerison et al. (1977) found that in the rat the reduction of circulating vasopressin levels by induced-water diuresis caused a 30% reduction in maximum renal adenylate cyclase activation by vasopressin *in vitro*. Conversely, the elevation of blood levels of vasopressin, either by administration of NaCl or by the chronic administration of a long-acting vasopressin analog, resulted in a 30% increase in the maximal activation of adenylate cyclase by vasopressin.

The administration of pharmacological concentrations of neurohypophysial peptides, however, produced a rapid and reversible reduction in renal adenylate cyclase responsiveness to vasopressin stimulation *in vitro*. The desensitization of vasopressin-stimulated activity was specific: Analogs with the greatest potencies as agonists produced the greatest desensitization. The reduction in activity did not appear to be the result of nonspecific alterations in catalytic activity because the desensitized enzyme remained responsive to NaF and Gpp(NH)p.

Desensitization of kidney adenylate cyclase has also been produced *in vitro*. Preincubation of membrane fractions from pig kidney with micromolar concentrations of vasopressin resulted in a 50–75% reduction of maximally stimulated adenylate cyclase activity when ATP was added (Roy et al., 1976). The effect of vasopressin in reducing maximal adenylate cyclase activity was dependent on the concentration of ATP. Desensitization was apparent with 1 mM ATP but was absent with a concentration of 0.1 mM. The reduction of maximally stimulatable enzyme activity did not appear to be due to the metabolism of vasopressin, because desensitization occurred when additional vasopressin was added during the adenylate cyclase assay. Desensitization was also achieved with two metabolically stable analogs. The degree of desensitization induced by the analogs was dose dependent. Maximum desensitization was obtained with concentrations of analogs that also gave maximal activation of adenylate cyclase. From these results, it seems likely that desensitization is somehow linked to the occupancy of the hormonal receptors involved in adenylate cyclase activation. Whether the process of desensitization is a reflection of a reduction in vasopressin receptor sites or the result of a modification in the coupling between receptor and adenylate cyclase remains to be determined. The Hill coefficients characterizing adenylate cyclase activation by two vasopressin analogs were not changed by desensitization. These results led Roy *et al.* (1973) to suggest that desensitization does not involve molecular events associated with receptor–adenylate cyclase coupling.

Although the precise mechanisms of desensitization are not understood, Rajerison *et al.* (1977) have suggested that vasopressin-sensitive adenylate cyclase activity in the kidney can be controlled by both positive and negative feedback mechanisms. Regulation by positive feedback would operate in the physiological range of circulating vasopressin levels, whereas negative regulation would become apparent by an increase in blood vasopressin to pharmacological levels.

IV. NEUROHYPOPHYSIAL HORMONE STIMULUS GENERATION

The nature of the primary stimulus generated by neurohypophysial hormone action on myoepithelial and myometrial cells is still speculative. In contrast, the primary actions of neurohypophysial hormones on anuran bladder and mammalian kidney tubule cells seem to involve the activation of membrane adenylate cyclase activity (for reviews, see Jard and Bockaert, 1975; Dousa and Valtin, 1976).

A. OXYTOCIN AND THE EXCITABLE MEMBRANE

Oxytocin has been shown by several workers to cause a slight, but definite, depolarization of the myometrial cell membrane, and to increase the frequency and duration of spike discharges (for a review, see Marshall, 1974). These effects of oxytocin were seen at physiological concentrations, 50–500 μU/ml. With greater doses (>10 mU/ml), the cell membrane was depolarized to a greater extent and the uterine muscles underwent sustained contractions (Marshall, 1974).

Marshall (1974) has postulated that the initial action of oxytocin is on the excitable surface membrane of the myometrial cell. Physiological concentrations of oxytocin would stimulate groups of the most sensitive cells to discharge action potentials, which by propagating over the muscle would recruit other cells into activity.

Studies of the effects of calcium on the uterine action potential under different sets of experimental conditions, including current clamp and voltage clamp conditions, led to the conclusion that calcium entry constitutes at least part of the depolarizing current (see Marshall, 1974).

In support of the proposed action of oxytocin upon membrane excitability, Csapo (1961b) reported that elevation of the extracellular K^+ concentration to 120 mM resulted in membrane depolarization and almost eliminated the electrical and mechanical effects of oxytocin on the parturient rabbit uterus. These findings, however, are not in accord with other studies which have shown that oxytocin can elicit contractions of the potassium-depolarized uterus (Evans *et al.*, 1958; Daniel *et al.*, 1962) and mammary strips (Moore and Zarrow, 1965; Polacek *et al.*, 1967). As pointed out in the study of Evans *et al.* (1958), exposure of an isolated segment of rat uterus to isotonic potassium solutions resulted in the reduction of the membrane potential of muscle cells to a level where all action potentials disappeared. Although no action potentials were generated, the depolarized muscles contracted in response to posterior pituitary extracts. The contractions, however, were weak in comparison to those of normal muscles.

Polacek and co-workers (1967) reported that mammary strips in Ringer solution containing 76 mM K_2SO_4 and 0.92 mM Ca^{2+} responded to oxytocin with qualitatively similar contractions of unimpaired intensity as in normal Tyrode solution. In summary, factors more than membrane excitation appear to be part of the stimulus generated by oxytocin.

B. Neurohypophysial Hormone-Sensitive Adenylate Cyclase Systems

Chase and Aurbach (1968) showed that most of the adenylate cyclase activity in the rat kidney that was stimulated by vasopressin was associated with crude membrane fractions from the medulla. Parathyroid hormone activated the enzyme primarily in the cortex. Several laboratories have since shown that the vasopressin-stimulated adenylate cyclase activity is associated with plasma membranes from the renal medulla of pigs, rats, and beef (Table IX). The stimulation results in an increase in the V_{max} of the adenylate cyclase reaction. In each of the studies cited in Table IX, a different set of Mg^{2+} and ATP concentrations was used. Birnbaumer and Yang (1974) have pointed out, however, that the ratio of vasopressin-stimulated to basal activities can differ with different Mg^{2+} and ATP concentrations. For example, an increase in the concentration of Mg^{2+} resulted in the selective stimulation of

TABLE IX

VASOPRESSIN-STIMULATED ADENYLATE CYCLASE IN
ENRICHED PLASMA MEMBRANE FRACTIONS FROM RENAL MEDULLA

Animal	Purification from homogenate (fold)	Vasopressin stimulation relative to basal activity	K_m (nM)	Reference
Pig	6	3	22	Campbell *et al.*, 1972
Rat	3–4	6	4–15	Neer, 1973b
Pig	5	4–6	5	Bockaert *et al.*, 1973
Beef	8–12	4–5	1	Birnbaumer and Yang, 1974
Rat	—	5–10	10–70	Rajerison *et al.*, 1974

basal adenylate cyclase activity with the loss of the relative stimulation by vasopressin. A change in the concentration of ATP from an optimum of 0.07 to 0.1 mM resulted in a selective loss of vasopressin-stimulated activity.

The mechanisms of neurohypophysial hormone activation of adenylate cyclase activity in broken cell preparations of the frog bladder could be distinguished from fluoride activation. Whereas both oxytocin- and NaF-stimulated activities resulted in an increased V_{max} of the enzyme reaction, oxytocin stimulation alone resulted in an increased affinity of adenylate cyclase for ATP (Bockaert *et al.*, 1972b). The oxytocin-stimulated enzyme system also appeared to have a nucleotide regulatory site. For example, oxytocin stimulation was maximal in the presence of 10 nM GTP and a substrate concentration of 10 μM ATP. The effect of GTP was reduced with increasing concentrations of ATP. The use of concentrations of GTP greater than 1 μM resulted in reductions in the ratio of stimulated to basal adenylate cyclase activities. Bockaert *et al.* (1972b) concluded that the adenylate cyclase system of frog bladder includes a regulatory site with an affinity for GTP and ATP. Because the GTP effect could be shown only with low concentrations of ATP, the affinity of the regulatory site for ATP appeared to be comparable to that for GTP. ATP may serve as an effector as well as a substrate for the adenylate cyclase system. For any given extent of saturation of the catalytic site, the occupancy of the regulatory site by nucleotide would increase the velocity of the adenylate cyclase catalyzed reaction. The increase in velocity would be higher in the presence of neurohypophysial hormone than under basal conditions. In other words, in addition to increasing the affinity of the catalytic site for ATP, vasopressin could increase the affinity of the regulatory site for both ATP and GTP.

The characteristics of the vasopressin-sensitive adenylate cyclase system in the kidney may be different from those of the enzyme in frog bladder. Birnbaumer *et al.* (1974) found that GTP inhibited the action of neurohypophysial hormones on adenylate cyclase activity in plasma membrane fractions from pig kidney medulla. Half-maximal inhibition occurred with 0.2 μM GTP. There was little effect of GTP on basal adenylate cyclase activity. Stimulation by neurohypophysial hormones was enhanced with concentrations of ATP greater than 10 μM; with concentrations of ATP less than 10 μM, hormone stimulation was low. Hormone stimulation was also enhanced by adenosine or AMP. The inhibitory effects of GTP, however, were still apparent in the presence of adenosine or AMP. Based on these observations, it was postulated that ATP could interact with the kidney medulla adenylate cyclase system at three sites: (a) the catalytic site; (b) regulatory site I, which enhances the response to neurohypophysial hormone (this effect could be mimicked by adenosine and AMP); and (c) regulatory site II, which can bind GTP, resulting in a stable state of the enzyme that is less susceptible to stimulation by occupied neurohypophysial receptors. The effects of neither GTP nor ATP appeared to be mediated by phosphorylation of components of the adenylate cyclase system, because non-phosphorylating analogs of GTP and ATP also were effective.

V. RELATIONSHIP BETWEEN STIMULUS GENERATION AND RESPONSE

At least two distinct events appear to reflect hormone–receptor interaction: binding of the hormone, and initiation of the signal which eventually leads to a response. Replacement of the tyrosine residue of oxytocin by various substituents led to losses in oxytocic activity and to the appearance of inhibitory activities (Rudinger *et al.*, 1972). Yet the affinities of the receptor sites for the series of analogs, as determined from pD_2 and pA_2 values, were very similar. This suggests that the tyrosine residue is involved primarily in stimulus generation and contributes little to the affinity of receptor sites for the peptide (Rudinger *et al.*, 1972). A separation between binding and response can also be seen with the oxytocin analogs shown in Table VI. These analogs, which have little or no oxytocic activity, competitively inhibited the binding of [^{3}H]oxytocin to uterine receptor sites (Soloff, 1976c).

The stimulation of adenylate cyclase activity by neurohypophysial hormones is not a simple linear function of receptor occupancy. Adenylate cyclase activation in renal membranes by vasopressin was 80% of maximum when 10% of the receptor sites were filled (Bockaert *et al.*, 1973). The phenomenon did not appear to be due to spare receptors, because saturation of the binding sites was required for maximal activation of adenylate cyclase. The binding of vasopressin was positively cooperative (Hill coefficient = 1.42), while vasopressin-stimulated adenylate cyclase activity was negatively cooperative (Hill coefficient = 0.35). The nonlinearity between the binding and activation of enzyme activity depended on the analog of oxytocin or vasopressin (Roy *et al.*, 1975a;b). With some analogs, the dose dependencies for receptor binding and adenylate cyclase activation were superimposable. In these cases it would appear that receptor–adenylate cyclase coupling is linear.

The recognition sites for vasopressin seem to develop separately ontogenetically from the sites involved in the activation of adenylate cyclase activity. The onset of vasopressin binding capacity preceded the appearance of enzyme responsiveness to vasopressin in kidney medulla–papillary membranes from immature rats (Rajerison *et al.*, 1976).

Any model depicting the coupling of binding to stimulus generation must be complex to properly account for the cooperative effects of vasopressin and for the regulatory effects of metal ions and nucleotides on adenylate cyclase activation. Although the details of coupling are not presently known, a model consisting of separate mobile receptor and effector molecules, both of which interact when the receptor is occupied by the hormone, might explain the observations of spare receptors, nonlinear coupling, differences in intrinsic activity, and desensitization (Swillens and Dumont, 1977).

A. The Role of Calcium in Oxytocin Action

Calcium is required for the oxytocic activity of a wide variety of agents, including neurohypophysial hormones. This subject has been reviewed by Marshall (1974), Jard and Bockaert (1975), and Wanner *et al.* (1977). When Ca^{2+} was removed from the medium bathing the uterus, the responsiveness to oxytocin disappeared within a period of minutes (for a review, see Marshall, 1974). Addition of Ca^{2+} restored the sensitivity of the myometrium to oxytocin. With submaximal concentrations of Ca^{2+}, however, oxytocin acted as a partial agonist (Krejčí *et al.*, 1964). Oxytocin action on mammary tissue is also dependent on extracellular Ca^{2+} (Moore and Zarrow, 1965; Polacek *et al.*, 1967; Lawson and Schmidt, 1972).

In these studies the origin of activator Ca^{2+} was not clear. After removal of Ca^{2+} from the extracellular medium, the decline in oxytocic activity was gradual, rather than abrupt. This suggests that activator Ca^{2+} may have arisen from intracellular stores that were exchangeable with the extracellular space. Alternatively, the gradual loss of oxytocic activity could be explained if Ca^{2+} were bound by connective tissue elements or by constituents of an extracellular compartment near the plasma membrane, but separated by a diffusion barrier. Ca^{2+} might be mobilized from these extracellular sites by oxytocin during the initial exposure to Ca^{2+}-free solutions. With time, however, the Ca^{2+} from these sites would be depleted, accounting for the gradual loss of uterine responsiveness (Marshall, 1974).

The determination of the source of activator calcium has not been easy because the influx and efflux curves for ^{45}Ca in contracting myometrium are complex and indicate that calcium is exchanging in a multicompartmental system (Krejčí and Daniel, 1970a,b; van Breemen et al., 1966).

An alternate approach to clarify the locus of activator calcium has been to characterize Ca^{2+} uptake by subcellular fractions from the myometrium. Several organelles may contribute to the movement of Ca^{2+} during contraction and relaxation. The plasma membrane is a barrier to extracellular Ca^{2+}, and probably is the site of a Ca^{2+} extrusion pump (Casteels and van Breemen, 1975; Hurwitz et al., 1973). The sarcoplasmic reticulum, which is relatively abundant in the myometrium when compared to other smooth muscle cells (Gabella, 1973; Devine et al., 1973), has been shown to bind Ca^{2+} (Carsten, 1969). By analogy with skeletal muscle, the myometrial sarcoplasmic reticulum may be a source of activator Ca^{2+} (Carsten, 1969). Mitochondria from myometrial cells take up Ca^{2+} and also may serve as a store of activator Ca^{2+}. Although uterine smooth muscle has a less developed sarcoplasmic reticulum compared to fast skeletal muscle, the uterine muscle does have a sufficient number of mitochondria (Gabella, 1973; Devine et al., 1973) to be involved in the control of contraction and relaxation of the uterus (Malmström and Carafoli, 1977).

1. Sarcolemma

Subcellular fractions enriched in sarcolemma have been prepared from human (Janis et al., 1976) and rat (Rangachari et al., 1976; Janis et al., 1977) myometrium. These preparations took up Ca^{2+} in an ATP-dependent manner. The sarcolemma is a logical site for activator calcium, because oxytocin action is initiated there (Soloff et al., 1977). The binding of oxytocin may be coupled to cell contraction by the movement of Ca^{2+} from the cell membrane to the myoplasm. Rangachari and co-workers (1976), however, have found that myometrial agonists such as $PGF_{2\alpha}$ and angiotensin, and relaxant drugs, had marginal if any effects on the uptake of ^{45}Ca by enriched plasma membrane preparations from rat myometrium. Calcium fluxes in the membrane preparations could be modified, however, with the ionophore A 23187. The addition of the ionophore greatly reduced the steady-state uptake of Ca^{2+} and also led to the release of previously accumulated Ca^{2+}. Similar results with ionophores have been reported by Janis and Daniel (1977).

An important role for sarcolemmal Ca^{2+} in uterine contraction has been deduced by Torok and Csapo (1976). Uterine strips from postpartum rabbits or from rabbits in late pregnancy (25 days) were made inexcitable to a 12 V/5 cm electrical field by removal of Ca^{2+} from the medium. The strips in Ca-free solution did undergo maximum tension, however, with a field of 50 V/5 cm. The tension induced by the 12 V/5 cm stimulus was obliterated by incubation of uterine strips from the postparturient rabbit with inhibitors of calcium uptake such as ruthenium red and Verapamil, whereas the tension induced with 50 V/5 cm was unaltered by these agents (Rubanyi and Csapo, 1977). These findings were interpreted to indicate that removal of extracellular Ca^{2+} depleted the amount of Ca^{2+} bound to the sarcolemma. The uterine strips were therefore unresponsive to an electrical field which normally would excite the myometrium in the presence of extracellular Ca^{2+}. However, the 50 V/5 cm field apparently by-passed the dependence of cell contraction on sarcolemmal Ca^{2+} by mobilizing intracellular stores of Ca^{2+}.

2. Sarcoplasmic Reticulum

Microsomal fractions from the myometrium of the cow (Carsten, 1969; 1973a), human (Carsten, 1973b; Batra, 1973), and rat (Batra and Daniel, 1971a,b) have been shown to take up Ca^{2+} in an ATP-dependent manner. Carsten (1974) has shown that the amount of Ca^{2+} taken up by microsomes from cow myometrium was inhibited *in vitro* in a dose-dependent fashion by the addition of PGE_2 and $PGE_{2\alpha}$, but not by the inactive $PGF_{1\beta}$. The inhibition of Ca^{2+} uptake by the uterotonic prostaglandins was greater with myometrial preparations from pregnant than nonpregnant cows. Oxytocin, in physiological concentrations, also inhibited the uptake of Ca^{2+} by the microsomal fraction; the inhibition was much greater in pregnant uteri. The greater effect of oxytocin on Ca^{2+} uptake in pregnancy is consistent with observations showing that the sensitivity of the uterus to oxytocin increases during pregnancy (see Section III,D,1). Further studies have indicated that the actions of PGE_2, $PGF_{2\alpha}$, and oxytocin in reducing Ca^{2+} uptake were due to an accelerated rate of release of Ca^{2+} from microsomes preloaded with ^{45}Ca (Carsten and Miller, 1977). The uterotonic agents were active when the microsomal preparations were preloaded with calcium in either the presence or absence of ATP.

Carsten's results suggest that the sarcoplasmic reticulum plays an important role in uterine contraction. The results, however, do not rule out the participation of the sarcolemma, because the microsomal fractions could have contained plasma membranes. Other workers have not observed effects of oxytocin on uterine microsomes. Oxytocin, 10 mU/ml, did not affect the rate of uptake of ^{45}Ca by microsomes from rat myometrium during a 10 minute incubation period (Batra and Daniel, 1971a). Batra (1972) also reported that 0.5 U/ml of oxytocin, a pharmacological amount, did not affect the uptake of ^{45}Ca by mitochondrial or microsomal fractions from human myometrium. However, these studies were conducted at a single time point, 20 minutes after the addition of oxytocin. The response of the intact uterus to oxytocin takes place in seconds.

3. *Mitochondria*

Calcium was taken up in an ATP-dependent manner by mitochondria from the myometrium of the cow (Carsten, 1969), human (Batra, 1973; Janis *et al.*, 1976; Malmström and Carafoli, 1977), and rat (Janis *et al.*, 1977). Isolated mitochondria took up Ca^{2+} in amounts far in excess of those needed to activate the contractile proteins (Batra, 1973). The maximum rate of Ca^{2+} accumulation was found to be faster in the mitochondrial fraction than in the microsomal fraction (Batra, 1973). However, oxytocic agents such as acetylcholine, prostaglandins, and oxytocin did not appear to have any influence on the uptake or release of Ca^{2+} by mitochondria (Batra, 1975). The experimental details of these studies were not given. Most of the Ca^{2+} associated with human myometrial mitochondria was discharged very rapidly by uncouplers of oxidative phosphorylation and ionophores (Malmström and Carafoli, 1977). It is likely that endogenous Ca^{2+} is maintained in a dynamic steady state and is available for rapid discharge into the sarcoplasm. This Ca^{2+}, therefore, does not appear to be sequestered inside the mitochondria as insoluble phosphate salts.

Although Ca^{2+} forms an integral part of the excitation–contraction sequence in the myometrium, the precise localization of activator Ca^{2+} and its movements and mobilization during contraction are still unknown. The potential sites of activator Ca^{2+} as reviewed by Wanner *et al.* (1977), are shown in Fig. 16. The possible mechanisms leading to increased myoplasmic Ca^{2+} concentrations include increased Ca^{2+} release from the cell surface, acceleration of Ca^{2+} movement from the extracellular space by a gate mechanism, release of Ca^{2+} from mitochondria and sarcoplasmic reticulum, and inhibition of calcium pumps involved in the extrusion of myoplasmic Ca^{2+}. The experimental evidence cited above indicates that Ca^{2+} is probably mobilized from both extra- and intracellular sites. A clear effect of oxytocin, however, has been shown only with microsomal fractions. The activity of acetylcholine also appears to involve intracellular Ca^{2+}. Increasing concentrations of extracellular Ca^{2+} caused graded contractions of K^+-depolarized uteri from the rat (Edman and Schild, 1962) and the human (Aronson and Batra, 1974). However, the myometrial response to acetylcholine was much faster than the response to increased concentrations of extracellular Ca^{2+}. These results suggested to Aronson and Batra (1974) that acetylcholine activated an intracellular pool of Ca^{2+}. In support of this conclusion were the findings that acetylcholine could induce contractions of human myometrium in Ca^{2+}-free medium. The contractions were of much less intensity than normal. Thus, it is probable that acetylcholine causes the mobilization of Ca^{2+} from intracellular sites.

Regardless of whether the intracellular source of Ca^{2+} is the sarcolemma, sarcoplasmic reticulum, mitochondria, or other organelles, the signal generated by the occupancy of receptor sites for oxytocin must be conducted from

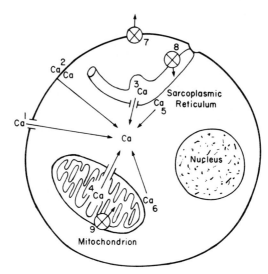

FIG. 16. Potential sites for the regulation of myoplasmic calcium concentrations include: (1) calcium channels in the plasma membrane, allowing extracellular Ca^{2+} to penetrate the cell membrane; (2) release of Ca^{2+} from binding sites on the cell surface; (3) calcium channels in the sarcoplasmic reticulum and (4) mitochondria; (5) release of Ca^{2+} from binding sites on the surfaces of the sarcoplasmic reticulum and (6) mitochondria; (7) inhibition of pumps which extrude Ca^{2+} from the myoplasm and which are located on the cell surface, (8) sarcoplasmic reticulum, or (9) mitochondrion.

the cell surface to the site of calcium release. The events coupling the binding of oxytocin and calcium release are unknown at the present time. Also unknown are the ways in which Ca^{2+} activates the myofilaments of uterine smooth muscle and mammary myoepithelial cells.

B. Cyclic Nucleotides

The actions of neurohypophysial hormones on amphibian bladder epithelium and mammalian kidney tubule cells appear to be mediated by cAMP (Orloff and Handler, 1967; Bär et al., 1970; Brown et al., 1963; Grantham and Burg, 1966; Hynie and Sharp, 1971a; Dousa et al., 1972; Roy et al., 1973). This subject has been reviewed in detail most recently by Jard and Bockaert (1975) and Dousa and Valtin (1976). Cyclic AMP may not be involved in all events related to vasopressin action, as pointed out by studies with artificial bilayer lipid membranes. Vasopressin, 0.2 nM, increased the permeability of black membranes constructed from egg phosphatidycholine by 69% (Graziani and Livne, 1973). Cyclic AMP, from 1 to 100 nM, had little or no effect. Although it is tempting to speculate that the water permeability effect of neurohypophysial peptides may not be mediated by cAMP, it should be emphasized that the concentrations of cAMP were low and that lipid bilayers may not accurately simulate the cell membrane.

It seems clear that cAMP is not involved in the actions of neurohypophysial hormones on the uterus and mammary gland (for reviews, see Jard and Bockaert, 1975; Korenman and Krall, 1977; Dousa, 1977). In fact, cAMP has been shown to inhibit spontaneous uterine contractions or contractions induced by oxytocin (Harbon and Clauser, 1971; Mitznegg *et al.*, 1970). There is good evidence that cAMP mediates uterine relaxation caused by β-adrenergic agents (Dobbs and Robison, 1968; Triner *et al.*, 1970; Mitznegg *et al.*, 1970, 1971; Harbon and Clauser, 1971; Polacek and Daniel, 1971; Bhalla *et al.*, 1972; Marshall and Kroeger, 1973; Vesin and Harbon, 1974). The depression of spontaneous contractions of the rat uterus by histamine was associated in a dose-dependent manner with the elevation of cAMP levels (Mitznegg *et al.*, 1975). It has been suggested that oxytocin may regulate uterine contractility by inhibiting cAMP production. Bhalla *et al.* (1972) showed that oxytocin decreased cAMP levels in uteri from ovariectomized rats in a dose-dependent manner. The levels of cAMP were initially elevated by the addition of isoproterenol to the incubation medium. The basis of the inhibition is uncertain because oxytocin did not affect either adenylate cyclase or cAMP phosphodiesterase activities (Bhalla *et al.*, 1972). Several other laboratories have found no effect of oxytocin on uterine cAMP levels, which had been elevated by prior treatment with catecholamines (Dobbs and Robison, 1968; Polacek and Daniel, 1971; Harbon and Clauser, 1971). It seems reasonable to conclude that cAMP is not involved in mediating the actions of neurohypophysial hormones on the uterus, although cAMP may be involved in the actions of β-adrenergic agents and of histamine.

The possible effects of oxytocin on adenylate cyclase activity in the mammary gland have received little attention. Adenylate cyclase activity reached maximum levels in the mammary glands of rats late in pregnancy, but fell continuously after parturition (Sapag-Hagar and Greenbaum, 1973). Levels of cAMP in the mammary glands changed correspondingly. Although the effects of oxytocin on adenylate cyclase activity were not studied, we surmise that the two are unrelated because the greatest sensitivity of the mammary gland to oxytocin occurs during lactation (Sala and Freire, 1974) when adenylate cyclase activity is declining.

A possible role for cGMP in uterine contraction has been suggested. Goldberg *et al.* (1975) reported that oxytocin stimulated a rapid accumulation of cGMP in uteri of diethylstilbestrol-treated rats while cAMP levels were unchanged. Other uterotonic agents, such as methacholine, serotonin, and $PGF_{2\alpha}$ also promoted increases in cGMP concentration. These studies,

which indicate that cGMP may mediate the action of neurohypophysial peptides on the uterus, have not been extended further. The role of cGMP
remains to be determined, but it may involve stimulation of cGMP-
dependent protein kinases, which have been shown to catalyze the phosphorylation of two microsomal proteins from guinea pig uterus (Casnellie
and Greengard, 1974). These two proteins were distinguishable from a third
protein, which was specifically phosphorylated as a result of cAMP stimulation. In other studies, oxytocin and other uterine contracting agents did not
affect the concentrations of cGMP in rat myometrium (Leiber *et al.*, 1978).

VI. MOLECULAR EVENTS MEDIATING
NEUROHYPOPHYSIAL HORMONE ACTION

A. ENDOMETRIAL PROSTAGLANDIN SYNTHESIS

Several laboratories have shown that oxytocin stimulated the release of
prostaglandins from the uterus *in vivo* (Sharma and Fitzpatrick, 1974;
Mitchell *et al.*, 1975; Roberts and McCracken, 1976). This response appears
to be the result of a direct action of oxytocin on endometrial cells. Roberts *et
al.* (1976) have shown that the incubation of ewe endometrium with oxytocin
resulted in a dose-dependent release of $PGF_{2\alpha}$ into the medium. The effect
of oxytocin was greatest in endometrial samples taken as estrus approached
and was maximum on the day of estrus. Oxytocin-stimulated $PGF_{2\alpha}$ accumulation fell off rapidly thereafter, reaching near baseline values after 5 days. In
contrast, $PGF_{2\alpha}$ synthesis by the sheep myometrium *in vitro* was relatively
low and unresponsive to oxytocin. The effect of oxytocin on the endometrial
$PGF_{2\alpha}$ release was paralleled by the concentration of high-affinity binding
sites for [^{3}H]oxytocin (see Fig. 12). These findings indicate that there is a
causal relationship between the binding of oxytocin and the synthesis of
$PGF_{2\alpha}$ by ewe endometrium.

The release of $PGF_{2\alpha}$ from the endometrium appears to account for the
luteolytic action of oxytocin in heifers (see Newcomb *et al.*, 1977, for references). Although $PGF_{2\alpha}$ is oxytocic, the endometrial release of prostaglandins does not seem to mediate the action of oxytocin on the myometrium.
Roberts and McCracken (1976) found that the myometrium responded to
oxytocin when the production of $PGF_{2\alpha}$ was suppressed *in vivo* with in-
domethacin. The amount of stimulation of $PGF_{2\alpha}$ release of oxytocin also did
not correspond to the uterotonic activity of the peptide at different times
during the estrous cycle.

B. cAMP-DEPENDENT PROTEIN KINASES

A general scheme for the diverse effects of cAMP in mediating hormone actions has been outlined by Krebs (1972). Increases in cAMP concentration would stimulate a greater portion of protein kinases to phosphorylate intrinsic proteins. The resulting phosphoproteins would be functionally altered to participate in the physiological responses to cAMP elevation. The phosphorylated state could be reversed by the dephosphorylation of the phosphoproteins by the action of phosphatase(s). The specificity of the hormone response could be due to the specific nature of the stimulatable protein kinases and their substrates. Cyclic AMP-dependent protein kinases appear to play a role in mediating the actions of vasopressin on target cells in the amphibian bladder and renal medulla.

1. Amphibian Bladder

Jard and Bastide (1970) demonstrated, in homogenates of epithelial cells isolated from frog bladder, a cAMP-dependent protein kinase that phosphorylated exogenous histone. The cytosol contained about 70% of the kinase activity, which had an apparent K_m for cAMP of 10 nM. Because the K_m was in the range of intracellular levels of cAMP, it was suggested that a protein kinase could be involved in cAMP-mediated effects in the bladder cells.

DeLorenzo et al. (1973) found that exposure of intact frog bladders to vasopressin or monobutyryl cAMP caused a 50–60% decrease in the level of phosphorylation of a specific protein (protein D) in membrane fractions from mucosal scrapings. Cyclic AMP produced the same effect in broken cell preparations. The concentration of cAMP producing a half-maximal decrease in phosphorylation was about 10 nM. These effects of vasopressin or cAMP preceded the stimulation of Na^+ transport, as measured by an increase in the electrical potential difference across the bladder epithelium.

These studies suggest that changes in the level of phosphorylation of a specific protein, presumably associated with the cell membrane, mediate the actions of neurohypophysial hormones on epithelial cells. Vasopressin appears to cause a decrease in the net rate of incorporation of ^{32}P into protein D by activating, via cAMP, a membrane-bound phosphoprotein phosphatase (DeLorenzo and Greengard, 1973). The hormone did not inhibit membrane-bound protein kinase activity (DeLorenzo and Greengard, 1973).

Further studies from Greengard's laboratory have extended the inverse correlation between sodium transport and the level of phosphorylation of protein D (Walton et al., 1975). Besides vasopressin and cAMP, theophylline, adenine, PGE_1, and $MnCl_2$ caused a decrease in the amount of radioactive phosphate in protein D and also stimulated active Na^+ transport across the toad bladder. Conversely, $ZnCl_2$ stimulated ^{32}P incorporation into protein D and inhibited Na^+ transport.

Ferguson and Twite (1974) also demonstrated that vasopressin stimulated dephosphorylation of a toad bladder protein comparable to protein D. Incubation of intact hemibladders with vasopressin, 50 mU/ml, produced a 40% reduction in phosphorylated protein D and maximal natriferic and hydroosmotic responses. However, at concentrations of vasopressin of 10 mU/ml, when a maximal natriferic response but no significant hydro-osmotic response was observed, there was no significant difference in phosphorylation of protein D from control and vasopressin-treated bladders. Contrary to the results of Walton *et al.* (1975), Ferguson and Twite concluded that dephosphorylation of protein D was associated with water flow rather than with Na^{2+} transport.

Notwithstanding important discrepancies in the findings from different laboratories, the sequence of events involved in vasopressin action might be

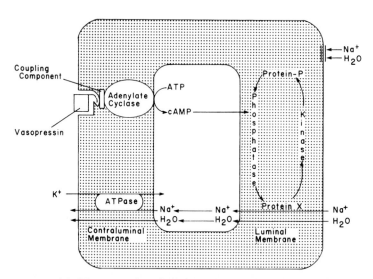

FIG. 17.   A model of the proposed mechanism by which vasopressin regulates the permeability of the luminal membrane of toad bladder epithelium. Vasopressin interacts with receptor sites on the contraluminal membrane. The occupancy of receptor is coupled to the activation of adenylate cyclase, which catalyzes an increase in intracellular cAMP. The cAMP diffuses across the cell to the luminal membrane, where it stimulates the activity of protein prosphatase. The increased enzyme activity causes an increased rate of conversion of protein X from a phosphorylated (Protein-P) to a dephosphorylated (Protein-X) state. Protein X is converted from the dephosphorylated state back to its phosphorylated state by the action of protein kinase. Na^+ and/or H_2O penetrates the luminal membrane at sites only where protein X is dephosphorylated, but not where it is phosphorylated. Adapted from Walton *et al.*, 1975.

as follows (Fig. 17): Vasopressin from the circulation interacts with a specific receptor on the basal surface of the mucosal epithelium. The occupation of the vasopressin receptor site is coupled to the activation of adenylate cyclase. This activation leads to an increased rate of production of cAMP, which diffuses across the cell to the inner surface of the luminal membrane. Increased levels of cAMP stimulate protein phosphatase activities at the luminal membrane, resulting in an increased conversion of phosphoprotein to a dephosphorylated state. Presumably, Na^+ and/or water could penetrate the luminal membrane more readily at sites where the protein is in the dephosphorylated form, but could not enter the cell as effectively when the protein remains phosphorylated. The effects of vasopressin could be reversed by conversion of the dephosphorylated protein back to the phosphorylated state by protein kinase.

2. Renal Medulla

The binding of cAMP to a regulatory subunit of cAMP-dependent protein kinase results in the dissociation of the holoenzyme complex into regulatory and active catalytic subunits (Gill and Garren, 1971; Reimann *et al.*, 1971; Krebs, 1972). Dousa and Barnes (1977) found that incubation of slices from bovine renal medulla with vasopressin resulted in an increased activation of protein kinase in the 40,000*g* supernatant fraction. The increase in activity was dose dependent and was paralleled by an increase in intracellular levels of cAMP. The increase in kinase activity was specific for vasopressin because an inert analog and other agents such as parathyroid hormone, histamine, and angiotensin II were without effect. These results were consistent with earlier findings on protein kinase activity in broken cell preparations (Dousa *et al*, 1972). Protein kinase in the cytosol of bovine kidney medulla catalyzed the phosphorylation of protein(s) in plasma membrane fractions; half-maximal stimulation occurred with 0.1 μM cAMP (Dousa *et al.*, 1972). The phosphorylation of membrane components was reversed by phosphoprotein phosphatase activity in the cytosol.

Although protein kinase activity was present in several subcellular fractions of medulla homogenates, the highest activity was found in the cytosol (Barnes *et al.*, 1975). Only activity in the cytosol was stimulated markedly by cAMP. Schwartz *et al.* (1974), however, showed that the cAMP-dependent kinase activity was located at the site of vasopressin-induced permeability changes, the luminal surface of epithelial cells from collecting ducts. The plasma membranes from tubular epithelium were resolved into luminal and contraluminal fractions by free-flow electrophoresis. Only the contraluminal membranes contained vasopressin-sensitive adenylate cyclase activity. The luminal membranes contained a cAMP-sensitive self-phosphorylating system that included both membrane-bound protein kinase and substrate(s).

Intrinsic protein kinase activity was not associated with contraluminal membranes. The separate sites of adenylate cyclase and cAMP-dependent protein kinase are consistent with the proposed model of vasopressin action.

Protein kinase activity in the cytosol may not be related to the phosphorylation of membrane proteins of the luminal surface (Barnes *et al.*, 1975). There appear to be several protein kinases in the cytosol of the renal medulla, at least one of which, glycogen synthase I kinase, is cAMP independent (Schlender and Reimann, 1975). There is evidence to suggest, however, that cAMP protein kinase activity associated with membrane proteins does arise from the cytosol. Dousa and Barnes (1977) found that incubation of slices of bovine renal medulla with vasopressin resulted in a marked decrease in the total amount of cAMP-dependent kinase in the 40,000g supernatant fraction, and an increase in extracts (300 mM NaCl) of the particulate fraction. The decrease in the cytosol was proportional to the dose of vasopressin and the concentration of endogenous cAMP. The effect of vasopressin was specific for protein kinase activity because lactate dehydrogenase activity and the concentration of free tubulin in the supernatant fraction were not changed. Both cAMP-dependent and cAMP-independent protein kinase activities in the particulate fraction were increased, indicating that both the holoenzyme and the catalytic subunit were translocated from the supernatant to the particulate fraction as a result of vasopressin treatment.

The translocation of protein kinase activity from the cytosol to the particulate fractions may be a generalized event associated with elevated cAMP levels. Cyclic AMP-associated decreases in total protein kinase activities have been found in cytosol fractions from the ovary (Spielvogel *et al.*, 1977), adrenal medulla (Costa *et al.*, 1976), liver (Castagna *et al.*, 1975), and uterus (Korenman *et al.*, 1974). The total protein kinase activity in particulate fractions from cardiac muscle appears to have been overestimated, however, because free catalytic subunit has been shown to bind nonspecifically both to particulate fractions from heterologous tissues and to denatured protein (Keely *et al.*, 1975). The translocation of the catalytic subunit could be mimicked in heart muscle by the addition of cAMP to homogenates prior to the separation of cytosol and particulate fractions (Corbin *et al.*, 1977). These results indicate that the translocation phenomenon may be an experimental artifact associated with the nonspecific binding of free catalytic subunit formed in response to elevated cAMP levels. However, the results of Dousa and Barnes (1977) indicated that both catalytic subunit and the holoenzyme were increased in particulate fractions from bovine renal medulla as a result of vasopressin treatment. How cAMP, which dissociates protein kinase, might activate the translocation of an intact holoenzyme remains to be determined.

The relative changes in cAMP levels in slices from bovine renal medulla in response to vasopressin were greater than the relative changes in protein kinase activation (Dousa and Barnes, 1977). These findings suggested to

Dousa and Barnes that only a certain portion of the cAMP generated in response to vasopressin was involved in the activation of protein kinases. Nevertheless, protein kinase activation by cAMP appears to be an integral step in the cellular action of vasopressin on the renal medulla. It remains to be clarified whether the process coupling the stimulation of the contraluminal surface of the tubular cell to the permeability response at the luminal surface is the transcellular migration of cAMP or of cAMP-dependent protein kinase. Also unknown are the specific protein substrates for vasopressin-stimulated protein kinases and the biochemical basis of phosphorylation induced permeability changes.

The present evidence indicates that the mechanisms of cAMP action in toad bladder epithelium and mammalian kidney tubule cells are different. Cyclic AMP stimulation of toad bladder cells appears to involve the activation of phosphoprotein phosphatase activity, whereas in kidney tubules protein kinase activity increases. The differences between the two target cells may be more apparent than real, however, if it could be shown that cAMP activates a protein D phosphatase kinase that would catalyze the phosphorylation and activation of protein D phosphatase (DeLorenzo and Greengard, 1973). Another explanation may be related to the observation that phosphorylation of regulatory components of bovine heart protein kinase facilitated the cAMP-dependent dissociation of the kinase into regulatory and catalytic subunits (Erlichman *et al.*, 1974). If protein D were the regulatory subunit, its dissociation from the holoenzyme might result in its accessibility to intracellular protein phosphatases, which would account for the dephosphorylation of protein D (Maeno *et al.*, 1975). The dephosphorylation of the dissociated regulatory subunit would then facilitate the reassociation of the regulatory and catalytic subunits into the holoenzyme (Rangel-Aldao and Rosen, 1976).

C. The Luminal Plasma Membrane

1. *Vasopressin-Induced Reorganization of the Luminal Membrane System*

Two mechanisms have been proposed to describe the changes in the permeability of the luminal membrane induced by vasopressin. Vasopressin may act (a) by increasing the size or the number of pores in the membrane (Grantham and Burg, 1966; Leaf and Hays, 1962) or (b) by altering the rate of diffusion of water across the membranes (Hays and Levine, 1974; Andreoli and Schafer, 1976). Regardless of which postulate will be proven correct, vasopressin has been shown to induce ultrastructural changes in the luminal membrane.

As demonstrated by freeze-fracture electron microscopy, oxytocin or vasopressin stimulated the reversible aggregation of intramembranous particles on the inner membrane fracture face of anuran bladder cells (Chevalier *et al.*, 1974; Kachadorian *et al.*, 1975). Several studies with different types of membranes have indicated that the intramembranous particles that form these aggregates are proteins that are intercalated with the membrane (see Kachadorian *et al.*, 1977b, for references). Vasopressin-induced aggregation occurred in the luminal membranes of granular cells of toad bladder, but not in membranes of nontarget cells from the bladder (Kachadorian *et al.*, 1975). The aggregation process appears to be involved in vasopressin action, because the frequency of aggregation sites per area of membrane was proportional to the vasopressin-induced osmotic water flow (Kachadorian *et al.*, 1975). The reorganization of membrane structure was not a consequence of water flow per se, but the result of hormone stimulation; aggregation of intramembranous particles induced by vasopressin occurred in the presence or absence of an osmotic gradient (Bourguet *et al.*, 1976; Kachadorian *et al.*, 1977b). Exposure of toad bladders to methohexital, a selective inhibitor of vasopressin-stimulated water flow, reduced both the vasopressin-induced alterations in luminal membrane structure and the hydro-osmotic response to the same extent (Kachadorian *et al.*, 1977a). Because sodium permeability was not affected by methohexital, the aggregation of intramembranous particles appears to be unique to the hydro-osmotic action of vasopressin.

Other lines of evidence have also indicated that vasopressin stimulates the reorganization of membrane components. Pietras (1976) found that treatment of isolated epithelial cells from frog bladders with vasopressin caused a marked polar concentration of clusters of binding sites for fluorescein-labeled concanavalin A. This response was inhibited by colchicine, which disrupts microtubules. The effects of vasopressin on the surface distribution of concanavalin A are similar to the surface modifications seen in lymphocytes and other cells in response to a variety of substances which interact with receptor sites on the plasma membrane (for a review, see Edelman, 1976).

2. Microtubules and Microfilaments

It has been postulated that the lateral mobility of cell surface receptors within the plane of the membrane is partly controlled by cytoplasmic microtubules and microfilaments (Fig. 18). Edelman (1976) has proposed a model for the surface-modulating assembly, in which the interaction of intramembranous proteins with microfilaments and associated proteins causes the lateral movement of the membrane proteins. The ends of the microfilaments are anchored to microtubules. Although the surface-modulating assembly model is still speculative, it may describe how vasopressin induces the aggregation of intramembranous particles in anuran bladder cells, and why inhibitors of microtubule and microfilament formation interfere with vasopressin action.

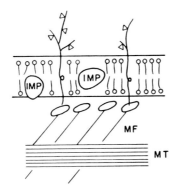

FIG. 18. The surface-modulating assembly. This model assumes that microfilaments (MF) interact with receptors possibly via a myosinlike structure. The other end of the microfilaments interacts with microtubules (MT). IMP = intramembranous particles. From Edelman, 1976.

Evidence supporting a role of microtubules and microfilaments in vasopressin action has been reviewed by Dousa and Valtin (1976). Microtubules are ubiquitous in eukaryotic cells. The tubules are thin, elongate, hollow-looking cylinders with an outside diameter of 200–300 Å. The walls of the tubules, which are polymers of tubulin, can be dissociated into soluble tubulin subunits in a reversible manner (Bryan, 1974; Olmsted and Borisy, 1973). Taylor *et al.* (1973, 1975) demonstrated that colchicine, vinblastine, and podophyllotoxin—substances which disrupt microtubules or prevent their assembly—blocked the hydro-osmotic response of intact toad hemibladders to vasopressin. These substances, however, did not affect basal levels of water movement or vasopressin-stimulated active transport of Na^+. The stimulation of osmotic water movement by exogenous cAMP was markedly reduced in hemibladders exposed to colchicine. Colchicine, therefore, interfered with vasopressin action at a molecular step(s) occurring after the stimulation of cAMP synthesis. In support of this conclusion, Dousa and Barnes (1974) found that colchicine and vinblastine did not affect the activities of vasopressin-activated adenylate cyclase and cAMP-phosphodiesterase in the renal medulla.

It has been assumed that the effects of colchicine were specifically directed at microtubules. However, colchicine has been found to inhibit activities that appear to be unrelated to microtubule formation, such as nucleoside uptake, cholinergic activity, and actomyosin ATPase activity in the brain (see Taylor *et al.*, 1973, for references).

Microfilaments, like microtubules, are polymers of protein subunits. The filaments are composed of subunits which resemble muscle actin and appear to be attached to, or to terminate near, cell membranes. Disruption of microfilaments in toad bladder epithelium with cytochalasin B resulted in an inhibition of the hydro-osmotic response to vasopressin with little or no effect on basal activity (Taylor *et al.*, 1973; Carasso *et al.*, 1973; Davis *et al.*, 1974; de Sousa *et al.*, 1974). Cytochalasin B appears to act at more than one site, because it inhibited vasopressin-stimulated increases in cellular cAMP (Davis *et al.*, 1974) as well as the hydro-osmotic activity of exogenous cAMP (Taylor *et al.*, 1973; Carasso *et al.*, 1973). Vasopressin-stimulated active transport of Na^+ was not affected by cytochalasin B (Taylor *et al.*, 1973; Davis *et al.*, 1974).

It is possible that microtubules and microfilaments are involved in structural changes of the lateral cell wall. For example, vasopressin stimulated an enlargement of the lateral intercellular spaces between renal tubule cells (Granthan, 1971; Tisher *et al.*, 1971) and frog bladder cells (Jard *et al.*, 1971). These findings have suggested that intercellular pathways may be involved in the transepithelial flow of water.

A clear relationship between cAMP-dependent protein kinase and substrates associated with purified microtubules, which has been shown in the brain (Goodman *et al.*, 1970; Reddington and Lagnado, 1973; Sandoval and Cuatrecasas, 1976; Shigekawa and Olsen, 1975; Sloboda *et al.*, 1975; Soifer, 1975), has not been found in vasopressin target cells. Dousa and Barnes (1974) showed that colchicine, in concentrations that disrupted microtubules in cells of the renal medulla, did not affect protein kinase activity.

VII. CONCLUDING COMMENTS

Some general statements concerning the state of the art of studies on the biochemical actions of neurohypophysial hormones and neurophysin can be made.

Current speculation, based on indirect evidence, indicates that the neurophysins and neurohypophysial hormones are synthesized as part of a larger precursor proneurophysin–hormone molecule. After cleavage of the complex, which involves at least two steps, the hormone and neurophysin are bound together noncovalently in storage granules in nerve endings in the neurohypophysis. On stimulation of the nerves, the complex is released into the bloodstream, where hormone and neurophysin dissociate. No definitive target site for the neurophysins has been identified.

Oxytocin causes contraction of two cells in mammals—myoepithelial and myometrial cells. The molecular events mediating the contractions are not yet known. There is abundant evidence that cAMP is not involved as a second messenger in the contractile response. It is clear that Ca^{2+} plays some role in coupling the occupancy of the oxytocin receptors and the contractile response. The sites and mechanisms of action of activator Ca^{2+}, however, remain to be demonstrated.

Our greatest understanding of the mechanisms of action of neurohypophysial hormones has been in the area of antidiuretic activity. The effects of vasopressin clearly appear to be mediated by cAMP and cAMP-dependent phosphatases and/or kinases. Although the stimulation of active Na^+ transport and water permeability are mediated by cAMP, the two processes appear to involve separate adenylate cyclases and intracellular pools of cAMP. A major question to be resolved is how the stimulus at the contraluminal surface of the cell is translated into a response at the luminal surface. The alterations in membrane permeability appear to involve the reorganization of the membrane structure. The biochemical mechanism underlying these ultrastructure changes is still speculative.

ACKNOWLEDGMENTS

Some of the studies in this review were supported by grants AM18383, HD8406, and contract NO1-CB-63983 from the National Institutes of Health. We thank Drs. Maurice Manning, Erwin Reimann, Judith Saffran, Murray Saffran, Linda Henderson, and Michael Wieder of this institution for their helpful comments. We also thank Solweig Soloff for bibliographic assistance, Cindy Licata for the typescript, and Jackie Ruffin for the graphics.

REFERENCES

Acher, R. (1974). *Handb. Physiol. Sect. 7: Endocrinol.* **4**, 119–130.
Alazard, R., Cohen, P., Cohen, J. S., and Griffin, J. H. (1974). *J. Biol. Chem.* **249**, 6895–6900.
Altura, B. M., and Altura, B. T. (1977). *Fed. Am. Soc. Exp. Biol. Proc.* **36**, 1853–1860.
Andreoli, T. E., and Schafer, J. A. (1976). *Annu. Rev. Physiol.* **38**, 451–500.
Argy, W. P., Jr., Handler, J. S., and Orloff, J. (1967). *Am. J. Physiol.* **213**, 803–808.
Aronson, S., and Batra, S. (1974). *Experientia* **30**, 768–769.
Aspeslagh, M. R., Vandesande, F., and Dierickx, K. (1976). *Cell Tissue Res.* **171**, 31–37.
Audhya, T. K., and Walter, R. (1977). *Arch. Biochem. Biophys.* **180**, 130–139.
Bai, K. S., and Martell, A. E. (1969). *J. Inorg. Nucl. Chem.* **31**, 1697–1707.
Balaram, P., Bothner-By, A. A., and Breslow, E. (1972). *J. Am. Chem. Soc.* **94**, 4017–4018.
Balaram, P., Bothner-By, A. A., and Breslow, E. (1973). *Biochemistry* **12**, 4695–4704.
Bär, H. P., Hechter, O., Schwartz, I. L., and Walter, R. (1970). *Proc. Natl. Acad. Sci. U.S.A.* **67**, 7–12.
Barnes, L. D., Hui, Y. S. F., Frohnert, P. P., and Dousa, T. P. (1975). *Endocrinology* **96**, 119–128.
Batra, S. (1972). *Am. J. Obstet. Gynecol.* **112**, 851–856.
Batra, S. (1973). *Biochim. Biophys. Acta* **305**, 428–432.
Batra, S. (1975). *In* "Calcium Transport in Contraction and Secretion" (E. Carafoli *et al.*, eds.), pp. 87–94. Am. Elsevier, New York.
Batra, S. C., and Daniel, E. E. (1971a). *Comp. Biochem. Physiol. A* **38**, 285–300.
Batra, S. C., and Daniel, E. E. (1971b). *Comp. Biochem. Physiol. A* **38**, 369–385.
Bentley, P. J. (1959). *J. Endocrinol.* **18**, 327–333.
Bentley, P. J. (1960). *J. Endocrinol.* **21**, 161–170.
Bentley, P. J. (1964). *J. Endocrinol.* **30**, 103–113.
Bentley, P. J. (1965). *J. Endocrinol.* **32**, 215–222.

Bentley, P. J. (1966). *Biol. Rev. Cambridge Philos. Soc.* **41**, 275–316.
Berde, B., and Boissonnas, R. A. (1968). *Handb. Exp. Pharmakol.* **23**, 802–870.
Berger, E., and Marshall, J. M. (1961). *Am. J. Physiol.* **201**, 931–934.
Bhalla, R. C., Sanborn, B. M., and Korenman, S. G. (1972). *Proc. Natl. Acad. Sci. U.S.A.* **69**, 3761–3764.
Birnbaumer, L., and Yang, P.-C. (1974). *J. Biol. Chem.* **249**, 7848–7856.
Birnbaumer, L., Nakahara, T., and Yang, P.-C. (1974). *J. Biol. Chem.* **249**, 7857–7866.
Bisset, G. W. (1968). *Handb. Exp. Pharmakol.* **23**, 475–544.
Bisset, G. W. (1974). *Handb. Physiol., Sect. 7: Endocrinol.* **4**, 493–520.
Bisset, G. W. (1976). *In* "Peptide Hormones" (J. A. Parsons, ed.), pp. 145–177. Univ. Park Press, Baltimore, Maryland.
Blumenstein, M., and Hruby, V. J. (1977). *Biochemistry* **16**, 5169–5177.
Blumenstein, M., Hruby, V. J., Yamamoto, D., and Yang, Y. (1977). *FEBS Lett.* **81**, 347–350.
Bockaert, J., Jard, S., Morel, F., and Montegut, M. (1970). *Am. J. Physiol.* **219**, 1514–1521.
Bockaert, J., Imbert, M., Jard, S., and Morel, F. (1972a). *Mol. Pharmacol.* **8**, 230–240.
Bockaert, J., Roy, C., and Jard, S. (1972b). *J. Biol. Chem.* **247**, 7073–7081.
Bockaert, J., Roy, C., Rajerison, R., and Jard, S. (1973). *J. Biol. Chem.* **248**, 5922–5931.
Bonne, D., and Cohen, P. (1975). *Eur. J. Biochem.* **56**, 295–303.
Bourguet, J., Chevalier, J., and Hugon, J. S. (1976). *Biophys. J.* **16**, 627–639.
Braun, T., Hechter, O., and Rudinger, J. (1969). *Endocrinology* **85**, 1092–1096.
Breslow, E. (1970). *Proc. Natl. Acad. Sci. U.S.A.* **67**, 493–500.
Breslow, E. (1974). *Adv. Enzymol.* **40**, 271–333.
Breslow, E. (1975). *Ann. N.Y. Acad. Sci.* **248**, 423–441.
Breslow, E., and Abrash, L. (1966). *Proc. Natl. Acad. Sci. U.S.A.* **56**, 640–646.
Breslow, E., and Gargiulo, P. (1977). *Biochemistry* **16**, 3397–3406.
Breslow, E., and Walter, R. (1972). *Mol. Pharmacol.* **8**, 75–81.
Breslow, E., and Weis, J. (1972). *Biochemistry* **11**, 3474–3482.
Breslow, E., Aanning, H. L., Abrash, L., and Schmir, M. (1971). *J. Biol. Chem.* **246**, 5179–5188.
Breslow, E., Weis, J., and Menendez-Botet, C. J. (1973). *Biochemistry* **12**, 4644–4653.
Brewster, A. I. R., Hruby, V. J., Glasel, J. A., and Tonelli, A. E. (1973). *Biochemistry* **12**, 5294–5304.
Brown, E., Clarke, D. L., Roux, V., and Sherman, G. H. (1963). *J. Biol. Chem.* **238**, PC852–PC853.
Brownstein, M. J., and Gainer, H. (1977). *Proc. Natl. Acad. Sci. U.S.A.* **74**, 4046–4049.
Bryan, J. (1974). *BioScience* **24**, 701–711.
Burford, G. D., and Pickering, B. T. (1972). *Biochem. J.* **128**, 941–944.
Caldeyro-Barcia, R., Melander, S., and Coch, J. A. (1971). *In* "Endocrinology of Pregnancy" (F. Fuchs and A. Klopper, eds.), pp. 235–285. Harper, New York.
Camier, M., Alazard, R., Cohen, P., Pradelles, P., Morgat, J.-L., and Fromageot, P. (1973). *Eur. J. Biochem.* **32**, 207–214.
Campbell, B. J., Woodward, G., and Borberg, V. (1972). *J. Biol. Chem.* **247**, 6167–6175.
Capra, J. D., Cheng, K. W., Friesen, H. G., North, W. G., and Walter, R. (1974). *FEBS Lett.* **46**, 71–74.
Carasso, N., Favard, P., and Bourguet, J. (1973). *J. Microsc. (Paris)* **18**, 383–400.
Carsten, M. E. (1969). *J. Gen Physiol.* **53**, 414–426.
Carsten, M. E. (1973a). *Gynecol. Invest.* **4**, 84–94.
Carsten, M. E. (1973b). *Am. J. Obstet. Gynecol.* **117**, 824–832.
Carsten, M. E. (1974). *Prostaglandins* **5**, 33–40.
Carsten, M. E., and Miller, J. D. (1977). *J. Biol. Chem.* **252**, 1576–1581.
Casnellie, J. E., and Greengard, P. (1974). *Proc. Natl. Acad. Sci. U.S.A.* **71**, 1891–1895.

Castagna, M., Palmer, W. K., and Walsh, D. A. (1975). *Eur. J. Biochem.* **55**, 193–199.

Casteels, R., and van Breemen, C. (1975). *Pfluegers Arch.* **359**, 197–207.

Chan, W. Y., and du Vigneaud, V. (1962). *Endocrinology* **71**, 977–982.

Chan, W. Y., Fear, B., and du Vigneaud, V. (1967). *Endocrinology* **81**, 1268–1277.

Chard, T., Hudson, C. N., Edwards, C. R. W., and Boyd, N. R. H. (1971). *Nature (London)* **234**, 352–354.

Chase, L. R., and Aurbach, G. D. (1968). *Science* **159**, 545–547.

Chauvet, M. T., Chauvet, J., and Acher, R. (1975). *FEBS Lett.* **52**, 212–215.

Chauvet, M. T., Chauvet, J., and Acher, R. (1976a). *FEBS Lett.* **62**, 89–92.

Chauvet, M. T., Codogno, P., Chauvet, J., and Acher, R. (1976b). *FEBS Lett.* **71**, 291–293.

Chauvet, M. T., Chauvet, J., and Acher, R. (1976c). *Eur. J. Biochem.* **69**, 475–485.

Chauvet, M. T., Codogno, P., Chauvet, J., and Acher, R. (1977). *FEBS Lett.* **80**, 374–376.

Chauvet, M. T., Codogno, P., Chauvet, J., and Acher, R. (1978). *FEBS Lett.* **88**, 91–93.

Cheng, K. W., and Friesen, H. G. (1972). *J. Clin. Endocrinol. Metab.* **34**, 165–176.

Chevalier, J., Bourguet, J., and Hugon, J. S. (1974). *Cell Tissue Res.* **152**, 129–140.

Civan, M. M., and Frazier, H. S. (1968). *J. Gen. Physiol.* **51**, 589–605.

Clegg, P. C., Hopkinson, P., and Pickles, V. R. (1963). *J. Physiol. (London)* **167**, 1–17.

Cohen, P., Griffin, J. H., Camier, M., Caizergues, M., Fromageot, P., and Cohen, J. S. (1972). *FEBS Lett.* **25**, 282–286.

Convert, O., Griffin, J. H., DiBello, C., Nicolas, P., and Cohen, P. (1977). *Biochemistry* **16**, 5061–5065.

Corbin, J. D., Sugden, P., Lincoln, T. M., and Keeley, S. L. (1977). *J. Biol. Chem.* **252**, 3854–3861.

Costa, E., Kurosawa, A., and Guidotti, A. (1976). *Proc. Natl. Acad. Sci. U.S.A.* **73**, 1058–1062.

Craig, L. C., Harfenist, E., and Paladini, A. C. (1964). *Biochemistry* **3**, 764–769.

Crankshaw, D. J., Branda, L. A., Matlib, M. A., and Daniel, E. E. (1978). *Eur. J. Biochem.* **86**, 481–486.

Csapo, A. (1950). *Am. J. Physiol.* **162**, 406–410.

Csapo, A. (1956). *Am. J. Anat.* **98**, 273–291.

Csapo, A. (1961a). *In* "Oxytocin" (R. Caldeyro-Barcia and H. Heller, eds.), pp. 100–123. Pergamon, Oxford.

Csapo, A. (1961b). *In* "Progesterone and the Defense Mechanism of Pregnancy" (G. E. W. Wolstenholme and M. P. Cameron, eds.), pp. 3–27. Churchill, London.

Cuatrecasas, P. (1974). *Annu. Rev. Biochem.* **43**, 169–214.

Daniel, E. E., Sehdev, H., and Robinson, K. (1962). *Physiol. Rev.* **42**, Suppl. 5, 228–260.

Davis, W. L., Goodman, D. B. P., Schuster, R. J., Rasmussen, H., and Martin, J. H. (1974). *J. Cell Biol.* **63**, 986–997.

Dax, E. M., Cumming, I. A., Lawson, R. A. S., and Johnston, C. I. (1977). *Endocrinology* **100**, 635–641.

Dean, C. R., Hope, D. B., and Kazic, T. (1968). *Br. J. Pharmacol.* **34**, 192P–193p.

DeLorenzo, R. J., and Greengard, P. (1973). *Proc. Natl. Acad. Sci. U.S.A.* **70**, 1831–1835.

DeLorenzo, R. J., Walton, K. G., Curran, P. F., and Greengard, P. (1973). *Proc. Natl. Acad. Sci. U.S.A.* **70**, 880–884.

de Mey, J., Dierickx, K., and Vandesande, F. (1975). *Cell Tissue Res.* **161**, 219–224.

de Sousa, R. C., Grosso, A., and Rufener, C. (1974). *Experientia* **30**, 175–177.

Devine, C. E., Somlyo, A. V., and Somlyo, A. P. (1973). *Philos. Trans. R. Soc. London, Ser. B* **265**, 17–23.

Dibona, D. R., Civan, M. M., and Leaf, A. (1969). *J. Membr. Biol.* **1**, 79–91.

Dierickx, K., Vandesande, F., and de Mey, J. (1976). *Cell Tissue Res.* **168**, 141–151.

Dobbs, J. W., and Robison, G. A. (1968). *Fed. Proc., Fed. Am. Soc. Exp. Biol.* **27**, 352.

Dousa, T. P. (1972). *Am. J. Physiol.* **222**, 657–662.

Dousa, T. P. (1977). *Fed. Proc. Fed. Am. Soc. Exp. Biol.* **36**, 1867–1871.
Dousa, T. P., and Barnes, L. D. (1974). *J. Clin. Invest.* **54**, 252–262.
Dousa, T. P., and Barnes, L. D. (1977). *Am. J. Physiol.* **232**, F50–F57.
Dousa, T. P., and Valtin, H. (1976). *Kidney Int.* **10**, 46–63.
Dousa, T. P., Sands, H., and Hechter, O. (1972). *Endocrinology* **91**, 757–763.
Dousa, T. P., Hui, Y. F. S., and Barnes, L. D. (1975). *Endocrinology* **97**, 802–807.
du Vigneaud, V. (1960). *Ann. N.Y. Acad. Sci.* **88**, 537–548.
Edelman, G. M. (1976). *Science* **198**, 218–226.
Edelman, G. M., Wang, J. L., and Yahara, I. (1976). *Cold Spring Harbor Conf. Cell Proliferation* **3** [Book A], 305–321.
Edman, K. A. P., and Schild, H. O. (1962). *J. Physiol. (London)* **161**, 424–441.
Erlichman, J., Rosenfeld, R., and Rosen, O. M. (1974). *J. Biol. Chem.* **249**, 5000–5003.
Evans, D. H. L., Schild, H. O., and Thesleff, S. (1958). *J. Physiol. (London)* **143**, 474–485.
Fain, J. N., and Loken, S. C. (1969). *J. Biol. Chem.* **244**, 3500–3506.
Ferguson, D. R., and Twite, B. R. (1974). *J. Endocrinol.* **61**, 501–507.
Fitzpatrick, R. J., and Walmsley (1965). *Adv. Oxytocin Res. Proc. Symp., 1964*, pp. 51–73.
Flouret, G., Terada, S., Yang, F., Nakagawa, S. H., Nakahara, T., and Hechter, O. (1977). *Biochemistry* **16**, 2119–2124.
Follett, B. K., and Bentley, P. J. (1964). *J. Endocrinol.* **29**, 277–282.
Foss, I., Sletten, K., and Trygstad, O. (1973). *FEBS Lett.* **30**, 151–156.
Fuchs, A. R. (1973). In "Endocrine Factors in Labour" (A. Klopper and J. Gardner, eds.), pp. 163–185. Cambridge Univ. Press, London and New York.
Gabella, G. (1973). *Philos. Trans. R. Soc. London, Ser. B* **265**, 7–16.
Gainer, H., Sarne, Y., and Brownstein, M. J. (1977a). *Science* **195**, 1354–1356.
Gainer, H., Sarne, Y., and Brownstein, M. J. (1977b). *J. Cell Biol.* **73**, 366–381.
Ganote, C. E., Grantham, J. J., Moses, H. L., Burg, M. B., and Orloff, J. (1968). *J. Cell Biol.* **36**, 355–367.
Gill, G. N., and Garren, L. D. (1971). *Proc. Natl. Acad. Sci. U.S.A.* **68**, 786–790.
Glasel, J. A., Hruby, V. J., McKelvy, J. F., and Spatola, A. F. (1973). *J. Mol. Biol.* **79**, 555–575.
Glasel, J. A., McKelvy, J. F., Hruby, V. J., and Spatola, A. F. (1976). *J. Biol. Chem.* **251**, 2929–2937.
Glickson, J. D. (1975). In "Peptides, Chemistry, Structure and Biology" (R. Walter and J. Meienhofer, eds.), pp. 787–802. Ann Arbor Sci. Publ., Ann Arbor, Michigan.
Goldberg, N. D., Haddox, M. K., Nicol, S. E., Glass, D. B., Sandford, C. H., Kuehl, F. A., Jr., and Estensen, R. (1975). *Adv. Cyclic Nucleotide Res.* **5**, 307–330.
Goodman, D. B., Rasmussen, H., DiBella, F., and Guthrow, C. E., Jr. (1970). *Proc. Natl. Acad. Sci. U.S.A.* **67**, 652–659.
Grantham, J. J. (1971). *Fed. Proc., Fed. Am. Soc. Exp. Biol.* **30**, 14–21.
Grantham, J. J., and Burg, M. B. (1966). *Am. J. Physiol.* **211**, 255–259.
Graziani, Y., and Livne, A. (1973). *Biochim. Biophys. Acta* **291**, 612–620.
Griffin, J. H., Alazard, R., and Cohen, P. (1973). *J. Biol. Chem.* **248**, 7975–7978.
Griffin, J. H., DiBello, C., Alazard, R., Nicolas, P., and Cohen, P. (1977). *Biochemistry* **16**, 4194–4198.
Hall, J. L., Swisher, J. A., Brannon, D. G., and Liden, T. M. (1962). *Inorg. Chem.* **1**, 409–413.
Hanlon, D. P., Watt, D. S., and Westhead, E. W. (1966). *Anal. Biochem.* **16**, 225–233.
Harbon, S., and Clauser, H. (1971). *Biochem. Biophys. Res. Commun.* **44**, 1496–1503.
Hays, R. M., and Levine, S. D. (1974). *Kidney Int.* **6**, 307–322.
Hope, D. B., and Wälti, M. (1971). *Biochem. J.* **125**, 909–911.
Hope, D. B., Wälti, M., and Winzor, D. J. (1975). *Biochem. J.* **147**, 377–379.
Huguenin, R. L., Stürmer, E., Boissonnas, R. A., and Berde, B. (1965). *Experientia* **21**, 68–69.

Hurwitz, L., Fitzpatrick, D. F., Debbas, G., and Landon, E. J. (1973). *Science* **179**, 384–386
Hynie, S., and Sharp, G. W. G. (1971a). *Biochim. Biophys. Acta* **230**, 40–51.
Hynie, S., and Sharp, G. W. G. (1971b). *J. Endocrinol.* **50**, 231–235.
Jakobs, K. H., Schultz, K., and Schultz, G. (1972). *Naunyn-Schmiedeberg's Arch. Pharmacol.* **273**, 248–266.
Janis, R. A., and Daniel, E. E. (1977). *In* "The Biochemistry of Smooth Muscle" (N. L. Stephens, ed.) pp. 653–671. Univ. Park Press, Baltimore, Maryland.
Janis, R. A., Lee, E. Y., Allan, J., and Daniel, E. E. (1976). *Pfluegers Arch.* **365**, 171–176.
Janis, R. A., Crankshaw, D. J., and Daniel, E. E. (1977). *Am. J. Physiol.* **232**, C50–C58.
Jard, S., and Bastide, F. (1970). *Biochem. Biophys. Res. Commun.* **39**, 559–566.
Jard, S., and Bockaert, J. (1975). *Physiol. Rev.* **55**, 489–536.
Jard, S., Bourguet, T., Favard, P., and Carasso, N. (1971). *J. Membr. Biol.* **4**, 124–147.
Jarvis, D., Ferrier, B. M., and du Vigneaud, V. (1965). *J. Biol. Chem.* **240**, 3553–3557.
Jošt, J., and Šorm, F. (1971). *Collect. Czech. Chem. Commun.* **36**, 234–245.
Jošt, K., and Rudinger, J. (1967). *Collect. Czech. Chem. Commun.* **32**, 1229–1241.
Kachadorian, W. A., Wade, J. B., and DiScala, V. A. (1975). *Science* **190**, 67–69.
Kachadorian, W. A., Levine, S. D., Wade, J. B., DiScala, V. A., and Hayes, R. M. (1977a). *J. Clin. Invest.* **59**, 576–581.
Kachadorian, W. A., Wade, J. B., Uiterwyk, C. C., and DiScala, V. A. (1977b). *J. Membr. Biol.* **30**, 381–401.
Kahn, C. R. (1976). *J. Cell Biol.* **70**, 261–286.
Katsoyannis, P. G., and du Vigneaud, V. (1958). *J. Biol. Chem.* **233**, 1352–1354.
Keely, S. L., Jr., Corbin, J. D., and Park, C. R. (1975). *Proc. Natl. Acad. Sci. U.S.A.* **72**, 1501–1504.
Kono, T., Crofford, O. B., and Park, C. R. (1969). *Diabetes* **18**, Suppl. 1, 335.
Korenman, S. G., and Krall, J. F. (1977). *Biol. Reprod.* **16**, 1–17.
Korenman, S. G., Bhalla, R. C., Sanborn, B. M., and Stevens, R. H. (1974). *Science* **183**, 430–432.
Krebs, E. G. (1972). *Curr. Top. Cell Regul.* **5**, 99–133.
Krejčí, I., and Daniel, E. E. (1970a). *Am. J. Physiol.* **219**, 256–262.
Krejčí, I., and Daniel, E. E. (1970b). *Am. J. Physiol.* **219**, 263–269.
Krejčí, I., and Polacek, I. (1968). *Eur. J. Pharmacol.* **2**, 393–398.
Krejčí, I., Polacek, I., Kupkova, B., and Rudinger, J. (1965). *In* "Oxytocin, Vasopressin and Their Structural Analogues" (J. Rudinger, ed.), pp. 117–131. Pergamon. Oxford.
Kumaresan, P., Anandarangam, P. B., Dianzon, W., and Vasicka, A. (1974). *Am. J. Obstet. Gynecol.* **119**, 215–223.
Lawson, D. M., and Schmidt, G. H. (1972). *Am. J. Physiol.* **222**, 444–449.
Leaf, A. (1967). *Am. J. Med.* **42**, 745–756.
Leaf, A., and Hays, R. M. (1962). *J. Gen. Physiol.* **45**, 921–932.
Legros, J. J., and Louis, F. (1973–1974). *Neuroendocrinology* **13**, 371–375.
Legros, J. J., Peeters, G., Marcus, S., DeGroot, A., and Reynaert, R. (1976). *Arch. Int. Physiol. Biochim.* **34**, 887–888.
Leiber, D., Vesin, M.-F., and Harbon, S. (1978). *FEBS Lett.* **86**, 183–187.
Lesniak, M. A., and Roth, J. (1976). *J. Biol. Chem.* **251**, 3720–3729.
Liggens, G. C., Grieves, S. A., Kendall, J. Z., and Knox, B. S. (1972), *J. Reprod. Fertil.*, Suppl. **16**, 85–103.
Lipson, L. C., and Sharp, G. W. G. (1971). *Am. J. Physiol.* **220**, 1046–1052.
Lord, S. T., and Breslow, E. (1978). *Biochem. Biophys. Res. Commun.* **80**, 63–70.
Maeno, H., Tetsufumi, U., and Greengard, P. (1975). *J. Cyclic Nucleotide Res.* **1**, 37–48.
Malmström, K., and Carafoli, E. (1977). *Arch. Biochem. Biophys.* **182**, 657–666.

Manning, M., Coy, E., and Sawyer, W. H. (1970). *Biochemistry* **9**, 3925–3929.
Manning, M., Lowbridge, J., Haldar, J., and Sawyer, W. H. (1977). *Fed. Proc., Fed. Am. Soc. Exp. Biol.* **36**, 1848–1852.
Markle, H. V., Warr, J. L., and Branda, L. A. (1978). *Can. J. Biochem.* (in press).
Marshall, J. M. (1974). *Handb. Physiol., Sec. 7: Endocrinol.* **4**, 469–492.
Marshall, J. M., and Kroeger, E. A. (1973). *Philos. Trans. R. Soc. London, Ser. B* **265**, 135–148.
Marumo, F., and Edelman, I. (1971). *J. Clin. Invest.* **50**, 1613–1620.
Menendez-Botet, C. J., and Breslow, E. (1975). *Biochemistry* **14**, 3825–3835.
Meraldi, J. P., Hruby, V. J., and Brewster, A. I. R. (1977). *Proc. Natl. Acad. Sci. U.S.A.* **74**, 1373–1377.
Michael, C. A., and Schofield, B. M. (1969). *J. Endocrinol.* **44**, 501–511.
Mitchell, M. D., Flint, A. P. F., and Turnbull, A. C. (1975). *Prostaglandins* **9**, 47–56.
Mitznegg, P., Heim, F., and Meythaler, B. (1970). *Life Sci.* **9**, Part I, 121–128.
Mitznegg, P., Hach, B., and Heim, F. (1971). *Life Sci.* **10**, Part I, 1285–1289.
Mitznegg, P., Schubert, E., and Fuchs, W. (1975). *Naunyn-Schmiedeberg's Arch. Pharmacol.* **287**, 321–327.
Moore, R. D., and Zarrow, M. X. (1965). *Acta Endocrinol. (Copenhagen)* **48**, 186–198.
Munsick, R. A., and Jeronimus, S. C. (1965). *Endocrinology* **76**, 90–96.
Munsick, R. A., Sawyer, W. H., and van Dyke, H. B. (1960). *Endocrinology* **66**, 860–871.
Needham, D. M., and Schoenberg, C. F. (1967). *In* "Cellular Biology of the Uterus" (R. M. Wynn, ed.), pp. 291–352. Appleton, New York.
Neer, E. J. (1973a). *J. Biol. Chem.* **248**, 3742–3744.
Neer, E. J. (1973b). *J. Biol. Chem.* **248**, 4775–4781.
Newcomb, R., Booth, W. D., and Rowson, L. E. A. (1977). *J. Reprod. Fertil.* **49**, 17–24.
Nicolas, P., Camier, M., Dessen, P., and Cohen, P. (1976). *J. Biol. Chem.* **251**, 3965–3971.
Nicolas, P., Dessen, P., Camier, M., and Cohen, P. (1978a). *FEBS Lett.* **86**, 188–192.
Nicolas, P., Wolff, J., Camier, M., DiBello, C., and Cohen, P. (1978b). *J. Biol. Chem.* **253**, 2633–2639.
North, W. G., and Valtin, H. (1977). *Anal. Biochem.* **78**, 436–450.
North, W. G., Walter, R., Schlesinger, D. H., Breslow, E., and Capra, J. D. (1975). *Ann. N.Y. Acad. Sci.* **248**, 408–422.
North, W. G., Valtin, H., Morris, J. F., and La Rochelle, F. T., Jr. (1977). *Endocrinology* **101**, 110–118.
Olmsted, J. B., and Borisy, G. G. (1973). *Annu. Rev. Biochem.* **42**, 507–540.
Orloff, J., and Handler, J. S. (1967). *Am. J. Med.* **42**, 757–768.
Peachey, L. D., and Rasmussen, H. (1961). *J. Biophys. Biochem. Cytol.* **10**, 529–553.
Pearlmutter, A. F. (1978). *Biochemistry*, in press.
Pearlmutter, A. F., and McMains, C. (1977). *Biochemistry* **16**, 628–633.
Pearlmutter, A. F., and Soloff, M. S. (1978). *J. Biol. Chem.*, in press.
Peek, J. C., and Watkins, W. B. (1977). *J. Endocrinol.* **72**, 5P–6P.
Peterson, M. J., and Edelman, I. S. (1964). *J. Clin. Invest.* **43**, 583–594.
Pickering, B. T. (1968). *J. Endocrinol.* **42**, 143–152.
Pickup, J. C., Johnston, C. I., Nakamura, S., Uttenthal, L. O., and Hope, D. B. (1973). *Biochem. J.* **132**, 361–371.
Pietras, R. J. (1976). *Nature (London)* **264**, 774–776.
Pliška, V., and Sachs, H. (1974). *Eur. J. Biochem.* **41**, 229–239.
Polacek, I., and Daniel, E. E. (1971). *Can. J. Physiol. Pharmacol.* **49**, 988–998.
Polacek, I., Krejčí, I., and Rudinger, J. (1967). *J. Endocrinol.* **38**, 13–24.
Ponec, J., and Licardus, B. (1977). *Endocrinol. Exp.* **11**, 235–240.

Rajerison, R. M., Marchetti, J., Roy, C., Bockaert, J., and Jard, S. (1974). *J. Biol. Chem.* **249**, 6390-6400.
Rajerison, R. M., Butlen, D., and Jard, S. (1976). *Mol. Cell. Endocrinol.* **4**, 271-285.
Rajerison, R. M., Butlen, D., and Jard, S. (1977). *Endocrinology* **101**, 1-12.
Rangachari, P. K., Pernollet, M.-G., and Worcel, M. (1976). *Eur. J. Pharmacol.* **40**, 291-294.
Rangel-Aldao, R., and Rosen, O. (1976). *J. Biol. Chem.* **251**, 7526-7529.
Reddington, M., and Lagnado, J. R. (1973). *FEBS Lett.* **30**, 188-194.
Reed, K. C., and Bygrave, F. L. (1975). *Anal. Biochem.* **67**, 44-54.
Reimann, E. M., Brostrom, C. O., Corbin, J. D., King, C. A., and Krebs, E. G. (1971). *Biochem. Biophys. Res. Commun.* **42**, 187-194.
Roberts, J. S., and McCracken, J. A. (1976). *Biol. Reprod.* **15**, 457-463.
Roberts, J. S., McCracken, J. A., Gavagan, J. E., and Soloff, M. S. (1976). *Endocrinology* **99**, 1107-1114.
Robinson, A. G. (1975). *Ann. N.Y. Acad. Sci.* **248**, 246-256.
Robinson, A. G., Michelis, M. F., Warms, P. C., and Davis, B. D. (1975). *Ann. N.Y. Acad. Sci.* **248**, 317-323.
Roy, C., Bockaert, J., Rajerison, R., and Jard, S. (1973). *FEBS Lett.* **30**, 329-334.
Roy, C., Barth, T., and Jard, S. (1975a). *J. Biol. Chem.* **250**, 3149-3156.
Roy, C., Barth, T., and Jard, S. (1975b). *J. Biol. Chem.* **250**, 3157-3168.
Roy, C., Rajerison, R., Bockaert, J., and Jard, S. (1975c). *J. Biol. Chem.* **250**, 7885-7893.
Roy, C., Guillon, G., and Jard, S. (1976). *Biochem. Biophys. Res. Commun.* **72**, 1265-1270.
Roy, C., Guillon, G., and Jard, S. (1977). *Biochem. Biophys. Res. Commun.* **78**, 67-73.
Rubanyi, G., and Csapo, A. I. (1977). *Life Sci.* **20**, 289-300.
Rudinger, J., Pliška, V., and Krejčí, I. (1972). *Recent Prog. Horm. Res.* **28**, 131-172.
Rudman, D., Chawla, R. K., Khatra, B. S., and Yodaiken, R. E. (1975). *Ann. N.Y. Acad. Sci.* **248**, 324-335.
Sachs, H., and Takabatake, Y. (1964). *Endocrinology* **75**, 943-948.
Sachs, H., Fawcett, P., Takabatake, Y., and Portonova, R. (1969). *Recent Prog. Horm. Res.* **25**, 447-491.
Sala, N. L., and Freire, F. (1974). *Biol. Reprod.* **11**, 7-17.
Sandoval, I. V., and Cuatrecasas, P. (1976). *Nature (London)* **262**, 511-514.
Sapag-Hagar, M., and Greenbaum, A. L. (1973). *Biochem. Biophys. Res. Commun.* **53**, 982-987.
Sawyer, W. H. (1977). *Fed. Proc., Fed. Am. Soc. Exp. Biol.* **36**, 1842-1847.
Sawyer, W. H., and Manning, M. (1973). *Annu. Rev. Pharmacol.* **13**, 5-17.
Scatchard, G. (1949). *Ann. N.Y. Acad. Sci.* **51**, 660-672.
Schlender, K. K., and Reimann, E. M. (1975). *Proc. Natl. Acad. Sci. U.S.A.* **72**, 2197-2201.
Schlesinger, D. H., Capra, J. D., and Walter, R. (1974). *Int. J. Pept. Protein Res.* **6**, 1-12.
Schlesinger, D. H., Ernst, M., Nicholas, A., Watkins, W. B., and Walter, R. (1975). *FEBS Lett.* **57**, 55-59.
Schroeder, B. T., Chakraborty, J., and Soloff, M. S. (1977). *J. Cell Biol.* **74**, 428-440.
Schwartz, I. L., Schlatz, L. J., Kinne-Saffran, E., and Kinne, R. (1974). *Proc. Natl. Acad. Sci. U.S.A.* **71**, 2595-2599.
Sharma, S. C., and Fitzpatrick, R. J. (1974). *Prostaglandins* **6**, 97-105.
Shigekawa, B. L., and Olsen, R. W. (1975). *Biochem. Biophys. Res. Commun.* **63**, 455-462.
Sim, M. K., and Chantharaksri, U. (1973). *Biochem. Pharmacol.* **22**, 1417-1422.
Sloboda, R. D., Rudolph, S. A., Rosenbaum, J. L., and Greengard, P. (1975). *Proc. Natl. Acad. Sci. U.S.A.* **72**, 177-181.
Soifer, D. (1975). *J. Neurochem.* **24**, 21-23.

Sokol, H. W., and Valtin, H. (1967). *Nature (London)* **214**, 314–316.

Soloff, M. S. (1975a). *Biochem. Biophys. Res. Commun.* **65**, 205–212.

Soloff, M. S. (1975b). *Biochem. Biophys. Res. Commun.* **66**, 671–677.

Soloff, M. S. (1976a). *In* "Methods in Receptor Research, Methods in Molecular Biology" (M. Blecher, ed.), pp. 511–513. Dekker, New York.

Soloff, M. S. (1976b). *In* "Hormone–Receptor Interaction: Molecular Aspects" (G. S. Levey, . ed.), pp. 129–151. Dekker, New York.

Soloff, M. S. (1976c). *Br. J. Pharmacol.* **57**, 381–386.

Soloff, M. S., and Swartz, T. L. (1973). *J. Biol. Chem.* **248**, 6471–6478.

Soloff, M. S., and Swartz, T. L. (1974). *J. Biol. Chem.* **249**, 1376–1381.

Soloff, M. S., Swartz, T. L., and Steinberg, A. H. (1974). *J. Clin. Endocrinol. Metab.* **38**, 1052–1056.

Soloff, M. S., Rees, H. D., Sar, M., and Stumpf, W. E. (1975). *Endocrinology* **96**, 1475–1477.

Soloff, M. S., Schroeder, B. T., Chakraborty, J., and Pearlmutter, A. F. (1977). *Fed. Proc., Fed. Am. Soc. Exp. Biol.* **36**, 1861–1866.

Soloff, M. S., Sadhukhan, P., Chakraborty, J., Senitzer, D., and Wieder, M. H. (1979a). *Endocrinology.* In press.

Soloff, M. S., Alexandrova, M., and Fernstrom (1979b). Submitted for publication.

Spielvogel, A. M., Mednieks, M. I., Eppenberger, U., and Jungmann, R. A. (1977). *Eur. J. Biochem.* **73**, 199–212.

Sunde, D. A., and Sokol, W. H. (1975). *Ann. N.Y. Acad. Sci.* **248**, 345–364.

Swillens, S., and Dumont, J. E. (1977). *J. Cyclic Nucleotide Res.* **3**, 1–10.

Takabatake, Y., and Sachs, H. (1964). *Endocrinology* **75**, 934–942.

Tasso, F., Picard, D., and Dreifuss, J. J. (1976). *Nature (London)* **260**, 621–622.

Taylor, A., Mamelak, M., Reaven, E., and Maffly, R. (1973). *Science* **181**, 347–350.

Taylor, A., Maffly, R., Wilson, L., and Reaven, E. (1975). *Ann. N.Y. Acad. Sci.* **253**, 723–737.

Thompson, E. E., Freychet, P., and Roth, J. (1972). *Endocrinology* **91**, 1199–1205.

Tisher, C. C., Bulger, R. E., and Valtin, H. (1971). *Am. J. Physiol.* **220**, 87–94.

Torok, I., and Csapo, A. I. (1976). *Prostaglandins* **12**, 253–269.

Triner, L., Vulliemoz, Y., Verosky, M., and Nahas, G. G. (1970). *Life Sci.* **9**, Part I, 707–712.

Trygstad, O., Foss, I., and Sletten, K. (1975). *Ann. N.Y. Acad. Sci.* **248**, 304–316.

Urry, D. W., and Walter, R. (1971). *Proc. Natl. Acad. Sci. U.S.A.* **68**, 956–958.

Urry, D. W., Ohnishi, M., and Walter, R. (1970). *Proc. Natl. Acad. Sci.* **66**, 111–116.

Uttenthal, L. O., and Hope, D. B. (1970). *Biochem. J.* **116**, 899–909.

van Breemen, C., Daniel, E. E., and van Breemen, D. (1966), *J. Gen. Physiol.* **49**, 1265–1297.

Vandesande, F., Dierickx, K., and de Mey, J. (1975). *Cell Tissue Res.* **156**, 189–200.

van Dyke, H. B., and Hastings, A. B. (1928). *Am. J. Physiol.* **83**, 563–577.

van Dyke, H. B., Chow, B. F., Greep, R. O., and Rothen, A. (1942). *J. Pharmacol. Expr. Ther.* **74**, 190–209.

van Leeuwen, F. W., and Swaab, D. F. (1977). *Cell Tissue Res.* **177**, 493–501.

Vesin, M. F., and Harbon, S. (1974). *Mol. Pharmacol.* **10**, 457–473.

Walter, R. (1977). *Fed. Proc., Fed. Am. Soc. Exp. Biol.* **36**, 1872–1878.

Walter, R., and Breslow, E. (1974). *Res. Methods Neurochem.* **2**, 247–279.

Walter, R., Glickson, J. D., Schwartz, I. L., Havran, R. T., Meienhofer, J., and Urry, D. W. (1972). *Proc. Natl. Acad. Sci. U.S.A.* **69**, 1920–1924.

Walter, R., Prasad, K. U. M., Deslauriers, R., and Smith, I. C. P. (1973). *Proc. Natl. Acad. Sci U.S.A.* **70**, 2086–2090.

Walter, R., Ballardin, A., Schwartz, I. L., Gibbons, W. A., and Wyssbrod, H. R. (1974). *Proc. Natl. Acad. Sci. U.S.A.* **71**, 4528–4532.

Walter, R., Smith, C. W., and Roy, J. (1976). *Proc. Natl. Acad. Sci. U.S.A.* **73**, 3054–3058.

Walter, R., Audhya, T. K., and Schlesinger, D. H. (1977a). *Fed. Proc., Fed. Am. Soc. Exp. Biol.* **36**, 1674.

Walter, R., Audhya, T. K., Schlesinger, D. H., Shin, S., Saito, S., and Sachs, H. (1977b). *Endocrinology* **100**, 162–174.

Walton, R. G., DeLorenzo, R. J., Curran, P. F., and Greengard, P. (1975). *J. Gen. Physiol.* **65**, 153–177.

Wanner, O., Crankshaw, D. J., and Pliška, V. (1977). *Mol. Cell. Endocrinol.* **6**, 281–292.

Watkins, W. B. (1972). *J. Endocrinol.* **55**, 577–589.

Watkins, W. B. (1973). *J. Endocrinol.* **59**, 17–29.

Watkins, W. B. (1976). *Cell Tissue Res.* **175**, 165–181.

Watkins, W. B., and Choy, V. J. (1976). *Neurosci. Lett.* **3**, 293–297.

Watkins, W. B., and Ellis, H. K. (1973). *J. Endocrinol.* **59**, 31–41.

Whittembury, G., Sugino, N., and Solomon, A. K. (1960). *Nature (London)* **187**, 699–701.

Wuu, T.-C., and Crumm, S. E. (1976a). *Biochem. Biophys. Res. Commun.* **68**, 634–639.

Wuu, T.-C., and Crumm, S. E. (1976b). *J. Biol. Chem.* **251**, 2735–2739.

Wuu, T.-C., Crumm, S. E., and Saffran, M. (1971). *J. Biol. Chem.* **246**, 6043–6063.

Zimmerman, E. A., Robinson, A. G., Husain, M. K., Acosta, M., Frantz, A. G., and Sawyer, W. H. (1974). *Endocrinology* **95**, 931–935.

CHAPTER 7

Biochemistry and Physiology of Cytokinins

Folke Skoog and Ruth Y. Schmitz

LIST OF ABBREVIATIONS

Ade = adenine

A = Ado = adenosine

m^6Ade = 6-methylaminopurine = N^6-methyladenine

bzl^3Ade = 3-benzyladenine

bzl^6Ade = 6-benzylaminopurine = N^6-benzyladenine

bzl^6A = bzl^6Ado = 6-benzylamino-9-β-D-ribofuranosylpurine = N^6-benzyladenosine

bzl^6AMP (also bzl^6ADP, bzl^6ATP) = N^6-benzyladenosine 5′-monophosphate (5′-disphosphate, 5′-triphosphate)

m^9bzl^6Ade = 6-benzylamino-9-methylpurine

$butyl^9bzl^6$Ade = 6-benzylamino-9-butylpurine

m^8-4-aza-3-deaza-bzl^6Ade = 6-benzylamino-8-methyl-4-aza-3-deazapurine = 8-benzylamino-2-methyl-s-triazolo [1,5-a]pyrazine

m^8-4-aza-1,3-deaza-bzl^6Ade = 6-benzylamino-8-methyl-1,3-deaza-4-azapurine = 8-benzylamino-2-methyl-s-triazolo [1,4-a]pyridine

fr^6Ade = 6-furfurylaminopurine = kinetin

fr^6A = fr^6Ado = 6-furfurylamino-9-β-D-ribofuranosylpurine = N^6-furfuryladenosine = ribosylkinetin = kinetin riboside

i^6Ade = 6-(3-methyl-2-butenylamino)purine = N^6-(Δ^2-isopentenyl)adenine

i^6A = i^6Ado = 6-(3-methyl-2-butenylamino)-9-β-D-ribofuranosylpurine = N^6-(Δ^2-isopentenyl)adenosine

i^6AMP (also i^6ADP, i^6ATP) = N^6-(Δ^2-isopentenyl)adenosine 5′-monophosphate (5′-diphosphate, 5′-triphosphate)

m^8i^6Ade = 6-(3-methyl-2-butenylamino)-8-methylpurine = N^6-(Δ^2-isopentenyl)-8-methylpurine

ms^2i^6Ade = 6-(3-methyl-2-butenylamino)-2-methylthiopurine = N^6-(Δ^2-isopentenyl)-2-methylthioadenine

ms^2i^6A = ms^2i^6Ado = 6-(3-methyl-2-butenylamino)-2-methylthio-9-β-D-ribofuranosyl-purine = N^6-(Δ^2-isopentenyl)-2-methylthioadenosine

HS^2i^6A = HS^2i^6Ado = 6-(3-methyl-2-butenylamino)-2-mercapto-9-β-D-ribofuranosyl-purine = N^6-(Δ-isopentenyl)-2-mercaptoadenosine

io^6Ade = 6-(4-hydroxy-3-methyl-2-butenylamino)purine = zeatin

io^6A = io^6Ado = 6-(4-hydroxy-3-methyl-2-butenylamino)-9-β-D-ribofuranosyl-purine = ribosylzeatin = zeatin riboside

ms^2io^6Ade = 6-(4-hydroxy-3-methyl-2-butenylamino)-2-methylthiopurine = 2-methylthiozeatin

ms²io⁶A = ms²io⁶Ado = 6-(4-hydroxy-3-methyl-2-butenylamino)-2-methylthio-9-β-D-ribofurano-
   sylpurine = 2-methylthiozeatin riboside = 2-methylthioribosylzeatin
ABA = 3-methyl-5-(1-hydroxy-4-oxo-2,6,6-trimethyl-2-cyclohexe-1-yl)-*cis,-trans*-2,4-penta-
   dienoic acid = abscisic acid = abscisin II = dormin
NAA = naphthaleneacetic acid
PAL = phenylalanine-ammonium lyase
2,4-D = 2,4-dichlorophenoxyacetic acid
tRNA^{Asn} = asparagine tRNA = asparagine transfer ribonucleic acid
tRNA^{Leu} = leucine tRNA
tRNA$^{Leu}_{5,6}$ = leucine tRNA$_5$ and leucine tRNA$_6$
tRNA^{Phe} = phenylalanine tRNA
tRNA$^{Phe}_I$ = phenylalanine tRNA$_I$
tRNA$^{Phe}_{II}$ = phenylalanine tRNA$_{II}$
tRNA^{Ser} serine tRNA
tRNA^{Tyr} = tyrosine tRNA
su$^{+Tyr}_{III}$ tRNA = tyrosine suppressor tRNA$_{III}$

I. INTRODUCTION

Cytokinins are a class of substances which in conjunction with other factors serve to regulate growth, morphogenesis, and development in plants. Some recent reports suggest that they have regulatory functions also in animals. They are arbitrarily defined as substances which promote cell division and growth of certain plant tissues, such as excised tobacco pith or callus, on specific nutrient media, in the same manner as does kinetin, the first compound of the class to be identified. This definition of cytokinins in terms of cell division is analogous to the definition of auxins as substances which promote elongation (enlargement) of plant cells in specified tests in the same manner as does indole-3-acetic acid (IAA). It serves to distinguish these two types of biologically active substances from one another and each of them from others, but it is understood that both cytokinins and auxins are required for cell division and growth and that both of these hormones are involved in all phases of plant growth and development.

Most if not all highly potent, naturally occurring cytokinins are N⁶-isopentenyl adenine derivatives. A summary of naturally occurring cytokinins, their sources and identification is presented in Table I. *N,N′*-Diphenylurea, isolated as a growth factor from coconut milk (Shantz and Steward, 1955), is included as it and many other phenylurea derivatives are active in promoting growth of tobacco tissue and are also active in most other assay systems.

The participation of cytokinins in the regulation of plant growth and development is observable at every stage in ontogeny and is reflected in every structural feature, from the composition and arrangement of macromolecular

TABLE I

CYTOKININ-ACTIVE COMPOUNDS OF NATURAL OCCURRENCE

Compound	Source	Reference	Remarks
Bases:			
i⁶Ade	*Corynebacterium fascians* culture filtrate	Klämbt *et al.*, 1966	Synthesized and tested before being found in nature (Cavé *et al.*, 1962; Rogozinska *et al.*, 1964; Hamzi and Skoog, 1964)
	Tobacco tissue	Einset and Skoog, 1973	
	Cotton ovules	Shindy and Smith, 1975	
	Agrobacterium tumefaciens culture filtrate	Kaiss-Chapman and Morris, 1977	
t-io⁶Ade (Zeatin)	Immature corn kernels	Letham *et al.*, 1964	Also reported from many other plant sources
	Rhizopogon roseolus	Miura and Miller, 1969	
	Tobacco tissue	Einset and Skoog, 1973	
	Cotton ovules	Shindy and Smith, 1975	
	Vinca rosea	Miller, 1975	
	A. tumefaciens culture filtrate	Kaiss-Chapman and Morris, 1977	
c-io⁶Ade (*cis*-Zeatin)	*C. fascians* culture filtrate	Scarbrough *et al.*, 1973	Not yet reported from higher plant source
	A. tumefaciens culture filtrate	Kaiss-Chapman and Morris, 1977	
H₂io⁶Ade (Dihydrozeatin)	*Lupinus luteus* seed	Koshimizu *et al.*, 1967	Natural isomer is (S)-(−)-dihydrozeatin (Fujii and Ogawa, 1972)
	Cotton ovules	Shindy and Smith, 1975	
ms²-c-io⁶Ade	*C. fascians* culture filtrate	Armstrong *et al.*, 1976b	

$(OH^{3,4'})^6Ade$	Immature corn kernels	Letham, 1973	N.B. Saturated sidechain; synthesized and tested before being found in nature (Leonard et al., 1968)
$(OH^{2,3,4'})^6Ade$	Immature corn kernels	Letham, 1973	N.B. Saturated side chain
OH^2io^6Ade	Immature corn kernels	Letham, 1973; Miller, 1965	Synthesized and tested before being found in nature (Hecht et al., 1970b)
Ribonucleosides			
i^6A	Tobacco callus	Dyson and Hall, 1972	
	Cotton ovules	Shindy and Smith, 1975	
	tRNA, Ser I&II, yeast	Zachau et al., 1966	
	tRNA, wheat germ	Burrows et al., 1970	
	tRNA, E. coli	Burrows et al., 1969	
ms^2i^6A	tRNA, E. coli	Burrows et al., 1968, 1969	Since found in certain tRNA's of all classes of organisms
	tRNA, pea shoots	Vreman et al., 1972	
t-io^6A (Ribosylzeatin)	Immature corn kernels	Letham, 1973	
	Tobacco tissue	Einset and Skoog, 1973	
	Cotton ovules	Shindy and Smith, 1975	
	A. tumefaciens culture filtrate	Kaiss-Chapman and Morris, 1977	
	tRNA, wheat germ[a]	Burrows et al., 1970	
	tRNA, pea shoots	Vreman et al., 1972	
	tRNA, A. tumefaciens	Chapman et al., 1976	
	tRNA, wheat germ	Taller et al., 1977	
	rRNA, wheat germ	Taller et al., 1977	

(continued)

TABLE I (continued)

Compound	Source	Reference	Remarks
c-io^{6}A (Cis-ribosylzeatin)	tRNA, spinach, corn and pea; tRNA, wheat germ[a]; tRNA, wheat germ; rRNA, wheat germ	Hall et al., 1967; Burrows et al., 1970; Taller et al., 1977; Taller et al., 1977	
H_2io^{6}A	Bean axes	Sondheimer and Tzou, 1971	
ms^{2}io^{6}A	tRNA, wheat germ[a]; tRNA, wheat germ[a]; tRNA, Pseudomonas aeruginosa[a]; tRNA, wheat germ[a]; rRNA, wheat germ[a]	Hecht et al., 1969a; Burrows et al., 1970; Thimmappaya and Cherayil, 1974; Taller et al., 1977; Taller et al., 1977	
ms^2-t-io^{6}A	tRNA, pea shoots	Vreman et al., 1972, 1974	
ms^2-c-io^{6}A	C. fascians, culture filtrate; tRNA, pea shoots; tRNA, A. tumefaciens, C. fascians, Rhizobium leguminosarum	Armstrong et al., 1976b; Vreman et al., 1972, 1974; Cherayil and Lipsett, 1977	Found only in those microorganisms associated with plant overgrowths
(COOH^{1}OH^{2}propyl)^{6}A	Immature corn kernels	Letham, 1973	
(COOH^{1,2}ethyl)^{6}A	Immature corn kernels	Letham, 1973	

Compound	Source	Reference	Remarks
$(OH^2bzl)i^6A$	*Populus × robusta*	Horgan *et al.*, 1973	Only finding to date of naturally occurring bzl⁶Ade derivative
Ribonucleotides: i^6AMP, i^6ADP, i^6ATP	Tobacco and *Acer* cells	Laloue *et al.*, 1974	Biosynthesized from [8-¹⁴C]i⁶Ade; the corresponding benzyl derivatives formed from [8-¹⁴C]bzl⁶Ade. Synthesized and tested before being found in nature (von Saltza, 1958)
$t\text{-}io^6AMP$	Immature corn kernels / Watermelon seeds	Letham, 1966 / Prakash and Maheshwari, 1970	
H_2io^6AMP	Bean axes	Sondheimer and Tzou, 1971	
Glucopyranosides: $(4\text{-}O\text{-}\beta\text{-}D\text{-}Gluc\text{-}io)^6Ade$	Soybean callus / *Populus alba* leaves[b] / Crown gall tissue of *Vinca rosea*	Horgan, 1975 / Letham *et al.*, 1977 / Morris, 1977; Peterson and Miller, 1977	Biosynthesized from [8-¹⁴C]io⁶Ade
$(4\text{-}O\text{-}\beta\text{-}D\text{-}Gluc\text{-}H_2io)^6Ade$	*Populus alba* leaves[b] / *Phaseolus vulgaris* leaves	Letham *et al.*, 1977 / Wang *et al.*, 1977	
$Gluc^7\text{-}io^6Ade$	Radish seedlings[b]	Parker and Letham, 1973	
$Gluc^9\text{-}io^6Ade$	Corn seedlings[b]	Parker and Letham, 1974	

(continued)

TABLE I (*continued*)

Compound	Source	Reference	Remarks
Gluc^{3}bzl^{6}Ade	Radish seedlings	Parker *et al.*, 1975	Biosynthesized from [^{3}H]bzl^{6}Ade. Not likely of natural occurrence but included here because the corresponding io^{6}Ade derivative may be of natural occurrence
Aminoacylated derivatives:			
Ala^{9}io^{6}Ade	*Lupinus angustifolius* seedlings	MacLeod *et al.*, 1975	First reported amino acid linked to N atom of purine ring in higher plants
[(NH$_2$)^3(COOH)^{3}propyl]^{3}i^{6}Ade (Discadenine)	*Dictyostelium discoides*	Abe *et al.*, 1976	Is a spore germination inhibitor in this slime mold. Has low cytokinin activity (Nomura *et al.*, 1977)
Miscellaneous:			
fr^{6}Ade (Kinetin)	Herring sperm, aged preparation of DNA	Miller *et al.*, 1955	Not yet found from plant source but possible biosynthetic route from 2'-deoxyadenosine demonstrated (Scopes *et al.*, 1976)
i^{3}Ade (Triacanthine)	*Gleditsia triacanthos*, young leaves	Cavé *et al.*, 1962	Active only after rearrangement to i^{6}Ade (Rogozinska *et al.*, 1964)
DPU (Diphenylurea)	Coconut milk	Shantz and Steward, 1955	Only reported occurrence; has definite cytokinin activity in tobacco but not in soybean callus

[a] Configuration not specified.
[b] Biosynthesized from [^{3}H]io^{6}Ade.

components in the walls, membranes, and organelles within individual cells to the kind, size, shape, and relative numbers of organs in mature plants. This review will deal mainly with biochemical and metabolic aspects of cytokinins, but a survey of physiological and striking morphogenetic effects is also included.

Reference is made to the following texts and reviews: Key (1969), Leopold and Kreidemann (1975), Steward (1972), Steward and Krikorian (1971), Thimann (1977), and Weaver (1972); and to more specialized accounts of cytokinins: Hecht (1978), Kulaeva (1973), Leonard (1974), and Skoog (1973a,b).

II. EFFECTS ON PHYSIOLOGICAL PROCESSES

A. CELL DIVISION AND ENLARGEMENT

Cytokinins were isolated on the basis of a requirement for growth of plant cells demonstrated in excised tobacco pith tissue (Jablonski and Skoog, 1954; Miller *et al.*, 1955), where kinetin was shown to be a key factor for cell division (Das *et al.*, 1956; Patau *et al.*, 1957). In this tissue, treatment with auxin alone satisfied exogenous requirements for cell enlargement, but both hormones were essential for cell division and continued growth and viability of the callus. In excised leaf tissue, on the contrary, exogenous cytokinin, but not auxin, promoted rapid cell enlargement of interveinal tissue which might then be followed by cell division, leading to clusters of callus and eventually to new meristems. In tissues exhibiting polar growth (excised roots, hypocotyls, and seedling stem segments), moderate to high cytokinin concentrations in short-term experiments tended to inhibit elongation and instead promoted growth in width. This has been correlated with a 90° shift in the orientation of cellulose fibrils in the cell walls (Hashimoto, 1961; Probine, 1965).

B. ORGANOGENESIS

The concept of multifactor quantitative chemical regulation of organ formation in plants was proposed by Skoog in 1949 (Skoog, 1950), on the basis of the effects of the interaction between auxin, adenine, and other factors in experiments with tobacco callus (Skoog, 1944), excised pith tissue (Skoog and Tsui, 1948, 1951), and horseradish root tissue (F. Skoog and R.L.N. Sastri, unpublished). This concept has now been supported by detailed studies of the interaction of hormones (auxins, cytokinins and gibberellins), substrates, and environmental factors in root formation on both excised stem segments (Leroux, 1973) and excised root tissues (Gautheret, 1966, 1969), as well as by numerous studies on the effects of cytokinins and auxins on bud formation in various plants (see Murashige, 1974).

The effect of cytokinin on organ formation in excised tobacco pith or callus tissue depends on its concentration and on the presence of other growth factors, especially auxin, in the nutrient medium. As illustrated in Fig. 1, in the presence of a moderately high, constant IAA concentration (other factors remaining the same), increasing kinetin concentrations from 0.02 to 10 mg/*l* led first to intensive root formation and development; next to rapid growth of undifferentiated callus consisting of large, thin-walled cells; then to profuse bud formation; then to the formation of a compact, firm callus, consisting of small, thick-walled cells; and lastly, to inhibition of growth (Skoog and Miller, 1957).

It should be emphasized that both auxin and cytokinin have been shown to be required for the growth and development of all kinds of organs. High auxin:cytokinin ratios not only promote root formation, but tend to inhibit bud formation; high cytokinin:auxin ratios, on the other hand, promote bud formation but repress the formation and growth of roots. The concentrations and ratio of cytokinin and auxin required for a particular morphogenetic response vary with the endogenous levels of the two hormones and with the concentrations of other factors, such as certain amino acids and phosphate, etc. (see Skoog and Armstrong, 1970). For example, horseradish root tissue,

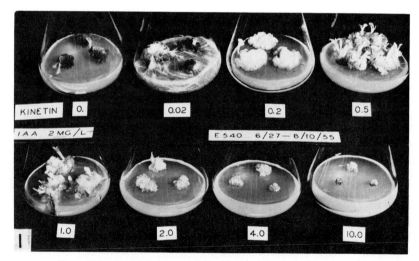

FIG. 1. Effect of kinetin concentration on growth and organ formation in tobacco tissue cultures. Exp. 540, 6/27 to 8/10/55. From Skoog and Miller, 1957.

which is rich in peroxidase, readily formed buds but not roots in the absence of hormones. Treatment with IAA alone in low concentration or in combination with cytokinins increased bud formation; a much higher auxin concentration was required for root formation, and an exceedingly high concentration of 2,4-D (a potent and more stable auxin than IAA) was required to repress bud formation completely (F. Skoog and   Sastri, unpublished). Similarly, alfalfa tissue cultures have been shown to form buds in response to treatment with 2,4-D; and kinetin was found to augment the effectiveness of the treatments (Saunders, 1973; Saunders and Bingham, 1975).

The strikingly quantitative relationship between auxin and cytokinin in the regulation of growth and morphogenesis, despite species variation, applies to dicotyledons (Murashige, 1974; Pierik, 1975), monocotyledons (Havránek and Novák, 1973; Nickell and Heinz, 1973), and gymnosperms (Brown and Sommer, 1975). It also applies to mosses (Gorton *et al.*, 1957; Hahn and Bopp, 1968; Szweykowska *et al.*, 1972), but factors other than cytokinins have been reported to induce gametophore formation in moss protonemata (Spiess *et al.*, 1972). This relationship is the basis of new methods in current practice for vegetative regeneration of plantlets of various horticultural and crop plants from excised tissue, excised meristems, cell suspension cultures, and protoplasts (Murashige, 1974, 1977; Nickell and Heinz, 1973). In fact, the utilization of appropriate, relatively high exogenous cytokinin levels is critical in the preparation of viable protoplasts (I. Takebe, private communication) as well as in their cultivation and for regeneration of plants (Takebe *et al.*, 1971; Melchers and Labib, 1974).

That quantitative hormonal regulation of growth and morphogenesis also functions in intact plants can be deduced from the differential distribution of cytokinin and auxin activities in tissues, and from the effect of interrupting their transport or of applying exogenous hormones to different parts of plants. It is strikingly illustrated by the formation of epiphyllous buds in the leaf notches of *Bryophyllum*, a process which is subject to phytochrome regulation and normally occurs only under a long-day light regime. Formation of plantlets could be prevented in a given leaf under long-day conditions by the application of auxin to its surfaces, and could be restored by subsequent cytokinin application. Plants kept on a short-day regime formed plantlets only on leaves treated with cytokinin, and this response could be prevented by treatment with auxin (Chailakhyan and Frolova, 1974; Dvořák and Radotínská-Ledinská, 1970). Environmental factors such as day length, light quality, temperature, etc. which affect regenerative capacities in plants may do so via influences on endogenous hormone levels, including cytokinin levels, as first indicated by analysis of bud and root formation in *Begonia* cuttings (Heide, 1965) and as supported by more recent evidence from various other plants. Species in which leaves do not normally form buds may be induced to do so by cytokinin treatments, as in the case of *Torenia* (Bajaj, 1972) and *Dendrophthoe* (Nag and Johri, 1970). The same applies to cotyledons and hypocotyls of *Lactuca* (Doershug and Miller, 1967) as well as to roots of intact *Passiflora caerulea* plants (Montaldi, 1972).

C. Differentiation of Tissues

Tissue differentiation, as well as the initiation of organ primordia, is regulated by hormones. Cytokinins are required for the initiation of tracheary elements and the development of vascular strands in tobacco callus (Torrey *et al.*, 1971). In the development of vascular strands in *Phaseolus* petiole segments, kinetin favored tracheid formation and lignification of sclerenchyma fibers and ray parenchyma, while at the same time it promoted cell division in the xylem parenchyma and cambium. On the other hand, IAA primarily promoted phloem development, specifically the radial expansion of ray and phloem parenchyma, and cell division in the parenchyma adjacent to the phloem strands (Oppenoorth, 1976). These findings suggest a mode by which the natural distribution of endogenous hormones may contribute to differentiation and orderly development of vascular tissues, the cytokinins ascending mainly in the xylem from the roots, and the auxins descending in the phloem and parenchyma.

D. Development of Stolons

In the development of stolons, auxin, cytokinin, and gibberellin all play a part, each having a major role: auxin and gibberellin in stolon formation and diageotropic outgrowth, and cytokinin in the formation of a new plant at the apex (Wareing and Phillips, 1970). In potato, cytokinins appear to trigger tuberization even under conditions adverse to normal tuber formation, such as high temperature, long-day photoperiod and the presence of exogenous ABA (abscisic acid or dormin) (Palmer and Smith, 1969, 1970; Smith and Palmer, 1970: Forsline and Langille, 1975).

E. Leaf Growth

Cytokinins have been shown to promote cell expansion of interveinal tissue of bean leaf discs and to replace a light requirement for continued growth (C.O. Miller, unpublished). Gibberellic acid, added to the nutrient media of budding tobacco tissue, markedly stimulated elongation of plantlet stems and leaves but repressed growth of laminar tissue; this led to spindly plants with narrow leaves, sometimes nearly devoid of interveinal tissue.

This effect was counteracted by high cytokinin concentrations. In fact, the cytokinin:gibberellin ratio in the medium determined the leaf shape, which varied from nearly round to straplike or needle-shaped as the ratio decreased (Engelke *et al.*, 1973). Spray applications of the hormones to growing points has comparable effects on later-developing foliage (Tronchet, 1968), suggesting that the characteristic leaf shapes of intact plants reflect relative endogenous levels of gibberellins and cytokinins. What may appear as an extreme case of cytokinin:gibberellin regulation of polar vs. nonpolar growth has been reported for the cactus *Opuntia polycanthus* (Mauseth and Halperin, 1975; Mauseth, 1976). Application of a high ratio of cytokinin:gibberellin or of cytokinin alone resulted in the development of leaves, while a low ratio or gibberellin alone promoted the formation of spines; intermediate ratios led to transitional forms. Auxin, in all but low concentrations, when combined with the above treatments, tended to oppose the effect of cytokinin. It is intriguing that leaf shapes stable enough to be used as common criteria for taxonomic classification may reflect small quantitative changes in the proportions of two minute cell constituents.

F. APICAL DOMINANCE

Apical dominance is a striking example of growth correlation, which includes the inhibition by the terminal bud of the development both of preformed lateral buds in the axils of leaves and stipules and of adventitious buds along the axis. This is probably the most studied case of regulation by one organ of the growth of other parts of the plant. Errera (1904) deduced that apical dominance was achieved through "internal secretion." Snow (1925, 1929), by surgical manipulation, obtained indirect evidence that an inhibitor derived from the young leaflets of the terminal bud is transported down the stem to the area where it exerts its effect, and it was shown (Thimann and Skoog, 1933, 1934) that auxin satisfied the specifications of the inhibiting agent, in being produced in by far the highest amounts in the terminal buds and being transported polarly down the stems of *Vicia* and *Pisum* plants. Furthermore, synthetic IAA, as well as extracted auxin, applied to the cut surface of decapitated plants under appropriate conditions, substituted effectively for the terminal buds (Skoog and Thimann, 1934). This effect of auxin has been confirmed in numerous species, and contrary reports, such as the claim for its limitation to legumes or failure to apply to *Coleus* (Jacobs, 1959), have been re-examined and refuted (Thimann *et al.*, 1971; F. Skoog, unpublished).

Interpretations of the nature of the inhibiting effect are almost as numerous as the investigators, but can be considered under two main categories, the so-called direct and indirect mechanisms of auxin action (see Phillips,

1969, 1975). The direct mechanism, according to which the action of auxin is exerted *directly* in the inhibited bud (Thimann and Skoog, 1934; Thimann, 1937) rather than *indirectly* through an influence exerted on growth of the main shoot (Müller, 1935; Gregory and Veale, 1957; Went, 1939), was supported by experiments showing that auxin promotes or inhibits growth of excised *Pisum* buds as a function of its concentration in a medium supplied with adequate nutrients, thus eliminating effects caused by nutrient deprivation (Skoog, 1939). In accordance with findings of interaction between IAA and its analogs in growth (Skoog *et al.*, 1942), it was postulated that regulation was achieved through a multifactor auxin reaction system in which proper balance between components would permit growth, and imbalance would depress or alter the pattern of growth. The search for components of such a system led to a demonstration of positive influences of phosphate, iron, carbohydrate, and adenine or adenosine levels on tissue growth and organ formation (Skoog, 1950; Skoog and Tsui, 1948, 1951) and eventually to the discovery of kinetin, which in turn led to the discovery of still more potent natural and synthetic N^6-substituted adenine derivatives.

Lateral buds in leaf axils of both intact and decapitated *Phaseolus* plants treated with IAA were released from apical dominance as expected with kinetin solution supplied through immersed leaf blades, debladed petioles, or the base of cut shoots (Schmid 1960).

Thimann and Wickson (1957; Wickson and Thimann, 1956, 1960) demonstrated the effectiveness of cytokinin application directly to lateral buds in *Pisum* in releasing them from apical dominance and showed that lateral buds of excised *Pisum* stem segments floated on a kinetin solution were similarly released whether the inhibition derived from the terminal buds on apical segments or from exogenous IAA in decapitated segments. They found that in the presence of the terminal bud, lateral buds released by cytokinin treatment would cease to grow unless they were subsequently provided with additional growth factors. Both auxin and gibberellin appeared to be required for their continued development. Similar positive effects of these hormones were reported by Davidson (1971) and others. However, in experiments with *Nicotiana glauca* (Engelbrecht, 1967), the lateral bud, in a leaf axil supplied with a high dosage of zeatin or ribosylzeatin alone, completely suppressed growth of the main axis and soon replaced it as the dominant shoot.

Studies by Davidson (1971) demonstrated a clear-cut quantitative relationship between the cytokinin dosage applied to lateral buds in peas and their subsequent rate of development and effectiveness in suppressing growth of the terminal shoot. The first observed effect was a rise in extractable auxin (IAA) from cytokinin-treated buds, detectable one to a few hours after treatment, and this further increased long before the onset of growth. At the same time, auxin production in the terminal buds decreased gradually until both growth and auxin production were completely suppressed by laterals which developed into main shoots. These results are in agreement with earlier evidence that the rate and location of auxin biosynthesis are important in correlation phenomena. In peas, the terminal bud suppressed auxin biosynthesis in inhibited lateral buds (Thimann and Skoog, 1934), as did IAA supplied to the cut surface of decapitated plants (F. Skoog, unpublished). In decapitated plants not supplied with IAA, all lateral buds started to produce auxin, but usually only one bud attained the level typical of the terminal bud. As it developed into a new shoot, it suppressed auxin production in the other laterals and stopped their growth.

That exogenous cytokinins promote auxin biosynthesis has been demonstrated in coleoptiles of derooted seedlings where it also restores the growth rate to the same level as in coleoptiles of intact seedlings (Jordan and Skoog, 1971). High exogenous cytokinin concentrations also induced auxin (IAA) synthesis to meet the requirements for growth of tobacco callus cultures (Jordan, 1971), and this regulation of IAA synthesis persisted indefinitely (2 years) in subcultures (Yamada, 1900) supplied with kinetin, as did cytokinin-regulated *de novo* synthesis of thiamine (Digby and Skoog, 1966; Dravnieks *et al.*, 1969; Dravnieks, 1971; Linsmaier-Bednar and Skoog, 1967).

It may be assumed, therefore, that a primary function of cytokinins in releasing buds from apical dominance is to promote synthesis of auxin and other growth factors. The facts that cytokinins applied to the terminal bud enhance its growth and apical dominance and that auxins and/or gibberellins applied to lateral buds after release by cytokinins enhance their development are consistent with this interpretation.

The influence of cytokinins in promoting growth of lateral buds and branching may include effects on mobilization of nutrients and assimilation products to growing points, a function of cytokinins which has been demonstrated in excised leaves (Mothes and Engelbrecht, 1961) and in decapitated plants (Pozsár and Kiraly, 1966). In this function the effectiveness of cytokinins may be augmented by the development of vascular connections between the stem and lateral buds, which occurs after a few days, i.e., long after the buds have been released from apical dominance either by decapitation (Work, 1950) or application of cytokinin (Davidson, 1971). This change in anatomy has been invoked repeatedly as a primary cause of the release of buds from apical dominance, since it was proposed by Moreland (1934), but it obviously cannot account for a shift in dominance which includes repression of growth of the terminal shoot by a lateral bud treated with cytokinin.

Attempts have been made to relate light intensities (Jackson and Field, 1972) and photoperiods (Tucker and Mansfield, 1972), which affect apical dominance in *Phaseolus* and *Xanthium*, respectively, to effects on endogenous hormone levels. But such analyses and their interpretation are difficult. Recent studies and reviews (Phillips, 1969, 1975) have stressed the importance of inhibitors and growth factors other than auxin as principal agents in correlative inhibition of lateral buds. Inasmuch as the development of lateral buds involves growth, it is clear that any factor which promotes or inhibits growth will also be involved in bud development and might conceivably become a limiting factor. For example, the phosphate concentration was shown to be limiting for the formation of buds in callus tissues supplied with certain relatively high concentrations of auxin and cytokinin (La Motte, 1960; Skoog, 1971), but this does not detract from the primary role of auxins in imposing and sustaining, and of cytokinins in abolishing, apical dominance. That these two hormones do in fact play the major roles in growth correlation phenomena is strikingly illustrated by false broom rape in tobacco, a disease involving excessive bud development from the root system. The disease has become prevalent with the use of chemicals which eliminate buds and lateral shoots in topped plants in the field. It can be induced experimentally by application of cytokinin to the root systems of normal plants, and it can be cured by application of auxin to the debudded stems (Hamilton *et al.*, 1972).

G. Rest Period of Buds and Dormancy and Germination of Seeds

Cytokinins function in triggering bud development in bulbs and seeds (Rakhimbaer and Solomina, 1975; Hussey, 1976), and have been shown to break the rest period of buds in some perennials. In the latter case, ABA and other inhibitors, rather than apical dominance, are principal causal agents, and their effects may be counteracted by cytokinin treatment. Cytokinins also counteract the effect of ABA in the regulation of stomatal opening and transpiration, and water transport can also be a factor in breaking the rest period of buds (F. Skoog, unpublished). In studies of changes in hormone content associated with the breaking of dormancy, Domanski and Kozlowski (1968) found a sharp rise in cytokinin activity associated with bud release in birch and aspen, and Dumbroff and Brown (1976) measured a peak of cytokinin activity in lateral roots of sugar maple just prior to bud break.

Plants have developed complex mechanisms, including both physical and chemical barriers, to regulate seed germination. Wareing and Saunders (1971) have reviewed the role of hormones in dormancy of buds and seeds. In cases where mechanical factors are involved in seed dormancy, exogenously supplied cytokinins may overcome it merely by promoting expansion of the cotyledons. In other cases, the applied cytokinins may help to counteract the effect of endogenous ABA or other inhibitors. Lettuce seed germination has been the subject of numerous studies which will be summarized briefly with special reference to cytokinin effects, but interactions of ethylene, gibberellic acid, ABA, and temperature, as well as of light, are involved.

Haber and Tolbert (1959) showed that the relative effectiveness of kinetin and gibberellic acid in promoting germination of light-sensitive lettuce seed depended on the temperature. Either hormone was extremely effective at moderate temperatures of 22° and 27°, but only kinetin was effective at 35° and only gibberellic acid at 7°. Similarly, Reynolds and Thompson (1973) found that kinetin was effective in overcoming high temperature-induced dormancy in the lettuce cultivar Arctic King. Keys *et al.* (1975) reported that in the case of thermodormancy of the cultivar Mesa, gibberellic acid, CO_2, and ethylene could completely reverse inhibition in the light, but that kinetin was also required in the dark. Miller (1956) found that kinetin greatly reduced but did not eliminate the light requirement for Grand Rapids seed germination, and Poggi-Pellegrini and Bulard (1976) reported that in order for kinetin to overcome ABA-induced dormancy in seed of this variety, either red light or gibberellic acid must be supplied. Khan and co-workers (Khan and Tolbert, 1965; Khan, 1968; Rao *et al.*, 1975, 1976), also using the cultivar Grand Rapids, have concluded that kinetin promotes germination by counteracting ABA and by enhancing polyribosome formation. Black, Bewley, and co-workers (Bewley and Fountain, 1972; Black *et al.*, 1974; Durley *et al.*, 1976; Fountain and Bewley, 1976) concluded from detailed studies of Grand Rapids lettuce seed germination that cytokinin, gibberellic acid, and ABA interact and control germination through modulation of protein synthesis. Dunlap and Morgan (1977) recently reported that the dormancy of the cultivar Premier Great Lakes could be induced by high temperature, ABA, or mannitol. Ethylene, kinetin, and gibberellic acid all tended to release the dormancy, and the presence of kinetin in addition to the other promoters was required at temperatures above 36°. Kinetin alone was effective in counteracting ABA or osmotic inhibition, but ethylene required the presence of gibberellic acid to be effective.

H. REPRODUCTIVE DEVELOPMENT

There is no evidence that cytokinins trigger reproductive development, i.e., floral induction, but there is much evidence that they participate in the subsequent process of flower formation. Bernier and co-workers (1977) have shown that in *Sinapis* transition from vegetative to floral buds starts with a wave of mitosis through the growing point. This wave could also be induced by cytokinin application, but it was not then followed by floral development. They suggested that cytokinin functions as a component of the "florigen complex." Cytokinins applied to the tips of tendrils excised from grape induced the formation of inflorescences (Srinivasan and Mullins, 1978) and increased the number of flowers per inflorescence formed on excised tobacco stem segments (Wardell and Skoog, 1969). In both cases the effect was on floral expression in tissue already in the reproductive phase, and the effect may have been primarily on branching, through release of apical dominance.

This interpretation was given for the increase in number of flowers found in *Bryophyllum* inflorescences treated with kinetin at an early stage (Catarino, 1964). Maturation of excised floral organs of tobacco has been achieved on media containing kinetin, but the organs did not elongate fully (Hicks and Sussex, 1970). Young grape inflorescences which would have produced only staminate flowers produced hermaphroditic or pistillate flowers after being dipped into cytokinin solutions (Hashizume and Iizuka, 1971; Negi and Olmo, 1966, 1972). This effect on sex does not hold for all species; Hugel (1976) found that, although cytokinin was required for the growth of excised floral primordia of two *Lemna* species, *L. paucifolia* and *L. gibba*, ethylene was required for pistillate and gibberellic acid for staminate flower development. Hugel suggested that the photoperiod regulates morphogenesis in this species by control of endogenous hormone production. Cytokinin also promotes floral development by the prevention of abscission under long-day conditions of certain varieties of *Phaseolus vulgaris*, presumably by counteracting high levels of ABA (Bentley *et al.*, 1975).

It has been proposed that cytokinins are required for fruit development especially in the early stages (Van Overbeek, 1968). Cytokinin promotes the *in vitro* formation of fruits from excised flowers (Tepfer *et al.*, 1966) and may markedly increase the number of carpels (Bilderback, 1972). Cytokinin applications to developing fruits on intact plants may increase the size of the fruit, as in the case of grapes (Van Overbeek and Loeffler, 1961), and may alter the shape of the fruit, as in the case of apples (Letham, private communication).

Parthenocarpic fruit development has been achieved by cytokinin application in relatively few cases, which include a species of fig (Crane and Van Overbeek, 1965); in most cases, auxin or gibberellic acid is required, but cytokinin may increase the effectiveness of these hormones.

III. CHEMISTRY AND STRUCTURE–ACTIVITY RELATIONSHIPS

A. METHODS OF CHEMICAL SYNTHESIS

Much of what is now known about cytokinin function is based on research utilizing synthetic cytokinins and cytokinin analogs. Excellent reviews of synthetic procedures have been presented by Grimm *et al.* (1968) and by Leonard (1974).

The synthesis of N^6-substituted adenine is usually accomplished by the displacement of a chloro, methylthio, or methylsulfonyl group in the 6 position of purine with the appropriate amine at reflux in ethanol or 1-butanol. This method may also be used for the synthesis of 2- and/or 8-substituted, N^6-substituted adenine derivatives, because the chloro and methylsulfonyl groups are much more reactive at the 6 position than the same or a poorer leaving group at the 2 and/or 8 positions. For example, when 2,6-bismethyl-thiopurine is treated with excess 3-methyl-2-butenylamine, the product is 2-methylthio-6-isopentenylaminopurine. This product may then be ribosidated. Alternatively, the starting compound may be a ribofuranosyl derivative from which the desired product may be purified by chromatography, or the 2′, 3′, and 5′ positions may be protected by benzoylation during the condensation procedure followed by debenzoylation in methanolic ammonia and purification by chromatography. Both methods have been used in the synthesis of 6-(4-hydroxy-3-methyl-*trans*-2-butenylamino)-2-methyl-thio-9-β-D-ribofuranosylpurine. Syntheses of specific cytokinins will be found in the references cited in Table I and in the section on structure–activity relationships (Section III). Recently, a new synthesis utilizing isoprene for zeatin and zeatin derivatives has been reported (Ohsugi *et al.*, 1974).

Synthesis of the optical isomers of dihydrozeatin has been achieved in two laboratories by special procedures (Corse and Kuhnle, 1972; Matsubara *et al.*, 1977). The latter group earlier had reported the synthesis of the mixed isomers (Koshimizu *et al.*, 1967).

Synthesis of the steroisomers of zeatin posed special problems because of *cis–trans* isomerization of the intermediates. Zeatin had already been synthesized in 1964 (Shaw and Wilson, 1964), but not until 1971 was *cis*-zeatin selectively synthesized by the use of cyclic intermediates which would assure the correct sterochemistry of the product (Playtis and Leonard, 1971; Leonard *et al.*, 1971). Recently, the *cis* and *trans* isomers of 2-methylthiozeatin have been obtained by stereoselective synthesis utilizing an alternate pathway which involves the incorporation of the methylthio group in the final step, to simplify the preparation of intermediates (Vreman *et al.*, 1974).

Two series of cytokinin antagonists have been synthesized by lengthy procedures using a final step similar to that used for N^6-substituted adenines as described above (Hecht *et al.*, 1971b, 1975; Hecht and Werner, 1973; Skoog *et al.*, 1975; Hecht, 1978).

B. ADENINE DERIVATIVES

The cytokinin activity of synthetic chemicals or isolated natural products is assessed by ability to promote the growth (increase in fresh weight) of cytokinin-dependent tobacco callus or other suitable material such as soybean callus, as compared to a known cytokinin, usually kinetin or N^6-Δ^2-isopentenylaminopurine (i^6Ade) (Linsmaier and Skoog, 1965; Miller, 1968; Murashige and Skoog, 1962). Rapid assays, such as those based on ability to prevent senescence or to promote budding in moss protonemata or leaf axils of peas, may be of value for detection and screening purposes. They are less suitable for quantitative determinations, because the relative activities of a series of compounds may vary considerably in different assays or in the same type of assay utilizing different plant species. For example, Letham (1967) found that kinetin was much more active than zeatin in a senescence assay, although the reverse was true in four other assays. Tahbaz (1977) compared the activities of 18 N^6-substituted adenine and adenosine derivatives in three assays (based on increase in area, fresh weight, and chlorophyll content) utilizing cucumber cotyledons, and found some marked differences within the assays as well as between any of these assays and the tobacco bioassay. Kuhnle *et al.* (1977) found ms^2i^6Ade (which has very low activity in the tobacco bioassay) to be more active than any of 15 other naturally occurring compounds in a senescence assay; fr^6Ade and bzl^6Ade were also very active. Even in assays based on cell division and growth of callus there may be marked differences between species, as in the case of two species of *Phaseolus* (Mok *et al.*, 1978). Differences in activity may reflect differences in the ability of given compounds to react with certain cell components and/or differences in their ability to resist degradation, for example by cytokinin oxidase. Thus it is desirable that assessment of relative activities be based on results obtained with a standard bioassay such as the tobacco bioassay.

Comparative studies have been carried out with several series of suitably modified adenine derivatives and adenine analogs. The results show that high potency (activity in the 10^{-11}–10^{-9} M range) is limited to adenine derivatives with N^6 substituents of restricted size and structure. However, many less potent cytokinins (active in the 10^{-9}–10^{-5} M range), as measured in terms of minimum concentration required for detectable activity, may be highly effective in terms of the total yield of tissue produced in response to an optimum supply of the chemical, and some weak cytokinins which cannot bring about a full response in terms of yield still elicit definite responses in high concentrations (10^{-5}–10^{-3} M range). Furthermore, certain additionally modified N^6-adenine derivatives are active down to $10^{-11} M$. Thus, the specific activities of cytokinins cover an extraordinary range of 9 orders of magnitude.

1. N^6 Side Chain Requirements

The isopentenyl group of i^6Ade may be said to be the parent side chain of high-potency cytokinins, conferring about 10 times higher activity than an isopentyl or *n*-pentyl group. The *n*-butyl or *n*-hexyl groups are only slightly less effective than the *n*-pentyl, but activity decreases rapidly with any further change in length of the *n*-alkyl chain, diminishing about 10-fold for each C atom added or subtracted. The isopentenyl polymers geranyl and farnesyl are moderately effective as N^6 substituents (Skoog *et al.*, 1967), probably because they may be readily metabolized to a shorter chain length, and/or possibly because they are unsaturated.

The structure of zeatin, 6-(4-hydroxy-3-methyl-*trans*-2-butenylamino)purine (*t*-io⁶Ade), the most potent natural cytokinin, incorporates the most effective characteristics in the side chain, i.e., an isopentenyl group unsaturated in the 2-position with a hydroxylated, terminal, *trans* methyl group. The following modifications of this side chain lower but do not completely eliminate cytokinin activity: a shift in the position of the hydroxyl group or the addition of more hydroxyl groups (with saturation of the side chain); a shift in the position of the double bond with or without loss of branching; a shift in the position of the methyl group; or, as indicated above, any change in chain length. Naturally occurring compounds incorporating such modifications are: *cis*-zeatin, which is ca. 50 times less active than zeatin (Vreman *et al.*, 1974), and dihydrozeatin, which is about 4 times less active (Schmitz *et al.*, 1972). It is of interest that the (+) optical isomer of dihydrozeatin is more active than the (−) isomer (Matsubara *et al.*, 1977; J. Corse and R. Y. Schmitz, unpublished).

For further reference to studies of compounds which incorporate the above-described side chain modifications, see Fawcett and Wright (1968), Kuraishi (1959), Leonard *et al.* (1968, 1969); Letham (1972), Rothwell and Wright (1967), Schmitz *et al.*, (1972), Shaw *et al.* (1971), and Skoog *et al.* (1967).

Cyclic N^6 side chains, may also confer high cytokinin activity as evidenced by kinetin (so far found in nature only as a degradation product of DNA) and bzl⁶Ade, a synthetic cytokinin. Saturation of the benzyl or furfuryl groups, reduction in ring size or increase to a bicyclic moiety, and elimination or lengthening of the carbon bridge all lower activity (Kuraishi, 1959; Skoog *et al.*, 1967). Substitution on the benzene ring usually lowers activity, being most detrimental when done in the *para* and least in the *ortho* position, as judged from tests of the methyl-, amino-, nitro-, hydroxy-, methoxy-, and chloro-benzyl adenine series (Kuraishi, 1959). It is of interest that N^6-(*o*-hydroxybenzyl)adenine has been recently identified as one of the constituents responsible for high cytokinin activity in extracts of poplar leaves (Horgan *et al.*, 1975) and that N^6-(*o*-chlorobenzyl)adenine was actually more active than bzl⁶Ade itself in a leaf disc expansion assay (Kuraishi, 1959).

The extent to which effects of $N^6,O^{2'}$-dibutyryladenosine-3',5'-monophosphate (DBcAMP), particularly its effects on motility and aggregation of animal cells, may be traced to cAMP activity as claimed, rather than to cytokinin activity conferred by its N^6-substituent, has been questioned (Johnson *et al.*, 1974). This compound has been used to test the activity of cAMP in a number of animal studies, but it should be noted that it has been shown to be an active cytokinin itself (Dekhuijzen and Overeem, 1972; Letham *et al.*, 1972), and other acylaminopurines have also been shown to have high cytokinin activity (Dekhuijzen and Overeem, 1972; Letham *et al.*, 1972; Martin *et al.*, 1973). Therefore, DBcAMP is not a suitable substance to use for the assessment of cAMP activity.

The cytokinin activity of ureidopurines is of interest not only because they are acylaminopurines, but more importantly because of their structural relationship to diphenylurea and its derivatives which have been shown to possess growth-promoting activity (Bruce and Zwar, 1966) and because of the presence of *N*-(purin-6-ylcarbamoyl)threonine adjacent to the anticodon in certain tRNA's (Chheda *et al.*, 1969; Schweizer *et al.*, 1970; Ishikura *et al.*, 1969). The most active member of a series of ureidopurines was 6-phenyl-ureidopurine, and this was 1/10 as active as bzl⁶Ade (McDonald *et al.*, 1971).

2. Essentiality of the N^6 Atom for Cytokinin Activity

The ability of carbon, oxygen, or sulfur to substitute for the exocyclic nitrogen atom of cytokinin-active adenine derivatives has been tested with two series of compounds incorporating either the isopentenyl or the benzyl side chain (Henderson *et al.*, 1975). Most of these derivatives proved to be very effective cytokinins, but the effect of the substituted atoms depended to some extent on the nature of the side chain. For instance, in the oxy series, 6-benzyloxypurine was nearly as active as bzl⁶Ade, but 6-isopentenyloxy-purine had very low activity; in contrast, in the thio series, the isopentenyl derivative was much more active than the benzyl derivative.

3. Effect of Additional Substituents on the Adenine Ring

Natural cytokinins may occur as ribonucleosides and ribonucleotides and also as free bases. A ribose moiety in the 9 position of N⁶-substitued adenine usually leads to an approximately 10-fold loss of activity. The mono-, di-, and triphosphates of kinetin riboside showed decreasing activity in that order, but all effectively promoted the growth of tobacco callus (von Saltza, 1958). A noncyclic 5'-monophosphate group did not affect the activity of i⁶Ado or bzl⁶Ado, but a 3',5'-cyclic monophosphate group lowered activity by a factor of 3, and DBcAMP was at least 100 times less active than these nucleotides (Schmitz *et al.*, 1975). cAMP itself had no detectable activity in these tests. These results are counter to the proposition that a high level of cAMP in plant tissues, resulting from inhibition of phosphodiesterases by "cyto-kinesins," regulates cell division (Wood *et al.*, 1972; Wood and Braun, 1973).

Other 9-substituted derivatives of cytokinin-active adenine derivatives have been synthesized and tested. Van Overbeek claimed that 6-benzyl-amino-9-tetrahydropyranylpurine (SD8339) is more readily transported than bzl^{6}Ade in tissues, and is therefore more active in senescence tests (Weaver and Van Overbeek, 1963). However, SD8339 is less active than bzl^{6}Ade in the tobacco bioassay. In tests designed to determine whether ribosidation in the 9 position is a prerequisite for cytokinin activity, m^{9}bzl^{6}Ade was assayed and found to be fairly active (Kende and Tavares, 1968). However, the 9-methyl group has been shown to be rapidly metabolized (Fox *et al.*, 1971). For this reason the 9-deaza-8aza analog of bzl^{6}Ade and its derivatives with methyl or ribosyl groups attached to the C atom replacing nitrogen in the 9-position of purine (so that these groups would be held by a stable C—C bond) were prepared (Hecht *et al.*, 1971b). As compared with bzl^{6}Ade, the analog and its methyl and ribosyl derivatives had definite but much reduced cytokinin activity, decreasing in the order stated. Hence it was concluded that ribosidation of adenine is not a requirement for cytokinin activity.

Substituents in the 2 position have been of particular interest, for the 2-methylthio derivatives of i^{6}Ade and zeatin occur naturally. A series of 2-chloro, 2-amino, 2-hydroxy, and 2-methylthio derivatives of i^{6}Ade, i^{6}Ado, and zeatin were compared for activity (Hecht *et al.*, 1970b). With regard to the bases, the methylthio and amino groups moderately and the hydroxy group markedly lowered activity, while the chloro group had no measurable effect on i^{6}Ade and actually slightly raised the activity of zeatin. Substitutions on i^{6}Ado lowered its activity slightly. It is of interest that of 20 cytokinins tried in an antisenescence test, ms^{2}i^{6}Ade was the most active but, as the authors stated, "Structure–activity relationships for chlorophyll retention did not parallel many of the relationships found for callus tissue growth stimulation" (Kuhnle *et al.*, 1977).

Because cytokinin-active adenine derivatives substituted in the 8 position are also likely candidates for natural occurrence, 18 derivatives of i^{6}Ade substituted in the 2, 8, or 2 and 8 positions with one of the following groups have been tested: methyl, chloro, sulfhydryl, methylthio, methylsulfonyl, and benzylthio (Dammann *et al.*, 1974). Each of the three members of the methyl-, methylthio-, and chloro-substituted series was highly active, the 8-substituted compound being the most active in each case, and in fact m^{8}i^{6}Ade was slightly more active than i^{6}Ade itself. This is in agreement with the earlier report of higher activity for 8-methylkinetin and 8-methyl-benzylaminopurine than for kinetin itself in a leaf senescence test (Kulaeva *et al.*, 1968). It is also consistent with the finding that 8-bromo derivatives of adenine, adenosine, and cAMP were weakly active as cytokinins at concentrations of 20 μM, whereas the parent compounds were inactive even at much higher concentrations (Schmitz *et al.*, 1975). Dammann *et al.* also found that disubstitution with the sulfhydryl group, which exists mainly as a ketonic tautomer, sharply lowered activity. The very weak activity of the disubstituted benzylthio and methylsulfonyl derivatives has been ascribed to their bulkiness and also to the electronegativity of the latter group. The methylsulfonyl series differed from all others in that the 8-substituted was less active than the 2-substituted derivative. It appears that the effect of these groups on cytokinin activity is primarily related to their electron-attracting properties but is also affected by their bulk. Chen *et al.* (1975) reported that the 8-hydroxy derivatives of zeatin and i[6]Ade were only slightly less active than the parent compounds, but that the 2,8-dihydroxy derivatives had much lower activity, in fact even lower than that of the corresponding 2-hydroxy compounds as reported by Hecht *et al.* (1970b).

4. Integrity of the Adenine Structure

As can be seen from the data in Table II, substitution of a C atom for any of the N atoms in the purine ring decreases but does not abolish the activity of cytokinin molecules. Rogozinska *et al.* (1973) assayed the 1-deaza and 3-deaza analogs of i[6]Ade and kinetin; the loss of N in the 1 position did not lower activity nearly so much as its loss in the 3 position. Hecht *et al.* (1975) found that loss of the N-7 atom of i[6]Ade had nearly as drastic an effect as that reported for loss of N-3. We are not aware of any analogs of i[6]Ade or kinetin lacking N-9, but the 9-deaza analog of bzl[6]Ade is a weak cytokinin, somewhat less active than 3-deaza-i[6]Ade or 3-deaza kinetin (Sugiyama *et al.*, 1977).

The effect of loss of more than one N atom has been determined for three bzl[6]Ade analogs: The 1,3-deaza analog was weakly active, the 1,3,7-deaza was very weakly active, and the 1,3,9-deaza was inactive (Torigoe *et al.*, 1972).

Analogs in which carbon atoms in the purine ring have been replaced by nitrogen atoms, i.e., aza analogs, also show loss in activity as compared to the parent compounds. Reports by Steward that 8-aza-kinetin had equal or higher activity than kinetin itself (Steward *et al.*, 1961) were not supported by adequate experimental data and have not been confirmed. When 8-aza-bzl[6]Ade, 8-aza-kinetin (Skoog *et al.*, 1967), and 8-aza-i[6]Ade (R. Y. Schmitz, unpublished) were tested in serial concentrations covering their active ranges, each of these compounds was less than 1/10 as active as its parent compound.

A number of analogs combining aza and deaza modifications have been tested, and all of them retained some cytokinin activity. The activities of the 1-deaza and the 8-aza-1-deaza analogs of i[6]Ade and of kinetin were about equal, but interestingly, the 8-aza-3-deaza analogs were more active than the corresponding 3-deaza analogs, especially in the case of the i[6]Ade analogs (Rogozinska *et al.*, 1973). The 8-aza-7-deaza analog of i[6]Ade had about half the activity of the 8-aza-9-deaza analog (Hecht *et al.*, 1975), which was in turn about half as active as the 8-aza-3-deaza analog. Low cytokinin activity has also been reported for two 8-methylated, aza–deaza analogs, m[8]-4-aza-3-deaza-bzl[6]Ade and m[8]-4-aza-1,3-deaza-bzl[6]Ade (Torigoe *et al.*, 1972).

TABLE II

RING-MODIFIED ANALOGS OF i[6]Ade, fr[6]Ade, AND bzl[6]Ade:
ACTIVITY IN THE TOBACCO ASSAY

Ring

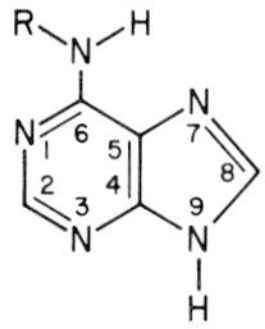

| Modifications | Side chain | | |
| | Isopentenyl | Furfuryl | Benzyl |
	Cytokinin activity[a] (μM)		
None	0.004[b]	0.003[c]	0.003[d]
1-Deaza	0.002[c]	0.04[c]	—
3-Deaza	1.0[c]	5.0[c]	—
7-Deaza	0.6[e]	—	—
9-Deaza	—	—	10.0[f]
1,3-Deaza	—	—	5.0[g]
1,3,7-Deaza	—	—	(Very weak)[g]
1,3,9-Deaza	—	—	(Inactive)[g]
8-Aza	0.009[h]	0.1[i]	0.01[i]
8-Aza-1-deaza	0.003[c]	0.4[c]	—
8-Aza-3-deaza	0.04[c]	1.0[c]	—
8-Aza-7-deaza	0.2[e]	—	—
8-Aza-9-deaza	0.09[e]	—	—
8-Me	—	—	—[j]
8-Me-4-aza-3-deaza	—	—	5.0[g]
8-Me-4-aza-1,3-deaza	—	—	5.0[g]

[a] Approximate minimum concentration at which growth starts to increase as a linear function of the log of concentration.

[b] From Schmitz *et al.*, 1975.

[c] From Rogozinska *et al.*, 1973.

[d] From McDonald *et al.*, 1971.

[e] From Hecht *et al.*, 1975.

[f] From Sugiyama *et al.*, 1977.

[g] From Torigoe *et al.*, 1972.

[h] From R. Y. Schmitz *et al.*, unpublished.

[i] From Skoog *et al.*, 1967.

[j] Very active in a senescence test; from Kulaeva *et al.*, 1968.

A total of 16 different 1-deaza-, 3-deaza-, and 1,3-deaza-2-aza analogs of assorted 6-acylaminopurines have been tested by Sugiyama *et al.* (1975). The difference in their side chain structures prevents strict comparisons of their activities with those of the above aza–deaza analogs, but the results are in agreement with the finding by Rogozinska *et al.* that loss in activity of the

3-deaza analogs is more drastic than for the 1-deaza analogs. The data of Rogozinska *et al.* indicate that the nature of the side chain affects the influence of ring substituents on activity. The sequence in order of activity found for the four kinetin analogs was the same as for the i^6Ade analogs, but the relative loss in activity was much greater for the kinetin series.

Even a modification as drastic as the expansion of the adenine nucleus to a tricyclic ring system does not necessarily destroy cytokinin activity, provided the product retains an appropriate spatial relationship between the side chain substituent and the ring system. A series of benzologs (i.e., stretched-out analogs formed by insertion of a benzyl ring between the pyrimidine and imidazole rings of i^6Ade and bzl^{6}Ade), were compared in the tobacco bioassay (Sprecker *et al.*, 1976). Of the three possible position isomers relating to the attachment of the imidazole ring, the linear analogs were effective as cytokinins at concentrations ca. 10^{-6} M as compared with ca. 10^{-9} M for the parent compounds. The distal and proximal analogs of i^6Ade were also weakly active, starting at ca. $10^{-5} M$, but the corresponding bzl^{6}Ade analogs were inactive at these concentrations.

Studies of structure–activity relationships of cytokinin-active molecules have failed to reveal their possession of any one specific structural property or chemical reactivity responsible for biological activity. Instead, it appears that the overall properties of the molecules, their configuration, size, charge, etc. determine their ability to function in a reactive system. A structural change in one part of a molecule may drastically affect or completely remove biological activity, but this effect may be modified or counteracted by concomitant structural changes in other parts of the molecule. The integrated properties of the molecule as a whole finally determine its capacity to function as a cytokinin.

C. Cytokinin Antagonists

In the work so far discussed alterations in the adenine ring have resulted in more or less severe loss in activity, but none of the above alterations were reported to have resulted in the development of cytokinin antagonist activity. Recent studies have shown that when certain alterations of the imidazo portion of the adenine nucleus are combined with certain modifications in the N^6 side chain and substitution at the 9 and/or other positions, cytokinin antagonist activity can be achieved (Hecht, 1978; Skoog *et al.*, 1973). The loss in cytokinin activity associated with successive steps in the modification of i^6Ade to 3-methyl-7-(3-methylbutylamino)pyrazolo[4,3-*d*]-pyrimidine, the first effective cytokinin antagonist to be developed (Hecht *et al.*, 1971a), is strikingly shown in Fig 2. All three changes—i.e., 9-deaza-8-

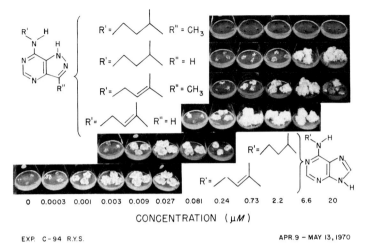

0   0.0003   0.001   0.003   0.009   0.027   0.081   0.24   0.73   2.2   6.6   20

CONCENTRATION (μM)

EXP. C-94 R.Y.S.   APR.9 – MAY 13,1970

FIG. 2. Steps in the conversion of i⁶Ade to a cytokinin antagonist and associated loss in cytokinin activity. From Skoog *et al.*, 1973.

aza modification, substitution on the inserted C atom, and saturation of the side chain—were required for the transformation to an effective cytokinin antagonist. In all, 14 pyrazolo[4,3-*d*]pyrimidine analogs with different side chains were synthesized and compared. Most effective were the *n*-pentyl, *n*-hexyl, and isopentyl derivatives.

The pyrazolo[4,3-*d*]pyrimidines, although effective antagonists, have the disadvantage of becoming toxic at concentrations as low as 2 μ M. For this reason, and in order to further define the structural features which determine cytokinin vs. antagonist activity, other series of analogs were synthesized and tested. By far the most effective to date have been 4-substituted 2-methylthiopyrrolo[2,3-*d*]pyrimidines, or 7-deaza analogs of 6-substituted 2-methylthio adenines (Skoog *et al.*, 1975). The activities of 11 pyrrolo-pyrimidines are given in Table III. The effectiveness of one of these, the cyclohexylamino derivative (compound 9 in Table III), in inhibiting growth of tobacco tissue, and the reversal of the effect by i⁶Ade, are shown in Fig. 3. One key feature in conferring antagonist activity in this series appears to be the 2-methylthio group; even in the presence of the isopentenyl or benzyl side chain, 2-methylthio analogs were effective anticytokinins. The most effective side chain in this series, however, was the cyclopentyl group. The pyrrolo[2,3-*d*]pyrimidines were more specific in their anticytokinin activity than the pyrazolo[4,3-*d*]pyrimidines, inhibiting the growth of tobacco callus at concentrations up to 20 μ M without evidence of toxicity.

The pyrrolo[2,3-*d*]pyrimidine cytokinin antagonists had the unexpected synergistic effect of increasing the effectiveness of high cytokinin concentra-

TABLE III

BIOLOGICAL ACTIVITY OF SUBSTITUTED 4-AMINOPYRROLO[2,3-d]PYRIMIDINES[a]

Compound no.	R	R'	R''	R'''	Range of conc. tested	Cytokinin activity min. conc. (μM) for		Growth inhibition min. conc. (μM) for	
						Detection	Maximum growth	Detection	Complete inhibition[d]
1		H	H	H	0.24–20	0.62	6.6	N.A.	—
2	H	H	H	H	0.24–20	5.8	>20	N.A.	—
3		SCH$_3$	H	H	0.24–20	N.A.[b]	—	N.A.	—
4		SCH$_3$	H	H	0.009–20	N.A.	—	0.24	2.2
5		SCH$_3$	H	H	0.027–20	N.A.	—	0.40	2.0
6		SCH$_3$	H	H	0.08–20	N.A.	—	0.1	1
7		SCH$_3$	H	H	0.009–20	N.A.	—	0.009	0.05
8		SCH$_3$	H	H	0.24–20	N.A.	—	6.6	>20
9		SCH$_3$	H	H	0.003–20	N.A.	—	0.05	0.60
10		SCH$_3$	H	H	0.24–20	N.A.	—	10	>20
11		H	CN	SCH$_3$	0.24–20	N.A.	—	20	N.R.[c]

[a] From Skoog et al., 1975.
[b] N.A. = not active.
[c] N.R. = not reached.
[d] In presence of 0.003 μM i^{6}Ade.

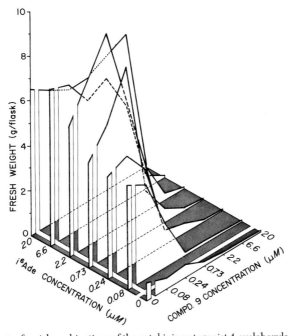

FIG. 3 Effects of serial combinations of the cytokinin antagonist 4-cyclohexylamino-2-methyl-thiopyrrolo [2,3-*d*]pyrimidine (compound 9, Table III) and i⁶Ade on fresh weight yield of tobacco callus. (Tested 12/6/74 to 1/10/75). From Skoog *et al.*, 1975.

tions in promoting bud formation in tobacco tissue cultures (Skoog *et al.*, 1975). For example, in Fig. 3, tissues in the five treatments with 20 μM i⁶Ade and 0.08–6.6 μM antagonist and in the two treatments with 2.2 or 6.6 μM each i⁶Ade and antagonist all formed buds, whereas none of the controls lacking antagonist differentiated. One possible conclusion from this interesting dual effect of the antagonists, also suggested by other evidence, is that cytokinin action in growth promotion and bud formation is exerted at separate sites.

Iwamura *et al.* (1974, 1976) have tested the anticytokinin activity of 4-alkylamino-7-(β-D-ribofuranosyl)pyrrolo[2,3-*d*]pyrimidines against kinetin, rather than i⁶Ade, in the tobacco bioassay. These tests thus are not strictly comparable to those described above. The results show that these chemicals may be growth inhibitory and toxic to the tissue, but the data do not support the conclusion that they are effective cytokinin antagonists.

Inhibition of growth has been obtained with certain substituted 7-deaza-8-aza adenine derivatives, i.e., by derivatives of 4-aminopyrazolo[3,4-*d*]pyrimidine (Hecht *et al.*, 1975), but this likewise appeared to be a case of general inhibition, in which the parent compound was almost as effective as its derivatives, and which could not be counteracted specifically by cytokinins.

Because the 2-methylthio group so effectively conferred anticytokinin activity on pyrrolo[2,3-*d*]pyrimidine derivatives, it was inserted in the corresponding position of a cytokinin-active and of an antagonist-active pyrazolo[4,3-*d*]pyrimidine:3-methyl-7-(3-methyl-2-butenylamino)-5-methyl-thiopyrazolo[4,3-*d*]pyridine and 3-methyl-5-methylthio-7-*n*-pentylamino-pyrazolo[4,3-*d*]pyrimidine, respectively(Hecht *et al.*, 1975). The effect was to slightly lower the activity of the cytokinin and, in contrast, to convert the antagonist into a weak cytokinin.

The results of analog testing thus strikingly confirm the conclusion drawn from cytokinin testing, that the overall combination of structural features rather than any single feature determines the biological activity of cytokinins.

D. Phenylurea and Derivatives

The demonstrated activity of *N,N'*-diphenylurea in promoting cell division in carrot tissue cultures (Steward and Shantz, 1956) has led to extensive testing for growth-promoting action of urea derivatives in various assay systems including tobacco callus cultures. Comparative studies of ca. 400 derivatives have shown that the R—NH—CO—NH moiety (where R is phenyl or other cyclic group and S may be substituted for O) is required for biological activity (Bruce and Zwar, 1966). Diphenylurea is 1000-fold less active than i^6Ade in the tobacco assay, but it can be used as a substitute for N^6-adenine derivatives to meet the cytokinin requirement for growth in tobacco callus. Tobacco tissue apparently adapts to utilize it more effectively in successive subcultures.

Diphenylurea is without activity in the soybean callus bioassay for cytokinins (Dyson *et al.*, 1972), a fact which has been used as evidence for the proposition that it must be metabolized before it is effective. Burrows and Leworthy (1976) have identified the major metabolite of radioactive diphenylurea supplied to tobacco callus as the *O*-β-D-glucoside. In this compound 17% of the radioactivity was recovered, but it was much less active than diphenylurea itself in promoting growth of tobacco callus, and was also inactive in soybean callus. It, therefore, was not the sought-after active metabolite. The possibility that diphenylurea might react with adenine in tissue to form 6-phenyladenine and/or 6-phenylureidopurine, both of which are moderately active cytokinins (McDonald *et al.*, 1971), has been examined but so far there have been no positive results (Burrows, 1976). It is of interest in this connection that 6-threonylcarbamoylpurine occurs naturally as the modified adenine nucleotide next to the 3' end of the anticodon in certain tRNA species responding to codons starting with the letter A. In the case of *E. coli* such modified tRNA species have been identified for all amino acids, except fMet and Arg, responding to codons of the "first letter A" group in the genetic code (Nishimura *et al.*, 1972). The 6-threonylureidopurine itself is inactive in the tobacco bioassay, but in view of the ring requirement for growth promoting activity of urea derivatives, cited above, perhaps the compound with the threonine in one of its two known lactone forms should be tested. However, the structurally analogous 6-benzoylamino- and 6-furfuroylamino-purines have questionable or no cytokinin activity. It is clear that relationships between urea derivatives and N^6-adenines with reference to their growth promoting activities deserve further inquiry.

IV. METABOLISM OF CYTOKININS

Available evidence on cytokinin metabolism is limited. Probable pathways of biosynthesis and degradation of cytokinins are summarized in Fig. 4.

A. FREE CYTOKININS

1. Biosynthesis

Most investigations into the origins of cytokinins have dealt with their occurrence as constituents of tRNA. Cytokinin-active ribonucleosides and free bases are readily obtained *in vitro* by the hydrolysis of tRNA with selective nucleases and/or acid (Armstrong *et al.*, 1976a). It has been suggested that the naturally occurring free bases and ribosides arise from this source (Hall, 1973). The immediate precursor of the isopentenyl side chain of i^6Ade in tRNA has been shown to be Δ^2-isopentenylpyrophosphate (Δ^2iPP) (Fittler *et al.*, 1968; Kline *et al.*, 1969). An enzyme, IPP-tRNA isopentenyltransferase, which catalyses the transfer of the isopentenyl group to the appropriate unmodified adenine residue in preformed tRNA molecules, has been partially purified from yeast (Kline *et al.*, 1969) and *E. coli* (Bartz and Söll, 1972; Rosenbaum and Gefter, 1972; Zubay *et al.*, 1971). *In vivo* incorporation of radioactive mevalonic acid into tRNA to form the i^6Ade residue has been observed in *Lactobacillus acidophilus* (Fittler *et al.*, 1968; Peterkofsky, 1968; Peterkofsky and Jesensky, 1969) and in tobacco callus (Chen and Hall, 1969). In the tobacco callus, the radioactive isopentenyl side chain appeared exclusively in i^6Ade. In a more recent study (Murai *et al.*, 1975) carried out under different conditions, about 40% of the [^{14}C]-mevalonic acid label which was incorporated into tRNA in tobacco callus was

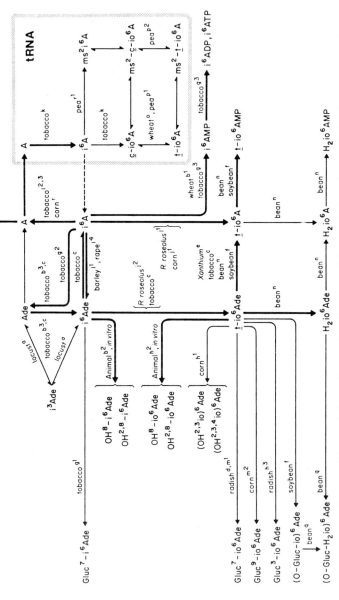

FIG. 4. Actual or possible metabolic pathways of cytokinin metabolism in higher plants and the plant-associated fungus *Rhizopogon roseolus*. References: a, Cavé *et al.*, 1962; b[1], Chen and Eckert, 1977; b[2], Chen *et al.*, 1975; b[3], Chen *et al.*, 1976a; c, Einset and Skoog, 1973; d, Gordon *et al.*, 1974; e, Henson and Wareing, 1977; f, Horgan, 1977; g[1], Laloue *et al.*, 1975; g[2], Laloue *et al.*, 1977a; g[3], Laloue *et al.*, 1977b; h[1], Letham, 1973; h[2], Letham *et al.*, 1967; h[3], Letham *et al.*, 1975; i, McLennon and Pater, 1973; j[1], Miura and Hall, 1973; j[2], Miura and Miller, 1969; k, Murai *et al.*, 1975; l[1], Pačes, 1976; l[2], Pačes and Kaminek, 1976; l[3], Pačes *et al.*, 1971; l[4], Pačes *et al.*, 1977; m[1], Parker and Letham, 1973; m[2], Parker and Letham, 1974; n, Sondheimer and Tzou, 1971; o, Taller *et al.*, 1977; p, Wang *et al.*, 1977; q, Whitty and Hall, 1974.

found to exist in the form of *cis*-zeatin, the major cytokinin-active species found in this preparation. The remainder of the ^{14}C-label in the tRNA apparently resulted from nonspecific incorporation of the products of [^{14}C]mevalonic acid metabolism.

The synthesis of io⁶Ade was demonstrated for the mycorrhizal fungus *Rhizopogon roseolus* by Miura and Miller (1969). Miura and Hall (1973) have since shown that both immature corn endosperm and the fungus can synthesize io⁶A from i⁶A, and suggest that this ready conversion accounts for the low or less than detectable levels of free i⁶Ade or i⁶A in plant extracts (Dyson and Hall, 1972). Because the io⁶A synthesized by the corn endosperm and fungus is in the *trans* configuration, tRNA presumably does not function as an intermediate. A cytokinin-autotrophic strain of tobacco callus has been shown to utilize radioactive Ade in the synthesis of free io⁶Ade, io⁶A, and i⁶Ade, as indicated by chromatographic evidence, whereas a cytokinin-dependent strain failed to produce detectable amounts of these compounds (Einset and Skoog, 1973).

The possibility that tRNA serves as an intermediate in the production of the free cytokinins and cytokinin ribonucleosides was not ruled out by this study, for the appearance of radioactive cytokinins was prevented by inhibitors of RNA synthesis. A report by Chen and Hall (1969) that mevalonic acid supplied to the nutrient medium of cytokinin-dependent tobacco tissue promotes growth and can satisfy the exogenous cytokinin requirement for this purpose could not be confirmed (McChesney, 1970; T. Murai and F. Skoog, unpublished). Recent studies suggest that alternate pathways of cytokinin biosynthesis do exist. Chen *et al.* (1976a) report that a cytokinin-autotrophic strain of tobacco tissue utilized a double-labeled glycerol analog, which apparently could not be incorporated into tRNA, to produce i⁶Ade. Taya *et al.* (1978) report that an enzyme preparation from *Dictyostelium discoides* produced i⁶Ade via i⁶AMP from IPP and AMP as the preferred substrate. cAMP, ADP, and ATP could serve as alternate substrates, but neither Ado nor Ade was utilized effectively in this system. Likely the same or a comparable system may function in other organisms. It should be noted that the presence of cAMP in higher plants, despite numerous reports, has not yet been unequivocally established.

The source of the methylthio group in ms²i⁶Ade and ms²io⁶Ade, which are constituents of certain tRNA's in microorganisms and green plants, is discussed below (Section V,D).

Small quantities of cytokinins are released by *in vitro* degradation of high molecular weight RNA (rRNA) preparations from wheat germ and *Pisum* (Taller *et al.*, 1977), but no information is available on the extent of this release *in vivo*.

The possibility that kinetin might be generated in living tissue under certain conditions is suggested by the work of Leonard and associates (Scopes *et al.*, 1976), who have demonstrated a possible intramolecular route for its genesis from 2'-deoxyadenylate units involving a head-to-tail transfer of deoxyribose from the 9 to the 3 position of the adenine nucleus via a cyclonucleoside, with subsequent elimination of the 1' and 3' polar groups, and $3 \rightarrow N^6$ intramolecular rearrangement leading to kinetin. The nature of the $3 \rightarrow N^6$ conversion was studied in detail by Leonard and Henderson (1975) using the conversion of $bzl^3 Ade$ to $bzl^6 Ade$ as a model. They showed that the rearrangement follows a contortional route involving opening and closing of both the pyrimidine and imidazole rings, during which the side chain does not leave its original nitrogen atom. The route of rearrangement was solved on the basis of synthesis of specifically ^{15}N-labeled $bzl^3 Ade$'s and comparison of the products of their autoclaving, by mass spectrometry and nmr $^{15}N-^1H$ coupling, with $bzl^6 Ade$'s specifically labeled with ^{15}N. The distribution of ^{15}N label in the products excluded a sequence of $N-3-\alpha-C$ solvolysis followed by $N^6-\alpha-C$ alkylation as a principal, even if not as a contributary, route of conversion.

This nonenzymatic pathway of cytokinin synthesis from nucleosides or other nucleic acid metabolites is of special interest as a ready-made mechanism for providing cell division factors for wound healing. Its effectiveness for this purpose may be greatly enhanced by the rapid, 10-fold increase in nuclease activity which occurs in wounded plant tissues (Sacher *et al.*, 1975) and possibly also by other factors.

2. *Occurrence*

The following are relatively rich sources of free cytokinins, particularly of zeatin and its derivatives: rapidly growing plant tissues such as young fruits including apples, plums, and corn endosperm (Letham and Miller, 1965; review by Kende, 1971); the mycorrhizal fungus *Rhizopogon roseolus* (Miura and Hall, 1973); and bacteria associated with overgrowths in plants (Cherayil and Lipsett, 1977; review by Greene 1977), and especially crown gall tissue (Miller, 1975). Earlier attempts to identify the cell division factor from the latter tissue led to the repeated claim for a separate class of "true cell division factors," cytokinesins, which are distinct from cytokinins (Wood and Braun, 1967; Wood *et al.*, 1969, 1972, 1974). With the demonstration of zeatin and its riboside (Miller, 1974, 1975) and of the corresponding glucosides (Peterson and Miller, 1976, 1977) in *Vinca rosea* crown gall tissue, and with evidence that ribosylzeatin is nearly inactive in promoting budding in *Funaria* (Whitaker and Kende, 1974; Spiess, 1975) (so that the bioassay used as a basis for the distinction is invalid), this claim no longer seems tenable in the absence of rigorous chemical identification of such compounds.

Dihydrozeatin has been found in young lupine seeds (Koshimizu *et al.*, 1967). It may well prove to be of more common occurrence, its glucoside having been isolated from poplar (Letham *et al.*, 1977) and bean (Wang *et al.*, 1977) leaves and its formation having been demonstrated in bean axes supplied with [8-^{14}C]-labeled zeatin (Sondheimer and Tzou, 1971). Immature sweet corn kernels yielded four adenine derivatives with highly modified side chains: 6-(3,4-dihydroxy- and 6-(2,3,4-trihydroxy-3-methylbutylamino)-purine; 6-(1-carboxy-2-hydroxypropylamino)-9-β-D-ribofuranosylpurine; and 6-(1,2-dicarboxyethylamino)-9-β-D-ribofuranosylpurine (Letham, 1973).

B. RIBONUCLEOSIDES

High levels of ribonucleosides are usually reported as early intermediates of cytokinin base metabolism. Henson and Wareing (1977) have correlated ribonucleoside levels with the physiological state of the plant tissue, reporting greater conversion of zeatin to zeatin ribonucleoside in senescing than in mature but still green leaves of *Xanthium pennsylvanicum*. Hordern *et al.* (1975) have isolated a nucleosidase from *Lactobacillus acidophilus* which rapidly converts i^{6}Ado to i^{6}Ade, and Pačes (1976) has demonstrated that barley leaves contain such an enzyme. This cleavage of i^{6}Ado was inhibited by io^{6}Ado, possibly by competition for the enzyme. Doree and Guern (1973) found no evidence of ribonucleosidase in *Acer* cell suspension cultures supplied with [8-^{14}C]kinetin or [8-^{14}C]bzl^{6}Ade, and they suggested that reported high concentrations of ribonucleosides might have resulted from phosphatase activity during lengthy extraction procedures.

C. RIBONUCLEOTIDES

There is ample evidence that exogenous cytokinin bases are converted to the corresponding 5'-nucleotides (McCalla *et al.*, 1962; Dyson *et al.*, 1972; Fox *et al.*, 1972; Gordon *et al.*, 1975; Parker and Letham, 1974; Horgan, 1977). Recently, there have been several reports that di- and triphosphates are also formed (Tzou *et al.*, 1973; Laloue *et al.*, 1974, 1977b). An adenosine kinase has been isolated from wheat germ which, although having the ability to phosphorylate Ade to AMP, ADP, and ATP, only forms the 5'-monophosphate i^{6}AMP from i^{6}Ade (Chen and Eckert, 1977). In a study of the phosphorylation of the riboside of i^{6}Ade, as compared to that of the base bzl^{6}Ade, by *Acer* cell suspension cultures, the following yields were reported: i^{6}AMP, 72%; i^{6}ADP and i^{6}ATP, 16%; and inosine-5'-nucleotide,

12% as compared to bzl⁶AMP, 28%; bzl⁶ADP and bzl⁶ATP, 6%; and remaining intact bzl⁶Ade; 30% (Laloue *et al.*, 1974).

D. Glucosylation

Numerous studies have revealed the presence of native cytokinin glucosides and/or have shown glucosides to be formed as primary metabolites of exogenous cytokinins. Loeffler and Van Overbeek (1964) first reported the isolation of two glycosides from radish seedlings which had been supplied with bzl⁶Ade, but the sugar moieties were not specified. Fox and co-workers (1972; Dyson *et al.*, 1972) found that the first products of bzl⁶Ade metabolism in soybean callus tissue were the ribonucleoside and ribonucleotide, but these soon declined in quantity and were no longer detectable after 120 hours. A more stable metabolite appeared within 4 hours, accounted for 20% of the labeled precursor by 48 hours, and was still present in quantity after 60 days. This metabolite was first reported as 6-benzylamino-7-glucofuranosylpurine (Deleuze *et al.*, 1972) but it has now been shown to have the pyranosyl conformation (Cowley *et al.*, 1975; Duke *et al.*, 1975). The labeled 7-glucoside was also produced by *Lupinus luteus* seedlings, potato tuber slices, and both autonomous and cytokinin-dependent tobacco callus tissues (Fox *et al.*, 1973). Fox and co-workers suggested that "the 7-glucoside alone of the BA [bzl⁶Ade] metabolites is protected from the action of the enzyme which degrades the bulk of the molecules by side chain cleavage, and the 7-glucoside may thus be the active form of cytokinin." The consensus now is rather that it is an inert storage form which can be reactivated as needed (Laloue, 1977; see also Van Staden and Papaphilippou, 1977). Letham and co-workers (Parker *et al.*, 1972; Parker and Letham, 1973) isolated the 7-glucoside of zeatin, which they named raphantin, from cotyledons of derooted radish seedlings which had been supplied with tritiated zeatin through the transpiration stream. The formation of this glucoside occurred in the cotyledons but not in the hypocotyl. As was shown later by Gordon *et al.* (1974), it also occurs in the roots.

Laloue and co-workers (1975, 1977a,b) report that cytokinin bases but not nucleosides are effectively glucosylated in the 7 position and suggest that this difference explains the higher growth promoting activity of the bases in bioassays. They found the absorption of i⁶Ade and i⁶Ado to be equally rapid in tobacco cell suspension cultures. The i⁶Ado was phosphorylated to i⁶AMP, i⁶ADP, and i⁶ATP, and these products were extensively degraded to Ado, AMP, ADP, and ATP. On the other hand most of the i⁶Ade was converted to the 7-glucoside, in which the side chain was protected from cleavage. These workers considered that 7-glucosylation was not merely a detoxification mechanism, as once suggested by Fox *et al.* (1973), for it occurred in tobacco suspension cultures even when the concentration of supplied cytokinin was very low (Gawer *et al.*, 1977). The 7-glucosyl derivative of bzl[6]Ade was absorbed slowly by the tobacco cell suspension cultures and was metabolized to bzl[6]AMP (Gawer *et al.*, 1977).

In corn seedlings the 9-glucoside was a major metabolite, but small quantities of the 7-glucoside were also formed (Parker and Letham, 1974). This is in contrast to the situation in radish seedlings, which were found to synthesize only small quantities of the 9-glucoside (Parker *et al.*, 1973; Parker and Letham, 1974) in addition to the 7-glucoside noted above. The role of the 9-glucoside in plant metabolism has not been established, but it is of interest that several years before the isolation of native glucosides of cytokinins, synthetic 6-benzylamino-9-glucofuranosylpurine had been shown to be readily transported in *Cicer arietinum* seedlings (Guern *et al.*, 1968).

Further studies of tritiated bzl[6]Ade metabolism in radish seedlings revealed the presence of a highly active minor metabolite (Wilson *et al.*, 1974) which was found to be 6-benzylamino-3-β-D-glucopyranosylpurine (Letham *et al.*, 1975). The relatively high activity of this 3-glucoside as compared to the 7- and 9-glucosides may be due to the fact that it is readily hydrolyzed by β-glucosidase, whereas 9-glucosides are only slowly attacked and 7-glucosides are resistant to this enzyme.

A fourth glucoside, 6-(4-O-β-D-glucopyranosyl-3-methyl-*trans*-but-2-enylamino)purine (O-glucosyl zeatin), has been identified in several plant tissues, including soybean callus (Horgan, 1975, 1977), lupine seedlings (Parker *et al.*, 1975), *Vinca rosea* crown gall tumor tissue (Peterson and Miller, 1977; Morris, 1977), and *Populus alba* leaves (Letham *et al.*, 1977). In the case of the crown gall tumor tissue, O-glucosyl zeatin and its riboside were detected when the tissue was supplied with a source of reduced nitrogen to ensure maximum cytokinin biosynthesis, thus suggesting that it, like the 7-glucoside and possibly other glucosides, is probably a storage form of cytokinin. Synthetic O-glucosyl zeatin was as active as zeatin or ribosylzeatin in the soybean callus assay (Van Staden and Papaphilippou, 1977), which is not surprising because O-glucosyl derivatives are readily hydrolyzed by β-glucosidases. This might account for the zeatin and ribosyl-zeatin which they found in the treated callus tissue.

Partially characterized glucosides have also been reported from a number of other plant species, including *Populus robusta* (Hewett and Wareing, 1973a,b), rice plants (Yoshida and Oritani, 1972), coconut milk (Van Staden, 1976a), and *Salix babylonica* (Van Staden, 1976b). In each of these cases the glucoside was reported to be readily hydrolyzed by β-glucosidase.

E. Aminoacylation

Two unusual metabolites, each containing an amino acid attached to a nitrogen atom of the adenine ring, have been reported, one from a higher plant and the other from a slime mold. Lupinic acid, β-[6-(4-hydroxy-3-methylbut-*trans*-2-enylamino)purine-9-yl]alanine, was found in 9 day old, derooted *Lupinus angustifolius* seedlings supplied with zeatin through the transpiration stream (Parker *et al.*, 1975; MacLeod *et al.*, 1975). Its *in vitro* synthesis was achieved with enzymes isolated from *Lupinus luteus* or *Citrullis vulgaris* seedlings, utilizing *O*-acetyl-L-serine and zeatin as substrates (Murakoshi *et al.*, 1977).

Discadenine, 3-(3-amino-3-carboxypropyl)-6-(3-methyl-2-butenylamino)-purine, has so far been isolated only from the slime mold, *Dictyostelium discoides*, in which it functions as a spore germination inhibitor (Abe *et al.*, 1976). Recrystallized discadenine was less than 10% as active as kinetin (i.e., only 1% as active as i^6Ade) in the tobacco bioassay (Nomura *et al.*, 1977). On the other hand, discadenine was active at 10^{-8} M as a spore germination inhibitor in *Dictyostelium*, while zeatin and i^6Ade were active at 10^{-5} M.

F. Oxidation of the Adenine Rings

One possible route of cytokinin inactivation is via formation of the 8-monohydroxy and 2,8-dihydroxy derivatives by the action of xanthine oxidase. This has been shown to occur in *in vitro* experiments with kinetin (Bergmann and Kwietny, 1958; Henderson *et al.*, 1962), zeatin (Letham *et al.*, 1967; Chen *et al.*, 1975), and i^6Ade (McLennon and Pater, 1973; Chen *et al.*, 1975). The only natural occurrence of a similar product which we have encountered is the finding of 2-hydroxy-zeatin in immature sweet corn kernels (Letham, 1973). In *in vitro* experiments only the bases and ribonucleosides reacted with xanthine oxidase, so that conversion to mononucleotides presumably would protect cytokinins from this enzyme.

G. Cleavage of the N^6 Side Chain

Studies utilizing [8-^{14}C]-labeled cytokinins have shown that side chain cleavage is a common fate of exogenous cytokinins. A cytokinin oxidase accomplishing this cleavage has been isolated from corn (Whitty and Hall, 1974) and tobacco (Pačes *et al.*, 1971). Paēs and Kaminek (1976) have reported that ribosylzeatin interferes with the cleavage of the isopentenyl side chain from i^6Ado and it is of interest that *t*-io^{6}Ado, which is more effective than c-io^{6}Ado in promoting growth, is also more effective in competing for the enzyme. Doree and Guern (1973) found that *Acer psuedoplatanus* cell suspension cultures maintained a constant level of N^6-substituted bases and ribonucleosides, which might indicate that any excess cytokinin supplied to the cells was eliminated by side chain cleavage. Sondheimer and Tzou (1971) could find no evidence of side chain cleavage by bean axes supplied with [8-^{14}C]-labeled zeatin. Little attention has been given to the fate of the side chain after cleavage, but Fox and Chen (1967) have reported that it was scavenged and incorporated into nucleic acids.

H. Cytokinin Binding

Evidence for the specific binding of cytokinin molecules to a protein component of ribosomes is now accumulating. Berridge *et al.* (1970) were the first to demonstrate cytokinin binding to Chinese cabbage leaf ribosomes, probably to the 83 S component, at the rate of 1 molecule of kinetin to 1.34 molecules of bzl^{6}Ade per ribosome. Fox and Erion (1975) and Erion and Fox (1975) detected two types of binding sites on ribosomes from wheat germ, one a low-affinity site similar to that described by Berridge *et al.*, the other a high-affinity protein which could be washed off the ribosome with 0.5 M KCl without loss of binding ability and which was saturated at the rate of 1 molecule of bzl^{6}Ade per ribosome. Fox and co-workers (Erion and Fox, 1977; Fox *et al.*, 1977) have further characterized this protein, reporting it to have a molecular weight of 140,000 and to consist of subunits of 54,000, 50,000, and 40,000 daltons. It is of interest that it binds kinetin, i^{6}Ade, and bzl^{6}Ade but not zeatin or certain other hydroxylated derivatives. By utilizing an antibody which was developed against the wheat germ protein, the presence of the cytokinin binding protein was traced throughout the life cycle of the barley plant. Present in dry seeds, it disappeared shortly after germination, was lacking in the vegetative parts, reappeared in reproductive tissues before fertilization, and remained present throughout seed formation.

Moore (1977, 1978), using affinity chromatography in the authors' laboratory, has isolated essentially the same material from wheat germ as that which Fox and co-workers have examined. Moore's data indicated that this binding moiety is a cytosolic protein of 122,000 daltons. Equilibrium dialysis revealed a kinetin–protein dissociation constant of 1.2×10^{-6} M and a saturation binding capacity of 1.5 moles of kinetin per mole of protein. The cytokinins i^{6}Ade and bzl^{6}Ade also showed high affinity for the protein, but neither zeatin nor *cis*-zeatin was bound. The i^{6}Ade (10 μM) completely abolished the binding of 10^{-7} M kinetin. A cytokinin antagonist, 4-(cyclopentylamino)-2-methylthiopyrrolo[2,3-d]pyrimidine, had no effect on kinetin binding. In contrast, a photoaffinity-labeled cytokinin, 2-azido-N^6-(Δ^2-isopentenyl)adenine (Theiler *et al.*, 1976; Theiler, 1977), at 7.5 × 10^{-5} M decreased the binding of 10^{-7} M [8-^{14}C]kinetin by 46% in darkness, and when the compound was photolyzed in the presence of protein before kinetin was introduced, the binding of the kinetin was reduced by 73%.

Takegami and Yoshida (1975, 1976, 1977; Yoshida and Takegami, 1977) have purified a 4500-dalton unit peptide from tobacco leaves which binds bzl^{6}Ade five times more effectively than it binds kinetin. These authors have suggested that bzl^{6}Ade stimulates an association between this peptide and 0.5 M KCl-washed 40 S ribosomal subunits.

Studies with moss indicate that cytokinin binding may be associated with the process of budding. Gardener *et al.* (1975, 1977), on the basis of competition between tritiated bzl^{6}Ade and other cytokinins, reported noncovalent binding of cytokinin bases to a subcellular particulate fraction of moss protonemata. Cytokinin ribonucleosides, which fail to promote budding in mosses, were poor competitors. On the basis of gel electrophoresis analysis, Bopp *et al.* (1977) have reported that there are three cytokinin-receptor proteins in moss protonemata which have attained the budding stage, and that these are lacking in protonemata which are still in the vegetative or caulonema stage.

LeJohn and co-workers (LeJohn and Cameron, 1973; LeJohn and Stevenson, 1973; LeJohn *et al.*, 1974; LeJohn, 1975) have studied a calcium binding glycoprotein present in the membrane of a filamentous, coenocytic water mold. The protein, which functions in calcium transport, also binds IAA, trytophan, and cytokinins. This type of binding protein has not yet been demonstrated in higher plants.

I. Plant Pathogens, Symbionts, and Cytokinin Biosynthesis

There is now considerable evidence that cytokinins generally play a role in plant–pathogen or symbiont interactions in which plant overgrowth is involved. This subject has been critically reviewed by Greene (1977) and Sequeira (1973). The first case to be studied was the disease caused by *Corynebacterium fascians*, known as fasciation disease or witches' broom and described in detail by Roussaux (1966). Samuels (1961) showed that the syndrome in infected pea seedlings (development of large numbers of lateral buds released from correlative inhibition, and growth in thickness of stems with concomitant inhibition of elongation) could be induced in the absence of bacteria by high dosages of kinetin applied to the seeds or seedlings. This was confirmed by Thimann and Sachs (1966), who also found that extracts of *C. fascians* cultures contain cytokinin activity.

In joint work between the laboratory of Professor N.J. Leonard at the University of Illinois and our own, three cytokinin-active preparations from culture filtrates were isolated as picrates (Klämbt *et al.*, 1966), and two of these were identified as i^6Ade and m^6Ade (Helgeson and Leonard, 1966). The third active constituent was identified later as c-io^6Ade (Scarbrough et al., 1973), and two additional active compounds have been identified as c-ms^2io^6Ade and t-io^6Ade (Armstrong *et al.*, 1976b). The presence of i^6A and io^6A, reported by Rathbone and Hall (1972), was confirmed in these studies on the basis of biological activity and chromatographic data. In tRNA hydrolysates, c-io^6A was identified (Einset and Skoog, 1977) and, on the basis of chromatography and biological activity data, both i^6A and ms^2io^6A were also present.

The same cytokinins with the following exceptions have been isolated from virulent cultures of *Agrobacterium tumefaciens* (collective data from Klämbt, 1967; Romanow *et al.*, 1969; Upper *et al.*, 1970; Einset *et al.*, 1977; Chapman *et al.*, 1976; Chen *et al.*, 1976b; Kaiss-Chapman and Morris 1977). Whereas c-io^6A was the predominant isomer found in *C. fascians* culture filtrate and in tRNA (as in plant tRNA generally), the *trans* isomer t-io^6A was reported for *A. tumefaciens* tRNA and the *trans/cis* ratio of io^6Ade in the culture filtrate was 85/15 (Kaiss-Chapman and Morris, 1977). In contrast, Cherayil and Lipsett (1977) reported only the *cis* isomer of ms^2io^6A in tRNA hydrolysate from *A. tumefaciens*. Furthermore, a zeatinlike, but more polar, cytokinin was found in *A. tumefaciens* culture filtrates (Einset *et al.*, 1977).

Relatively high cytokinin activities, mainly in fractions corresponding to zeatin and zeatin derivatives, have been found in culture filtrates of *Rhizobium* species which invade legume roots and induce nodules in which they fix nitrogen (Giannattasio and Coppola, 1969; Phillips and Torrey, 1970, 1972). High activities were also found in the bacteroid-containing nodules. The cytokinins in neither the *Rhizobia* nor the nodules have been rigorously identified, but they behaved as zeatin and zeatin derivatives and appeared to be the same as found in normal root tissue. The highest activity was in the nodule apices (Syōno *et al.*, 1976); it has been suggested that *Rhizobia* may both synthesize cytokinins and activate their synthesis in the nodule tissue.

The nodules caused by endophytes in *Alnus*, *Casuarina*, *Myrica*, *Comptonia*, and others were also found to have higher contents of cytokinins, tentatively designated as zeatin and its derivatives, than did normal root tissue (Henson and Wheeler, 1977a,b; Torrey *et al.*, 1977).

Cultures of several mycorrhizal fungi (Miller, 1968; Miura and Miller,

1969), *Plasmodiophora brassica* (Dekhuijzen and Overeem, 1971), and various rusts and mildews which prevent senescence (cause green islands) and/or bring about overgrowths in host tissues (Engelbrecht, 1967; Abou-Mandour and Volk, 1971) have been reported to raise the level of zeatin in the infected tissues.

Similarly, bodies of insects which cause leaf galls, including *Stigmella* (Engelbrecht, 1971; Engelbrecht *et al.*, 1969) *Dryocosmus* (Ohkawa, 1974) and *Erythrina latissima* (Van Staden, 1975), were found to contain high concentrations of io^6Ade and io^6A which were not derived from the host plants.

Leaf nodules of *Ardesia* species have a high cytokinin content (Edwards and La Motte, 1975), and *Chromobacterium lividum* isolated from leaf nodules exhibited high cytokinin activity in culture (Pereira *et al.*, 1972). Even if the bacteria were not the cause of the leaf nodules, they must have had an important symbiotic relationship with the plant, because sterilized seeds produced stunted seedlings which soon died unless infected with the bacterium or supplied with exogenous cytokinin.

Various free living bacteria have been tested for cytokinin production with positive results, including phosphate-solubilizing bacteria in the rhizosphere and the *Azotobacter* species *A. paspali*, *A. vinlandii*, and *A. beijerinckii* (Barea *et al.*, 1976). When the root systems of tomato seedlings were dipped in cultures of these species before planting, they grew better than the controls (Azcón and Barea, 1975). In tests of four African soils, those associated with roots of *Acacia mearnsii* having *Rhizobium*-induced nodules or *Pinus patula* having mycorrhiza had the highest cytokinin contents, including a fraction coeluting with zeatin (Van Staden and Dimalla, 1976).

Pedersén and Fridborg (1972) and Pedersén (1973) have shown that sea water in beds of kelp (*Fucus-Ascophyllum*) is a rich source of i^6Ade, which likely is derived at least in part from associated microbes; contents of up to 80 $\mu g/l$ were recorded in late summer. Evidence was obtained that the cytokinin in sea water stimulated the growth of brown algae and affected their morphology, as was earlier reported for *Ulva* (Provasoli, 1958).

Unlike most normal tissue, excised crown gall tissue is capable of indefinite growth in subcultures on nutrient media without added cytokinins and other growth factors. Cultures derived from gall tissue of plants infected with different species of *Agrobacterium* or different strains of *A. tumefaciens* vary in growth rates and differ in morphological traits over a wide range, but, at least in the case of tobacco, the variation is within the same range as for normal tissue supplied with different combinations of cytokinin, auxin, and nutrients. The tumor tissue produces relatively high concentrations of cytokinins, which in cultures of *Vinca rosea* crown gall tissue were mainly $t\text{-}io^6Ade$ and $t\text{-}io^6A$ (Miller, 1975), but on media supplemented with NH_2 nitrogen, high concentrations of the corresponding $4'\text{-}O'$-glucosides were also produced (Peterson and Miller, 1977). The biosynthetic capacity of the tissue was retained in cultures free from bacteria.

Braun and co-workers (Braun and Wood, 1976; Turgeon *et al.*, 1976) report that biosynthetic capacities characteristic of crown gall tumor tissues were ordinarily retained in vegetative tissues of plants regenerated from tumor cells but were eliminated during meiosis in the process of sexual reproduction. In contrast, insect galls (Pelet *et al.*, 1960) and other overgrowths, with the possible exception of viral tumors, apparently do not synthesize enough cytokinin for indefinite growth *in vitro*.

Consistent with the above findings, the pathogenicity (i.e., the capacity to induce uncontrolled, continuous growth) of *Agrobacterium* species and strains has been shown to be dependent on a large plasmid—the Ti plasmid (Van Larebeke *et al.*, 1974)—a specific small DNA segment of which is required (Chilton *et al.*, 1977) and is retained and functional in transformed tumor cells. Recurring claims to the contrary, oncogenicity has been generally considered to be a unique property of *Agrobacterium* species, and the required Ti plasmid may be unique to *Agrobacteria*. However, it has now been transmitted to *Rhizobium* species, which have thereby acquired the capacity to induce crown gall presumably by serving as alternate vehicles for the insertion of the Ti plasmid into the cells of the host plant (Hooykaas *et al.*, 1977).

High cytokinin content in culture filtrates was found to be associated with pathogenicity of *A. tumefaciens* in surveys comparing virulent and avirulent, plasmidcured strains (Einset *et al.*, 1977; Kaiss-Chapman and Morris, 1977). In comparisons of the virulent *A. tumefaciens* strain C58 and the derived avirulent strain C58-5, the former yielded much higher cytokinin activity, including io⁶Ade and a more polar cytokinin, but the avirulent strain without the Ti plasmid also yielded small amounts of activity in fractions cochromatographing with io⁶Ade. Kaiss-Chapman and Morris included tests on a third strain, derived from the plasmid-cured strain, into which the Ti plasmid from the virulent parent strain had been reintroduced and pathogenicity thus restored. High cytokinin content and the presence of io⁶Ade as well as i⁶Ade were found in the virulent parent strain. As expected, only i⁶Ade and much lower total cytokinin activity were found in the plasmidless strain; but unexpectedly, this was also found true for the third strain, in which the plasmid had been reintroduced and virulence restored. These results do not exclude a function of plasmids in regulating zeatin biosynthesis or relevance of zeatin synthesis to growth of crown gall tissue, but if they are confirmed in further studies, the mechanism of cytokinin participation in gall formation must be more complex than anticipated from early findings.

Corynebacterium fascians strains also contain plasmids (Doyle, 1977), and high cytokinin content in culture filtrates has been associated with pathogenicity. The total cytokinin content was found to vary greatly with the strain, but was by far the lowest in a strain which was avirulent after a plasmid had been eliminated (M. E. Doyle, N. Murai, R. Hanson, and F. Skoog, unpublished). Relationships of plasmids in *Rhizobia* or other bacteria to cytokinin biosynthesis have not been examined.

The pattern emerging from the above studies is that the capacity to synthesize zeatin and zeatin derivatives which normally are only found in plants is also a common feature of the pathogens and symbionts, including bacteria, fungi, and insects, which cause overgrowths. It appears that both in virulent *Agrobacterium* species and strains and in *Corynebacterium fascians* strains the capacity to produce zeatin may be associated with plasmids. This may also be the case in *Rhizobia* which cause nodule formation in roots and are known to contain plasmids, and in other bacteria which cause overgrowths in their hosts. In the case of the fungi and insects discussed above, there is no direct evidence for or against the possibility that zeatin biosynthesis may be regulated by extranuclear DNA.

In the case of crown gall tissue, synthesis by bacteria in the plant may contribute to the total cytokinin content, but increased synthetic activity by the host tissue which persisted after the bacteria have been eliminated and was retained in progeny would seem to be more important.

Rhizobia and other organisms which must enter the plant to cause overgrowth probably synthesize the required cytokinins. If they also stimulate biosynthesis by the host cells, they do so only as long as they are present. *Corynebacterium* brings about fasciation from outside the plant, and there is no evidence that it enters plant cells or affects their capacity to synthesize cytokinins. In the case of the nonparasitic microflora which produce the cytokinins required for normal development of brown algae, etc., the available evidence suggests that i^6Ade is the main cytokinin, and there is no evidence that the synthesis of zeatin is involved.

It seems logical to assume that in crown gall the Ti plasmid provides one or more genes required for tumor induction and growth, but, as far as the hormones required for continuous growth are concerned, the necessary mechanisms for their synthesis already exist in the host tissue, even if in a repressed state, so that no structural or regulatory gene for synthesis of a specific hormone need be introduced. As to the biosynthesis of zeatin by the pathogens and symbionts, they presumably originally acquired this capacity through transfer of genes from plants. The question may be raised, therefore, whether the plasmid DNA which activates hormone biosynthesis and induces tumor growth and which is considered by plasmid authorities as a case of effective transfer and functioning of prokaryote DNA in eukaryote cells is not originally derived from plants in the distant past and eventually reintroduced and utilized successfully by *Agrobacteria* in their exploitation of host metabolism. Whatever the original source of the tumor-forming plasmid DNA, further investigation of plant hormone biosynthesis and plant–parasite interactions may provide new insight into mechanisms regulating both normal and abnormal growth and development.

V. CYTOKININS IN NUCLEIC ACIDS

A. KINDS OF CYTOKININS IN RNA OF DIFFERENT ORGANISMS

Acid- or enzyme-hydrolyzed RNA preparations from every kind of organism so far examined in detail have been found to contain cytokinin-active ribonucleosides. It appears that i^6A is universally present, and it is the only cytokinin reported to date in animals. The cytokinin commonly associated with green plants is io^6A, and normally the *cis* isomer predominates in the tRNA's and in the two rRNA's which have been examined. The methylthio derivatives ms^2i^6A and ms^2io^6A have also been isolated from higher plant RNA's (Vreman *et al.*, 1974; Taller *et al.*, 1977), but they may be restricted to chloroplasts and possibly other organelles.

The kinds of cytokinin in microorganisms are of special interest. The major cytokinins generally present in bacteria are i^6A and ms^2i^6A (see Skoog and Armstrong, 1970), but in plant-associated microorganisms io^6A and ms^2io^6A may also be present (Chapman *et al.*, 1976; Cherayil and Lipsett, 1977; Greene, 1977; Thimmappaya and Cherayil, 1974). In *Euglena* io^6A has been found in cytoplasmic tRNA and ms^2io^6A exclusively in chloroplast tRNA (Swaminathan and Bock, 1977; Swaminathan *et al.*, 1977). This would seem to support the views of Fairfield and Barnett (1971) regarding the evolution of eukaryotic organelles. They reported that base Y (see below) is found exclusively in tRNA^{Phe} of cytoplasmic origin in *Neurospora* and *Euglena*, and in neither the mitochondrial tRNA of the former nor the chloroplast tRNA of the latter. In this scheme the methylthiolated cytokinins would be characteristic of prokaryotes, and would be restricted to organelles of possible prokaryotic origin, in eukaryotes. The occurrence of the cytokinins i^6A and ms^2i^6A in tRNA^{Phe} of *E. coli* (Armstrong *et al.*, 1969b; Bartz *et al.*, 1970b; Nishimura *et al.*, 1969) and the occurrence of base Y instead of a cytokinin-active base in the corresponding position of phenylalanine tRNA in yeast (RajBhandary *et al.*, 1967) and wheat germ (Dudock *et al.*, 1969) also fit into this scheme, as does the finding of ms^2io^6A in chloroplast tRNA^{Phe} and the fluorescent base Y in cytoplasmic tRNA^{Phe} of beans (Guillemaut *et al.*, 1976). Two of three strains of mycoplasma tRNA which have been tested contained cytokinin activity (D. J. Armstrong and D. Söll, unpublished).

B. CYTOKININ-CONTAINING tRNA SPECIES

The proportion of the total tRNA molecules which contain a cytokinin-active base is no more than 20% in *E. coli* or yeast and is much less in plants and animals. Recoveries of cytokinins from hydrolysates of certain purified tRNA species reach values of one active base per 80–100 nucleotides, suggesting the presence of only one such base per molecule of tRNA, and this has been borne out by base-sequence analyses (see Barrell and Clark, 1974).

The number of tRNA species which contain cytokinins as well as the number of cytokinins is greater in microorganisms and plants than in animals. Cytokinins are located exclusively in those tRNA species which respond to codons starting with U. In *E. coli* (Armstrong *et al.*, 1969b; Bartz *et al.*, 1970b; Doctor *et al.*, 1969; Nishimura *et al.*, 1969; Yamada *et al.*, 1971), cytokinin-containing tRNA species exist for all amino acids with codon assignments in the U group (i.e., phenylalanine, leucine, serine, tyrosine, cysteine, and tryptophan). The same is true for *Lactobacillus acidophilus*, with the exception of tRNA^{Phe} (Peterkofsky and Jesensky, 1969). In yeast, cytokinin-containing tRNA species have been found which code for serine (Zachau *et al.*, 1966) tyrosine (Madison *et al.*, 1967; Madison and Kung, 1967) and cysteine (Hecht *et al.*, 1969b; Armstrong *et al.*, 1969a). In this organism, phenylalanine tRNA contains the base Y (RajBhandary *et al.*, 1967), a more highly modified purine derivative (Blobstein *et al.*, 1975) which, although inactive, can be degraded to produce an active cytokinin (Hecht *et al.*, 1970a).

In all animal tRNA's which have been tested, cytokinin activity is restricted to tRNA^{Ser} (Skoog and Armstrong, 1970). The same is true for *Drosophila* tRNA, the only tRNA of insect origin which has so far been examined in detail (White *et al.*, 1975). It contains seven tRNA^{Ser} subspecies, three of which respond to codons in the U group and these contain i^{6}A. In higher plants the association of cytokinins with specific tRNA species has been examined in some detail in only a few cases. In wheat germ, Dudock *et al.* (1969) reported finding a base related to base Y in tRNA^{Phe}, and D. J. Armstrong (private communication) determined that two tRNA^{Ser} subspecies and a minor tRNA^{Leu} species accounted for most if not all of the cytokinin activity. In pea roots, c-io^{6}A has been isolated from tRNA^{Leu} (Babcock and Morris, 1973; Einset *et al.*, 1976). In tobacco callus, preliminary observations have indicated that several tRNA species contain cytokinin activity. It is of interest that ms^2i^6A has been identified in so-called "unique" tRNA species coded for by bacteriophage T4 in *E. coli*, i.e., in tRNA^{Leu} (Pinkerton *et al.*, 1973) and tentatively in tRNA^{Ser} (Barrell *et al.*, 1974).

It appears, therefore, that the number of amino acids for which there are cytokinin-active tRNA's varies with the phylum, but it should be recognized that cytokinin activity is often associated with minor tRNA species, such as subspecies of tRNA^{Leu} (Zilbertstein *et al.*, 1976), and these may readily have escaped detection.

No tRNA species responding to codons other than those in the U group have been found to contain cytokinins. The cases of tRNA^{Leu} and tRNA^{Ser} which have subspecies responding to codons starting with C and A, respectively, as well as to U, strikingly illustrate this point. The tRNA^{Leu} from plant sources has been shown to contain six subspecies of which only tRNA$^{Leu}_{5+6}$ respond to codons starting with U, and these are the subspecies which contain a cytokinin (work from our laboratory and that of J. H. Cherry, unpublished). Likewise, in *E. coli* and yeast only the tRNA^{Leu} subspecies responding to codons in the UUA or UUG have cytokinin activity. In *Drosophila*, two out of the three tRNA^{Ser} subspecies which contain cytokinin have been shown to respond to UCN codons, and three out of the four subspecies which do not contain cytokinin have been shown to respond to AG^u_c codons (White *et al.*, 1975).

C. Locus and Functional Role of the Cytokinin in tRNA

In all cases where base sequences of cytokinin-containing tRNA species have been determined, the cytokinin-active nucleoside has been the N^6-substituted adenosine located in the position adjacent to the 3' end of the anticodon and has been the middle member of a triple A sequence. In two cases where base exchanges in tRNA have resulted in U codons, these modified tRNA's have also been shown to contain i^6A.

Modifications which confer cytokinin activity on the adenine next to the 3' end of the anticodon have been shown not to affect the amino acid-accepting ability of the tRNA but to enhance the efficiency of binding the tRNA to the mRNA–ribosome complex, as demonstrated for the i^6A residue adjacent to the anticodon in yeast tRNA^{Ser} (Fittler and Hall, 1966) or in yeast tRNA^{Tyr} (Furuichi and Ukita, 1970). Gefter and Russell (1969) compared the acceptor activities and binding efficiencies of three tRNA's in tyrosine-suppressor mutant strains of *E. coli*, which differed in possessing ms^2i^6A, i^6A, or unmodified A. No difference was found in amino acid-acceptor activity, but the affinities of the three tRNA's for the mRNA–ribosome complex were in the proportions of 100:54:14, respectively. This demonstrates that both the isopentenyl group in the N^6 position and the methylthio group in the 2 position of the modified adenosine base enhance the functional effectiveness of the tRNA. They also indicate that modified adenosine may enhance the specificity of codon recognition, the tRNA without the modified base being less effective in distinguishing between the UAG and CAG codons. Similarly, Faulkner and Uziel (1971) ascribed the inability of iodine-treated tRNA^{Phe} from *E. coli* to function in *in vitro* polyphenylalanine peptide biosynthesis to its failure to bind to the mRNA–polyribosome complex as a result of the iodine reaction with the ms^{2}i^{6}A moiety. A mutant yeast tRNA containing 2% of the normal complement of i^{6}A accepted normal levels of amino acids *in vitro*, but *in vivo* the function of a suppressor tRNA lacking i^{6}A was markedly impaired, apparently at a step in protein synthesis subsequent to tRNA aminoacylation (H. M. Laten, J. W. Gorman, and R. M. Bock, unpublished).

The nature of the action of the modified base Y next to the anticodon has been investigated in a few cases. Fuller and Hodgson (1967) stated that base Y serves to assure correct codon recognition, and Ghosh and Ghosh (1970) suggested that it affects the configuration of the loop containing the anticodon. Such a change in configuration resulting from excision of Y by mild acid treatment has been reported by Pongs and Reinwald (1973). A similar function of i^{6}A has been considered.

Unfortunately, the hope raised by the above findings for an understanding of the growth regulatory function of cytokinins at the molecular level has not yet been fulfilled.

D. SOURCE OF THE CYTOKININ MOIETY IN tRNA

In vitro studies have shown that the isopentenyl group is derived from mevalonic acid via isopentenylpyrophosphate (IPP) (Peterkofsky, 1968; Fittler *et al.*, 1968; Kline *et al.*, 1969; Hall, 1970; Vickers and Logan, 1970; Murai *et al.*, 1975). A study by Gefter (1969) indicates that in those tRNA's containing the cytokinin-active component ms^{2}i^{6}A, cysteine is the source of the sulfur molecule, and S-adenosyl methionine is the source of the methyl group. The isopentenyl and methylthio substituents become attached to specific adenine moieties of particular tRNA molecules during their maturation. The extent to which the cytokinin-active modifications are produced depends on the availability of appropriate precursors and adequate nutrients. A strain of *Bacillus subtilis* cultured in an enriched medium synthesized tRNA $_{II}^{Phe}$, containing ms^{2}i^{6}A, whereas the same strain cultured in a minimal glucose salt medium synthesized tRNA $_I^{Phe}$, which contained simply i^{6}A (Arnold *et al.*, 1977). By providing IPP, Zubay *et al.* (1971) were able to bring about a 4-fold increase in the *in vitro* synthesis of su $_{III}^{tTyr}$ tRNA. Conversely, by limiting the amount of mevalonic acid available to *Lactobacillus acidophilus*, Litwack and Peterkofsky (1971) caused the tRNA produced to be 50% deficient in i^{6}Ade as compared to the normal tRNA produced by this organism. And *E. coli* mutant defective in methylation capacity was deficient in ms^{2}i^{6}A and instead may have produced i^{6}A and HS^{2}i^{6}A or related compounds (D. Söll, D. J. Armstrong, and P. F. Agris, unpublished). A case of particular interest concerns the production of i^{6}Ade-containing tRNA by a *Mycoplasma* species which does not normally produce detectable quantities of cytokinin-active tRNA. This was accomplished by supplying the organism with IPP and an enzyme from *E. coli* (Bartz *et al.*, 1970a).

Attempts to determine whether exogenous cytokinins must be incorporated into tRNA as an essential step for function in growth regulation have so far yielded only negative results (see Section F, below).

E. PRESENCE OF CYTOKININS IN rRNA

Although early examinations of rRNA failed to reveal cytokinin activity, more effective fractionation of rRNA hydrolysates obtained by acid treatment and/or by combined treatments with nucleases and phosphatases have demonstrated the presence of cytokinin activity in certain fractions (Murai *et al.*, 1977; Taller *et al.*, 1977). The evidence obtained with different selective cleavage enzymes indicates that cytokinins are present as constituents of rRNA and occur in base sequences different from those in which they occur in tRNA. Their localization within the rRNA molecules has not been established. The total activity of the separated cytokinins is much greater than could be derived from the tRNA and 5 S RNA which were present as contaminants in the preparations. In the case of wheat germ rRNA and also of *Pisum* rRNA, three cytokinin species have been tentatively identified on the basis of chromatographic analysis: *c*-io^{6}A, *t*-io^{6}A, and ms^{2}io^{6}A. The total cytokinin content in rRNA may be appreciable, about 15% that of tRNA, but the concentration in terms of the proportion of cytokinin-active nucleotides is much lower in the rRNA.

F. INCORPORATION OF EXOGENOUS CYTOKININS INTO RNA

The extent of incorporation of exogenous cytokinins into tRNA varies but is generally considered to be far less than would be needed for replacement of the endogenous cytokinins normally found in certain tRNA species. It has not been possible to show that incorporation is an integral part of cytokinin function in the regulation of growth. Using double-labeled bzl[6]Ade, Walker *et al.* (1974) were able to demonstrate incorporation of the intact base into RNA of tobacco callus at the rate of one molecule of bzl[6]Ado recovered per 10,000 molecules of tRNA. However, a much larger proportion (15 times as much) of the exogenously supplied bzl[6]Ade was shown to be incorporated into the rRNA (Armstrong *et al.*, 1976b). The same holds for the incorporation of kinetin into tobacco callus RNA. More than 90% of the labeled cytokinin in RNA was found in the rRNA fraction (Murai *et al.*, 1977). The yields were 1 kinetin molecule per 110,000 bases in the rRNA hydrolysates as compared to 1 per 290,000 in the tRNA hydrolysates. The recovery is equivalent to 1 fr[6]A per 3600 molecules of tRNA. This is in contrast to earlier reports by Elliot and Murray (1972), who found no significant incorporation of butyl[9]bzl[6]Ade into soybean callus but reported transbenzylation to occur at the rate of 1 molecule per 755–2210 molecules of tRNA.

The use of double-labeled bzl[6]Ade in the experiments of Walker *et al.*, noted above, clearly showed that the base was incorporated intact into the tRNA and that the recovered bzl[6]A did not arise from transbenzylation between the free base and the adenine already present in the tRNA chain. This has been confirmed by Jouanneau *et al.* (1977), who obtained incorporation intact and in higher amounts than reported above in short-term experiments with tobacco cell suspension cultures.

That cytokinin-active moieties in tRNA can arise by enzyme-catalyzed isopentenylation and methiolation of adenosine in the nucleotide chain of preformed tRNA has been discussed above. No evidence has been presented that free cytokinins incorporated into tRNA or rRNA are inserted into specific loci. It is worth noting, however, that incorporation of an exogenous base intact at a specific site in tRNA can occur. This has been elegantly demonstrated by Okada *et al.* (1976), who showed that ^{14}C-labeled guanine will replace the base Q (a highly modified guanine derivative) as the first base of the anticodons of purified *E. coli* tRNA[Tyr], tRNA[His], tRNA[Asn], and tRNA[Asp], all of which contain base Q, and respond to NA codons, and into none of 14 other tRNA's which respond to various other codons. The reaction is catalyzed by a rabbit reticulocyte lysate. The same enzyme activity was detected in a number of other systems. It serves also for the incorporation of ^{14}C]guanine in place of endogenous guanine in yeast tRNA, which does not contain base Q. As the enzyme does not replace guanine in the first position of the anticodon of several tRNA species of *E. coli*, which respond to codons other than NA$_C^U$, it presumably functions to replace Q or G only when one of these is present in the first position of anticodons responding to the NA$_C^U$ codons. The insertion of the base into the tRNA need not involve rupture of the phosphate linkages in the nucleotide chain. No such enzyme-catalyzed incorporation of cytokinin-active bases into specific sites in tRNA species has yet been found.

VI. EFFECTS OF CYTOKININS ON METABOLISM

A. RESPIRATION AND DIGESTION

Early studies attempting to relate auxin effects on growth to a slight stimulation of total respiration or to the activation of specific respiratory systems failed to reveal any significant relationship. Similarly, cytokinins alone ordinarily stimulate only slightly the respiratory rates of growing tissue, but combined auxin and cytokinin treatments which permit continuous growth of excised tissue *in vitro* sustain respiration at highly increased rates, roughly in accordance with the extent of growth promotion, as first shown in tobacco tissue cultures (E. H. Newcomb, unpublished, 1956). Similarly, in potato tuber slices on an auxin-containing nutrient medium, the initally high respiration rate dropped after 3 days when kinetin was also supplied, in which case the high rate of respiration and growth were sustained for more than 3 weeks (Kikuta et al., 1977). Kinetin promoted glucose metabolism via the pentose phosphate pathway, apparently by increasing the availability of NADP, and concomitantly promoted DNA synthesis.

In soybean callus either kinetin or zeatin treatment increased the rate of respiration after a 3 hour lag period (Moore and Miller, 1972). Inhibitor studies suggested that glycolysis and the tricarboxylic acid cycle were promoted and that ATP levels were not directly affected. In tobacco callus, the high cytokinin concentrations required for organ formation resulted in less than optimal growth of tissue and correspondingly lower than optimal respiratory rates during the first days of the treatment, but after ca. 2 weeks, when differentiation appeared, there was a sharp rise in respiration in the shoot-forming tissue. Glucose, fructose, or maltose, but not sorbitol, could substitute for sucrose as an adequate carbohydrate source (Thorpe and Meier, 1972; Thorpe, 1974). Earlier studies of the role of carbohydrates in organogenesis in tobacco tissue cultures (Thorpe and Murashige, 1968, 1970) had shown that the most dramatic effect of the high cytokinin concentrations required for bud formation was a sharp increase in starch content within 4 hours of transferring tissues to "bud forming media" and that shoots formed only in those areas of the callus which contained heavy starch deposits.

Starch presumably served primarily as an energy source, but a role in osmotic regulation was not excluded. The enzymology of the starch accumulation is not clear (Palmer, 1976; Häggman and Haapala, 1971).

Not only starch synthesis but generally the formation of high-polymer carbohydrates from monosaccharides and disaccharides and the formation of glycosides of various kinds are promoted by high cytokinin concentrations (Wright and Bowles, 1974). In the case of scopoletin in tobacco tissue cultures, the equilibrium between it and its glucoside (scopolin), or other scopoletin glycosides, has been shown to be regulated by the exogenous cytokinin:auxin ratio (Sargent and Skoog, 1960, 1961; Skoog and Montaldi, 1961). Cytokinin–auxin regulation of deoxyisoflavone synthesis in soybean callus on solid and liquid media has been reported (Miller, 1969). Also, in this case cytokinins promote glucoside synthesis.

Petunia mesophyll protoplasts supplied with a relatively high concentration of zeatin (ca. 5 μM) only exhibited a temporary increase in respiration as compared with controls for the first 4 hours and then a sharp decrease (Kull and Hoffman, 1975). The respiratory rate of senescing tissue is usually depressed by treatment with cytokinins, which may be functionally significant with respect to prevention or retardation of cytolysis and chlorophyll loss. First found by Richmond and Lang (1957), this effect has been widely observed (Dedolph *et al.*, 1962; Goldthwaite, 1974; Kuhnle *et al.*, 1977; Van Overbeek and Loeffler, 1962; Wade and Brady, 1971) and may have practical utility in storage of fruits and vegetables.

B. PROTEIN METABOLISM

1. General

The maintenance of normal protein levels is a primary factor in cytokinin-induced retardation of senescence. Neither general consensus of opinion nor definitive proof as to whether this is due primarily to enhanced protein synthesis or to reduced rates of protein degradation has resulted from the numerous studies which have focused on this process. Evidence that cytokinins retard protein degradation includes decreased activity of ribonuclease, deoxyribonuclease, and peptidase in kinetin-treated senescing barley leaves (Atkin and Srivastava, 1969) and retention of chlorophyll, proteins, and lipids in kinetin-treated detached tobacco leaves (Balz, 1966). Kuraishi (1968) deduced from measurements of [^{14}C]leucine incorporation into *Brassica* leaf discs that proteins which had been synthesized during the 24 hours preceding kinetin treatment were retained, but he could find no evidence of kinetin-promoted synthesis. Recently, Kuraishi (1976) has reaffirmed his earlier conclusion that cytokinins delay senescence by counteracting protein breakdown rather than by stimulating synthesis. Similarly, Tavares and Kende (1970) have reported that bzl[6]Ade retarded senescence in corn leaves by retarding protein breakdown, and they could find no evidence for an increase in protein content. Mizrahi *et al.* (1970) studied protein turnover in detached *Tropaeolum majus* leaves in the presence of $^{14}CO_2$. There was no net increase in protein content in kinetin-treated leaves, but the older, unlabeled, protein synthesized before treatment broke down faster than newly synthesized protein, resulting in an increase in the specific activity of the proteins.

Results of studies utilizing labeled amino acids indicate that cytokinins stimulate protein synthesis. Examples are the increased incorporation of [14C]valine by young barley leaves (Kulaeva and Klyachko, 1965); of [14C]leucine by lettuce cotyledons (Knypl and Chylinska, 1973), of [14C]alanine by detached, senescing barley leaves (Atkin and Srivastava, 1970); and of ^{35}S by suspensions of tobacco cells (Jouanneau and Péaud-Lenoël, 1967). Klämbt reported cytokinin-induced protein synthesis in an *in vitro* system which included dialyzed polysomes from which endogenous cytokinins presumably had been lost. Cytokinins may stimulate the synthesis of specific proteins rather than overall net protein synthesis. Fankhauser and Erismann (1969) reported an increase in protein synthesis in *Lemna minor*, detectable within 2 minutes and reaching its maximum in 30 minutes. The RNA level was also increased, but not so markedly. On the basis of sedimentation data, they concluded that the protein increase could be accounted for by an increase in structural proteins. McCombs and Ralph (1972) found rapid increases, i.e., within 1 hour, in the protein, DNA, and RNA contents of *Spirodela oligorrhiza* plants treated with cytokinin. No effects on specific proteins were demonstrated, but they suggested that protein kinases were probably involved. Sekiya and Yamada (1974) demonstrated changes in specific proteins of tobacco callus by the use of DEAE-cellulose column chromatography, polyacrylamide gel electrophoresis, and immunological methods. New protein bands were associated with morphological changes, specifically the formation of shoots, as a result of cytokinin treatment.

Takegami (1975a,b) found evidence for both prevention of degradation and promotion of synthesis in tobacco leaf discs. The incorporation of [14C]leucine was increased by bzl[6]Ade in the absence of inhibitors of protein synthesis; in the presence of cycloheximide, which completely prevented [14C]leucine incorporation, relatively high protein levels were maintained by bzl[6]Ade. Simpson and Torrey (1977) demonstrated marked accumulation of soluble protein as a result of cytokinin treatment of pea root cortical explants, but this increase did not begin until after the first 48 hours following excision. A high rate of protein turnover was indicated by the rapid uptake of [^{14}C]leucine, also during the first 48 hours, when the tissues were recovering from the wounding caused by excision.

As to the site of cytokinin action, Sekiya and Yamada (1974) considered that their evidence (for the appearance of new proteins) supported the hypothesis that cytokinins affect gene repression and gene derepression. On the other hand, both Klämbt (1976) and Muren and Fosket (1977), on the basis of cytokinin effects on polyribosome formation and RNA synthesis, conclude that the action is at the translation stage of protein synthesis.

Burrows (1975) has reviewed the ways in which cytokinins might exert their diverse growth regulatory functions by participating or interfering with one or more of the successive steps in gene-controlled protein biosynthesis in accordance with currently acceptable molecular biology concepts, and he has tried to evaluate and integrate the fragmentary evidence for and against different alternatives. It may be concluded from his analysis that, except for their demonstrated function in codon recognition in the case of certain tRNA's (which has not yet been related specifically to the growth regulatory function of exogenous cytokinins), cytokinins, like other hormones, apparently do or could interact at several stages in protein biosynthesis. Which of these possible ways is involved in a particular case remains to be determined.

2. Effects on Enzyme Activity

Cytokinins affect the activity of many enzymes, enhancing activity in some cases and inhibiting it in others. The physiological state of the tissue has a bearing on the response to cytokinin treatment, and this should be kept in mind when considering the effects reported below. In time-course studies, particularly when developmental processes such as seed germination or plastid development are followed, changing patterns of enzyme activity emerge.

The activities of enzymes involved in photosynthesis are highly sensitive to cytokinins. Treharne *et al.* (1970) reported stimulation of carboxydismutase synthesis by cytokinin and gibberellic acid treatments of fully expanded leaves of dwarf bean, but found no effect on plastid rRNA; this suggested that the enzyme was synthesized in the cytoplasm. The influences of kinetin on the development of the photosynthetic apparatus in rye seedlings have been studied in detail by Feierabend (1969, 1970a,b). In the initial stages of germination, only the production and/or activation of cytoplasmic enzymes was stimulated by kinetin, but after 96 hours there was exclusive stimulation of photosynthetic enzymes. Enzymes of the reductive pentose phosphate cycle were particularly sensitive, especially carboxydismutase and NADP-dependent glyceraldehyde phosphate dehydrogenase. Auxin-induced inhibition of the production of these two enzymes was counteracted by kinetin in young seedlings but not in older seedlings, and kinetin could not reverse the inhibition of carboxydismutase synthesis by cycloheximide or chloramphenicol. As plastids developed, the activity of glucose-6-phosphate dehydrogenase, an enzyme of the oxidative pentose phosphate cycle, declined. Treatment with kinetin alone could not halt this decline, but when it was combined with high levels of the auxin NAA, plastid development was arrested and high levels of the enzyme were maintained.

In further studies (DeBoer and Feierabend, 1974), kinetin restored high enzyme activity in the leaves (as distinct from the coleoptiles) of derooted, dark-grown rye seedlings. The increase in activity of the microbody enzymes glycolate oxidase and hydroxypyruvate reductase and of the photosynthetic enzymes was more marked than of the mitochondrial enzymes fumarase and cytochrome oxidase; it was also more marked than of glucose-6-phosphate dehydrogenase or the increase in total protein content. In the coleoptiles, in contrast, root removal prolonged enzyme activity and protein synthesis in darkness; exposure to light or treatment with cytokinin actually decreased enzyme activity and accelerated proteolysis.

Recently, Romanko *et al.* (1976) carried out a similar study of the effect of kinetin on enzyme activities in etiolated, derooted rye seedlings; they report that enzymes of the oxidative pentose phosphate cycle were especially sensitive to cytokinin treatment. Of the chloroplast enzymes, the activities of ribulose-5-phosphate kinase, ribulose diphosphate carboxylase, and "malic" enzyme were increased, but no significant effect was found on ribulose-5-phosphate isomerase. Of the cytoplasmic enzymes, the activities of 6-phosphogluconate dehydrogeanse and phosphoenolpyruvate carboxylase were slightly increased, and a decrease in the activity of glucose-6-phosphate dehydrogeanse was prevented. No measurable effect was found on the activities of acid pyrophosphatase, p-nitrophenylphosphatase, and fructose diphosphatase. The authors proposed that kinetin activated rather than induced synthesis of these enzymes and postulated that cytokinin acts at the transcription and translation levels by increasing all types of RNA either by influencing template activation of chromatin or by acting on RNA polymerase systems.

The stimulation by cytokinins of photosynthetic enzymes in cucumber cotyledons has been followed by Harvey *et al.* (1974). Ribulose diphosphate carboxylase and NADP-dependent glyceraldehyde-3-phosphate dehydrogenase activities were enhanced by cytokinin in the dark, but cytokinin was not required for their activation in the light. Because inhibitors of protein synthesis prevented cytokinin-stimulated activation of the former but not the latter enzyme, actual synthesis was presumed to be involved in the activation of the former but not of the latter.

The activation of mitochondrial and microbody enzymes in sunflower cotyledons is of interest, because in these organs reserve fats are mobilized during germination. Theimer *et al.* (1976) compared the appearance of microbody enzymes in rooted vs. derooted sunflower seedlings. Derooting resulted in early loss in enzyme activity. Kinetin prevented much of the loss in activity of the glyoxysomal enzymes catalase and isocitrate lyase, and markedly enhanced the activities of the peroxisomal enzymes glycolate oxidase and hydroxypyruvate reductase. The latter effect was highly specific, suggesting both that endogenous cytokinins formed in the roots may modulate the normal shift from glyoxysomes to peroxisomes and that nitrate supply is involved in this effect.

The course of the appearance of key enzymes in sunflower cotyledons has been described by Servettaz *et al.* (1976). Treatment with bzl[6]Ade in the dark had an effect strikingly similar to that of white light, rapidly increasing the activities of the glyoxysomal enzymes isocitrate lyase and malate synthetase during the first 3 days, and then accelerating their decay from the third to the fifth day. The peroxisomal enzymes glycolate reductase and glycolate oxidase showed an even greater increase in activity over a more extended time period. Cytokinin effects on mitochondrial enzymes were more variable. Cytochrome C oxidase and succinate dehydrogenase activities were markedly increased after the second day, while particulate malate dehydrogenase and fumarase activities were only slightly enhanced. A marked increase in the respiration rate over the first 3 days, which did not parallel cytochrome oxidase activity, was considered to be the result of an overall increase in metabolic activity.

Stimulation of nitrate reductase activity by cytokinins has been observed in a number of instances. In *Agrostema githago* seedlings, bzl[6]Ade was found to induce *de novo* synthesis of this enzyme (Hirschberg *et al.*, 1972). Nitrate was shown to have an additive stimulatory effect, which was sensitive to different inhibitors (Kende *et al.*, 1971; Kende and Shen, 1972; Dilworth and Kende, 1974). In fenugreek cotyledons (Parkash, 1972, 1973) and cucumber cotyledons (Knypl, 1973), nitrate and cytokinin have been reported to synergistically stimulate nitrate reductase activity. In the leaves of green pepper, the activity of this enzyme followed a circadian rhythm, the phase of which could be shifted by cytokinin treatment (Steer, 1976). Regulation of nitrate reductase activity appeared to take place in the leaves and possibly also in the roots and/or stem, for the rate of transport of nitrate appeared to be involved. In excised pea roots, on the other hand, kinetin treatment decreased the activity of nitrate reductase after 9 and 24 hours of incubation, while nitrite reductase activity was slightly enhanced after 9 hours and slightly decreased after 24 hours (Sahulka, 1972). In freshly excised tobacco leaf discs kept in the light, there was a sharp rise from a normally low to a high level of nitrate reductase activity which persisted for ca. 4 days. Exogenous kinetin had a slight stimulatory effect discernible only during the second half of the first day (Grierson *et al.*, 1977).

Cytokinin effects on peroxidase and IAA oxidase activities are of special interest in that they may reflect the intimate quantitative interaction of the two types of hormones in growth regulation. Increased activities of both these enzymes but not of catalase, as reported for cytokinin concentrations which inhibit growth of *Lens culinaris* roots (Gaspar and Xhaufflaire, 1967, 1968), may be typical. In other reports, one of the two enzyme activities is increased and the other decreased, or both may be decreased by certain cytokinin treatments. Perhaps more significant are changes in isozyme patterns in these enzymes brought about by hormone treatments. It has long been known that auxins drastically affect these patterns (Galston *et al.*, 1968; Lee, 1971b). Lee (1971a, 1972, 1974) has studied the effects of multiple hormone treatments including cytokinin effects on tobacco cultures in detail. An 0.2 μM concentration of kinetin was optimal for stimulation of isoperoxidases, which could be resolved into three bands, and also for two fast-moving IAA oxidase bands. The latter, which were especially sensitive to kinetin, increased in parallel with cytokinin-induced increase in dry weight and were localized to cytoplasmic-, plasma membrane-, and ribosome-rich fractions. The IAA oxidase/peroxidase ratio was especially high in the plasma membrane-rich fraction. Because peroxidase was the more sensitive to high (supraoptimal) cytokinin concentrations, these would further increase the IAA oxidase/peroxidase ratio. This differential effect might have a bearing on the striking morphological changes brought about by high exogenous cytokinin concentrations in tobacco callus.

Endogenous hormone regulation of α-amylase activity is a complex process. Gibberellins are generally credited with a key role, but cytokinins, ABA, and auxins have also been shown to be involved. The effect of kinetin on gibberellic acid-induced α-amylase synthesis in barley seeds was studied by Verbeek *et al.* (1969, 1973). There was no effect until after the third day, when amylase synthesis normally declines; this decline was accelerated by kinetin, and the effect of kinetin was opposed by IAA. In studies by Khan and Downing (1968) of hormone interactions in this same system, ABA completely inhibited both growth and α-amylase production, and the inhibition of both processes was reversed by kinetin but not by gibberellin treatment alone. However, subsequent to reversal of the ABA inhibition with kinetin, treatment with gibberellin promoted further enzyme production. In bean cotyledons, the response to hormone is different. Kinetin was found to promote α-amylase activity, but gibberellic acid and IAA were without effect (Gepstein and Ilan, 1970). Also in wheat seeds, cytokinins rather than gibberellins seem to trigger α-amylase production.

In the moss *Ceratodon purpureus*, enzyme changes in protonemata, relative to differentiation and development brought about by hormone treatments, have been investigated by Szweykowska and co-workers

(Schneider and Szweykowska, 1974, 1975). Ribonuclease activity decreased for the first 24 hours after treatment with cytokinin and then increased, reaching a maximum in 5 days coincidental with a peak in bud formation, as did peroxidase and acid phosphatase activities. tRNA–Nucleotidyltransferase activity rose more quickly, being detectable 1–3 hours after treatment with i^6Ade.

In bean callus, cytokinin stimulation of vascularization was associated with peak activities of phenylalanine ammonia lyase and UDP:1–3 glucan glucosyltransferase (Haddon and Northcote, 1975, 1976). Similarly, development of the plasma membrane in bzl^{6}Ade-treated cucumber cotyledons kept in the dark coincided with marked increases in the activities of ribulose-1,5-diphosphate carboxylase and NADP-dependent glyceraldehyde phosphate dehydrogenase (Harvey *et al.*, 1974). Cytokinin-induced lignification in tobacco cells grown in liquid culture coincided with a marked increase in caffeic acid-o-methyltransferase (Yamada and Kuboi, 1976; Kuboi and Yamada, 1976). An influence of cytokinins in the medium in promoting lignin formation and relatively high lignin/pectin ratios in the cell walls was first demonstrated by Koblitz (1962) in carrot tissue cultures and has been confirmed in other systems (Bergmann, 1964; Koblitz, 1964). This influence of cytokinins and auxins on cell wall composition may be related to their influences on cell expansion and organization in tissue differentiation and organogenesis (Halperin and Minocha, 1973). *myo*-Inositol utilization for pectin synthesis is inhibited by high bzl^{6}Ade concentrations (Verma *et al.*, 1976).

Additional instances of enhanced enzyme activity are the following: adenine–phosphoribosyltransferase in soybean callus and senescing barley leaves (Nicholls and Murray, 1968); leucine aminotransferase in pea buds (Choudhary *et al.*, 1976); and glutamate dehydrogenase in pea roots (Sahulka, 1972) and in soybean (Soulen and Olson, 1969). In the latter two reports, IAA was also required for the enhancement of glutamate dehydrogenase.

Reports of decreased enzyme activities as a result of cytokinin treatment are less numerous, but the effect has been considered functionally significant in some instances, such as decreased activity of protease in senescing oat leaves (Martin and Thimann, 1972); of nucleases (Birmingham and Mc-Lachlan, 1972) and ribonuclease in various tissues (Hodge and Sacher, 1975; Palmer and Baker, 1973; Shibaoka and Thimann, 1970; Srivastava, 1968; Udvardy *et al.*, 1967); and of adenine deaminase (Schlee *et al.*, 1966).

In most cases, cytokinin effects on enzymes are dependent on or modified by other factors. For example, in the work by Steinhart *et al.* (Mann *et al.*, 1963; Steinhart *et al.*, 1964) on germinating barley, early cytokinin treatments hastened the appearance and increased the magnitude of peak tyraminemethylferase activity in the seedling. This enzyme was not markedly affected by treatments at later stages, at which times certain other enzymes, not earlier affected, showed increased activities. It may be concluded that the cytokinin effect is to hasten and enhance the total process of gene-controlled protein biosynthesis, and that the particular enzymes which would be activated by treatment at a given time would be in accordance with a programed sequence of gene derepression. This relationship of the response to the developmental stage of the treated tissue no doubt applies generally.

C. Nucleic Acid Metabolism

Increased nucleic acid content is a common consequence of cytokinin treatment both in actively proliferating tissue, such as tobacco callus, and in senescing material, such as detached barley leaves. In excised tobacco pith, some DNA synthesis was initiated by kinetin treatment, but exogenous cytokinin and auxin were both required for continued synthesis (Patau *et al.*, 1957). Detailed cytological examination of mitosis and division of polyploid cells showed that the promoting effect of cytokinins is not limited to one specific stage in the cell cycle. Jouanneau and De Marsac (1973) utilized synchronized tobacco cell suspension cultures to correlate the cytokinin requirement with DNA synthesis during successive stages of the cell cycle. Exogenous cytokinin was required throughout the 18 hour lag period in order for the first cell division to occur, but the amount of DNA synthesized was the same in the presence or the absence of cytokinin. Thus, they postulate that cytokinins regulate a separate process taking place throughout the premitotic period which is independent of DNA synthesis, but both processes are requisite for mitosis. Bamberger (1971) has proposed that cytokinins may react directly with DNA to form complexes which stabilize DNA structure, thus modulating DNA metabolism.

Increases in the levels of total RNA of various kinds, as well as in the level of DNA, have been ascribed to effects of cytokinins leading either to increase of nucleic acid synthesis (Burdett and Wareing, 1966; Carpenter and Cherry, 1966; Erismann and Fankhauser, 1967; Cherry, 1967; Srivastava, 1967a,b; Schneider *et al.*, 1969; Bick *et al.*, 1970; Matthysse and Abrams, 1970; Zwar, 1973) or to prevention of degradation by inhibition of nuclease activity (Srivastava and Ware, 1965; Sodek and Wright, 1969; Wyen *et al.*, 1972; Birmingham and MacLachlan, 1972).

Enhancement of RNA synthesis may be very rapid: Erismann and Fankhauser (1967) found an increase in all species of RNA within 1 hour after treatment of *Lemna minor* with kinetin. Although many workers have reported the synthesis of all species of RNA to be about equally enhanced, there are several cases of more specific effects. Cherry (1967) has reported marked stimulation of ^{32}P incorporation especially into "S_2RNA" as compared to other RNA's in peanut cotyledons treated with bzl[6]Ade. The contents of tRNA$_{5\&6}^{Leu}$ were preferentially increased by cytokinin treatment of soybean cotyledons (Anderson and Cherry, 1969; Bick *et al.*, 1970). In excised pea roots, a cytokinin-induced rapid increase in RNA appeared to be due mainly to an increase in total tRNA, including but not exclusively tRNA^{Leu} (J. W. Einset, unpublished). Shininger and Polley (1977) report a gradual increase in RNA synthesis, caused by kinetin treatment in pea root explants, which was detectable after 9 hours and resulted in a 2- to 4-fold higher RNA content after 24 hours.

The effect on nucleases may also be rapid. Wyen *et al.* (1972) measured a decrease in activity after 2 hours in excised oat leaves, and most of this loss was in a relatively specific endoribonuclease which yields $2',3'$-cyclic phosphates, while the endonuclease which yields $5'$-nucleotides was only slightly affected.

The physiological condition of treated cells may determine their capacity to respond to cytokinin treatments and the resulting effect on nucleic acid metabolism. For example, a water deficit may result in increased ribonuclease activity which cannot be counteracted by cytokinin treatment (Arad *et al.*, 1973). Schneider *et al.* (1969) found that total RNA content was dramatically increased in bud-forming protonema cells as compared with nondifferentiating cells of the moss *Funaria hygrometrica*. In this case, the base composition of the RNA was altered in the direction of increased DNA-like RNA.

In addition to enhancing rRNA levels, cytokinin treatments lead to increased ribosome populations and promote the formation of polysomes, as shown for detached barley leaves (Srivastava and Arglebe, 1968), pumpkin cotyledons (Kliachko *et al.*, 1973), and soybean callus (Short *et al.*, 1974). Gordon *et al.* (1975) reported that in radish cotyledons the cytokinin effect was specific for membrane-bound (not cytoplasmic) ribosomal RNA and that it could only be measured after a lag period, indicating that it was an indirect effect. Wainfan and Landsberg (1971) have reported that in *in vitro* studies with animal and bacterial systems, cytokinin-active ribonucleosides (i[6]Ado, io[6]Ado, fr[6]Ado, and bzl[6]Ado) competitively inhibited the rate of methyl transfer from $^{14}CH_3$-adenosylmethionine, thus causing the formation of methyl-deficient tRNA.

Although not all workers have obtained positive effects of cytokinin treatments (Chaly and Setterfield, 1972), and Simard (1971) even failed to confirm the enhanced thymidine incorporation into DNA of excised tobacco pith tissues, the majority of the evidence to date suggests that cytokinins play an important role in regulating both DNA and RNA metabolism in plants. It seems that both the total levels of RNA classes and the content and functioning of certain specific RNA species are affected.

D. EFFECTS ON ORGANNELLES, MEMBRANES, PIGMENTS, AND OTHER CELL CONSTITUENTS

The retention of chlorophyll in senescing leaves treated with cytokinins, as noted earlier, forms the basis of rapid cytokinin assays utilizing either excised leaf tissue (Kuraishi, 1959; Osborne and McCalla, 1961; Goldthwaite and Laetsch, 1967; Letham, 1967) or attached leaves (Varga and Bruinsma, 1973). Cytokinin-stimulated synthesis of chlorophyll in excised cotyledons is also the basis for rapid bioassays (Fletcher and McCullagh, 1971a,b; Fletcher et al., 1973), as are the syntheses of betacyanin (amaranthin) (Köhler and Conrad, 1966; Bigot, 1968; Conrad, 1971; Biddington and Thomas, 1973) and anthocyanin (Mishra, 1966).

The effect of cytokinins applied to discrete areas of intact plants may be different. For example, growth and viability of treated leaves of bean plants were enhanced, but senescence of untreated leaves on the same plant was advanced by mobilization of metabolites to the treated leaves (Leopold and Kawaze, 1964; Pozsár and Kiraly, 1966). Seth and Wareing (1967) reached the same conclusion from studies on excised bean peduncles. There is evidence that cytokinin synthesized in the apical meristem controls mobilization of nutrients from the rest of the plant and hastens senescence of lower leaves, as does kinetin applied to the cut stem tip of decapitated plants (Pozsár and Kiraly, 1964). Similarly, in detached leaves, regenerated roots or applied cytokinins regulate transport and prevent senescence (Mothes, 1964; Parthier, 1964). The onset of senescence has been correlated with decreased production of cytokinins by the roots (Sitton et al., 1967).

Many investigators have ascribed cytokinin effects on mobilization and transport to the formation and maintenance of organelles and membrane structures, upon which the synthesis of chlorophyll and other cell constituents depend. Stetler and Laetsch (1965) studied chloroplast formation in tobacco tissue cultures. Tissues maintained in the light without cytokinin developed undifferentiated plastids only; when supplied with kinetin but kept in the dark, lamellae formed but did not fuse into grana; well-developed chloroplasts only formed when both light and kinetin were present. Harvey et al. (1974) reported similar findings for cucumber cotyledons. The development of plastid membranes in the dark was permitted and the appearance of grana in the light was hastened by bzl^{6}Ade. It also increased the synthesis in the dark of two enzymes—ribulose-1,5-diphosphate carboxylase and NADP-dependent glyceraldehyde phosphate dehydrogenase—by 75% and 50% respectively.

Kulaeva and Romanko (1967) reported that amino acid incorporation was markedly increased by cytokinin treatment of washed chloroplasts from mature leaves, but that the hormone had no effect when the chloroplasts had been isolated from senescent leaves. Kulaeva and co-workers (Sveshnikova *et al.*, 1968) have made detailed comparative studies of membrane structure in chloroplasts and of cytokinin effects on its preservation in mature leaves and reconstruction in senescent leaves of tobacco. Treatment with bzl[6]Ade inhibited degradation (destruction of the grana and lamellae of the stroma) of the chloroplasts in treated halves of aged green leaves. In aged yellow leaves, containing chloroplasts devoid of grana and filled with osmophilic globules, after 5 days of bzl[6]Ade treatment there was substantial decrease in globules, reappearance of lamellae, and formation of grana in chloroplasts in the treated halves of the leaves. After 12 days, when chloroplast degeneration in the untreated halves was complete, in the treated halves the new grana contained 5–7 lamellae, chlorophyll had formed, and the chloroplasts were photosynthetically functional. Concomitant activation of RNA, DNA, and protein synthesis, as well as restoration of mitochondrial structures, was observed. Similar positive results were obtained with kohlrabi (Mlodianowski and Kwintkiewicz, 1973).

The above positive effects of cytokinin treatment were obtained with detached leaves or cotyledons or with cultured tissue. In intact jackbean plants, Alberte and Naylor (1975) failed to find any effect of kinetin on chlorophyll synthesis or chloroplast formation in developing leaves, but it can be assumed that in this case endogenous hormone was already present. Dennis *et al.* (1967) reported that exogenous cytokinins actually enhanced senescence by overstimulating chloroplast membrane production in young leaves.

Membrane integrity is clearly an important factor in senescence phenomena, including the loss of chlorophyll. Ferguson and Simon (1973) related rapid water loss and marked decrease in phosphatidyl choline content to loss of membrane integrity in senescing cucumber cotyledons, but unfortunately they did not include cytokinin effects in their study. Richmond *et al.* (1971), on the basis of [14C]leucine incorporation by isolated chloroplasts, concluded that the effect of kinetin was related to membrane hydration and permeability rather than to the machinery of protein synthesis. Choe and Thimann (1975), working with isolated chloroplasts, confirmed that the production of enzymes outside the chloroplast is a major factor in the control of senescence. Banerji and Kumar (1975) have ascribed the kinetin-induced retention of Hill reaction capability in isolated spinach chloroplasts to retained integrity of the chloroplast membrane.

β-Cyanin (amaranthin) biosynthesis in *Amaranthus* cotyledons maintained in the dark requires an exogenous cytokinin supply (Bamberger and Mayer, 1960). The synthesis of this pigment is normally regulated by the phytochrome system, red light (R, 660 nm) favoring synthesis and far red light (FR, 730–735 nm) reversing red light stimulation. Colomas and Bulard (1975) demonstrated that FR could prevent R-stimulated synthesis even in the presence of kinetin. Gibberellic acid inhibited the synthesis of this pigment in the light but did not prevent the synthesis induced by kinetin in the dark (Kinsman *et al.*, 1975). Stobart and Kinsman (1977) found that kinetin, in promoting the synthesis of betacyanin, mimicked light in increasing the pools of tyrosine and dopa-oxidase, while gibberellic acid limited the availability of tyrosine.

The synthesis of anthocyanin in detached *Impatiens balsamina* petals was shown to be promoted by kinetin (Klein, 1959), and the content was doubled in detached wheat leaves which had been maintained in the light for 5 days (Mishra, 1966). Similar promotive effects were obtained in radish seedlings (Straub and Lichtenthaler, 1973). In red cabbage, cytokinin-promoted anthocyanin synthesis has been related to membrane permeability (Pecket and Bassim, 1974; Bassim and Pecket, 1975). A 5 minute exposure to FR nullified the effects of a 15 minute immersion of the seedling roots in kinetin solution, and no evidence was found for an effect of kinetin on PAL activity.

Carotenoid pigment content and its regulation by hormones in cultured carrot callus derived from roots varied with the genetic source, individual roots, and stock cultures (Mok *et al.*, 1976). In cultures derived from a red-pigmented root and supplied with serial combinations of 2,4-D and cytokinin, the color of the callus ranged from bright red to pale or bright yellow as the proportions of hormones varied from the extreme of no cytokinin to no 2,4-D. This quantitative shift in pigmentation in response to an increasing cytokinin/2,4-D ratio reflected a shift from carotenoid to xanthophyll synthesis and was due mainly to cytokinin inhibition of, and possibly to 2,4-D promotion of, lycopene synthesis. However, in some subcultures derived from the same source, pigmentation was not subject to quantitative regulation by hormone treatments.

Cytokinin regulation of IAA and thiamine biosynthesis has been referred to in the discussion on apical dominance. Undoubtedly, the synthesis of additional growth factors and levels of metabolites are similarly influenced by cytokinins.

It has been suggested that cytokinin enhances permeability of membranes through effects on their fatty acid content. Donaldson *et al.* (1969) ascribed the kinetin-induced increase in fatty acid content of spinach leaves mainly to α-linolenic acid, apparently as a result of decreased degradation rather than of enhanced synthesis. Schaeffer and co-workers (Schaeffer and Sharp, 1971; Schaeffer *et al.*, 1972) found incorporation of Me-^{14}C from methionine into polar and neutral fatty acids to be enhanced in bzl[6]Ade-treated dormant buds; the increase occurred before a burst in nucleic acid synthesis could be detected, and it was considered to be evidence in support of a cytokinin effect on membrane permeability. In onion epidermal cells, kinetin treatment did have a highly significant effect on the permeability constant, but the osmotic value was not affected, and it was suggested that an effect on membrane proteins might be involved (Feng and Unger, 1972). In leaves of *Coleus* or *Populus*, treatment with either kinetin or zeatin increased the linolenic acid content, while in leaves of *Impatiens* the palmitic acid content was raised according to Kull and Buxenstein (1974), who speculated that inhibition by cytokinin of two kinases (glucose 6-isomerase and glucose-6-phosphate dehydrogenase) would restrict glucose metabolism and favor UDP-glucose isomerization to UDP-galactose, which in turn would increase synthesis of linolenic acid-containing galactolipids.

There is some evidence that cytokinins affect nutrient uptake and translocation. Calcium and cytokinin have been found to have similar effects on certain aspects of membrane functioning as well as on cell wall metabolism. In senescing corn leaf discs, calcium and bzl[6]Ade were reported to have similar and additive effects in maintaining chlorophyll and protein contents, preventing water efflux, and minimizing increase in free space (Poovaiah and Leopold, 1973). All these effects could be related to the preservation of cell membranes. On the other hand, calcium, unlike cytokinin, inhibited anthocyanin synthesis in "red" cabbage seedlings whether the synthesis had been promoted by a 5 minute exposure to red light or by kinetin treatment in the dark (Bassim and Pecket, 1975). The authors suggested that "the molecular configuration of the phytochrome molecule affects the ability of the membrane to bind Ca^{2+} and that this in turn affects the permeability to substrates which are required for anthocyanin biosynthesis." Expansion of Chinese cabbage leaf discs was promoted by calcium as well as by bzl[6]Ade or kinetin (Ralph *et al.*, 1972, 1976) and was correlated with inhibition of phosphorylation by the kinases bound to membrane proteins, smooth cell membranes, and chloroplast lamellae, as measured in the presence of free [^{32}P]ATP. The effect of cytokinin on membrane phosphorylation appeared to be specific and not the result of a general competition with ATP. The authors speculated that the cytokinins modified protein phosphorylation by control of protein kinases in a manner comparable to that of cAMP in the regulation of phosphorylation in animals.

Cytokinin effects on monovalent ion transport are less definite. Enhanced uptake of the K^+ and Rb^+ cations, but no effect on the uptake of Na^+, has been reported for kinetin treatment of detached sunflower cotyledons (Ilan *et al.*, 1971). An inhibitory effect of bzl[6]Ade on Na^+ uptake by intact primary leaves of bean was observed in the expansion stage, but not found in fully expanded leaves (Jacoby and Dagan, 1970), and the Tris-induced uptake of Na^+ and Rb^+ by storage tissue of *Beta vulgaris* was repressed by kinetin or by bzl[6]Ade (Van Steveninck, 1972).

VII. CONCLUDING REMARKS

We have attempted to review the present status of cytokinin biochemistry and to bring together the available evidence to show that cytokinins serve important regulatory functions in all phases of development and vital activities of plants. There is a broad spectrum of cytokinin effects with impressive potential usefulness, but knowledge of the nature of cytokinin action at the molecular level is sparse. Present information indicates a need for further study of the function of cytokinins not merely as nucleotide constituents of tRNA's and rRNA's, but in terms of their association with proteins and possible roles, analogous to those of steroid hormones, in activating membrane function and thus in regulating chromosome anabolism and gene expression. Such a mode of cytokinin action at multiple sites could account for the observed stimulation of DNA and RNA synthesis, rapid induction or modification of metabolic activities, directional transport or mobilization, and resulting long-term influences on composition and morphology of plants.

ACKNOWLEDGMENTS

Work reported from this laboratory and the preparation of the manuscript were supported in part by the National Science Foundation Research Grant BMS72-02226, Mod. 5. We thank Mr. Hardy F. Moore for his contribution to the section on cytokinin binding. The authors gratefully acknowledge the benefits of many years of enjoyable and fruitful collaboration with colleagues and students in our own and other laboratories. We are especially indebted to Professors Nelson J. Leonard, University of Illinois-Urbana; Sidney M. Hecht, Massachusetts Institute of Technology; Donald J. Armstrong, Oregon State University; and Robert M. Bock, University of Wisconsin-Madison.

REFERENCES

Abe, H., Uchiyama, M., Tanaka, Y., and Saito, H. (1976). *Tetrahedron Lett.* p. 3807.
Abou-Mandour, A. A., and Volk, O. H. (1971). *Z. Pflanzenphysiol.* **65**, 240–247.

Alberte, R. S., and Naylor, A. W. (1975). *Plant Physiol.* **55**, 1079–1081.
Anderson, M. B., and Cherry, J. H. (1969). *Proc. Natl. Acad. Sci. U.S.A.* **62**, 202–209.
Arad, S. M., Mizrahi, Y., and Richmond, A. E. (1973). *Plant Physiol.* **52**, 510–512.
Armstrong, D. J., Skoog, F., Kirkegaarde, L. H., Hampel, A. E., Bock, R. M., Gillam, I., and Tener, C. M. (1969a). *Proc. Natl. Acad. Sci. U.S.A.* **63**, 504–511.
Armstrong, D. J., Burrows, W. J., Skoog, F., Roy, K. L., and Söll, D. (1969b). *Proc. Natl. Acad. Sci. U.S.A.* **63**, 834–841.
Armstrong, D. J., Murai, N., Taller, B. J., and Skoog, F. (1976a). *Plant Physiol.* **57**, 15–22.
Armstrong, D. J., Scarbrough, E., Skoog, F, Cole, D. L., and Leonard, N. J. (1976b). *Plant Physiol.* **58**, 749–752.
Arnold, H. H., Raettig, R., and Keith, G. (1977). *FEBS Lett.* **73**, 210.
Atkin, R. A., and Srivastava, B. I. S. (1969). *Physiol. Plant.* **22**, 742–750.
Atkin, R. A., and Srivastava, B. I. S. (1970). *Physiol. Plant.* **23**, 304–315.
Azcón, R., and Barea, J. M. (1975). *Plant Soil* **43**, 609–619.
Babcock, D. F., and Morris, R. O. (1973). *Plant Physiol.* **52**, 292–297.
Bajaj, Y. P. S. (1972). *Z. Pflanzenphysiol.* **66**, 284–287.
Balz, H. P. (1966). *Planta* **70**, 207–236.
Bamberger, E., and Mayer, A. (1960). *Science* **131**, 1094.
Bamberger, E. S. (1971). *Phytochemistry* **10**, 957.
Banerji, D., and Kumar, N. (1975). *Biochem. Biophys. Res. Commun.* **65**, 940–944.
Barea, J. M., Navarro, E., and Montoya, E. (1976). *J. Appl. Bacteriol.* **40**, 129–134.
Barrell, B. G., and Clark, B. F. C. (1974). "Handbook of Nucleic Acid Sequences." Johnson-Bruvvers Ltd., Oxford.
Barrell, B. G., Seidman, J. G., Guthrie, C., and McClain, W. H. (1974). *Proc. Natl. Acad. Sci. U.S.A.* **71**, 413–416.
Bartz, J., and Söll, D. (1972). *Biochimie* **54**, 31–39.
Bartz, J., Kline, L. K., and Söll, D. (1970a). *Biochem. Biophys. Res. Commun.* **40**, 1481–1487.
Bartz, J., Söll, D., Burrows, W. J., and Skoog, F. (1970b). *Proc. Natl. Acad. Sci. U.S.A.* **67**, 1448–1453.
Bassim, T. A. H., and Pecket, R. C. (1975). *Phytochemistry* **14**, 731–734.
Bentley, B., Morgan, C. B., Morgan, D. G., and Saad, F. A. (1975). *Nature (London)* **256**, 121.
Bergmann, F., and Kwietny, H. (1958). *Biochim. Biophys. Acta* **28**, 100–103.
Bergmann, L. (1964). *Planta* **62**, 221–254.
Bernier, G., Kinet, J. M., Jacqmard, A., Havelange, A., and Bodson, M. (1977). *Plant Physiol.* **60**, 282–285.
Berridge, M. V., Ralph, R. K., and Letham, D. S. (1970). *Biochem. J.* **119**, 75–84.
Bewley, J. D., and Fountain, D. W. (1972). *Planta* **102**, 368–371.
Bick, M. D., Liebke, H., Cherry, J. H., and Strehler, B. L. (1970). *Biochim. Biophys. Acta* **204**, 175–182.
Biddington, N. L., and Thomas, T. H. (1973). *Planta* **111**, 183–186.
Bigot, C. (1968). *C. R.Hebd. Seances Acad. Sci.* **266**, 349–352.
Bilderback, D. E. (1972). *Am. J. Bot.* **59**, 525–527.
Birmingham, B. C., and MacLachlan, G. A. (1972). *Plant Physiol.* **49**, 371–375.
Black, M., Bewley, J. D., and Fountain, D. W. (1974). *Planta* **117**, 145–152.
Blobstein, S. H., Gebert, R., Grunberger, D., Nakanishi, K., and Weinstein, I. B. (1975). *Arch. Biochem. Biophys.* **167**, 668–673.
Bopp, M., Overlach, U., Erichsen, I., and Knoop, B. (1977). *Plant Growth Regul., Proc. Int. Conf. Plant Growth Subst., 9th, 1976* Abstract, pp. 43–45.
Braun, A. C., and Wood, H. N. (1976). *Proc. Natl. Acad. Sci. U.S.A.* **73**, 496–500.
Brown, C. L., and Sommer, A. E. (1975). "An Atlas of Gymnosperms Cultured in Vitro." Georgia Forest Research Council, Macon.

Bruce, M. I., and Zwar, J. A. (1966). *Proc. R. Soc. London, Ser. B* **165**, 245–265.

Burdette, A. N., and Wareing, P. F. (1966). *Planta* **71**, 20–26.

Burrows, W. J. (1975). *Curr. Adv. Plant Sci.* **21**, 837–847.

Burrows, W. J. (1976). *Planta* **130**, 313–316.

Burrows, W. J., and Leworthy, D. P. (1976). *Biochem. Biophys. Res. Commun.* **70**, 1109–1114.

Burrows, W. J., Armstrong, D. J., Skoog, F., Hecht, S. M., Boyle, J. T. A., Leonard, N. J., and Occolowitz, J. (1968). *Science* **161**, 691–693.

Burrows, W. J., Armstrong, D. J., Kaminek, M., Skoog, F., Bock, R. M., Hecht, S. M., Dammann, L. G., Leonard, N. J. and Occolowitz, J. (1969). *Biochemistry* **8**, 3071–3076.

Burrows, W. J., Armstrong, D. J., Kaminek, M., Skoog, F., Bock, R. M., Hecht, S. M., Dammann, L. G., Leonard, N. J. and Occolowitz, J. (1970). *Biochemistry* **9**, 1867–1872.

Carpenter, W. J. G., and Cherry, J. H. (1966). *Biochim. Biophys. Acta* **114**, 640–642.

Catarino, F. M. (1964). *Port. Acta Biol.* **8**, 267–284.

Cavé, A., Deyrup, J. A., Goutarel, R., Leonard, N. J., and Monseur, X. G. (1962). *Ann. Pharm. Fr.* **20**, 285–292.

Chailakhyan, M. K., and Frolova, I. A. (1974). *Proc. Acad. Sci. USSR* **215**, 999–1002, (Engl. transl. 29–31).

Chaly, N., and Setterfield, G. (1972). *Planta* **108**, 363–368.

Chapman, R. W., Morris, R. O., and Zaerr, J. B. (1976). *Nature (London)* **262**, 153–154.

Chen, C.-M., and Eckert, R. L. (1977). *Plant Physiol.* **59**, 443–447.

Chen, C.-M., and Hall, R. H. (1969). *Phytochemistry* **8**, 1687–1695.

Chen, C.-M., Smith, O'B. C., and McChesney, J. D. (1975). *Biochemistry* **14**, 3088–3093.

Chen, C.-M., Eckert, R. L., and McChesney, J. D. (1976a). *FEBS Lett.* **64**, 429–434.

Chen, C.-M., Eckert, R. L., and McChesney, J. D. (1976b). *Phytochemistry* **15**, 1565.

Cherayil, J. D., and Lipsett, M. N. (1977). *J. Bacteriol.* **131**, 741–744.

Cherry, J. H. (1967). *Ann. N.Y. Acad. Sci.* **144**, 154–168.

Chheda, G. B., Hall, R. H., Magrath, D. I., Mozejko, J., Schweizer, M. P., Stasiuk, L., and Taylor, P. R. (1969). *Biochemistry* **8**, 3278.

Chilton, M.-D., Drummond, M. H., Merlo, D. J., Sciaky, D., Montoya, A. L., Gordon, M. P., and Nester, E. W. (1977). *Cell* **11**, 263–271.

Choe, H. T., and Thimann, K. V. (1975). *Plant Physiol.* **55**, 828–834.

Choudhary, J., Sopory, S. K., and Guhamukherjee, S. (1976). *Experientia* **32**, 1517–1518.

Colomas, J., and Bulard, C. (1975). *Planta* **124**, 245–254.

Conrad, K. (1971). *Biochem. Physiol. Pflanz.* **162**, 327–333.

Corse, J., and Kuhnle, J. (1972). *Symp. Phytochem. Soc. Am., 13th, 1972.*

Cowley, D. E., Jenkins, I. D., and MacLeod, J. K. (1975). *Tetrahedron* **11**, 1015–1019.

Crane, J. C., and Van Overbeek, J. (1965). *Science* **147**, 1468.

Dammann, L. C., Leonard, N. J., Schmitz, R. Y. and Skoog, F. (1974). *Phytochemistry* **13**, 329–336.

Das, N. K., Pätau, K., and Skoog, F. (1956). *Physiol. Plant.* **9**, 640–651.

Davidson, D. R. (1971). Ph.D. Thesis, University of Wisconsin, Madison.

DeBoer, J., and Feierabend, J. (1974). *Z. Pflanzenphysiol.* **71**, 261.

Dedolph, R. R., MacLean, D. C., and Wittwer, S. H. (1962). *Plant Physiol.* **37** Suppl., 35.

Dekhuijzen, H. M., and Overeem, J. C. (1971). *Physiol. Plant Pathol.* **1**, 151–162.

Dekhuijzen, H. M., and Overeem, J. C. (1972). *Phytochemistry* **11**, 1669–1672.

Deleuze, G. G., McChesney, J. D., and Fox, J. E. (1972). *Biochem. Biophys. Res. Commun.* **48**, 1426–1432.

Dennis, D. T., Stubbs, M., and Coultate, T. P. (1967). *Can. J. Bot.* **45**, 1019–1024.

Digby, J., and Skoog, F. (1966). *Plant Physiol.* **41**, 647–652.

Dilworth, M. G., and Kende, H. (1974). *Plant Physiol.* **54**, 821–825.

Doctor, P. B., Loebel, J. E., Sodd, M. A., and Winter, D. B. (1969). *Science* **163**, 693–695.

Doershug, M. R., and Miller, C. O. (1967). *Am. J. Bot.* **54**, 410–413.

Domanski, R., and Kozlowski, T. T. (1968). *Can. J. Bot.* **46**, 397–403.

Donaldson, R., Loesher, W., and Newman, D. W. (1969). *Am. J. Bot.* **56**, 1167–1172.

Doree, M., and Guern, J. (1973). *Biochim. Biophys. Acta* **304**, 611–622.

Doyle, M. E. (1977). *Am. Soc. Microb., Abstr. Annu. Meet.* p. 142.

Dravnieks, D. E. (1971). Ph.D. Thesis, University of Wisconsin, Madison.

Dravnieks, D. E., Skoog, F., and Burris, R. H. (1969). *Plant Physiol.* **44**, 866–870.

Dudock, B. S., Katz, G., Taylor, E. K., and Holley, R. W. (1969). *Proc. Natl. Acad. Sci. U.S.A.* **62**, 941.

Duke, C. C., Liepa, A. J., MacLeod, J. K., Letham, D. S., and Parker, C. W. (1975). *J. Chem. Soc., Chem. Commun.* pp. 964–965.

Dumbroff, E. B., and Brown, D. C. W. (1976). *Can. J. Bot.* **54**, 191–197.

Dunlop, J. R., and Morgan, P. W. (1977). *Plant Physiol.* **60**, 222–224.

Durley, R. C., Bewley, J. D., Railton, I. D., and Pharis, R. P. (1976). *Plant Physiol.* **57**, 699–703.

Dvořák, M., and Radotínská-Ledinská, V. (1970). *Biol. Plant.* **12**, 125–133.

Dyson, W. H., and Hall, R. H. (1972). *Plant Physiol.* **50**, 616–621.

Dyson, W. H., Fox, J. E., and McChesney, J. D. (1972). *Plant Physiol.* **49**, 506–513.

Edwards, W. J., and La Motte, C. E. (1975). *Plant Physiol.* **56**, 425–428.

Einset, J. W., and Skoog, F. (1973). *Proc. Natl. Acad. Sci U.S.A.* **70**, 658–660.

Einset, J. W., and Skoog, F. (1977). *Biochem. Biophys. Res. Commun.* **79**, 1117–1121.

Einset, J. W., Swaminathan, S., and Skoog, F. (1976). *Plant Physiol.* **58**, 140–142.

Einset, J. W., Greene, E. M., Skoog, F., Doyle, E., and Hanson, R. S. (1977). *Plant Physiol.* **59**, Suppl., 109.

Elliot, D. C., and Murray, A. W. (1972). *Biochem. J.* **130**, 1157–1160.

Engelbrecht, L. (1967). *Wiss. Z. Univ. Rostock, Math.-Naturwiss. Sci.* **16**, 647–649.

Engelbrecht, L. (1971). *Biochem. Physiol. Pflanz.* **162**, 9–27.

Engelbrecht, L., Orban, U., and Heese, W. (1969). *Nature (London)* **233**, 319–321.

Engelke, A. L., Hamzi, H. Q., and Skoog, F. (1973). *Am. J. Bot.* **60**, 491–495.

Erion, J. L., and Fox, J. E. (1975). *Plant Physiol.* **56**, Suppl., 28.

Erion, J. L., and Fox, J. E. (1977). *Plant Physiol.* **59**, Suppl., 83.

Erismann, K. H., and Fankhauser, M. (1967). *Experientia* **23**, 621–622.

Errera, L. (1904). *Bull. Soc. R. Bot. Belg.* **42**, 17.

Fairfield, S. A., and Barnett, W. E. (1971). *Proc. Natl. Acad. Sci. U.S.A.* **68**, 2972–2976.

Fankhauser, M., and Erismann, K. H. (1969). *Planta* **88**, 332–334.

Faulkner, R. D., and Uziel, M. (1971). *Biochim. Biophys. Acta* **238**, 464–474.

Fawcett, C. H., and Wright, S. T. C. (1968). *Phytochemistry* **7**, 1719–1725.

Feierabend, J. (1969). *Planta* **84**, 11–29.

Feierabend, J. (1970a). *Planta* **94**, 1–15.

Feierabend, J. (1970b). *Z. Pflanzenphysiol.* **62**, 70–82.

Feng, K. A., and Unger, J. W. (1972). *Experientia* **28**, 1310–1311.

Ferguson, C. H. R., and Simon, E. W. (1973). *J. Exp. Bot.* **24**, 307–316.

Fittler, F., and Hall, R. H. (1966). *Biochem. Biophys. Res. Commun.* **25**, 441–446.

Fittler, F., Kline, L. K., and Hall, R. H. (1968). *Biochemistry* **7**, 940–944.

Fletcher, R. A., and McCullagh, D. (1971a). *Can. J. Bot.* **49**, 2197–2202.

Fletcher, R. A., and McCullagh, D. (1971b). *Planta* **101**, 88–90.

Fletcher, R. A., Teo, C., and Ali, A. (1973). *Can. J. Bot.* **51**, 937.

Forsline, P. L., and Langille, A. R. (1975). *Can. J. Bot.* **54**, 2513–2516.

Fountain, D. W., and Bewley, J. D. (1976). *Plant Physiol.* **58**, 530–536.

Fox, J. E., and Chen, C.-M. (1967). *J. Biol. Chem.* **242**, 4490–4494.

Fox, J. E., and Erion, J. L. (1975). *Biochem. Biophys. Res. Commun.* **64**, 694–700.

Fox, J. E., Sood, C. K., Buckwalter, B., and McChesney, J. D. (1971). *Plant Physiol.* **47**, 275–281.

Fox, J. E., Dyson, W. H., Sood, D., and McChesney, J. D. (1972). *In* "Plant Growth Substances" (D. J. Carr, ed.), pp. 449–458. Springer-Verlag, Berlin and New York.

Fox, J. E., Cornette, J., Deleuze, G., Dyson, W. H., Giersak, G., Niu, P., Zapata, J., and McChesney, J. D. (1973). *Plant Physiol.* **52**, 627–632.

Fox, J. E., Dobbins, J., Russell, D., Starr, A., and Erion, J. (1977). *Plant Physiol.* **59**, Suppl., 84.

Fujii, T. and Ogawa, N. (1972) *Tetrahedron Lett.*, 3075–3078.

Fuller, W., and Hodgson, A. (1967). *Nature (London)* **215**, 817–821.

Furuichi, Y., and Ukita, T. (1970). *Biochem. Biophys. Res. Commun.* **41**, 797–803.

Galston, A. W., Lavee, S., and Siegel, B. Z. (1968). *In* "Biochemistry and Physiology of Plant Growth Substances" (F. Whightman and G. Setterfield, eds.), pp. 455–472. Runge Press, Ottawa.

Gardener, G., Sussman, M. R., and Kende, H. (1975). *Plant Physiol.* **56**, Suppl., 28.

Gardener, G., Sussman, M. R., and Kende, H. (1977). *Plant Growth Regul., Proc. Int. Conf. Plant Growth Subst. 9th, 1976* Abstract, pp. 103–104.

Gaspar, T., and Xhauflaire, A. (1967). *Planta* **72**, 252–257.

Gaspar, T., and Xhauflaire, A. (1968). *Physiol. Plant.* **21**, 792–799.

Gautheret, R.-J. (1966). *Congr. Colloq. Univ. Liege* **38**, 83–94.

Gautheret, R.-J. (1969). *Am. J. Bot.* **56**, 702–717.

Gawer, M., Laloue, M., Terrine, C., and Guern, J. (1977). *Plant Sci. Lett.* **8**, 267–274.

Gefter, M. L. (1969). *Biochem. Biophys. Res. Commun.* **36**, 435.

Gefter, M. L., and Russell, R. L. (1969). *J. Mol. Biol.* **39**, 145–157.

Gepstein, S., and Ilan, I. (1970). *Plant Cell Physiol.* **11**, 819–822.

Ghosh, K., and Ghosh, H. P. (1970). *Biochem. Biophys. Res. Commun.* **40**, 135–143.

Giannattasio, M., and Coppola, S. (1969). *G. Bot. Ital.* **103**, 11–17.

Goldthwaite, J. (1974). *Plant Physiol.* **54**, 399–403.

Goldthwaite, J. J., and Laetsch, W. M. (1967). *Plant Physiol.* **42**, 1757–1762.

Gordon, M. E., Letham, D. S., and Parker, C. W. (1974). *Ann. Bot. (London)* [N.S.] **38**, 809–826.

Gordon, M. E., Letham, D. S., and Beever, J. E. (1975). *Physiol. Plant.* **35**, 27–33.

Gorton, B. S., Skinner, C. G., and Eakin, R. E. (1957). *Arch. Biochem. Biophys.* **66**, 493–496.

Greene, E. M. (1977). M.S. Thesis, University of Wisconsin, Madison.

Gregory, F. G., and Veale, J. A. (1957). *Symp. Soc. Exp. Bot.* **11**, 1–20.

Grierson, D., Chambers, S. E., and Penniket, L. P. (1977). *Planta* **134**, 29–34.

Grimm, W., Fujii, T., and Leonard, N. J. (1968). *In* "Synthetic Procedures in Nucleic Acid Chemistry" (W. W. Zorbach and R. S. Tipson, eds.), Vol. 1, pp. 212–214. Wiley, New York.

Guern, J., Doree, M., and Sadorge, S. (1968). *In* "Biochemistry and Physiology of Plant Growth Substances" (F. Whightman and G. Setterfield, eds.), pp. 1155–1167. Runge Press, Ottawa.

Guillemaut, P., Martin, R., and Weil, J. H. (1976). *FEBS Lett.* **63**, 273–277.

Haber, A. H., and Tolbert, N. E. (1959). *In* "Photoperiodism and Related Phenomena in Plants and Animals," Publ. No. 55, pp. 197–206. Am. Assoc. Adv. Sci., Washington, D.C.

Haddon, L. E., and Northcote, D. H. (1975). *J. Cell Sci.* **17**, 11–26.

Haddon, L. E., and Northcote, D. H. (1976). *J. Cell Sci.* **20**, 47–56.

Häggman, J., and Haapala, H. (1971). *Physiol. Plant.* **24**, 548–551.

Hahn, H., and Bopp, M. (1968). *Planta* **83**, 115–118.

Hall, R. H. (1970). *Prog. Nucleic Acid Res. Mol. Biol.* **10**, 57–86.
Hall, R. H. (1973). *Annu. Rev. Plant Physiol.* **24**, 415–444.
Hall, R. H., Csonka, L., David, H., and McLennon, B. (1967). *Science* **156**, 69–71.
Halperin, W., and Minocha, S. (1973). *Can. J. Bot.* **51**, 1347–1354.
Hamilton, J. L., Lowe, R. H., and Skoog, F. (1972). *Plant Physiol.* **50**, 303–304.
Hamzi, H. Q., and Skoog, F. (1964). *Proc. Natl. Acad. Sci. U.S.A.* **51**, 76–83.
Harvey, B. M. R., Lu, B. C., and Fletcher, R. A. (1974). *Can. J. Bot.* **52**, 2581–2586.
Hashimoto, T. (1961). *Bot. Mag.* **74**, 110.
Hashizume, T., and Iizuka, M. (1971). *Phytochemistry* **10**, 2653–2656.
Havránek, P., and Novák, F. J. (1973). *Z. Pflanzenphysiol.* **68**, 308–318.
Hecht, S. M. (1978). *Bioorg. Chem.* (in press).
Hecht, S. M., and Werner, D. (1973). *J. Chem. Soc., Perkin Trans.* **17**, 1903–1905.
Hecht, S. M., Leonard, N. J., Burrows, W. J., Armstrong, D. J., Skoog, F., and Occolowitz, J. (1969a). *Science* **166**, 1272–1274.
Hecht, S. M., Leonard, N. J., Occolowitz, J., Burrows, W. J., Armstrong, D. J., Skoog, F., Bock, R. M., Gillam, I., and Tener, G. M. (1969b). *Biochem. Biophys. Res. Commun.* **35**, 205–209.
Hecht, S. M., Bock, R. M., Leonard, N. J., Schmitz, R. Y., and Skoog, F. (1970a). *Biochem. Biophys. Res. Commun.* **41**, 435–440.
Hecht, S. M., Leonard, N. J., Schmitz, R. Y., and Skoog, F. (1970b). *Phytochemistry* **9**, 1173–1180.
Hecht, S. M., Bock, R. M., Schmitz, R. Y., Skoog, F., and Leonard, N. J. (1971a). *Proc. Natl. Acad. Sci. U.S.A.* **68**, 2608–2610.
Hecht, S. M., Bock, R. M., Schmitz, R. Y., Skoog, F., Leonard, N. J., and Occolowitz, J. L. (1971b). *Biochemistry* **10**, 4224–4228.
Hecht, S. M., Frye, R. B., Werner, D., Hawrelak, S. D., Skoog, F., and Schmitz, R. Y. (1975). *J. Biol. Chem.* **250**, 7343–7351.
Heide, O. M. (1965). *Physiol. Plant.* **18**, 891–920.
Helgeson, J. P., and Leonard, N. J. (1966). *Proc. Natl. Acad. Sci. U.S.A.* **56**, 60–63.
Henderson, T. R., Skinner, C. G., and Eakin, R. E. (1962). *Plant Physiol.* **37**, 552–555.
Henderson, T. R., Frihart, C. R., Leonard, N. J., Schmitz, R. Y., and Skoog, F. (1975). *Phytochemistry* **14**, 1687–1690.
Henson, I. E., and Wareing, P. F. (1977). *New Phytol.* **78**, 27–33.
Henson, I. E., and Wheeler, C. T. (1977a). *J. Exp. Bot.* **28**, 205–214.
Henson, I. E., and Wheeler, C. T. (1977b). *Z. Pflanzenphysiol.* **84**, 179–182.
Hewett, E. W., and Wareing, P. F. (1973a). *Plant Physiol.* **29**, 386–389.
Hewett, E. W., and Wareing, P. F. (1973b). *Planta* **112**, 225–234.
Hicks, G. S., and Sussex, I. M. (1970). *Can. J. Bot.* **48**, 133–139.
Hirschberg, K., Hubner, G., and Boriss, H. (1972). *Planta* **108**, 333–337.
Hodge, E. T., and Sacher, J. A. (1975). *Biochem. Physiol. Pflanz.* **168**, 433–441.
Hooykaas, P. J. J., Klapwijk, P. M., Nuti, M. P., Schilperoort, R. A., and Rörsch, A. (1977). *J. Gen. Microbiol.* **98**, 477–484.
Hordern, J., Johnson, R. H., and McLennon, B. D. (1975). *Can. J. Microbiol.* **21**, 633–638.
Horgan, R. (1975). *Biochem. Biophys. Res. Commun.* **65**, 352–357.
Horgan, R. (1977) *Plant Growth Regul., Proc. Int. Conf. Plant Growth Subst., 9th, 1976* Abstract, pp. 150–151.
Horgan, R., Hewett, E. W., Purse, J. G., and Wareing, P. F. (1973). *Tetrahedron* **30**, 2827–2828.
Horgan, R., Hewett, E. W. M., Morgan, J. M., Purse, J. G., and Wareing, P. F. (1975). *Phytochemistry* **14**, 1005–1008.

Hugel, B. (1976). Z. *Pflanzenphysiol.* **80**, 298–305.
Hussey, G. (1976). *Ann. Bot. (London* [N.S.] **40**, 1323–1326.
Ilan, I., Gilad, T., and Reinhold, L. (1971). *Physiol. Plant.* **24**, 337–341.
Ishikura, H., Yamada, Y., Murao, K., Saneyoshi, M., and Nishimura, S. (1969). *Biochem. Biophys. Res. Commun.* **37**, 990–996.
Iwamura, H., Ito, T., Kumazawa, Z., and Ogawa, Y. (1974). *Biochem. Biophys. Res. Commun.* **57**, 412–416.
Iwamura, H., Kumazawa, Z., Nagato, S., and Okuda, S. (1976). *Agric. Biol. Chem.* **40**, 1653–1654.
Jablonski, J., and Skoog, F. (1954). *Physiol. Plant.* **7**, 16–24.
Jackson, D. I., and Field, R. J. (1972). *Ann. Bot. (London)* [N.S.] **36**, 525–532.
Jacobs, W. P. (1959). *Dev. Biol.* **1**, 527–533.
Jacoby, B., and Dagan, J. (1970). *Physiol. Plant.* **23**, 397–403.
Johnson, G. S., D'Armento, M., and Carchman, R. A. (1974). *Exp. Cell Res.* **85**, 47–56.
Jordan, W. R. (1971). Ph.D. Thesis, University of Wisconsin, Madison.
Jordan, W. R., and Skoog, F. (1971). *Plant Physiol.* **48**, 97–99.
Jouanneau, J.-P., and De Marsac, N. T. (1973). *Exp. Cell Res.* **77**, 167–174.
Jouanneau, J.-P., and Péaud-LeNoël, C. (1967). *Physiol. Plant.* **20**, 834–850.
Jouanneau, J.-P., Gander, J.-C., and Péaud-LeNoël, C. (1977). *Plant Growth Regnl. Proc. Int. Conf. Plant Growth Subst., 9th, 1976* Abstract, 174–176.
Kaiss-Chapman, R. W., and Morris, R. O. (1977). *Biochem. Biophys. Res. Commun.* **76**, 453–459.
Kende, H. (1971). *Int. Rev. Cytol.* **31**, 301–338.
Kende, H., and Shen, T. C. (1972). *Biochim. Biophys. Acta* **286**, 118–125.
Kende, H., and Tavares, J. (1968). *Plant Physiol.* **43**, 1244.
Kende, H., Hahn, H., and Kays, S. E. (1971). *Plant Physiol.* **48**, 702–706.
Key, J. E. (1969). *Annu. Rev. Plant Physiol.* **20**, 449–474.
Keys, R. D., Smith, O. E., Kumamoto, J., and Lyon, J. L. (1975). *Plant Physiol.* **56**, 826–829.
Khan, A. A. (1968). *Plant Physiol.* **43**, 1463–1465.
Khan, A. A., and Downing, R. D. (1968). *Physiol. Plant.* **21**, 1301–1307.
Khan, A. A., and Tolbert, N. E. (1965). *Physiol. Plant.* **18**, 41–43.
Kikuta, Y., Harada, T., Akamine, T., and Tagawa, T. (1977). *Plant Cell Physiol.* **18**, 361–370.
Kinsman, L. T., Pinfield, N. J., and Stobart, A. K. (1975). *Planta* **127**, 207–212.
Klämbt, D. (1967). *Naturwiss. Reihe* **16**, 623–625.
Klämbt, D. (1976). *Plant Cell Physiol.* **17**, 73–76.
Klämbt, D., Theis, G., and Skoog, F. (1966). *Proc. Natl. Acad. Sci. U.S.A.* **56**, 52–59.
Klein, A. O. (1959). Ph.D. Thesis, Indiana University, Bloomington.
Kliachko, N. L., Iakovleva, L. A., and Kulaeva, O. N. (1973). *Dokl. Akad. Nauk SSSR* **211**, 1235–1238.
Kline, L., Fittler, F., and Hall, R. H. (1969). *Biochemistry* **8**, 4361.
Knypl, J. S. (1973). *Z. Pflanzenphysiol.* **70**, 1–11.
Knypl, J. S., and Chylinska, K. M. (1973). *Z. Pflanzenphysiol.* **70**, 414–420.
Koblitz, H. (1962). *Faserforsch. Textiltech.* **13**, 231–234 and 310–317.
Koblitz, H. (1964). *Flora (Jena)* **154**, 511–546.
Köhler, K. H., and Conrad, K. (1966). *Biol. Rundsch.* **4**, 36–37.
Koshimizu, K., Kusaki, T., Mitsui, T., and Matsubara, S. (1967). *Tetrahedron* **14**, 1317–1320.
Kuboi, T., and Yamada, Y. (1976). *Phytochemistry* **15**, 397–400.
Kuhnle, J. A., Fuller, G., Corse, J., and Mackey, B. E. (1977). *Physool. Plant* **41**, 14–21.
Kulaeva, O. N. (1973). "Cytokinins, Their Structure and Function." USSR Acad. Sci., Moscow.
Kulaeva, O. N., and Klyachko, N. L. (1965). *Dokl. Akad. Nauk SSSR* **164**, 458–461.
Kulaeva, O. N., and Romanko, E. G. (1967). *Dokl. Biol. Sci. (Engl. Transl.* **177**, 464.

Kulaeva, O. N., Cherkasov, V. M., and Tretyakova, G. S. (1968). *Dokl. Biochem. (Engl. Transl.)* 1-6, 39–42.

Kull, U., and Buxenstein, R. (1974). *Phytochemistry* 13, 39–44.

Kull, U., and Hoffman, F. (1975). *Biol. Plant.* 17, 31–37.

Kuraishi, S. (1959). *Sci. Pap. Coll. Gen. Educ. Univ. Tokyo* 9, 67–104.

Kuraishi, S. (1968). *Physiol. Plant.* 21, 78–83.

Kuraishi, S. (1976). *Plant Cell Physiol.* 17, 875–886.

Laloue, M. (1977). *Planta* 134, 273–276.

Laloue, M., Terrine, C., and Gawer, M. (1974). *FEBS Lett.* 46, 45–50.

Laloue, M., Gawer, M., and Terrine, C. (1975). *Physiol Veg.* 13, 781–796.

Laloue, M., Gawer, M., Terrine, C., and Guern, J. (1977a). *Plant Growth Regul. Proc. Int. Conf. Plant Growth Subst., 9th, 1976* Abstract, pp. 211–213.

Laloue, M., Terrine, C., and Guern, J. (1977b). *Plant Physiol.* 59, 478–483.

La Motte, C. E. (1960). Ph.D. Thesis, University of Wisconsin, Madison.

Lee, T. T. (1971a). *Plant Physiol.* 47, 181–185.

Lee, T. T. (1971b). *Plant Physiol.* 48, 56–59.

Lee, T. T. (1972). *Can. J. Bot.* 50, 2471.

Lee, T. T. (1974). *Phytochemistry* 13, 2445–2454.

Le John, H. B. (1975). *Can. J. Biochem.* 53, 768–778.

Le John, H. B., and Cameron, L. E. (1973). *Biochem. Biophys. Res. Commun.* 54, 1053–1060.

Le John, H. B., and Stevenson, R. M. (1973). *Biochem. Biophys. Res. Commun.* 54, 1061–1066.

LeJohn, H. B., Cameron, L. E., Stevenson, R. M., and Meuser, R. U. (1974). *J. Biol. Chem.* 249, 4016–4020.

Leonard, N. J (1974). *Recent Adv. Phytochem.* 7, 21–56.

Leonard, N. J., and Henderson, T. R. (1975). *J. Am. Chem. Soc.* 97, 4990–4999.

Leonard, N. J., Hecht, S. M., Skoog, F., and Schmitz, R. Y. (1968). *Proc. Natl. Acad. Sci. U.S.A.* 59, 15–21.

Leonard, N. J., Hecht, S. M., Schmitz, R. Y., and Skoog, F. (1969). *Proc. Natl. Acad. Sci. U.S.A.* 63, 175–182.

Leonard, N. J., Playtis, A. J., Skoog, F., and Schmitz, R. Y. (1971). *J. Am. Chem. Soc.* 93, 3056–3058.

Leopold, A. C., and Kawase, M. (1964). *Am. J. Bot.* 51, 294–298.

Leopold, A. C., and Kreidemann, P. E. (1975). "Plant Growth and Development." McGraw-Hill, New York.

Leroux, R. (1973). *Rev. Cytol. Biol. Veg.* 36, 1–132.

Letham, D. S. (1969). *New Zealand J. Agr. Res.* 12, (1) 1–20.

Letham, D. S. (1966). *Life Sci.* 5, 1999–2004.

Letham, D. S. (1967). *Planta* 74, 228–242.

Letham, D. S. (1972). *Phytochemistry* 11, 1023–1025.

Letham, D. S. (1973). *Phytochemistry* 12, 2445–2456.

Letham, D. S., and Miller, C. O. (1965). *Plant Cell Physiol.* 6, 355–359.

Letham, D. S., Shannon, J. S., and McDonald, I. R. (1964). *Proc. Chem. Soc., London* p. 30.

Letham, D. S., Shannon, J. S., and McDonald, I. R. C. (1967). *Tetrahedron* 23, 479–486.

Letham, D. S. Parker, C. W., and Gordon, M. E. (1972). *Physiol. Plant.* 27, 285–290.

Letham, D. S., Wilson, M. M., Parker, C. W., Jenkins, I. D., MacLeod, J. K., and Summons, R. E. (1975). *Biochim. Biophys. Acta* 399, 61–71.

Letham, D. S., Parker, C. W., Duke, C. C., Summons, R. E., and MacLeod, J. K. (1977). *Ann. Bot. (London)* [N.S.] 41, 261–264.

Linsmaier, E. M., and Skoog, F. (1965). *Physiol. Plant.* **18**, 100–127.

Linsmaier-Bednar, E. M., and Skoog, F. (1967). *Planta* **72**, 146–154.

Litwack, M. D., and Peterkofsky, A. (1971). *Biochemistry* **10**, 994–1000.

Loeffler, J. E., and Van Overbeek, J. (1964). *In* "Régulateurs naturels de la croissance végétale" (J. P. Nitsch, ed.), pp. 77–82. CNRS, Paris.

McCalla, D. R., Moore, D. J., and Osborne, D. (1962). *Biochim. Biophys. Acta* **55**, 522–528.

McChesney, J. D. (1970). *Can. J. Bot.* **48**, 2357–2359.

McCombs, P. J. A., and Ralph, R. K. (1972). *Biochem. J.* **129**, 403–418.

McDonald, J. J., Leonard, N. J., Schmitz, R. Y., and Skoog, F. (1971). *Phytochemistry* **10**, 1429–1439.

McLennon, B. D., and Pater, A. (1973). *Can. J. Biochem.* **51**, 1123–1125.

MacLeod, J. K., Summons, R. E., Parker, C. W., and Letham, D. S. (1975). *J. Chem. Soc., Chem. Commun.* pp 809–810.

Madison, J. T., and Kung, H.-K. (1967). *J. Biol. Chem.* **242**, 1324–1330.

Madison, J. T., Everett, G. A., and Kung, H.-K. (1967). *J. Biol. Chem.* **242**, 1318–1323.

Mann, J. D., Steinhart, C. E., and Mudd, S. H. (1963). *J. Biol. Chem.* **238**, 676–681.

Martin, C., and Thimann, K. V. (1972). *Plant Physiol.* **49**, 64–71.

Martin, J. H., Fox, J. E., and McChesney, J. D. (1973). *Phytochemistry* **12**, 749–752.

Matsubara, S., Shiojiri, S., Fujii, T., Ogawa, N., Imamura, K., Yamaguchi, K., and Koshimizu, K. (1977). *Phytochemistry* **16**, 933–938.

Matthysee, A. G., and Abrams, M. (1970). *Biochim. Biophys. Acta* **129**, 511–518.

Mauseth, J. D. (1976). *Am. J. Bot.* **63**, 1295–1301.

Mauseth, J. D., and Halperin, W. (1975). *Am. J. Bot* **62**, 869–877.

Melchers, G., and Labib, G. (1974). *Mol. Gen. Genet.* **135**, 277–296.

Miller, C. O. (1956). *Plant Physiol.* **31**, 318–319.

Miller, C. O. (1965). *Proc. Natl. Acad. Sci. U.S.A.* **54**, 1052–1058.

Miller, C. O. (1968). *In* "Biochemistry and Physiology of Plant Growth Substances" (F. Wightman and G. Setterfield, eds.), pp. 1043–1046. Runge Press, Ottawa.

Miller, C. O. (1969). *Planta* **87**, 26–35.

Miller, C. O. (1974). *Proc. Natl. Acad. Sci. U.S.A.* **71**, 334–338.

Miller, C. O. (1975). *Proc. Natl. Acad. Sci. U.S.A.* **72**, 1883–1886.

Miller, C. O., Skoog, F., Okumura, F. S., von Saltza, M. H., and Strong, F. M. (1955). *J. Am. Chem. Soc.* **77**, 2662.

Mishra, D. (1966). *Naturwissenschaften* **12**, 307–308.

Miura, G., and Hall, R. H. (1973). *Plant Physiol.* **51**, 563–569.

Miura, G., and Miller, C. O. (1969). *Plant Physiol.* **44**, 372–376.

Mizrahi, Y., Amir, J., and Richmond, A. E. (1970). *New Phytol.* **69**, 355–362.

Mlodianowski, F., and Kwintkiewicz, M. (1973). *Protoplasma* **76**, 211–226.

Mok, M. C., Gabelman, W. H., and Skoog, F. (1976). *J. Am. Soc. Hortic. Sci.* **101**, 442–449.

Mok, M. C., Mok, D. W. S., and Armstrong, D. J. (1978). *Plant Physiol.* **61**, 72–75.

Montaldi, E. R. (1972). *Z. Pflanzenphysiol.* **67**, 43–44.

Moore, H. F. (1977). *Plant Physiol.* **59**, Suppl., 17.

Moore, H. F. (1978). Ph.D. Thesis, University of Wisconsin, Madison.

Moore, T. S., and Miller, C. O. (1972). *Plant Physiol.* **50**, 594–598.

Moreland, C. F. (1934). *N.Y., Agric. Exp. Stn., Ithaca, Mem.* **167**, 3–28.

Morris, R. O. (1977). *Plant Physiol.* **59**, 1029–1033.

Mothes, K. (1964). *In* "Régulateurs naturels de la croissance végétale" (J. P. Nitsch, ed.), pp. 131–140. CNRS, Paris.

Mothes, K., and Engelbrecht, L. (1961). *Phytochemistry* **1**, 58–62.

Müller, A. M. (1935). *Jahrb. Wiss. Bot.* **81**, 497–540.

Murai, N., Armstrong, D. J., and Skoog, F. (1975). *Plant Physiol.* **55**, 853–858.
Murai, N., Taller, B. J., Armstrong, D. J., Skoog, F., Micke, M. A., and Schnoes, H. K. (1977). *Plant Physiol.* **60**, 197–202.
Murakoshi, I., Ikegami, F., Ookawa, N., Haginiwa, J., and Letham, D. S. (1977). *Chem. Pharm. Bull.* **25**, 520–522.
Murashige, T. (1974). *Annu. Rev. Plant Physiol.* **25**, 135–166.
Murashige, T. (1977). *HortScience* **12**, 127–130.
Murashige, T., and Skoog, F. (1962). *Physiol. Plant.* **15**, 473–497.
Muren, R. C., and Fosket, D. E. (1977). *J. Exp. Bot.* **28**, 775–784.
Nag, K. K., and Johri, B. M. (1970). *Planta* **90**, 360–364.
Nagao, M. A., and Rubinstein, B. (1975). *Bot. Gaz. (Chicago)* **136**, 366–371.
Nagao, M. A., and Rubinstein, B. (1976). *Bot. Gaz. (Chicago)* **137**, 39–44.
Negi, S. S., and Olmo, H. P. (1966). *Science* **152**, 1624–1625.
Negi, S. S., and Olmo, H. P. (1972). *Am. J. Bot.* **59**, 851–857.
Nicholls, P. B., and Murray, A. W. (1968). *Plant Physiol.* **43**, 645–648.
Nickell, L., and Heinz, D. J. (1973). *In* "Genes, Enzymes, and Populations" (A. Srb, ed.), Basic Life Sciences Vol. 2, pp. 109–128. Plenum, New York.
Nishimura, S. (1972). *Prog. Nucleic Acid Res. Mol. Biol.* **12**, 49–85.
Nishimura, S., Yamada, Y., and Ishikura, H. (1969). *Biochim. Biophys. Acta* **179**, 517–520.
Nomura, T., Tanaka, Y., Abe, H., and Uchiyama, M. (1977). *Phytochemistry* **16**, 1819–1820.
Ohkawa, M. (1974). *HortScience* **9**, 458–459.
Ohsugi, M., Ichimoto, I., and Ueda, H. (1974). *J. Agric. Chem. Soc.* **48**, 373–378.
Okada, N., Harada, F., and Nishimura, S. (1976). *Nucleic Acids Res.* **3**, 2593–2603.
Oppenoorth, J. M. (1976). *Proc. R. Soc. London, Ser. C* **79**, 299.
Osborne, D., and McCalla, D. R. (1961). *Plant Physiol.* **36**, 219–221.
Pačes, V. (1976). *Biochem. Biophys. Res. Commun.* **72**, 830–839.
Pačes, V., and Kaminek, M. (1976). *Nucleic Acids Res.* **3**, 2309–2314.
Pačes, V., Werstiuk, E., and Hall, R. H. (1971). *Plant Physiol.* **48**, 775–778.
Pačes, V., Rosenberg, I., Kaminek, M., and Holy, A. (1977). *Collect. Czech. Chem. Commun.* **42**, 2452–2458.
Palmer, C. E. (1976). *Z. Pflanzenphysiol.* **77**, 345–349.
Palmer, C. E., and Baker, W. G. (1973). *Ann. Bot. (London)* [N.S.] **37**, 85–93.
Palmer, C. E., and Smith, O. E. (1969). *Plant Cell Physiol.* **10**, 657–664.
Palmer, C. E., and Smith, O. E. (1970). *Plant Cell Physiol.* **11**, 303–314.
Parkash, V. (1972). *Planta* **102**, 372–373.
Parkash, V. (1973). *Indian J. Exp. Biol.* **11**, 55.
Parker, C. W., and Letham, D. S. (1973). *Planta* **114**, 199–218.
Parker, C. W., and Letham, D. S. (1974). *Planta* **115**, 337–344.
Parker, C. W., Letham, D. S., Cowley, D. E., and MacLeod, J. K. (1972). *Biochem. Biophys. Res. Commun.* **49**, 460–467.
Parker, C. W., Wilson, M. M., Letham, D. S., Cowley, D. E., and MacLeod, J. K. (1973). *Biochem. Biophys. Res. Commun.* **55**, 1370–1376.
Parker, C. W., Letham, D. S., Wilson, M. M., Jenkins, I. D., MacLeod, J. K., and Summons, R. E. (1975). *Ann. Bot. (London)*]N.S.] **39**, 375–376.
Parthier, B. (1964). *Flora (Sena)* **154**, 230–244.
Patau, K., Das, N. K., and Skoog, F. (1957). *Physiol. Plant.* **10**, 949–966.
Pecket, R. C., and Bassim, T. A. H. (1974). *Phytochemistry* **13**, 1395–1400.
Pedersén, M. (1973). *Physiol. Plant.* **28**, 101–105.
Pedersén, M., and Fridborg, G. (1972). *Experientia* **28**, 111.
Pelet, F., Hildebrandt, A. C., Riker, A. J., and Skoog, F. (1960). *Am. J. Bot.* **47**, 186–195.

Pereira, A. S. R., Hovwen, P. J. W., Deurenberg-Vos, H. W. J., and Pey, E. B. F. (1972). Z. Pflanzenphysiol. 68, 170–177.
Peterkofsky, A. (1968). Biochemistry 7, 472–482.
Peterkofsky, A., and Jesensky, C. (1969). Biochemistry 8, 3798–3804.
Peterson, J. B., and Miller, C. O. (1976). Plant Physiol. 57, 393–399.
Peterson, J. B., and Miller, C. O. (1977). Plant Physiol. 59, 1026–1028.
Phillips, D. A., and Torrey, J. G. (1970). Physiol. Plant. 23, 1057–1063.
Phillips, D. A., and Torrey, J. G. (1972). Plant Physiol. 49, 11–15.
Phillips, I. D. J. (1969). In "Physiology of Plant Growth and Development" (M. B. Wilkins, ed.), pp. 163–202. McGraw-Hill, New York.
Phillips, I. D. J. (1975). Annu. Rev. Plant Physiol. 26, 341–367.
Pierik, R. L. M. (1975). Acta Hortic. 54, 71–82.
Pinkerton, T. C., Paddock, G., and Abelson, J. (1973). J. Biol. Chem. 248, 6348.
Playtis, A. J., and Leonard, N. J. (1971). Biochem. Biophys. Res. Commun. 45, 1–5.
Poggi-Pellegrini, M.-C., and Bulard, C. (1976). Physiol. Plant. 36, 40–46.
Pongs, O., and Reinwald, E. (1973). Biochem. Biophys. Res. Commun. 50, 357–363.
Poovaiah, B. W., and Leopold, A. C. (1973). Plant Physiol. 52, 236–239.
Pozsár, B. I., and Kiraly, Z. (1964). In "Host-Parasite Relations" (Z. Kiraly and G. Ubrizsy, eds.), pp. 199–210. Publ. Plant Pro. Res. Inst., Budapest, Hungary.
Pozsár, B. I., and Kiraly, Z. (1966). Phytopathol. Z. 56, 297–309.
Prakash, R., and Maheshwari, S. C. (1970). Physiol. Plant. 23, 792–799.
Probine, M. C. (1965). Proc. R. Soc. London, Ser. B 161, 526–627.
Provasoli, L. (1958). Biol. Bull. (Woods Hole, Mass.) 114, 375–384.
RajBhandary, U. L., Chang, S. H., Stuart, A., Faulkner, R. D., Hoskinson, R. M., and Khorana, H. G. (1967). Proc. Natl. Acad. Sci. U.S.A. 57, 751–758.
Rakhimbaer, I. R., and Solomina, V. F. (1975). Sov. Plant Physiol. (Engl. Transl.) 22, 517–519.
Ralph, R. K., McCombs, P. J. A., Tener, G., and Wojcik, S. J. (1972). Biochem. J. 130, 901–912.
Ralph, R. K., Bullivant, S., and Wojcik, S. (1976). Biochim. Biophys. Acta 421, 319–327.
Rao, V. S., Sankhla, N., and Khan, A. A. (1975). Plant Physiol. 56, 265–266.
Rao, V. S., Braun, J. W., and Khan, A. A. (1976). Plant Physiol. 57, 446–449.
Rathbone, M. P., and Hall, R. H. (1972). Planta 108, 93–102.
Reger, B. J., Fairfield, S. A., Epler, J. L., and Barnett, W. E. (1970). Proc. Natl. Acac. Sci. U.S.A. 67, 1207–1213.
Reynolds, T., and Thompson, T. A. (1973). Physiol. Plant. 28, 516–522.
Richmond, A. E., and Lang, A. (1957). Science 125, 650–651.
Richmond, A. E., Sachs, B., and Osborne, D. J. (1971). Physiol. Plant. 24, 176–180.
Rogozinska, J. H., Helgeson, J. P., and Skoog, F. (1964). Physiol. Plant. 17, 165–176.
Rogozinska, J. H., Croon, C., and Salemink, C. A. (1973). Phytochemistry 12, 2087–2092.
Romanko, E. G., Selivankina, S. Y., Yu, S., and Ohmann, E. E. (1976). Sov. Plant Physiol. (Engl. Transl.) 23, 460–466.
Romanow, I., Chalvignac, M. A., and Pochon, J. (1969). Ann. Inst. Pasteur, Paris 117, 58–63.
Rosenbaum, N., and Gefter, M. L. (1972). J. Biol. Chem. 247, 5675–5680.
Rothwell, K., and Wright, S. T. C. (1967). Proc. R. Soc. London, Ser. B 167, 202–223.
Roussaux, J. (1966). C. R. Hebd. Seames Acad. Sci., Ser, D 263, 1077–1080.
Sacher, J. A., Morgan, E. J., and De La Rosa, D. (1975). Plant Physiol. 56, 442–449.
Sahulka, J. (1972). Biol. Plant. 14, 330–336.
Samuels, R. M. (1961). Ph.D. Thesis, Indiana University, Bloomington.
Sargent, J. A., and Skoog, F. (1960). Plant Physiol. 35, 934–941.
Sargent, J. A., and Skoog, F. (1961). Physiol. Plant. 14, 504–519.

Saunders, J. W. (1973). Ph.D. Thesis, University of Wisconsin, Madison.

Saunders, J. W., and Bingham, E. T. (1975). *Am. J. Bot.* **62**, 850–858.

Scarbrough, E., Armstrong, D. J., Skoog, F., Frihart, C. R., and Leonard, N. J. (1973). *Proc. Natl. Acad. Sci. U.S.A.* **70**, 3825–3829.

Schaeffer, G. W., and Sharpe, F. T., Jr. (1971). *Physiol. Plant.* **25**, 456–460.

Schaeffer, G. W., St. John, J. B., and Sharpe, F. T., Jr. (1972). *Biochim. Biophys. Acta* **261**, 38–43.

Schlee, D., Reinbothe, H., and Mothes, K. (1966). *Z. Pflanzenphysiol.* **54**, 223–236.

Schmid, M. S. (1960). M.S. Thesis, University of Wisconsin, Madison.

Schmitz, R. Y., Skoog, F., Playtis, A. J., and Leonard, N. J. (1972). *Plant Physiol.* **50**, 702–705.

Schmitz, R. Y., Skoog, F., Vincze, A., Walker, G. C., Kirkegaard, L. H., and Leonard, N. J. (1975). *Phytochemistry* **14**, 1479–1484.

Schneider, J., and Szweykowska, A. (1974). *Z. Pflanzenphysiol.* **72**, 95–106.

Schneider, J., and Szweykowska, A. (1975). *Biochem. Physiol. Pflanz.* **167**, 207–217.

Schneider, M. J., Lin, J. C. J., and Skoog, F. (1969). *Plant Physiol.* **44**, 1207–1210.

Schweizer, M. P., McGrath, K., and Baczynsky, L. (1970). *Biochem. Biophys. Res. Commun.* **40**, 1046–1052.

Scopes, D. I. C., Zarnack, W., Leonard, N. J., Schmitz, R. Y., and Skoog, F. (1976). *Phytochemistry* **15**, 1523–1526.

Sekiya, J., and Yamada, Y. (1974). *Bull. Inst. Chem. Res., Kyoto Univ.* **52**, 246–255.

Sequeira, L. (1973). *Annu. Rev. Plant Physiol.* **24**, 353–380.

Servettaz, O., Cortesi, F., and Longo, C. P. (1976). *Plant Physiol.* **58**, 659–572.

Seth, A. K., and Wareing, P. F. (1967). *J. Exp. Bot.* **18**, 65–77.

Shantz, E. M., and Steward, F. C. (1955). *J. Am. Chem. Soc.* **77**, 6351–6354.

Shaw, G., and Wilson, D. V. (1964). *Proc. Chem. Soc., London* p. 231.

Shaw, G., Smallwood, B. M., and Steward, F. C. (1971). *Phytochemistry* **10**, 2329–2336.

Shibaoka, H., and Thimann, K. V. (1970). *Plant Physiol.* **46**, 212–220.

Shindy, W. W., and Smith, O. E. (1975). *Plant Physiol.* **55**, 550–554.

Shininger, T. L., and Polley, L. D. (1977). *Plant Physiol.* **59**, 831–835.

Short, K. C., Tepfer, D. A., and Fosket, D. E. (1974). *J. Cell Sci.* **15**, 75–87.

Simard, A. (1971). *Can. J. Bot.* **49**, 1541–1550.

Simpson, S. F., and Torrey, J. G. (1977). *Plant Physiol.* **59**, 4–9.

Sitton, D., Itai, C., and Kende, H. (1967). *Planta* **73**, 296–300.

Skoog, F. (1939). *Am. J. Bot.* **26**, 702–707.

Skoog, F. (1944). *Am. J. Bot.* **31**, 19–24.

Skoog, F. (1950). *Annee Biol.* **26**, 545–562.

Skoog, F. (1971). *Colloq. Int. CNRS* **193**, 115–135.

Skoog, F. (1973a). *Biochem. Soc. Symp.* **38**, 195–215.

Skoog, F. (1973b). *In* "Genes, Enzymes and Populations" (A. M. Srb, ed.). Basic Life Sciences Vol. 2, Chapter 11, pp. 147–184. Plenum, New York.

Skoog, F., and Armstrong, D. J. (1970). *Annu. Rev. Plant Physiol.* **21**, 359–384.

Skoog, F., and Miller, C. O. (1957). *Symp. Soc. Exp. Biol.* **11**, 118–131.

Skoog, F., and Montaldi, E. (1961). *Proc. Natl. Acad. Sci. U.S.A.* **47**, 36–49.

Skoog, F., and Thimann, K. V. (1934). *Proc. Natl. Acad. Sci. U.S.A.* **20**, 480–485.

Skoog, F., and Tsui, C. (1948). *Am. J. Bot.* **35**, 782–787.

Skoog, F., and Tsui, C. (1951). *In* "Plant Growth Substances" (F. Skoog, ed.), pp. 263–285. Univ. Wisconsin Press, Madison.

Skoog, F., Schneider, C., and Malan, P. (1942). *Am. J. Bot.* **29**, 598–606.

Skoog, F., Hamzi, H. Q., Szweykowska, A. M., Leonard, N. J., Carraway, K. L., Fujii, T., Helgeson, J. P., and Loeppky, R. N. (1967). *Phytochemistry* **6**, 1169–1192.

Skoog, F., Schmitz, R. Y., Bock, R. M., and Hecht, S. M. (1973). *Phytochemistry* **12**, 25–37.

Skoog, F., Schmitz, R. Y., Hecht, S. M., and Frye, R. B. (1975). *Proc. Natl. Acad. Sci. U.S.A.* **72**, 3508–3512.

Smith, O. E., and Palmer, C. E. (1970). *Physiol. Plant.* **23**, 599–606.

Snow, R. (1925). *Ann. Bot. (London)* **39**, 841–859.

Snow, R. (1929). *New Phytol.* **28**, 345–358.

Sodek, L., and Wright, S. T. C. (1969). *Phytochemistry* **8**, 1629–1640.

Sondheimer, E., and Tzou, D.-S. (1971). *Plant Physiol.* **47**, 516–520.

Soulen, T. K., and Olson, L. C. (1969). *Planta* **86**, 205.

Spiess, L. D. (1975). *Plant Physiol.* **55**, 583–585.

Spiess, L. D., Lippincott, B. B., and Lippincott, J. A. (1972). *Am. J. Bot.* **59**, 233–241.

Sprecker, M. A., Morrice, A. G., Gruber, B. A., Leonard, N. J., Schmitz, R. Y., and Skoog, F. (1976). *Phytochemistry* **15**, 609–613.

Srinivasan, C., and Mullins, M. G. (1978). *Plant Physiol.* **61**, 127–130.

Srivastava, B. I. S. (1967a). *Ann. N.Y. Acad. Sci.* **144**, 260–278.

Srivastava, B. I. S. (1967b). *Biochim. Biophys. Acta* **145**, 169–171.

Srivastava, B. I. S. (1968). *Biochem. Biophys. Res. Commun.* **32**, 533–538.

Srivastava, B. I. S., and Arglebe, C. (1968). *Physiol. Plant.* **21**, 851–857.

Srivastava, B. I. S., and Ware, G. (1965). *Plant Physiol.* **40**, 62–64.

Steer, B. T. (1976). *Plant Physiol.* **57**, 928–932.

Steinhart, C. E., Mann, J. D., and Mudd, S. H. (1964). *Plant Physiol.* **39**, 1030–1038.

Stetler, D. A., and Laetsch, W. M. (1965). *Science* **149**, 1387–1388.

Steward, F. C., ed. (1972). "Plant Physiology: A Treatise," Vol. 6B. Academic Press, New York.

Steward, F. C., and Krikorian, A. D. (1971). "Plants, Chemicals and Growth." Academic Press, New York.

Steward, F. C., and Shantz, E. M. (1956). *In* "The Chemistry and Mode of Action of Plant Growth Substances" (R. L. Wain and F. Wightman, eds.), pp. 165–186. Butterworth, London.

Steward, F. C., Shantz, E. M., Pollard, J. K., Mapes, M. O., and Mitra, J. (1961). *In* "Synthesis of Molecular and Cellular Structure" (D. Rudnick, ed.), pp. 193–246. Ronald, New York.

Stobart, A. K., and Kinsman, L. T. (1977). *Phytochemistry* **16**, 1137–1143.

Straub, V., and Lichtenthaler, H. K. (1973). *Z. Pflanzenphysiol.* **70**, 308–321.

Sugiyama, T., Kitamura, E., Kubokawa, S., Kobayashi, S., Hashizume, T., and Matsubara, S. (1975). *Phytochemistry* **14**, 2539–2544.

Sugiyama, T., Matsubara, S., Kobayashi, S., and Hashizume, T. (1977). *Agric. Biol. Chem.* **41**, 605–606.

Sveshnikova, I. N., Kulaeva, O. N., and Bolyakina, Y. P. (1968). *Electron Microsc., Proc. Int. Congr. 6th 1966*, p. 327.

Swaminathan, S., and Bock, R. M. (1977). *Biochemistry* **16**, 1355–1359.

Swaminathan, S., Bock, R. M., and Skoog, F. (1977). *Plant Physiol.* **59**, 558–563.

Syōno, K., Newcomb, W., and Torrey, J. G. (1976). *Can. J. Bot.* **54**, 2155–2162.

Szweykowska, A., Korcz, I., Jaskiewicz-Mroczkowska, B., and Metelska, M. (1972). *Acta Soc. Bot. Pol.* **41**, 408–409.

Tahbaz, F. (1977). *Bull. Soc. Bot. Fr.* **124**, 255–264.

Takebe, I., Labib, G., and Melchers, G. (1971). *Naturwissenschaften* **58**, 318–320.

Takegami, T. (1975a). *Plant Cell Physiol.* **16**, 407–416.

Takegami, T. (1975b). *Plant Cell Physiol.* **16**, 417–426.

Takegami, T., and Yoshida, Y. (1975). *Biochem. Biophys. Res. Commun.* **67**, 782–789.

Takegami, T., and Yoshida, Y. (1976). *Biochem. Biophys. Res. Commun.* **68**, 1035.

Takegami, T., and Yoshida, Y. (1977). *Plant Cell Physiol.* **18**, 337–346.

Taller, B. J., Murai, N., Armstrong, D. J., and Skoog, F. (1977). *Plant Physiol.* **59**, Suppl., 17.

Tavares, J., and Kende, H. (1970). *Phytochemistry* **9**, 1763-1770.

Taya, Y., Tanaka, Y., and Nishimura, S. (1978). *Nature (London)* **271**, 545-546.

Tepfer, S. S., Karpoff, A. J., and Greyson, R. I. (1966). *Am. J. Bot.* **53**, 148-157.

Theiler, J. B. (1977). Ph.D. Thesis, University of Illinois, Urbana.

Theiler, J. B., Leonard, N. J., Schmitz, R. Y., and Skoog, F. (1976). *Plant Physiol.* **58**, 803-805.

Theimer, R. R., Anding, G., and Matzner, P. (1976). *Planta* **128**, 41-48.

Thimann, K. V. (1937). *Am. J. Bot.* **24**, 407-412.

Thimann, K. V. (1977). "Hormones in the Whole Life of Plants." Univ. of Massachusetts Press, Amherst.

Thimann, K. V., and Sachs, T. (1966). *Am. J. Bot.* **53**, 731-739.

Thimann, K. V., and Skoog, F. (1933). *Proc. Natl. Acad. Sci. U.S.A.* **19**, 714-716.

Thimann, K., and Skoog, F. (1934). *Proc. R. Soc. London, Ser. B* **114**, 317-339.

Thimann, K. V., and Wickson, M. (1957). *Union Int. Sci. Biol., Ser. B* **34**, 47-50.

Thimann, K. V., Sachs, T., and Mathur, K. N. (1971). *Physiol. Plant.* **24**, 68-72.

Thimmappaya, B., and Cherayil, D. (1974). *Biochem. Biophys. Res. Commun.* **60**, 665-672.

Thorpe, T. A. (1974). *Physiol. Plant.* **30**, 77-81.

Thorpe, T. A., and Meier, D. D. (1972). *Physiol. Plant.* **27**, 365-369.

Thorpe, T. A., and Murashige, T. (1968). *Science* **160**, 421-422.

Thorpe, T. A., and Murashige, T. (1970). *Can. J. Bot.* **48**, 277-285.

Torigoe, Y., Akiyama, M., Hirobe, M., Okamoto, T., and Isogai, Y. (1972). *Phytochemistry* **11**, 1623-1630.

Torrey, J. G., Fosket, D. E., and Hepler, P. K. (1971). *Am. Sci.* **59**, 338-352.

Torrey, J. G., Callahan, D., and Bowes, B. (1977). *Plant Physiol.* **59**, Suppl., 50.

Treharne, K. J., Stoddart, J. L., Pughe, J., Paranjothy, K., and Wareing, P. F. (1970). *Nature (London)* **228**, 129-131.

Tronchet, A. (1968). *Ann. Sci. Univ. Besancon, Bot.* [3] **5**, 3-8.

Tucker, D. J., and Mansfield, T. A. (1972). *Planta* **102**, 140-150.

Turgeon, R., Wood, H. N., and Braun, A. C. (1976). *Proc. Natl. Acad. Sci. U.S.A.* **73**, 3562-3564.

Tzou, D. S., Galson, E. C., and Sondheimer, E. (1973). *Plant Physiol.* **51**, 894-897.

Udvardy, J., Farkas, G. L., Marré, E., and Forte, G. (1967). *Physiol. Plant.* **20**, 781-788.

Upper, C. D., Helgeson, J. P., Kemp, J. D., and Schmidt, C. J. (1970). *Plant Physiol.* **45**, 543-547.

Van Larebeke, N., Engler, G., Holsters, M., Van den Elsacker, S., Zaenen, I., Schilperoort, R. A., and Schell, J. (1974). *Nature (London)* **252**, 169-170.

Van Overbeek, J. (1968). *Sci. Am.*, **219**, 75-81.

Van Overbeek, J., and Loeffler, J. E. (1965). *Food Sci. Technol., Proc. Int. Cong., 1st, 1962* Vol. 4, p. 357.

Van Staden, J. (1975). *Plant Sci. Lett.* **5**, 227-230.

Van Staden, J. (1976a). *Physiol. Plant.* **36**, 123-126.

Van Staden, J. (1976b). *Physiol. Plant.* **36**, 225-228.

Van Staden, J., and Dimalla, G. G. (1976). *Planta* **130**, 85-88.

Van Staden, J., and Papaphilippou, A. P. (1977). *Plant Physiol.* **60**, 649-650.

Van Steveninck, R. F. M. (1972). *Physiol. Plant.* **27**, 43-47.

Varga, A., and Bruinsma, J. (1973). *Planta* **111**, 91-93.

Verbeek, R., Van Onckelen, H., and Gaspar, T. (1969). *Physiol. Plant.* **22**, 1192-1199.

Verbeek, R., Van Onckelen, H., and Gaspar, T. (1973). *Physiol. Plant.* **29**, 208-211.

Verma, T. C., Tavares, J., and Loewus, F. A. (1976). *Plant Physiol.* **57**, 241-244.

Vickers, J. D., and Logan, D. M. (1970). *Biochem. Biophys. Res. Commun.* **41**, 741-747.

von Saltza, M. H. (1958). Ph.D. Thesis, University of Wisconsin, Madison.

Vreman, H. J., Skoog, F., Frihart, C. R., and Leonard, N. J. (1972). *Plant Physiol.* **49**, 848–851.

Vreman, H. J., Schmitz, R. Y., Skoog, F., Playtis, A. J., Frihart, C. R., and Leonard, N. J. (1974). *Phytochemistry* **13**, 31 38.

Wade, N. L., and Brady, C. J. (1971). *Aust. J. Biol. Sci.* **24**, 165–168.

Wainfan, E., and Landsberg, B. (1971). *FEBS Lett.* **19**, 144–148.

Walker, G. C., Leonard, N. J., Armstrong, D. J., Murai, N., and Skoog, F. (1974). *Plant Physiol.* **54**, 737–743.

Wang, T. L., Thompson, A. G., and Horgan, R. (1977). *Planta* **135**, 285–288.

Wardell, W. L., and Skoog, F. (1969). *Plant Physiol.* **44**, 1402–1406.

Wareing, P. F., and Phillips, I. D. J. (1970). "The Control of Growth and Differentiation in Plants." Pergamon, Oxford.

Wareing, P. F., and Saunders, P. F. (1971). *Annu. Rev. Plant Physiol.* **22**, 261–288.

Weaver, R. J. (1972). "Plant Growth Substances in Agriculture." Freeman, San Francisco, California.

Weaver, R. J., and Van Overbeek, J. (1963). *Calif. Agric.* **17**, 12.

Went, F. W. (1939). *Am. J. Bot.* **26**, 109–117.

Whitaker, B. D. and Kende, H. (1974) *Planta* **121**, 93–96.

White, B. N., Dunn, R., Gillam, I., Tener, G. M., Armstrong, D. J., Skoog, F., Frihart, C. R., and Leonard, N. J. (1975). *J. Biol. Chem.* **250**, 515–521.

Whitty, C. D., and Hall, R. H. (1974). *Can. J. Biochem.* **52**, 789–799.

Wickson, M., and Thimann, K. V. (1956). *Plant Physiol.* **31**, Suppl., 28.

Wickson, M., and Thimann, K. V. (1960). *Physiol. Plant.* **13**, 539–559.

Wilson, M. M., Gordon, M. E., Letham, D. S., and Parker C. W. (1974). *J. Exp. Bot.* **25**, 725–733.

Wood, H. N., and Braun, A. C. (1967). *Ann. N.Y. Acad. Sci.* **144**, 244–250.

Wood, H. N., and Braun, A. C. (1973). *Proc. Natl. Acad. Sci. U.S.A.* **70**, 447–450.

Wood, H. N., Braun, A. C., Brandes, H., and Kende, H. (1969). *Proc. Natl. Acad. Sci. U.S.A.* **62**, 349–356.

Wood, H. N., Lin, M. C., and Braun, A. C. (1972). *Proc. Natl. Acad. Sci. U.S.A.* **60**, 403–406.

Wood, H. N., Rennekamp, M. E., Bowen, D. Y., Field, F. H., and Braun, A. C. (1974). *Proc. Natl. Acad. Sci. U.S.A.* **71**, 4140–4143.

Work, R. (1950). M.S. Thesis, University of Wisconsin, Madison.

Wright, K., and Bowles, R. H. (1974). *J. Cell Sci.* **16**, 433–444.

Wyen, N. V., Erdei, S., Udvardy, J., Bagi, G., and Farkas, G. L. (1972). *J. Exp. Bot.* **23**, 37–44.

Yamada, Y., and Kuboi, T. (1976). *Phytochemistry* **15**, 395–396.

Yamada, Y., Nishimura, S., and Ishikura, H. I. (1971). *Biochim. Biophys. Acta* **247**, 170–174.

Yoshida, K., and Oritani, T. (1972). *Plant Cell Physiol.* **13**, 337–343.

Yoshida, K., and Takegami, T. (1977). *J. Biochem. (Tokyo)* **81**, 791–800.

Zachau, H. C., Dütting, D., and Feldmann, H. (1966). *Angew. Chem., Int. Ed. Engl.* **5**, 422.

Zilberstein, A., Dudock, B., Berissi, H., and Revel, M. (1976). *J. Mol. Biol.* **108**, 43–54.

Zubay, G., Cheong, L., and Gefter, M. (1971). *Proc. Natl. Acad. Sci. U.S.A.* **68**, 2195–2197.

Zwar, J. A. (1973). *J. Exp. Bot.* **24**, 701–710.

CHAPTER 8

Steroid Hormone Receptors in the Central Nervous System

Ivan Lieberburg and Bruce S. McEwen

I. INTRODUCTION

It has long been known that removal of the steroid-producing glands, the gonads and the adrenals, produced pronounced behavioral alterations. The Greek naturalist and philosopher Aristotle (ca. 330 B.C.) was the first to record the behavioral changes in roosters and other animals following castration (cf. Dorfman and Shipley, 1956). Much later, but still before the modern era, A. A. Berthold (1849) proved by transplantation studies with testes that

415

the loss of crowing behavior and sexual activity as a result of orchidectomy of roosters is due to a testicular humoral agent (later identified as testosterone) and not simply to the denervation of the testes. Once steroids became available, it was noted that behavioral and neuroendocrine deficits which appeared after surgical removal of the gonads or adrenals could be markedly reversed by the systemic administration of appropriate steroid preparations. Though it was assumed that the steroids were interacting directly with the brain and pituitary to produce these changes, rigorous proof was lacking.

Such proof came in 1957, when Harris and co-workers demonstrated that complete female sexual behavior could be restored in ovariectomized cats by implanting a small amount of crystalline stilbestrol di-n-butyrate (a synthetic estrogen) into the hypothalamus. This work was confirmed and extended by other groups who demonstrated that female sexual behavior could be induced in ovariectomized rats by hypothalamic implants of crystalline estradiol-17β (E_2) (Lisk, 1962), and that male sexual behavior could be restored in orchidectomized rats by preoptic area implants of crystalline testosterone (T) (Davidson, 1966a). Various control experiments verified that these effects were not due to neural damage incurred during the implantation procedure, nor were they accompanied by substantial diffusion of steroid into the periphery.

With the introduction of tritium-labeled steroids of high specific activity in the 1960's, many laboratories began to examine the ability of various brain regions to retain the steroids after systemic administration (cf. McEwen *et al.*, 1972c, for review). These *in vivo* tissue uptake studies revealed a striking parallel between the brain regions which demonstrated the highest ^{3}H steroid retention after systemic administration and the regions in which the steroids were shown to act after intracranial implantation (cf. McEwen *et al.*, 1972c). At the same time, Jensen's and Gorski's groups (cf. Jensen and DeSombre, 1973; Gorski *et al.*, 1968) played a key role in elucidating a cellular mechanism of estradiol action in the uterus whereby the hormone binds to cytoplasmic receptor proteins, which then enter the cell nucleus and interact directly with the chromatin to alter RNA formation and ultimately protein synthesis. Because estrogens and androgens produce most of their behavioral and neuroendocrine effects with latencies of hours or days (cf. McEwen and Luine, 1978), it appears likely that these steroids may be interacting at the genomic level with brain cells. This may also be the case for progestins, glucocorticoids, and mineralocorticoids.

Stimulated by this possibility, much work has been done toward identifying and characterizing steroid hormone receptor systems in the brain and pituitary gland. The purpose of this chapter is to summarize the present status of knowledge concerning these steroid receptors. First, technical aspects of measuring neural and pituitary steroid receptors will be dealt with; then, the topographic distribution of these receptors, their physical and chemical properties, and evidence that they mediate specific neuroendocrine and behavioral responses will be summarized. The discussion will also deal with the likely involvement of estrogen and androgen receptors in sexual differentiation of the brain. The existence of possible nonclassical steroid–central nervous system (CNS) interactions will also be discussed.

II. TECHNICAL ASPECTS OF MEASURING STEROID BINDING TO PUTATIVE RECEPTORS IN BRAIN AND PITUITARY

A. DEFINITIONS OF TERMS

We will attempt to define some of the most salient terms as they are used in the work under consideration in this chapter. The reader should also consult King and Mainwaring (1974) and Westphal (1971) for additional definitions and for more general discussion of technical aspects of receptor measurement.

Uptake refers to entry of hormone into the tissue *in vitro* or *invivo*. *Retention* implies a holding or delaying of the departure of the hormone from the tissue, and it may be explained by the existence in the tissue of *binding sites*. The two assumptions underlying the interpretation of uptake experiments are (a) that there are a finite number of binding sites which will become saturated by high enough levels of hormone and (b) that certain brain regions possess these sites while other brain regions lack them. Are these binding sites also *"receptors"*? Binding refers to what is observed, while receptors are postulated to exist in order to explain an observed hormone effect.

The term *receptor* has been defined as "an intracellular component almost certainly proteinaceous, responsible for the specific and high affinity binding of a selected steroid hormone and playing an integral part in its mechanism of action" (Mainwaring, 1976). The receptor concept was first introduced by Paul Ehrlich (cf. Himmelweit, 1960) as a mediator of drug effects. It was Ehrlich's proposition that small molecules, such as certain drugs, toxins, and hormones, were made up of two structural components: the haptophore, which combined with the receptor; and the ergophore, which initiated the biological response. As far as steroid–receptor interactions are now understood, this notion is now modified by the proposition that the ergophore is actually part of the receptor itself.

Clark (1933) proposed that the dose–response curve observed for a particular drug could be directly related to receptor occupation if each drug–receptor interaction were a quantum event resulting in a biological effect.

Clark's idea was modified (Kier, 1970) by the notion that receptor sites need not be fully occupied in order for a biological effect to appear, nor was receptor occupation necessarily linearly correlated with the intensity of the effect. This conclusion is of particular importance for steroid research, as it has been demonstrated that there is an excess of steroid receptors in many mammalian tissues (King and Mainwaring, 1974). In this connection, a major problem with the use of the term *receptor* to refer to steroid binding sites in tissues is that in a number of situations steroids have been demonstrated to bind to these putative receptors without apparently initiating the expected biological effect (King and Mainwaring, 1974; Gorski and Gannon, 1976).

Throughout this chapter we adopt the generally accepted practice that "receptor" means a macromolecular component of a tissue which binds the hormone with high affinity and stereospecificity and which carries the hormone into the cell nuclear compartment.

Steroids circulate in the blood in concentrations as low as 0.4 nM (estradiol) and approaching 1 μM (glucocorticoids: see Table I). Because the blood–brain barrier is permeable to most steroids, and because steroids gain entry into most, if not all, brain cells, it stands to reason that the putative steroid receptors might have dissociation constants which reflect the blood concentration of the steroids. Indeed, this appears to be the case, but the range of K_d's at 0°–4° is much narrower than the range of blood concentrations (Table I). One thing which this comparison does not take into consideration is the presence in blood of carrier proteins such as transcortin which bind the steroid.

Binding to putative receptors, represented by K_d's in Table I, is referred to as *high-affinity* binding. *Low-affinity* binding refers to steroid interactions with macromolecules having higher K_d values. There is virtually no information pro or con which implicates low-affinity binding in biological effects of steroids. (Low-affinity serum binding, e.g., of glucocorticoids by transcortin, is presumed to attenuate biological effectiveness of steroids; cf. Thompson and Lipmann, 1974.) The tendency to assume exclusive involvement of high-affinity binding in biological effects of steroids is largely based on the consideration that a low-affinity binding site would be so poorly occupied by circulating endogenous levels of the steroid as to preclude significant numbers of bound hormone molecules being present to exert an effect. It should also be noted that so-called low-affinity binding sites are frequently found in steroid nonresponsive brain regions which lack the high-affinity sites.

An important property of high-affinity binding sites is stereospecificity and selectivity in binding various steroids. For example, estrogen receptors prefer 17β over 17α estradiol and bind poorly or not at all most androgens, progestins, or glucocorticoids, while androgen receptors prefer 5α over 5β

TABLE I

COMPARISON OF STEROID BLOOD LEVELS AND DISSOCIATION CONSTANTS OF BRAIN STEROID RECEPTORS

Hormone	Level in serum (nM)	References	Estimated K_d[a] (nM)	References
Estradiol	0.04 early diestrus 0.15 proestrus	Smith et al., 1975	0.1	Ginsburg et al., 1975
Aldosterone	0.14 salt replete 1.4 salt depleted	Gomez-Sanchez et al., 1976	1.5	Anderson and Fanestil, 1976
Testosterone	10–17 normal male	Kalra and Kalra, 1977	0.5–1	Naess, 1976
Progesterone	30 diestrus 160 proestrus	Smith et al., 1975	2–4	MacLusky et al., 1978
Corticosterone	400 pm resting 1000 stress	de Kloet and McEwen, 1976c	4–6	de Kloet et al., 1975

[a] K_d's measured in brain cytosols at 0°–4°.

dihydrotestosterone and have vastly lower binding affinities for estrogens, progestins, and glucocorticoids (cf. McEwen and Luine, 1978, for discussion).

A final term to be considered is the *binding capacity*, as demonstrated by such techniques as a Scatchard analysis of binding. Though it has always been found that there are more low-affinity than high-affinity binding sites, the limited capacity of the high-affinity sites really adds little to our understanding of their potential roles. The comfort in finding low capacity of high-affinity sites may be a prejudice related to Clark's (1933) idea that total receptor capacity should be substantially or totally occupied when the maximum biological effect is taking place.

B. EXPERIMENTS INVOLVING *in Vivo* INJECTION OF ³H STEROID OR *in Vitro* INCUBATION OF INTACT TISSUE WITH ³H STEROIDS

1. General Considerations

a. In Vivo Studies.   With the exception of the radioimmunoassay, gas–liquid chromatographic, and exchange assays (Sections II,B,6 and II,B,7), the techniques described in this section rely on the measurement of the uptake and retention of ³H steroids of high specific radioactivity (20–100 Ci/mmole) by means of autoradiography or liquid scintillation counting. In such experiments, the steroid-producing glands must be removed in order to prevent occupation of receptor sites by endogenous hormone. The time interval between gland removal and ³H steroid injection must be chosen with some caution to allow for clearance of endogenous steroid but at the same time bearing in mind that various aspects of the animal's physiology may change as a result of the anhormonal status.

Some of the changes which do influence uptake of ³H steroids are changes in the number of receptor sites, such as has been observed for glucocorticoid receptors after adrenalectomy (McEwen and Wallach, 1973), and changes in the liver metabolism of steroids (Gustafsson *et al.*, 1977). In addition, a more general consideration for hormone replacement therapy in anhormonal animals is the gradual change in levels of hormone-dependent enzymes in the absence of the hormone, which requires time for reinstatement after the start of replacement therapy and which may explain the time lag observed for full restoration of behavioral responsiveness to gonadal steroids in long-term gonadectomized rats (see McEwen *et al.*, 1978, for discussion).

In administering the ³H steroid, it is ideal to give a dose which will approximate the normal physiological blood levels. However, this would require constant infusion of hormone and involve both large amounts of ³H steroid and great expense. One laboratory (LeMaire *et al.*, 1974) has produced satisfactory results using this technique to examine rat CNS uptake of

[3]H corticosterone, but they minimized the expense by reducing the specific radioactivity of the isotope. Most work on this topic has involved the pulse injection of ^{3}H steroid intraperitoneally, subcutaneously, or intravenously, in all of which cases the blood level of steroid rises rather rapidly at first and then falls rapidly from the peak. The animal is usually killed and the brain tissue sampled during the declining phase (30 minutes to 4 hours following injection), and the blood levels at sacrifice do not indicate what they were at the peak, when tissue levels of specifically retained and bound hormone were determined.

A very important aspect of *in vivo* administration of ^{3}H steroids is the biotransformation of the steroid which occurs both centrally in the brain and pituitary and peripherally in the liver, kidneys, and gut. As will be discussed below, steroid metabolism serves not only to inactivate the hormone, but in some instances, particularly in the case of testosterone, metabolism serves to produce more active forms of the steroid. Many of the initial *in vivo* uptake

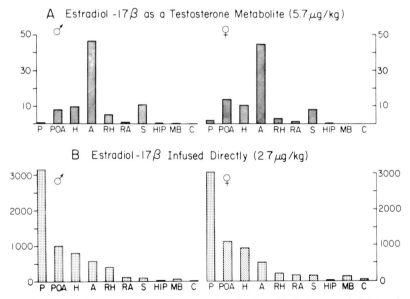

FIG. 1. Levels of estradiol-17β (E$_2$) in cell nuclear fractions (fmdes/mg DNA). (A) Levels of radioactivity identified as E$_2$ present in brain cell nuclear fractions 2 hours after [^{3}H]T administration (5.7 μg/kg) to castrated–adrenalectomized adult male and female rats. (B) Levels of radioactivity present in brain cell nuclear fractions 2 hours after [^{3}H]E$_2$ administration (2.7 μg/kg) to castrated–adrenalectomized adult male and female rats. Abbreviations: P, whole pituitary; POA, preoptic area; H, basomedial hypothalamus; A, cortico-medial amygdala; RH, rest of hypothalamus; RA, rest of amygdala; S, septum; HIP, hippocampus; MB, midbrain–central gray; C, parietal cerebral cortex. From Lieberburg and McEwen, 1977.

studies with androgens failed to take this into consideration. When levels of testosterone (T), estradiol (E_2), and 5α-dihydrotestosterone (DHT) and their metabolites were measured in serum 2 hours after intravenous administration of 3–6 μg/kg doses to gonadectomized–adrenalectomized rats, 20% of E_2 was unchanged but only 3% of T and DHT was unmetabolized (Lieberburg and McEwen, 1977; Lieberburg *et al.*, 1977a; I. Lieberburg, unpublished). And, as will be seen below, brain radioactivity reflects this pattern (Figs. 1 and 2). Thus, the comparison of total tissue radioactivity with total serum radioactivity can be very misleading.

The occurrence of biotransformation of androgens has important implications for the route of administration of ^{3}H steroid. In our recent *in vivo* studies, we have used only intravenous (i.v.) infusion, because it allows a greater exposure of all tissues to the initial circulatory passage of the authentic steroid. We found that while i.v. and subcutaneous (s.c.) injection of [^{3}H]DHT result in similar serum total radioactivity 2 hours later, s.c. injection results in undetectable serum levels of DHT and i.v. injection results in about 3% authentic DHT (I. Lieberburg, unpublished). E_2 is metabolized more slowly, and intravenous and subcutaneous routes seem to produce more or less equal patterns and levels of CNS uptake and retention.

    b. In Vitro Studies.   Another approach to measuring steroid uptake and retention is to incubate brain or pituitary slices or fragments with ^{3}H

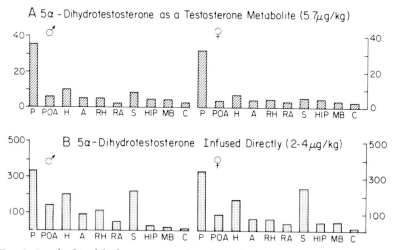

FIG. 2. Levels of 5α-dehydrotestosterone (DHT) in cell nuclear fractions (f moles/mg DNA). (A) Levels of radioactivity identified as DHT present in brain cell nuclear fractions 2 hours after [^{3}H]T administration (5.7 μg/kg) to castrated–adrenalectomized adult male and female rats. (B) Levels of radioactivity present in cell nuclear fractions 2 hours after [^{3}H]DHT administration (2–4 μg/kg) to castrated–adrenalectomized adult male and female rats. Abbreviations are identical to those used in Fig. 1. From Lieberburg and McEwen, 1977.

steroids. This relatively inexpensive technique permits precise determination of concentration of hormone, time, and temperature of incubation, and it allows for measurement of central steroid metabolism without interference from peripheral organs. Furthermore, there is no interference from serum steroid binding proteins (see McEwen and Wallach, 1973). Such proteins, except for CBG, are not important in blood of mature rats, but sex steroid binding globulin is an important factor in other species, such as the rhesus monkey. Tissue uptake studies *in vitro*, however, suffer from a number of serious drawbacks. First, the size of the tissue fragment may limit access of steroid (as well as oxygen and nutrients) to some of the innermost cells. Second, viability of CNS tissue *in vitro* may be short-lived and may be nonuniform throughout the tissue fragment. Third, *in vitro* incubations at 37° are not optimal because the tissue survives better only at lower temperatures (see McEwen and Wallach, 1973). Finally, high-affinity binding is lower *in vitro* than *in vivo* in relation to low-affinity and nonspecific binding of ^{3}H steroid (see McEwen and Wallach, 1973).

2. Autoradiography

Autoradiography is the most powerful technique for documenting the anatomical distribution of steroid-concentrating neurons in the CNS. Although usually performed on tissue labeled *in vivo* by ^{3}H steroids, it has recently been possible to carry out autoradiography on neonatal mouse brain explants in tissue culture and to demonstrate selective retention of [^{3}H]estradiol by neurons in the preoptic region of the newborn mouse brain, after *in vitro* exposure to the hormone (J. L. Gerlach, C. D. Toran-Allerand, and B. S. McEwen, unpublished). The autoradiographic technique, which is discussed in detail in a number of reviews (Rogers, 1973; Stumpf and Roth, 1966; Tuohimaa, 1970; Stumpf, 1971), is most easily carried out by placing 6–8 μm frozen sections directly onto emulsion-coated slides in the dark, allowing the sections to thaw, and placing them in a dark, dry place in the cold for exposure of 3–12 months. Development of the emulsion at the end of this time is followed by histological fixation and staining of sections and results in good localization of ^{3}H steroid and adequate preservation of tissue structures. Alternatives to this "thaw-mount" procedure (cf. Stumpf and Roth, 1966; Anderson and Greenwald, 1969) involve modifications in the way tissue is handled prior to exposure to the photographic emulsion. These include exposure of frozen sections of tissue containing radioactive steroid to osmic acid vapor followed by dipping of slides in emulsion (Pfaff, 1968); application of frozen sections without thawing to emulsion-coated slides (Appleton, 1968) and freeze-drying of sections before application to emulsion-coated slides (Stumpf and Roth, 1966). The latter method minimizes diffusion of soluble substances but is most difficult in terms of the success of

getting good contact between tissue and emulsion. And it must be emphasized that it is not necessary to go to such lengths as freeze-drying tissue
to obtain good autoradiograms of steroid retention by intracellular receptors;
rather, the "thaw-mount" procedure is quite sufficient for most purposes.

Because the β particle produced by decay of tritium has such a low
energy, the path length of the track is only $1\text{--}2\,\mu\text{m}$ (Feinendegen, 1967), and
as a result the sections must be kept as thin as possible ($6\,\mu\text{m}$ is usually the
thinnest one can routinely obtain). Following development of the photographic emulsion, the reduced silver grains appear as brown or black against
the tissue background, which is usually stained with cresyl violet or other
histological stains to increase the resolution of cellular structures. Tissue
structure is usually not well preserved, but is adequate for identification
of major anatomical and cellular structures (i.e., nuclei, perinuclear cytoplasm).

If there were no selective retention of the steroid by cells or their organelles, the pattern of distribution of silver grains would be random. While
this appears to be the case for background labeling of neuropil and of brain
regions lacking receptors, regions of the brain containing steroid receptors
show a distinct localization of silver grains over neuron cell bodies, particularly over the region of the cell nucleus (Fig. 3). One problem is how to
analyze this distribution. There are two choices: to count grains per unit
area, or to count grains per cell. The first alternative includes less intensely
labeled areas such as neuropil with heavily labeled cell nuclei; the second
alternative ignores the neuropil and does not take into consideration the size
of the cell. The solution most frequently employed is to define criteria for
identifying a labeled cell—usually, this means a grain density over a cell body
or cell nuclear region which is five times that of the grain density over the
neuropil. Such cells are easily recognized by visual inspection through the
microscope, and this facilitates the mapping of such cells onto representative
atlas drawings of the CNS (see Pfaff and Keiner, 1973; Warembourg,
1975a,b), although it does bias the results toward only the most heavily
labeled cells.

There are a number of other considerations in the evaluation of autoradiography as a technique for studying steroid receptors in brain tissue.
Because the energy of the β decay permits the particle to travel only a few
microns, cells which contain isotopic steroid but which are far away from the
emulsion will appear to be less intensely labeled than those which are close
to the emulsion. In fact, most autoradiograms show unlabeled cells in the
proximity of heavily labeled cells: whether these unlabeled cells lack receptors or have simply not registered on the emulsion as a result of their distance is difficult to ascertain with available techniques. Another problem,
based on the criteria used for judging a cell to be labeled, is that some cells

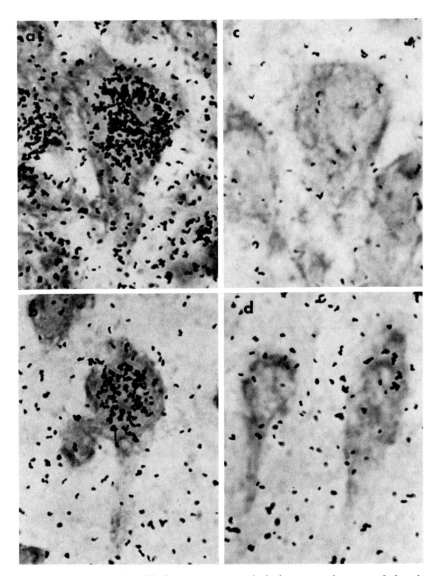

FIG. 3. Autoradiographs of [³H]corticosterone uptake by hippocampal neurons of adrenalectomized male rats. (a) and (b) Control uptake of [³H]corticosterone. (c) and (d) Uptake of [³H]corticosterone in presence of 3 mg unlabeled corticosterone injected to compete for binding sites (photographs by Mr. John Gerlach, from McEwen and Pfaff, 1973).

and, indeed, cellular compartments other than the nucleus, may contain some receptor-bound steroid but simply not register because of the low density of labeling. Such may be the case with glial cells and glucocorticoid receptors, because there is evidence that cultured glial cells have such receptors which mediate induction of glycerol phosphate dehydrogenase (de Vellis *et al.*, 1974). The most informative test for establishing the existence of high-affinity, low-capacity steroid receptor sites in any cellular compartment is to carry out competition experiments with unlabeled steroids, but because of the time-consuming nature of autoradiography such studies have been carried out rarely and only with respect to cell nuclear labeling (see Anderson and Greenwald, 1969; McEwen and Pfaff, 1973). Competition studies are a necessity in evaluating the significance of autoradiographic results from [^{3}H]testosterone because of the above-mentioned metabolism of this steroid which results in the labeling of both androgen and estrogen receptor sites (see Sheridan *et al.*, 1974a,b).

3. Tissue Uptake

Tissue uptake studies can be performed *in vivo* or *in vitro* employing liquid scintillation counting to measure labeled steroid after the tissue is either solubilized or homogenized and extracted with appropriate organic solvents such as methylene chloride (see McEwen *et al.*, 1970a,b; Perez-Palacios *et al.*, 1973). Tissue uptake is quick and easy, but it has a number of serious drawbacks. The first is that limited-capacity binding resulting from receptors occupies only a small proportion of total uptake—this is more true with *in vitro* uptake than with *in vivo* uptake, and it varies as a function of the relative amount of steroid receptor in the tissue. The second drawback is that steroid metabolites account for a large proportion of label in tissue. This is compounded by the fact that contaminating blood radioactivity *in vivo* contributes other metabolites, unless blood is removed by perfusion through the heart with Dextran–saline during killing. A third problem is that tissue contains other binding sites besides receptors, including the steroid-metabolizing enzymes, and thus limited capacity uptake is not necessarily synonymous with receptor content. For these reasons, tissue uptake studies have been replaced by other techniques which involve some degree of receptor isolation such as subcellular fractionation.

A problem which is common to all biochemical studies of steroid receptors in brain is that neuroanatomical localization is only as fine as the dissection of brain regions. Thus, such studies should always be conducted in conjunction with autoradiographic maps of steroid localization. A number of dissection schemes have been worked out in this laboratory and are described in various publications (McEwen *et al.*, 1969, 1975a; McEwen and Pfaff, 1970).

4. Steroid Binding to Macromolecules Soluble in Low Ionic Strength Buffers

This approach is conceptually closer to examining steroid binding to receptors than is tissue uptake. The tissue, labeled *in vivo* or *in vitro*, is
homogenized in a low ionic strength buffer, usually Tris or phosphate (the
problem of buffer choice and homogenization conditions will be treated in
Section II,C,1), and macromolecules binding steroid are isolated by high-
speed centrifugation and then measured in the cytosol fraction by a number
of separation procedures such as gel filtration on Sephadex beads or electrophoresis or sucrose density gradients. Labeling of intact tissue *in vitro* or
in vivo necessitates that the time to tissue disruption be rather short before
many of the cytosol macromolecules are translocated into the cell nuclear
compartment. *In vitro* labeling of cytosol after preparation permits one to
study cytosol macromolecules without regard to such time factors. As will be
discussed in Section II,C, rigorous criteria must be applied before a cytosol
binding macromolecule is called a receptor. Once again, steroid-
metabolizing enzymes and contaminating serum binding proteins such as
transcortin or α-fetoprotein may confuse the issue.

5. Cell Nuclear Uptake

According to the generally accepted model of steroid hormone action, the
final destination of the hormone is the cell nucleus and it reaches this or-
ganelle by translocation from the cytoplasm attached to a cytoplasmic receptor. In the brain and pituitary, as in most tissues, one sees cell nuclear
retention of ^{3}H steroid which reaches a peak between 1 and 2 hours after
intraperitoneal or intravenous administration (see McEwen *et al.*, 1972c,
1975a; de Kloet *et al.*, 1975). Such measurements depend on the isolation of
a pure cell nuclear fraction. The procedure, which we routinely use (McEwen
and Zigmond, 1972), which is modified from that described earlier
(Lovtrup-Rein and McEwen, 1966), involves homogenization of tissue in the
presence of a nonionic detergent, Triton X100, and a final centrifugation in
2.0 M sucrose to float away cytoplasmic debris. Purity of the nuclear fraction
is indicated by the absence of cytoplasmic debris in preparations viewed by
light and electron microscopy and by the low activity of cytochrome C
oxidase in nuclear preparations (McEwen and Zigmond, 1972). The nuclear
preparation contains an assortment of nuclear sizes, representing, undoubtedly, cell nuclei from large and small neurons as well as various types of glial
cells (McEwen *et al.*, 1972b).

In addition to measuring total radioactivity in isolated brain and pituitary
cell nuclei by extraction with organic solvents, it is possible, as in other
steroid-sensitive tissues, to recover ^{3}H steroid attached to receptors after salt

extraction of the cell nuclear pellet. Whereas salt extraction of cell nuclei containing *in vivo* bound [³H]corticosterone (McEwen and Plapinger, 1970), [³H]estradiol (Mowles *et al.*, 1971), and ³H androgens (Lieberburg *et al.*, 1977a) with 0.4 *M* KCl typically removes only 60–70% of total radioactivity, recent work in our laboratory has established conditions whereby nearly 100% of total [³H]estradiol can be extracted from brain cell nuclear pellets (Roy and McEwen, 1977). This procedure differs from others in that the nuclear pellet is first suspended in a Tris buffer without salt, following which an equal volume of 0.8 *M* KCl containing buffer is added and allowed to stand in the cold for 30 minutes. This procedure does not, however, extract all nuclear bound [³H]estradiol from uterine nuclear preparations, a finding in agreement with other laboratories, although the percentage of residual radioactivity by this method is lower than that generally reported (Roy and McEwen, 1977).

Other procedures for obtaining "nuclear bound" hormone involve homogenization of tissue in low ionic strength buffers without sucrose, under which conditions cell nuclei aggregate and lose their shape and structure. Extensive washing of pellets after low-speed centrifugation yields a fraction enriched in DNA compared to the whole homogenate, and this fraction is then used for the analysis of receptor-bound hormone (Clark *et al.*, 1972). This method of preparing chromatin from whole tissue leaves open the possibility that cytosol receptor may be trapped in the preparation. Such a chromatin fraction can also be prepared from isolated brain cell nuclei, and it has been shown to retain receptor-bound [³H]estradiol after *in vivo* injection (R. E. Whalen, personal communication).

It is accepted procedure to normalize the nuclear bound radioactive hormone on the basis of protein and/or DNA in the fraction. Insofar as most brain cells appear to be diploid, standardization to DNA content is actually an estimate of the hormone content per cell. One must not forget, however, that not all cells in a given brain region bind the hormone (see Section II,B,2 above), and thus the measure is an average of responsive and nonresponsive cells. Normalization of bound hormone to protein content of the nuclear fraction has the advantage of allowing a comparison with tissue radioactivity expressed per unit of tissue protein. Insofar as the protein content per unit volume of cell nuclei is similar to that of brain tissue, the ratio of steroid/protein in nuclei to steroid/protein in tissue is a rough estimate of the relative concentration of hormone in the nuclear compartment. This is probably a superior method of expressing results than simply indicating the percentage of tissue radioactivity recovered in the nuclear pellet, because brain cell nuclear mass (as percent of tissue mass) is as low as 2% in midbrain and brainstem and as high as 8% in cerebellum (McEwen *et al.*, 1972b).

6. Radioimmunoassay, Radioenzymatic, and Gas–Liquid Chromatographic Analysis of Steroids

Radioimmunoassay (RIA) and its predecessor, competitive protein binding assay, has been used to measure endogenous levels of steroid in brain tissue. The advantage of this approach, and of the exchange assay to be discussed below, is that normal physiological levels of hormone can be measured (see Butte *et al.*, 1972; Carroll *et al.*, 1975). Recently, it has become possible to go beyond tissue levels of steroids to measurements of steroids in the purified cell nuclear fraction from the brain. This has so far been done successfully for corticosterone and has revealed the pattern and degree of occupation of cell nuclear receptors by morning, afternoon, and stress levels of hormone (B. S. McEwen, B. S. Stephenson, and L. C. Krey, unpublished). There are peculiar problems associated with RIA, centering around the ability of other steroids or of other tissue constituents to interfere with the assay and give a false positive value. This kind of problem can be circumvented by chromatography of the extracts prior to RIA.

Another procedure used successfully to measure progestins and androgens in brain tissue is gas–liquid chromatography (GLC) (Raisinghani *et al.*, 1968; Robel *et al.*, 1973). GLC provides a more positive identification of the endogenous steroid but it lacks sensitivity (400 pg required for GLC compared to 10 pg for RIA).

A third procedure for analysis of endogenous steroids involves the use of enzymatic reactions to label the steroid with [³H]methyl or other groups. This approach has recently been applied by Paul and Axelrod (1977) to measure endogenous levels of 2-hydroxyestradiol in brain. Methyl groups are enzymatically transferred to the steroid from [³H]methyl-labeled methionine, after which the steroid is purified by chromatographic techniques. This principle might be used in the future to measure other endogenous steroids, employing tritium-labeled acetic anhydride or tritium-labeled borohydride.

7. Nuclear Exchange Assays

Whereas we will deal here with assays designed to measure cell nuclear receptor–steroid complexes by exchange of radiolabeled for endogenous steroid, similar procedures can be applied to measurement of cytosol receptor occupation (see Section II,C). Exchange procedures are not only cheaper than uptake studies with ³H steroids, they also enable one to measure endogenous steroid occupation of receptors. Exchange assays are free of artifacts of RIA because they take advantage of the stereospecificity of the receptor itself, and they are also more sensitive than GLC. Finally, exchange assays permit the measurement of occupied receptors in nuclei, regardless of what has caused the receptor to translocate from the cytoplasm to the nucleus. (Thus, for example, antiestrogens as well as estradiol or DES can be measured on nuclear receptors by exchange.)

The first exchange assay for estradiol was developed by Clark and coworkers (Anderson *et al.*, 1972) and applied by that group first to the uterus and later to the brain (Clark *et al.*, 1972; Anderson *et al.*, 1973). Their procedure utilized a chromatin fraction prepared from tissue by homogenization in low ionic strength buffers followed by low-speed centrifugation and washing of the pellet. Exchange assays were run on the washed pellet and require large amounts of material (see Anderson *et al.*, 1973). They also tend to produce variable results when applied to estrogen receptors in adult brain (E. Roy and G. Wade, personal communications; B. S. McEwen, unpublished).

Westley and Salaman (1976) modified the technique of Clark by using purified cell nuclei and running exchange assays on nuclei in isotonic sucrose. They also used brain tissue from newborn rats. Their results indicated nuclear receptor levels one-tenth or less of those shown by [³H]estradiol injection. Reasons for this discrepancy have only recently emerged as an exchange assay was worked out in our laboratory (Roy and McEwen, 1977). As noted above, Roy first established conditions for salt-extracting virtually all nuclear estradiol receptor, which permitted him to run the exchange assay on the extract rather than on a less tractable nuclear pellet or chromatin pellet. Roy found that low temperature ($0°$–$4°$) and reducing agents such as dithiothreitol are essential during the preparation of the extracts, and that a presumed protease inhibitor, bacitracin, must be present in the extracts in order to prevent degradation. Exchange assays were run at $25°$, as also is the case with the other exchange assays described above. Roy found that his exchange values were identical to results obtained by injecting [³H]estradiol into immature and adult rats, but there is still a discrepancy of 2- to 5-fold between uptake and exchange estimates of receptor occupancy in the newborn rat brain (MacLusky *et al.*, 1978). This discrepancy remains to be resolved, but we suspect that it may be due to higher protease activity and we plan to use higher bacitracin levels, among other procedures, in an attempt to overcome it.

Thus far, the exchange assays have not been extended to the measurement of steroid–receptor complexes in the brain other than those with estrogens.

C. MEASUREMENT OF NEURAL AND PITUITARY CYTOSOL RECEPTORS *in Vitro*

1. General Considerations

Many studies of neural and pituitary steroid hormone receptors have made extensive use of measurements of soluble macromolecular receptors in cytosol preparations (e.g., 100,000 $g \times 60'$ supernatants). Before summarizing the individual techniques which have been used to measure these cytosol receptors, it is well to note some of the peculiarities and problems encountered in working with neural and pituitary receptors, which in large part dictate the best techniques for their measurement. With respect to the tissues themselves, the low concentration of receptors and their regional localization within the brain together with receptors for other classes of steroid hormones necessitate the use of methods which are sensitive and steroid-specific.

On the technical level, a primary concern is the efficient extraction of receptors from the tissues, minimizing entrapment and stabilizing them from degradation. To maintain the integrity of the receptors against oxidation of essential sulfhydryl groups, one uses a reducing agent such as dithiothreitol, β-mercaptoethanol, or thioglycerol in the homogenizing buffer. Of these three reducing agents, we have had the best success with dithiothreitol (N. J. MacLusky, unpublished). The standard hypotonic buffer used in many laboratories consists of Tris (about 10 mM) in the presence of EDTA (1–2 mM) at pH 7.4. It should be noted that there is no systemic comparison of Tris with other buffers such as HEPES or phosphate with regard to receptor yield or stability. The hypotonicity facilitates disruption of cells and organelles and the EDTA chelates divalent cations. It has been noted that steroid binding is reduced if one omits EDTA and supplements the buffers with a divalent cation such as Mg (N. J. MacLusky, unpublished). Although, as noted, hypotonicity is a valuable tool in receptor extraction from the tissue, the addition of glycerol (10%) to the homogenizing medium has been favored by Fox and co-workers (Fox and Johnston, 1974) on the grounds that it seems to increase the yield of receptor. Finally, the precise method of homogenization has never been examined systematically with regard to receptor yield. The brain and pituitary are soft tissues and are easily disrupted by hand-operated or low-speed, motor-driven, Teflon–glass homogenizers, and we favor these over more violent methods of tissue disruption because of the decreased chances of heating or foaming.

In spite of the desirability of preparing a highly concentrated cytosol from a tissue in which the steroid receptor content is low, the yield of receptor from the tissue does tend to suffer as the concentration of the homogenate is increased (N. J. MacLusky, unpublished). It is interesting that pituitary and brain tissue differ somewhat in this respect. For estradiol receptors undergoing extraction at a tissue/volume ratio of 5–10%, in a Tris–EDTA–dithiothreitol buffer containing glycerol, the pituitary shows virtually complete extraction after one homogenization, whereas the hypothalamus requires three homogenizations to remove all the receptor from the tissue.

After preparing the cytosol and incubating it with ³H steroid, various techniques may be employed for separating bound from free steroid. These will now be reviewed and evaluated as to whether they may be successfully applied to the measurement of neural and pituitary steroid receptor sites.

2. Equilibrium Dialysis

The principal merit of the equilibrium dialysis procedure for measuring a dissociable binding equilibrium is its thermodynamic validity. However, several serious problems make it undesirable for use on brain steroid receptors. For one thing, it is cumbersome, and processing multiple samples is difficult. Further, it takes time, during which receptors may be degraded. In addition, it is very insensitive, because unbound steroid is present on both sides of the membrane and represents a baseline on which the bound steroid must be detected. It is probably for this reason that the technique has been used only for pituitary and neural estrogen receptors (Korach and Muldoon, 1973, 1974), which are present in relatively large amounts compared to androgen receptor sites. Glucocorticoid and progestin receptors are too labile to survive equilibrium dialysis.

3. Sucrose Density-Gradient Centrifugation

This and all the other techniques are nonequilibrium procedures and rely on the relative stability of the hormone–receptor complex for achieving a separation from unbound steroid. Density gradients are usually made of 5–20% sucrose in Tris–EDTA–dithiothreitol buffer, although glycerol may be substituted for sucrose with good results (McEwen et al., 1972a). At low ionic strengths, most steroid–receptor complexes sediment at 7–9 S (Table III), and this is characteristic not only of brain and pituitary but of other target tissues. Because of the 10–24 hours required to effect sedimentation and the attendant disequilibration, sucrose density-gradient centrifugation is not an adequate procedure for estimation of dissociation constant or binding capacity.

4. Gel Filtration Chromatography

This procedure takes advantage of differences in molecular size between free steroid and receptor-bound steroid, and in certain instances (e.g., nonpolar steroids as estradiol and filtration gels as Sephadex LH20) utilizes the affinity of the steroid for the gel as an additional separation technique. Gels include Sepharose, Sephadex G25 or G100, and the polyacrylamide and agarose gels of Biorad. Sephadex G200 (fractionation range 5000–800,000) is ideal for estimating molecular sizes of receptors, but for running multiple determinations (e.g., Scatchard analysis of K_d and binding capacity) Sephadex LH20 (hydroxypropylated form of G25) is ideal when used in mini-columns made up in disposable Pasteur pipets. LH20 chromatography gives better yields of neural estrogen receptor than chromatography on

Sephadex G25 (see Table II). This may be due to a retention of some of the receptor by the gel, as has been observed for mammary cytosols (Godefroi and Brook, 1973). As already noted, LH20 possess a moderate affinity for many steroids and is able to adsorb free steroid and even strip steroid from low-affinity sites (e.g., serum albumin) without significantly affecting the high-affinity, receptor-bound steroids. While most neural and pituitary steroid receptor complexes are quite stable in the presence of LH20, the progestin–receptor complex tends to dissociate somewhat more rapidly and requires speed and care when being handled by this method (N. J. Mac-Lusky, unpublished). In addition, running columns with three or more different bed volumes permits, by graphical extrapolation, the estimation of 100% receptor levels at a hypothetical gel bed volume of zero (Samperez *et al.*, 1974). Once such controls for dissociation have, where necessary, been incorporated, the mini-column technique has the obvious advantage of enabling one to process large numbers of samples simultaneously with good estimates of apparent K_d's and numbers of binding sites.

5. Adsorption by Dextran-Coated Charcoal

Exposure of cytosol to dextran-coated charcoal followed rapidly by centrifugation is a convenient method for removing the free steroid, while leaving receptor-bound steroid in solution (Korenman *et al.*, 1969). Like the LH20 mini-columns, the charcoal has a moderate affinity for steroids and thus can strip away a good deal of the low-affinity binding to cytosol proteins if left in contact long enough. It has been our experience and that of others that charcoal produces much higher levels of noncompetable binding than either LH20 or G25 (Table II). For this reason and because of the generally

TABLE II

COMPETABLE E_2 RECEPTOR LEVELS PRESENT IN PITUITARY AND LIMBIC (HYPOTHALAMUS, PREOPTIC AREA, AND AMYGDALA) CYTOSOLS AS DEMONSTRATED BY VARIOUS PROCEDURES

	Dextran charcoal[a]	Protamine sulfate[b]	LH20[c]	G25[c]
Pituitary[d]	280(292,12)[e]	253(287,34)	296(305,9)	116(119,2)
Limbic	17.5(31.4,13.9)	30.7(83.8,53.1)	25.9(29.4,3.5)	17.2(19.3,1.1)

[a] Method of Baxter and Tomkins, 1971.

[b] Method of Steggles and King, 1970.

[c] Method of Ginsburg *et al.*, 1974.

[d] Tissues from 1 week ovariectomized–adrenalectomized adult female rats. Dissection according to McEwen *et al.*, 1975a. Tissues homogenized in 0.32 M sucrose, 0.01 M phosphate pH 7.3, 0.1 M β-mercaptoethanol. Final cytosol protein concentrations: 1.3 mg/ml, pituitary; 1.9 mg/ml, limbic. Cytosols incubated at 4° for 2.5 hours with 1 nM [^{3}H]E_2 ± 1 μM unlabeled E_2.

[e] Competable fmoles/mg cytosol protein (total binding, noncompeted binding).

higher results obtained with LH20, we prefer this method. It should be noted that charcoal adsorption is a particularly good, rapid method for removing unbound steroid with little increase in volume, and it is useful as a preparative step before density-gradient centrifugation or isoelectric focusing.

6. Protamine or Ammonium Sulfate Precipitation

King *et al.*, 1969) noted that polycations, such as protamine polylysine, and the monovalent cation ammonium will precipitate the uterine estrogen receptor, and protamine sulfate precipitation was applied successfully to an analysis of neural and pituitary estrogen receptors that same year (Vertes and King, 1969). Protamine sulfate precipitation has also been used to precipitate glucocorticoid–receptor complexes of brain (McEwen *et al.*, 1972a). Like charcoal for the analysis of estrogen receptors, protamine yields rather high levels of noncompetable radioactivity, particularly in brain cytosols (see Table II).

As a preparative tool, ammonium sulfate has a distinct advantage over protamine sulfate because the precipitate in the former case is readily redissolved, thus permitting further analysis with other techniques (see de Kloet and McEwen, 1976a,b).

7. Hydroxylapatite Adsorption

Hydroxylapatite adsorption of receptor was originally applied to uterine cytosol estrogen receptors using a column procedure (Erdos *et al.*, 1970). More recently, it has been used in a batch procedure (Pavlik and Coulson, 1976a). The technique produces reliable estimates of apparent K_d's and binding capacities, at least for uterine estrogen receptors (Pavlik and Coulson, 1976a). However, estimates of these parameters for pituitary and hypothalamic cytosol estrogen receptors are widely at variance with those obtained by other techniques (Pavlik and Coulson, 1976b). The reasons for the discrepancy require further study.

8. DNA-Cellulose Chromatography

The use of DNA-cellulose in the analysis of neural and pituitary steroid receptors was first reported by Plapinger and co-workers (1973). Serum binding proteins do not adhere strongly to DNA-cellulose (Plapinger *et al.*, 1973; Fox and Johnston, 1974; de Kloet and McEwen, 1976a), whereas intracellular receptorlike macromolecules of brain and pituitary origin do adhere (Fox, 1977; de Kloet and McEwen, 1976a,b; MacLusky *et al.*, 1977). Like other target tissue steroid receptors, most brain and pituitary receptors elute between 0.1 and 0.4 *M* salt, although warming of the receptor in the presence of steroid results in a shift in ionic strength required for elution

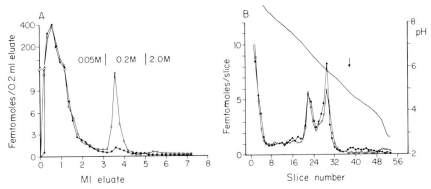

FIG. 4. Effect of thermal activation on hippocampal [³H]dexamethasone binding. Hippocampal cytosol equilibrated at 0°–2° with 10^{-8} M [³H]dexamethasone was divided into two parts. One part was "activated" by incubation for 15 minutes at 25°. The remainder ("nonactivated") was kept on ice. Samples of the cytosols were then subjected to polyacrylamide gel isoelectric focusing and DNA-cellulose chromatography. (A) DNA-Cellulose chromatography. 200 μl samples of each cytosol were applied to DNA-cellulose columns (0.5 ml bed volume). The columns were then eluted with buffer containing 5 mM Tris·HCl, 1 mM EDTA, 1 mM 2-mercaptoethanol, and 5% glycerol at pH 7.4. At the points indicated, the ionic strength of the eluant was increased by the addition of either 0.2 M or 2.0 M NaCl. ●, nonactivated. ○, activated. (B) Isoelectric focusing. 50 μl samples of cytosol were applied to each gel and focused as described in MacLusky *et al.* (1977). Lines with symbols indicate the quantities of [³H]dexamethasone, in fmoles, recovered from each gel slice (left-hand ordinate). The plain line indicates the pH gradient within the gels (right-hand ordinate). The vertical arrow shows the position of the horse spleen ferritin marker. ●, nonactivated. ○, activated. From MacLusky *et al.*, 1977.

(Fox, 1977; MacLusky *et al.*, 1977). In the case of the estrogen receptor, this "activation" is accompanied by a shift in sedimentation coefficient from 4 to 5 S in a parallel manner to what is observed for uterine receptors (Fox, 1977). In the case of neural glucocorticoid receptors, there is no indication whether activation results in altered sedimentation behavior, but it is clear that activation is not accompanied by a drastic shift in net charge (Fig. 4) (MacLusky *et al.*, 1977).

9. *Electrophoresis and Isoelectric Focusing*

Electrophoresis has been applied for examination of brain and pituitary steroid receptors using a variety of supporting media: 0.9% agar plus 0.1% agarose (Davies *et al.*, 1975); 3.25% acrylamide plus 0.5% agarose (Naess *et al.*, 1975); 7% polyacrylamide with a 4% acrylamide stacking gel (McEwen *et al.*, 1972a); and Pharmacia PAA4 acrylamide gradient gels (Kato, 1977). The gradient gels are particularly useful for estimating molecular sizes.

Isoelectric focusing has been applied to the measurement of CNS steroid receptors by a number of authors (see Fig. 4) (Gustafsson *et al.*, 1976; Naess *et al.*, 1975; MacLusky *et al.*, 1977). Focusing in acrylamide gels is prefered over focusing in sucrose density gradients, as two groups (Naess *et al.*, 1975; MacLusky *et al.*, 1977) have noted that CNS proteins tend to precipitate as they reach their isoelectric point in sucrose solutions. Because the steroid-receptor complex tends to dissociate during the run, care must be taken to focus rapidly. This is particularly true for progestin and glucocorticoid sites, which should be focused within 6 hours; the more stable androgen and estrogen sites can be focused for periods around 16 hours without appreciable dissociation. To increase the reliability of the gradients and to minimize cathodal drift, the recent advance of Nguyen and Crambach (1977) of employing amino acids rather than strong acids and bases as the anolyte and catholyte is currently being applied to the examination of CNS steroid receptors (N. J. MacLusky, unpublished).

III. NEURAL AND PITUITARY STEROID RECEPTORS IN RELATION TO FUNCTION

A. CLASSIFICATION AND PROPERTIES OF NEURAL AND PITUITARY RECEPTORS

With the techniques reviewed in Section II, it has been possible to identify receptors for the five major classes of steroid hormones. The major features of these receptors are summarized in Table III. Those receptors which we know well enough have sedimentation coefficients in the range of 6–9 S and appear to be highly thermolabile proteins with sulfhydryl groups essential for steroid binding activity. Each class of receptor gives evidence of a highly selective, stereospecific binding site, which ensures minimal crosstalk between steroids and heterologous receptor systems. Further, each class of receptor has a unique regional distribution pattern within the brain. Within some of these patterns, however, are certain parallels and even overlaps.

The most contrasting patterns of receptor distribution are those of estrogens and glucocorticoids, and although there are both types of receptors in some brain areas, there is no evidence, pro or con, concerning the dual presence of these two receptor systems in a single cell. In this connection, the progestin receptor is unique, showing inducibility by estrogen in pituitary, preoptic area, and hypothalamus, which implies strongly the dual occurrence of estrogen and progestin receptors within certain cells (see MacLusky *et al.*, 1978). The distribution of androgen receptors is similar to that of estrogen receptors, yet there is no indication that both types of receptors

TABLE III

PROPERTIES OF STEROID RECEPTORS IN NEURAL AND PITUITARY TISSUE IN RELATION TO BRAIN ANATOMY AND STEROID METABOLISM

Class of steroid	Cytosol receptor properties[a]	Specificity of receptor[b]	Brain areas of highest receptor[c]	Steroid metabolism by brain
Estrogen	$\simeq$8 S, P, SH, TL[d]	DES>$E_2\beta$>2OHE_2>$E_3$$\equiv$E$\equiv$$E_2\alpha$ >3βAol>3αAol>T[d]	[^{3}H]E_2: pit, hyp, POA, amygd[g,h]	2-Hydroxylation (2OHE_2)[o]
Androgen	6–9 S, P, SH, TL[d]	T$\equiv$DHT>CypAc>P>$E_2\beta$=F[d]	[^{3}H]DHT: pit, sept, POA, hyp, amygd[i,j]	Δ4–5 Reduction (5α,βDHT)[p] 3-Keto reduction (3α,βAol) Aromatization ($E_2\beta$)
Progestin	7 S[d,e]	R5020>d Norgestrel>P >>$E_2\beta$>B>T>dex[e]	[^{3}H]R5020: pit, hyp, POA[e]	Δ4–5 Reduction (5α,βDHP)[p-r] 3-Keto reduction (3α,βPol) 20-α-Hydroxylation
Glucocorticoid	7 S, P, SH, TL[d]	B$\equiv$dex$\equiv$F>DOC$\equiv$P>ald >T$\equiv$$E_2$[d]	[^{3}H]B: hippo, sept, amygd[k-m]; [^{3}H]DEX: pit	Acetylation[s,t]
Mineralocorticoid		Binds ald, dex, Spironolactone[f]	[^{3}H]ALD similar to [^{3}H]B distribution[n]	

[a] P, proteinaceous; SH, essential sulfhydryl groups; TL, thermolabile; S, sedimentation coefficient.

[b] DES, diethylstilbestrol; $E_2\beta$, estradiol-17β; 2OHE_2, 2-hydroxyestradiol-17β; E_3, estriol; E_2, estrone, $E_2\alpha$, estradiol-17α; 3β Aol, 3β,5α-androstanediol; 3α,5α-androstanediol; T, testosterone; DHT, 5α-dihydrotestosterone; R5020, 17, 21-dimethyl-19-norpregna-4,9-diene-3,20-dione; B, corticosterone; dex, dexamethasone; F, cortisol; DOC, deoxycorticosterone; P, progesterone; ald, aldosterone; 5α,B DHP, 5α and β forms of dihydroprogesterone; 3α,β Pol, 3α and β forms of 5α- and β-dihydroprogesterone.

[c] Brain structures: hyp, hypothalamus; POA, preoptic area; amygd, amygdala; sept, septum; pit, pituitary gland; hippo, hippocampus.

[d] McEwen and Luine, 1978.
[e] N. J. MacLusky et al., unpublished.
[f] Anderson and Fanestil, 1976.
[g] Pfaff and Keiner, 1973.
[h] Zigmond and McEwen, 1970.
[i] Lieberburg and McEwen, 1977.
[j] Sar and Stumpf, 1977.
[k] McEwen et al., 1976.
[l] Warembourg, 1975a.
[m] Warembourg, 1975b.
[n] Ermisch and N. J. MacLusky, unpublished.
[o] Fishman, 1976.
[p] McEwen, 1978b.
[q] Karavolas and Nuti, 1976.
[r] Feder and Marrone, 1977.
[s] Purdy and Axelrod, 1968.
[t] Grosser and Axelrod, 1968.

may be present within a single cell type. For glucocorticoid receptors, the striking difference in *in vivo* distribution of [³H]corticosterone, a naturally occurring hormone, and [³H]dexamethasone, a synthetic steroid, has been interpreted in terms of the demonstrated presence of at least two classes of glucocorticoid receptors of overlapping hormonal specificity which differ from each other in regional distribution within the brain. Mineralocorticoid receptors are the most inadequately studied, and it is principally a competition experiment with spironolactone (a mineralocorticoid antagonist) which points to their existence separate from glucocorticoid receptors (Anderson and Fanestil, 1976). The *in vivo* distribution of [³H]aldosterone in ADX rats is very similar to that of [³H]corticosterone, and this may indicate that the two steroids bind to the same receptors or that two receptor systems have a parallel regional distribution.

The final feature of Table III concerns steroid metabolism by brain and pituitary. Metabolism is not essential for receptor binding in the case of estrogens and glucocorticoids. Hydroxylation at the 2 position of estradiol and acetylation at the 21 position of corticosterone subserve as yet unknown roles in the brain. The extensive metabolism of progesterone by neural and pituitary tissue is likewise of unknown functional significance. Only in the case of androgen metabolism do we have some idea of its functional significance, and this will be discussed below in Section III,E.

B. NEUROENDOCRINE AND BEHAVIORAL EFFECTS OF STEROIDS

Estrogens, androgens, and glucocorticoids exert "negative feedback" control over the secretion of anterior pituitary protein hormones (Table IV). Estrogens, in addition, produce the facilitatory effects on LH secretion which lead to ovulation; in rodents such as the rat, progesterone acts synergistically with estrogen to facilitate this process (see Table IV). Besides neuroendocrine regulation, steroid hormones also influence various aspects of behavior. Some of these behaviors are highly specialized in relation to the class of steroid, e.g., salt appetite in the case of mineralocorticoids and sexual and aggressive behavior in the case of androgens, estrogens, and progestins. Other of these behaviors are related to the general circumstances under which the hormones are secreted, e.g., extinction of conditioned avoidance behavior, in which the aversive motivation for the behavior is a stressor which normally evokes glucocorticoid secretion (Table IV). However, other behaviors influenced by gluco- and mineralocorticoids are not so easily categorized and relate more to global functions of the nervous system: e.g., detection and recognition of sensory information; paradoxical or dreaming-type sleep; mood and affective state (Table IV). In this connection it should

TABLE IV

BEHAVIORAL AND NEUROENDOCRINE EFFECTS OF STEROID HORMONES

Class of steroid	Effects	References
Estrogen	Facilitates ovulation Negative feedback Regulates body weight Facilitates locomotor activity Facilitates proceptive, receptive (sexual) behavior	Flerkó, 1966 Wade, 1972 Pfaff *et al.*, 1974
Androgen	Negative feedback Promotes aggressive behavior Promotes copulatory behavior	Davidson, 1966b Bronson and Desjardins, 1971 Hart, 1974
Progestin	Facilitates ovulation Facilitates receptive (sexual) behavior	Feder and Marrone, 1977
Glucocorticoid	Negative feedback Modifies diurnal ACTH pattern Modifies sensory detection and recognition thresholds Suppresses paradoxical sleep Facilitates extinction of conditioned avoidance behavior Influences mood, affective state	McEwen, 1977, 1978a
Mineralocorticoid	Regulates salt appetite Mediates prestimulation effect on avoidance behavior	McEwen, 1978a

be noted that estrogen effects on body weight regulation and locomotor activity are, at least among rodents, rather specialized effects which are related to the change-over from food searching activity to mating.

C. EVIDENCE FOR INVOLVEMENT OF THE GENOME IN STEROID ACTION

The cellular mechanism of steroid hormone action implicated by the existence of macromolecular receptors which translocate hormone to the cell nucleus is an activation of the genome leading to RNA and protein synthesis. Although there exist very few experimental data on this point for many of the behavioral and neuroendocrine effects summarized in Table V, there is some

TABLE V

BLOCKADE OF ESTROGEN AND GLUCOCORTICOID EFFECTS BY RNA AND PROTEIN SYNTHESIS INHIBITORS

Effect	Drug[a]	Route of administration[b]	References
Estradiol			
Blockade of negative feedback	Act D	S	Schally *et al.*, 1969
Blockade of positive feedback	Act D	S	Jackson, 1972; Kalra, 1975
	Cyclo	S	Jackson, 1973
Blockade of E_2 sensitization	Act D	S	Debeljuk *et al.*, 1975;
of pituitary responsiveness			Kalra, 1975
to LHRH			
Blockade of ovulation	Act D	S	Barros and Austin, 1968
Blockade of E_2-induced	Act D	IC	Terkel *et al.*, 1973
lordosis	Cyclo	IC	Quadagno and Ho, 1975
Dexamethasone			
Blockade of negative feedback	Act D	S	Fleischer and Battarbee, 1967;
			Arimura *et al.*, 1969

[a] Act D = actinomycin D; cyclo = cycloheximide.
[b] S = systemic; IC = intracranial.

evidence for certain effects of estrogens and glucocorticoids derived from the use of an RNA synthesis inhibitor, actinomycin D, and a protein synthesis inhibitor, cycloheximide (Table V). Several of these drug effects have been shown to be reversible (Terkel *et al.*, 1973; Quadagno and Ho, 1975). All the effects summarized in Table V require additional information regarding the extent and specificity of inhibition of RNA or protein synthesis, and it would be well to obtain parallel information with other macromolecular synthesis inhibitors. Nevertheless, the data on hand are completely consistent with the view that estradial and glucocorticoids exert these effects via an activation of genomic activity, and this in turn is consistent with the overall picture of the cellular mechanism of steroid hormone action on many target cells.

D. EFFECTS OF ESTROGENS AND GLUCOCORTICOIDS ON CELLULAR AND BIOCHEMICAL EVENTS IN BRAIN AND PITUITARY

There are many indications of the kinds of effects which steroid hormones have on brain and pituitary function at the cellular and biochemical levels. These are illustrated for estrogens in Table VI and for glucocorticoids in Table VII. Among the steroid effects on the pituitary are facilitatory and inhibitory effects on pituitary hormone synthesis, as well as facilitatory and

TABLE VI
Estrogen Effects on Cellular and Biochemical Events in Pituitary and Hypothalamus

Tissue	Effects	References
Pituitary	DNA polymerase activity	Mastro and Hymer, 1973
	Levels of RNA	Robinson and Leavitt, 1971
	Synthesis of FSH decreased	Miller et al., 1977
	Preprolactin in RNA increased	Stone et al., 1977
	Sensitivity to LH-RH	Vilchez-Martinez et al., 1974
	Short-term E_2 (2–4 hours)	Tang and Spies, 1975
	Long-term E_2 (10–24 hours)	Drouin et al., 1976
	Sensitivity to TRH	De Lean et al., 1977
Hypothalamus	Neuronal electrical activity	Bueno and Pfaff, 1976
	Neuronal thresholds for stimulation of ovulation	Kubo et al., 1975
	Release and/or synthesis of LH-RH	Araki et al., 1975; Kalra, 1976
	Turnover of neurotransmitter	Cardinali and Gomez, 1977
	Induction of enzymes	McEwen and Luine, 1978
	Amino acid incorporation	Litteria and Thorner, 1974
	RNA synthesis	Peck, 1978

TABLE VII
Glucocorticoid Effects on Cellular and Biochemical Events in Pituitary and Neural Tissue

Tissue	Effects	References
Pituitary	Induction of pregrowth hormone mRNA	Tushinski et al., 1977
	Inhibition of ACTH synthesis, release	Sayers and Portanova, 1974
		Watanabe et al., 1973
	Inhibition of pituitary response to CRF	Russell et al., 1969
Brain	Inhibition of single unit electrical activity	Pfaff et al., 1971
	Alters GABA transport by synaptosomes	Miller et al., 1978
	Alters 5HT transport and release by synaptosomes	Vermes et al., 1976
	Alters tryptophan uptake and exerts permissive influence on 5HT biosynthesis	Sze, 1976
	Alters tyrosine uptake in brain	Diez et al., 1977
	Induces PNMT	Pohorecky and Wurtman, 1971
	Increases tyrosine hydroxylase activity	Hanbauer et al., 1975
		Kizer et al., 1974
	Inhibits release of CRF activity	Jones et al., 1977
	Induction of glutamine synthetase in neural retina	Morris and Moscona, 1970
	Induction of glycerol phosphate dehydrogenase in brain and glial cells	de Vellis and Inglish, 1973

inhibitory effects on pituitary sensitivity to releasing factors. In the brain, steroid effects range from alterations in electrical activity of brain regions which contain appropriate hormone receptors to effects on amino acid incorporation and nucleic acid synthesis and the induction of a number of enzymes; and they include a variety of effects on both the biosynthesis, inactivation, and reuptake of transmitter candidates. What we lack at this point is a step-by-step analysis of the critical events by which a steroid, acting in any given brain region, brings about the neural conditions sufficient for the appearance of a neuroendocrine or behavioral response. One approach, which we are pursuing at present, is to try to establish by localized hormone implants a brain region in which estradiol action is sufficient to produce lordosis behavior and/or to facilitate ovulation, and then to study in great detail the chemistry of this region as it is influenced by systemic estrogen administration.

E. Uniqueness of Testosterone Action in the Brain and Pituitary

Testosterone (T) is unique among the steroids affecting the brain for a number of reasons. First, it produces both activational effects on behavior and neuroendocrine function (Table IV) and organizational effects during early brain development which affect these same parameters. With respect to its organizational influences, T alters the neuroendocrine system of the developing mammal during a circumscribed "critical period," and these effects are permanent for the life of the animal. Second, T is unique in producing these effects in that much of its action requires local conversion within brain and pituitary to other steroid metabolites. In a sense, T is a prehormone.

Much of the information regarding these actions of T has been gathered using the laboratory rat. Comparisons with other species have been reviewed elsewhere (McEwen, 1978b). Unless otherwise noted, what follows is a discussion of the action of T in the albino rat. T is the major circulating androgen in the male rat, reaching stable serum levels of 2–5 ng/ml in adulthood (see Table I). 5α-Dihydrotestosterone (DHT) is the other major circulating androgen in the male, at serum levels roughly 1/10 that of T. The female rat possesses circulating T, the levels of which fluctuate during the estrous cycle, reaching peak values of 170 pg/ml on proestrus and minimum values of 120 pg/ml on the day of estrus (Falvo *et al.*, 1974). T has been implicated in the control of male sexual behavior and in the control of gonadotropin secretion in the male rat. Castration results in a loss of male sexual behavior and an increase of LH and FSH secretion (Austin and Short,

1972). These postcastration effects can be blocked by exogenous T. In the female rat, T (or perhaps DHT) has been implicated in the maintenance of the midcycle secretion of FSH (Gay and Tomacari, 1974).

There is little doubt that T is acting directly on the brain and pituitary in achieving these effects. However, these central effects of T are complicated by the presence of a wide spectrum of T metabolizing enzymes in neural and pituitary tissue (Fig. 5). Probably the two most important enzymes are 5α-reductase and aromatiase. 5α-Reductase is an NADPH-dependent, micro-

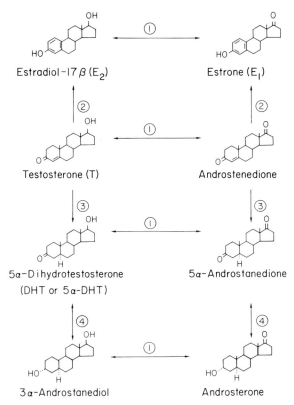

FIG. 5. Testosterone-metabolizing enzymes present in neural tissues of the rat. Indicated enzymes: (1) 17β-hydroxysteroid dehydrogenase [17β-hydroxysteroid: NAD(P) oxidoreductase, EC 1.1.1.51], present mainly in cytosol fraction of all brain regions (Rommerts and Van der Molen, 1971; (2) aromatizing enzyme or aromatase [NAD(P)- and O_2-dependent], probably associated with microsomal fraction, present only in limbic–hypothalamic structures (Naftolin *et al.*, 1975; (3) 5α-reductase [5α-steroid: NAD(P) Δ^4-oxidoreductase, EC 1.3.1.99], present mainly in microsomal fraction of all brain regions (Rommerts and Van der Molen, 1971); (4) 3α-hydroxysteroid dehydrogenase [3α-hydroxysteroid: NAD(P) oxidoreductase, EC 1.1.1.50]; present mainly in cytosol fraction of all brain regions (Rommerts and Van der Molen, 1971).

somally associated enzyme, capable of irreversibly converting T to DHT or androstenedione (A) to 5α-androstanedione (Rommerts and Van der Molen, 1971). 5α-Reductase is present in all regions of male and female rat brains, although its activity is somewhat higher in midbrain central gray area than in other brain regions, and its activity increases dramatically in the pituitary (but not in the brain) after castration (Denef *et al.*, 1973). The aromatizing enzyme or aromatase irreversibly converts T to E_2 or A to estrone (E_1) (Naftolin *et al.*, 1975). This microsomally associated enzyme, also present in the brains of both sexes, requires molecular oxygen and NADPH for its action.

Whereas 5α-reductase is ubiquitous throughout the brain, aromatase is present only in hypothalamus and in limbic structures and is apparently absent from the pituitary and cerebral cortex (Naftolin *et al.*, 1975). The aromatase activity present in the medial preoptic area and the basomedial hypothalamus of the male is greater than that found in the female, but the male values decrease to female levels following orchidectomy (Kobayashi and Reed, 1977). These *in vitro* demonstrations of T metabolizing activity suggested the potential for *in situ* metabolism. An early *in vivo* study by Stern and Eisenfeld (1971) demonstrated the presence of greater amounts of [³H]DHT in neural tissues than in the plasma after a [³H]T injection to castrated adult male rats. This lends added support to the notion that DHT formation has functional significance.

The reason for the interest in neural T metabolism is that many of the actions of T can be mimicked by one or more of its metabolites. The postcastration loss of male sexual behavior can be attenuated by exogenously administered E_2 or by other aromatizable androgens (i.e., androgens with a 4–5 double bond and no –11 axial group, as well as certain other structural features; Perez-Palacios *et al.*, 1975; Schwarzel *et al.*, 1973). Nonaromatizable androgens, such as DHT, are incapable of restoring complete sexual behavior in rats, although they can produce profound peripheral effects (Perez-Palacios *et al.*, 1975). In addition, implantation of T or E_2 directly into the preoptic area (a brain region related to male sexual behavior) will restore the behavior in castrated males (Davis and Barfield, 1978; Johnston and Davidson, 1972). Similarly placed DHT or cholesterol implants are ineffective (Johnston and Davidson, 1972; Christensen and Clemens, 1974). However, the most convincing evidence that aromatization of T to E_2 in the preoptic area is related to male sexual behavior is the demonstration by Christensen and Clemens (1975) that simultaneous application of a potent aromatase inhibitor, 1,4,6-androstatriene-3,17-dione (ATD) with either T or E_2 in the preoptic area will substantially block the T-induced male sexual behavior, but will not affect the E_2-induced behavior. Thus, it would appear that the *in situ* aromatization of T to E$_2$ in the preoptic area may be necessary for the normal maintenance of male sexual behavior in the intact animal.

Castration of the male rat is also accompanied by a rise in gonadotropin secretion, which can be suppressed by systemically administered or intrahypothalamically implanted T as well as by E$_2$ and DHT (McEwen *et al.*, 1972c; Motta *et al.*, 1970; Beyer *et al.*, 1971; Plapinger and McEwen, 1978; Swerdloff *et al.*, 1972). Swerdloff and co-workers (1972) have hypothesized that T is mediating this effect through its 5α-reduced metabolite, DHT. Their conclusion was based on the observation that exogenously administered DHT and other 5α-reduced androgens suppressed LH and FSH in castrates with a time course similar to that of T. On the other hand, E$_2$ suppressed gonadotropin much faster and at much lower doses. This circumstantial evidence does not eliminate E$_2$ as a possible candidate, though it does make its involvement less likely.

In more direct experiments (L. C. Krey, I. Lieberburg, R. J. Robbins, E. J. Roy, and B. S. McEwen, unpublished) we have tested the ability of the aforementioned aromatase inhibitor ATD to block T-mediated suppression of LH secretion. At ATD levels which resulted in the virtual absence of E$_2$ production in the brain, T still produced an apparently normal time course of LH suppression in castrates. These experiments support conclusions of Swerdloff *et al.* (1972) indicating that under certain circumstances neural aromatization is unnecessary to achieve T-mediated negative feedback. It should be noted that J. Weisz and co-workers (personal communication) have recently demonstrated that a potent 5α-reductase inhibitor (4-androstene-3-one-20-carboxylic acid) is also incapable of blocking T-mediated negative feedback in castrated male rats. It is therefore possible that T itself may be capable of acting by negative feedback to regulate gonadotropin secretion in the male.

Our particular interest in this problem of T metabolism has been to define the role played by CNS and pituitary steroid receptors in the action of T. The behavioral and neuroendocrine evidence alluded to tends us to indicate that both estrogen and androgen receptor sites may be involved to some degree. In fact, it appears that both classes of sites are occupied by [3H]-metabolites after [3H]T is administered to OVX-ADX adult rats of either sex; i.e., [3H]E$_2$, [3H]T, and [3H]DHT are recovered from highly purified brain and pituitary cell nuclei under conditions in which we expect virtually all nuclear radioactivity to be associated with receptor sites (see Figs. 1 and 2). These three metabolites account for virtually all of the cell nuclear radioactivity (Lieberburg and McEwen, 1975b, 1977). However, their respective regional patterns are quite different, because [3H]E$_2$ {as a metabolite of [3H]T} distributes as a function of aromatase activity; i.e., highest levels of [3H]E$_2$ are found in corticomedial amygdala, medial preoptic area, and basomedial hypothalamus. The pituitary, despite its high levels of E_2 receptors, has no cell nuclear-associated E_2 as a T metabolite, because of the absence of aromatase in this tissue (Naftolin *et al.*, 1975).

The conclusion, that E_2 derived from T will substantially occupy estrogen receptors in aromatase-rich areas of the brain, has been confirmed for intact and and T-treated castrate male rats using [^{3}H]E_2 injections to measure occupied sites (Ogren *et al.*, 1976). In these experiments cell nuclear uptake of [^{3}H]E_2 was reduced from control levels by roughly 30–50% in the preoptic area, hypothalamus, and the amygdala, while the pituitary was unaffected. Similar results have been obtained in our laboratory (E. J. Roy, I. Lieberburg, R. J. Robbins, L. C. Krey, and B. S. McEwen, unpublished) wherein we measured endogenously occupied cell nuclear E_2 receptors in T-treated castrates employing an exchange assay (Roy and McEwen, 1977). We also made the concordant observation that the aromatase inhibitor, ATD, would substantially block the appearance of nuclear-translocated estrogen receptor, arguing that locally derived E_2 was mediating the receptor translocation. We are currently conducting experiments which employ varying doses of ATD, in an attempt to directly correlate the magnitude of various parameters of male sexual behavior with cell nuclear estrogen receptor occupation in the brain, particularly in the preoptic area.

As mentioned above, following [^{3}H]T administration to GX-ADX adult rats, cell nuclear-associated [^{3}H]T and [^{3}H]DHT display a very distinct regional pattern. The levels of both steroids accumulate to the greatest degree in pituitary, septal, and hypothalamic cell nuclei. This pattern is identical to the one observed following administration of [^{3}H]DHT (see Fig. 2). It would appear that cell nuclear androgen receptors can recognize T as well as DHT. The CNS receptors also bind antiandrogens such as cyproterone acetate and are stereospecific for the 5α vs. the 5β form of DHT (Lieberburg *et al.*, 1977a). In agreement with this is the demonstration that there is a substantial occupation of nuclear sites in intact males, which disappears following GX-ADX (Lieberburg *et al.*, 1977a). It would be interesting to know what percentage of the androgen sites are occupied by T and DHT.

The physiological evidence alluded to above suggests a role for unmetabolized T. Additional support for this concept comes from the work of Robel and co-workers (1973). Using an electron capture technique, they measured ambient T and DHT levels in various neural and peripheral structures of intact male rats, and found that in the pituitary T was present at 25 × plasma levels, while DHT levels were not significantly different from those in plasma. However, they also demonstrated a 10-fold greater amount of T in this region than in plasma. As these were whole tissue levels, one cannot extrapolate to the levels of receptor occupation; still, it seems likely that unmetabolized T may itself play some role in the CNS, perhaps with regard to gonadotropin regulation (see above).

F. Testosterone Metabolism and Brain Sexual Differentiation

In the developing rat, T influences a wide variety of neuroendocrine functions and behaviors measured in adulthood. The organizing effect of T is usually complete by the fifth postnatal day, as most manipulations after this time are ineffective. Some adult parameters which are affected by neonatal T are listed in Table VIII. Some of these T effects can be produced only by aromatizable androgens or estrogens (1 and 2); while one (3) can be produced by T and not by E_2; and one (4) can be produced by either T, DHT, or E_2. These physiological data suggest that separate androgen and estrogen receptors exist in the developing rat brain, which may mediate some of the same, as well as some different functions.

As in the adult, both 5α-reductase and aromatase are present in the neonatal CNS (Denef *et al.*, 1974; Naftolin *et al.*, 1975). The regional pattern of these enzymes is similar to that observed in the adult, in that 5α-reductase is ubiquitous in neural structures, though high in the pituitary (Denef *et al.*, 1974), while aromatase is present in limbic and hypothalamic structures and absent from the cortex and pituitary. When [³H]T is administered to neonatal rats, the pattern of metabolites recovered in the tissues reflects the enzyme distribution (Weisz and Philpott, 1971; Weisz and Gibbs, 1974; Lieberburg and McEwen, 1975a).

TABLE VIII

Some Behavioral and Neuroendocrine Parameters Measured in Adult Rats
Which are Organized by Neonatal Exposure to Testosterone

Effect	Comments	References
Anovulatory sterility or the ability to produce an LH surge	Aromatizable androgens and estrogens are effective; nonaromatizable androgens are ineffective	Plapinger and McEwen, 1977
Female sexual behavior	Aromatizable androgens and estrogens are effective; nonaromatizable androgens are ineffective.	Plapinger and McEwen, 1977
Saccharin taste preference	T effective, E_2 ineffective	Wade and Zucker, 1969
Levels of steroid metabolizing enzymes in liver	T, DHT, and E_2 are all effective; epitestosterone and etiocholanolone ineffective	Gustafsson and Stenberg, 1976 deMoor *et al.*, 1977

However, the involvement of receptors in T-mediated sexual differentiation of the brain was more difficult to pin down. Initial attempts to locate estrogen receptors in the newborn CNS were confounded by the presence of a serum estrogen binding protein, α-fetoprotein (AFP), which is present in very high levels before and shortly after birth but falls to low levels by the third week of life. The problem of interference and masking by AFP has been solved by means of the use of synthetic estrogens which have a low affinity for AFP but a high affinity for the true estrogen receptor (McEwen *et al.*, 1975b).

Various groups have now demonstrated that the perinatal E_2 receptor is very similar in its properties to the adult rat E_2 receptor (Barley *et al.*, 1974; McEwen *et al.*, 1975b; MacLusky *et al.*, 1976; Westley and Salaman, 1977). However, the regional distribution of these receptors in neonates is different from that which is found in adulthood. In addition to those regions of the CNS in which estrogen receptors are found in the adult (hypothalamus, preoptic area, and amygdala), the neonatal brain contains high levels of receptors in the cerebral cortex (Barley *et al.*, 1974; McEwen *et al.*, 1975b; MacLusky *et al.*, 1976; Westley and Salaman, 1977). An early study indicated that the transition from the neonatal pattern to the adult pattern occurred somewhere between the days 10 and 25 of life (McEwen *et al.*, 1975b).

These initial observations prompted us to examine in more detail the ontogeny of the neural estrogen receptor system. There are two phases in this development. Initially, there is a rapid phase from 1 to 2 days prenatally until postnatal day 5, wherein the receptors increase rapidly in all brain regions. This is followed by a second slower phase, extending to postnatal day 25, during which the estrogen receptor distribution in the CNS is transformed into the adult pattern (N. J. MacLusky, J. Lieberburg, and B. S. McEwen, unpublished; N. J. MacLusky, C. Chaptal, and B. S. McEwen, unpublished). This second phase is not simply brought about by a decline of cortical receptors to adult levels; rather, it involves dynamic changes in receptor content over time in various brain regions. Cortical estrogen receptors first peak at day 10, and fall between days 10 and 15. Hypothalamic and pituitary receptors increase rapidly between days 3 and 10, and level off thereafter until day 25. In contrast, levels in the preoptic area and the septum increase gradually throughout the first three weeks of life; while levels in the amygdala change little from day 3 onward.

A significant feature of this developmental pattern is the initial rapid rise of receptor levels around the time of birth, and the differentiation of the cortical receptors between days 10 and 15. Both periods are accompanied by greatly elevated plasma concentrations of estrogen (Döhler and Wuttke, 1975). We were therefore interested to know if the estrogen receptors, present in the CNS of both sexes at approximately equal levels, were occupied to any extent by endogenous estrogens. In addition, we wished to know if estrogen produced from circulating T in males was occupying estrogen receptor sites, thus supporting a role for the conversion of T to E_2 in brain sexual differentiation (aromatization hypothesis).

In an attempt to estimate the degree of occupation of brain estrogen receptors, we have used a recently developed estrogen exchange assay (Roy and McEwen, 1977) to measure the number of estrogen receptors present in cell nuclei from female rats at one day before birth, and at postnatal days 3, 10, and 25. A summary of the results is as follows: Occupied cell nuclear estrogen receptor sites were not detectable in limbic tissues, or in cerebral cortex from rats at postnatal day 3 or younger; at day 10, occupied receptors were barely detectable in limbic tissues at less than 5% of the nuclear saturation capacity, but again, no occupied receptors were detected within the cerebral cortex. These observations can be ascribed entirely to the protective influence of AFP. In the male rat, E_2 can be formed *in situ* in limbic tissues via aromatization of plasma T (Lieberburg and McEwen, 1975a). In cell nuclei isolated from limbic brain tissue of male rats one day before birth, or five days after birth, estrogen receptor sites are clearly demonstrable, to about 15% of saturation capacity (N. J. MacLusky, I. Lieberburg, and B. S. McEwen, unpublished). This finding is in accord with the report of Westley and Salaman (1976) that occupied estrogen receptors can be recovered in male, but not female, limbic brain cell nuclei at postnatal day 5, and that this occupation disappears following orchidectomy. Thus, it would appear that endogenous T, via *in situ* aromatization to E_2 in the male, is able to occupy CNS estrogen receptor sites, while endogenous estrogens in either sex do not reach receptors in the brain as a result of their substantial binding to AFP.

If estrogen receptors play a key role in sexual differentiation of the brain, within the constraints of the aromatization hypothesis, then we can make certain predictions. Blocking the conversion of T to E_2 should attenuate the sterilizing effects of exogenous T, but not those of exogenous estrogens. This approach has met with some success: barbiturates and SKF-525A (an inhibitor of P-450) will reduce the sterilizing effects of exogenous T but have not yet been tested with E_2 (Clemens, 1974; Sutherland and Gorski, 1972). It is assumed that these drugs reduce the extent of aromatization by competing directly with T for the microsomal aromatase system, particularly at hydroxylation sites on the enzyme complex (Anders, 1971; Clemens, 1974). However, these agents are not very specific, and they seem to interact with a number of microsomal enzyme systems (Anders, 1971). Another prediction would be that antiestrogens, which occupy estrogen receptor sites but ideally produce no estrogenic effect of their own, could attenuate the sterilizing effects of exogenous T or E_2. Using the antiestrogen MER-25 in conjunction with exogenous T, workers have obtained both positive (MacDonald and Doughty, 1973–1974) and negative results (Brown-Grant, 1974; Hayashi, 1974); the uncertainty of the effect might be attributable to the weak antiestrogenic properties of MER-25 (Lerner, 1964).

Recently, several new and better drugs have become available, which make testing of the aromatization hypothesis far more feasible than before. Two such drugs we have examined are the potent antiestrogen CI-628 (Chazal *et al.*, 1975), and a relatively specific aromatase inhibitor, 1,4,6-androstatriene-3,17-dione (ATD) (Schwarzel *et al.*, 1973). Following *in vivo* treatment of neonatal female rats with ATD or CI-628, there is a reduction of greater than 75% in $[^3H]E_2$ recovered from cell nuclear receptors in the hypothalamus, preoptic area, and amygdala after the administration of $[^3H]T$, without alterations in levels of tissue or nuclear $[^3H]T$ or of $[^3H]DHT$ (Lieberburg *et al.*, 1977b). Under virtually identical experimental conditions, ATD and CI-628 attenuate the effects on sexual differentiation of exogenous T in females or endogenous T in males (McEwen *et al.*, 1977). It therefore seems that aromatization of T is necessary if sexual differentiation of the rat brain is to occur.

One problem with confirming the aromatization hypothesis is the demonstration that cyproterone acetate (CA) is able to attenuate the sterilizing effects of exogenous T (Arai and Gorski, 1968). CA is mainly antiandrogenic in its properties (Neumann and Steinbeck, 1974). We wish to understand the biochemical mechanism through which CA produces its protective effect. Various modes of action seem possible: CA could be interfering with the interaction of E_2 (formed from T) with the estrogen receptor; or, perhaps more directly, CA could be limiting the substrate, T, for neural aromatization, competing with T for the enzyme either competitively or noncompetitively, or repressing the enzyme genomically, or of course any combination of the above. All these potential modes of action of CA would be reflected in a lowering of nuclear and tissue levels of E_2 following T administration.

To test these possibilities, neonatal female rats were treated with various chronic and acute doses of CA ranging from 0.6 to 2.0 mg/rat/day. The animals were then treated with $[^3H]$diethylstilbestrol (DES), a synthetic estrogen. At no dose did CA produce any alteration in $[^3H]DES$ nuclear uptake in the CNS, indicating that it was probably not acting by interfering with the estrogen receptor mechanism. In parallel experiments, CA-treated animals showed normal levels of $[^3H]E_2$ in CNS tissue and cell nuclei following $[^3H]T$ administration. Thus, it would appear that CA was not competing with T for aromatase either, nor was the enzyme substantially repressed following CA treatment. CA substantially reduced $[^3H]T$ and $[^3H]DHT$ in

CNS cell nuclei after [³H]T administration. Tissue levels of [³H]T were reduced, but not significantly, indicating that the nuclear levels were not simply reflecting tissue levels. This observation indicates the presence of a CNS cell nuclear androgen receptor in the neonatal rat brain, but also confuses the picture obtained with CI-628 and ATD. Though the CA data do not disprove the aromatization hypothesis, they certainly do not support it. Clearly, further work is needed in defining CA's action, and in resolving this apparent discrepancy.

There is no evidence to suggest that androgen receptors appear in the rat brain before birth. They are present in the neonatal CNS by postnatal days 1–5, at a level approximately 1/10 of that observed in the gonadectomized adult rat (I. Lieberburg, N. J. MacLusky, and B. S. McEwen, unpublished; Kato, 1976). Subsequently, the receptor levels increase gradually over the first four weeks of life. The neonatal CNS androgen receptors exhibit properties typical of the receptors found in the adult animal. They sediment in low ionic strength glycerol gradients at approximately 8 S; they bind to DNA-cellulose with the same affinity; they exhibit high affinity for the antiandrogen cyproterone or its 17α-acetate, CA, and low affinity for the synthetic estrogen DES. It is noteworthy that high levels of androgen receptors do not appear in the developing cerebral cortex, in marked contrast to the estrogen receptor system (see above).

These cytosol androgen receptors are probably capable of translocating the steroid into the cell nucleus. Part of the evidence for this has been mentioned in the previous section regarding the ability of CA to decrease [³H]T and [³H]DHT levels in CNS cell nuclei after [³H]T administration. Recently, we have gathered evidence that these ³H-androgens are macromolecular bound. Following *in vivo* [³H]T administration to neonatal female rats, CNS cell nuclei were subjected to salt extraction to remove receptor proteins, followed by Sephadex G-200 filtration or protamine sulfate precipitation of the extract. The macromolecular bound steroid was then extracted with organic solvents and subjected to analysis. Both G-200 and protamine revealed a substantial amount of [³H]T and [³H]DHT, as well as of [³H]E₂, bound to macromolecules which were extracted from the nuclear compartment. The specificity of this androgen nuclear receptor has recently been tested with a tritiated synthetic androgen, 17α-methyl-4,9,11-estratriene-17β-ol-3-one (RU-1881), which was generously supplied to us by Dr. J. P. Raynaud, Roussel-Uclaf (Romainville, France). This androgen is also bound *in vivo* to macromolecules in the nuclear compartment, demonstrable by LH20 gel filtration. Unlabeled androgens, such as T, administered in excess with the [³H]1881, are able to compete away the nuclear binding, while unlabeled estrogens have no effect (I. Lieberburg, N. J. MacLusky, and B.

S. McEwen, unpublished). Additional experiments are in progress to determine whether these androgen receptors, which are present in the brain at the time of sexual differentiation, play some role in the process.

IV. CONCLUDING REMARKS

In this chapter we have attempted to define steroid receptor systems in the brain and to describe some of the ways of measuring them in the central nervous system (CNS) and pituitary, and to point out some technical problems which may be encountered. The evidence supporting receptor involvement in neuroendocrine function was also summarized. According to this now "classical" scheme of steroid action, the steroid receptor complex initiates genomic events by altering cell nuclear metabolism and production of specific messenger RNA's. The circumstantial evidence for the role of this "inductive" mechanism of steroid hormones in the CNS and pituitary may be classified into three categories: temporal, pharmacological, and neurochemical (McEwen and Luine, 1978). That is, following steroid administration, a lag time of hours or days generally precedes the appearance of most neuroendocrine effects. In addition, there are reports that steroid antagonists which occupy and render the steroid receptors inactive, as well as inhibitors of RNA and protein synthesis, can reversibly block some steroid effects. Finally, correlative studies of steroid effects on pituitary and brain RNA and protein metabolism provide some neurochemical evidence for altered metabolic states resulting from enhanced steroid secretion or from steroid administration. Measurements of brain and pituitary enzyme activities as a function of steroid administration also point to a variety of "inductive" effects on cellular metabolism. Where these effects have been examined in detail they appear to be the direct result of steroid action at the receptor level, although the definitive proof of this relationship is lacking (McEwen and Luine, 1978).

There are now reports describing steroid-mediated neuroendocrine events which do not appear to involve the genome (McEwen *et al.*, 1978). Some of these effects occur with such short latencies as to preclude genomic involvement. This is true of rapid (<5 minute) electrical responses of neurons to iontophoretically or systemically applied steroids (Feldman and Sarne, 1970; Kelly *et al.*, 1977; Mandelbrod *et al.*, 1974; Phillips and Dafny, 1971; Ruh and Steiner, 1967). This may also apply to the very rapid attenuation of pulsatile LH release by intravenous estradiol which is mimicked by an α-adrenergic blocking agent, phenoxybenzamine (Blake, 1974; Blake *et al.*, 1974; Knobil, 1974). Another example is the fast negative feedback effect of glucocorticoids on the ability of hypothalamic synaptosomes to release corticotropin-releasing factor (CRF) (Edwardson and Bennett, 1974). There is also the glucocorticoid stimulation of the uptake of tryptophan by synaptosomes (Neckers and Sze, 1975).

Although we can reasonably exclude genomic involvement in these phenomena, we cannot exclude the involvement of some kind of steroid receptors. Many of these rapid effects seem to involve or are accompanied by changes in ion permeability and other processes originating in the cell surface. From studies of other steroid target tissues, there is some evidence indicating the presence of classical steroid receptors on the cell surface (Pietras and Szego, 1977; Suyemitsu and Terayama, 1975). The implication is that these receptors perform an integral role in cellular functioning. These surface-bound receptors have been invoked to explain the saturable and temperature-dependent nature of the steroid's entry into the target cell (see Pietras and Szego, 1977), a process which was originally thought to be achieved solely by passive diffusion (see Gorski and Gannon, 1976). However, more recently, these surface receptors in endometrial cells have been implicated in mediating rapid estrogen effects on calcium ion flux across the cell membrane (see Pietras and Szego, 1975). Changes in the conformation of membrane-bound receptor following binding of the steroid could sterically alter nearby ion channels, resulting in an increase in ion permeability. Because Ca^{2+} influx is required for neurotransmitter release, it is conceivable that rapidly induced steroid-mediated changes in neuronal firing rates could be achieved through this mechanism. The potential involvement of the steroid receptor in this process is evidenced by the recent findings of Kelly *et al.* (1977) that iontophoretically applied 17β-estradiol hemisuccinate will dramatically alter the firing rates of preoptic area septal neurons, while the 17α epimer is without effect.

Another potential mechanism of action involving the receptor could be at the synaptic level. It is possible that steroid receptors present in the cytoplasm within synaptic terminals could regulate neurotransmitter synthesis, packaging, and release independently of the involvement of the cell nucleus. The aforementioned evidence demonstrating glucocorticoid effects on synaptosomal release of CRF may indicate that such a mechanism is involved. Thus, we are faced with the possibility that steroid receptors performing other than classical roles may exist in parts of neurons other than the perinuclear cytoplasm. In this light, it is interesting to note that certain regions of the brain which have been considered steroid nonresponsive, such as the cerebral or cerebellar cortex, demonstrate very little nuclear concentration of steroids, such as androgens or glucocorticoids, using either biochemical or autoradiographic techniques; yet, these regions possess quite substantial amounts of cytosol receptor which can be measured *in vitro* (Sar and Stumpf, 1977; Barley *et al.*, 1975). The issue then becomes whether or not these putative receptors are functional, and if so, where they reside intracellularly and what functions they perform. This is one of the directions which future research must take in defining the roles played by steroid receptors in the functioning of the CNS.

ACKNOWLEDGMENTS

Research in the authors' laboratory is supported by research grant NS 07080 from the USPHS and by an institutional grant RF 70095 from the Rockefeller Foundation. The authors wish to acknowledge the essential role played by their colleagues in the laboratory whose work is cited in the review: Dr. Lewis Krey, Dr. Victoria Luine, Dr. Neil MacLusky, Dr. Jerrold Meyer and Dr. Edward Roy. The authors also would like to thank Ms. Freddi Berg for editorial assistance.

REFERENCES

Anders, M. W. (1971). *Annu. Rev. Pharmacol.* **11**, 37–56.
Anderson, C. H., and Greenwald, S. S. (1969). *Endocrinology* **85**, 1160–1165.
Anderson, J., Clark, J. H., and Peck, E. J., Jr. (1972). *Biochem. J.* **126**, 561–567.
Anderson, J. N., Peck, E. J., Jr., and Clark, J. H. (1973). *Endocrinology* **93**, 711–717.
Anderson, N. S., III, and Fanestil, D. D. (1976). *Endocrinology* **98**, 676–684.
Appleton, T. C. (1968). *Acta Histochem., Suppl.* **8**, 115–133.
Arai, Y., and Gorski, R. A. (1968). *Proc. Soc. Exp. Biol. Med.* **127**, 590–593.
Araki, S., Ferin, M., Zimmerman, E. A., and Vande Wiele, R. L. (1975). *Endocrinology* **96**, 644–650.
Arimura, A., Bowers, C. Y, Schally, A. V., Saito, M., and Miller, M. C. (1969). *Endocrinology* **85**, 300–311.
Austin, C. R., and Short, R. V., eds. (1972). "Reproduction in Mammals," Vol. 3. Cambridge Univ. Press, London and New York.
Barley, J., Ginsburg, M., Greenstein, B. D., MacLusky, N. J., and Thomas, P. J. (1974). *Nature (London)* **252**, 259–260.
Barley, J., Ginsburg, M., Greenstein, B. D., MacLusky, N. J., and Thomas, P. J. (1975). *Brain Res.* **100**, 383–393.
Barros, C., and Austin, C. R. (1968). *Endocrinology* **83**, 177–179.
Baxter, J. D., and Tomkins, G. D. (1971). *Proc. Natl. Acad. Sci. U.S.A.* **68**, 932–937.
Berthold, A. A. (1949). *Arch. Anat., Physiol. Wiss. Med.* **16**, 42–46.
Beyer, C., Morali, G., and Cruz, M. L. (1971). *Endocrinology* **89**, 1158–1161.
Blake, C. A. (1974). *Endocrinology* **95**, 999–1004.
Blake, C. A., Norman, R. L., and Sawyer, C. H. (1974). *Neuroendocrinology* **16**, 22–35.
Bronson, F. H., and Desjardins, C. (1971). *In* "The Physiology of Aggression" (B. E. Elfthériou and J. P. Scott, eds.), pp. 43–64 Plenum, New York.
Brown-Grant, K. (1974). *J. Endocrinol.* **62**, 683–684.
Bueno, J., and Pfaff, D. W. (1976). *Brain Res.* **101**, 67–78.
Butte, J. C., Kakihana, R., and Noble, E. P. (1972). *Endocrinology* **90**, 1091–1100.
Cardinali, D. P., and Gomez, E. (1977). *J. Endocrinol.* **73**, 181–182.
Carroll, B. J., Heath, B., and Jarrett, D. B. (1975). *Endocrinology* **97**, 290–300.
Chazal, G., Faudon, M., Gogan, F., and Rotsztejn, W. (1975). *Brain Res.* **89**, 245–254.

Christensen, L. W., and Clemens, L. G. (1974). *Endocrinology* **95**, 984–990.

Christensen, L. W., and Clemens, L. G. (1975). *Endocrinology* **97**, 1545–1551.

Clark, A. J. (1933). "The Mode of Action of Drugs on Cells." Arnold, London.

Clark, J. H., Campbell, P. S., and Peck, E. J. (1972). *Neuroendocrinology* **77**, 218–228.

Clemens, L. G. (1974). *In* "Reproductive Behavior" (W. Montagna and W. A. Sadler, eds.), pp. 23–53. Plenum, New York.

Davidson, J. M. (1966a). *Endocrinology* **79**, 783–794.

Davidson, J. M. (1966b). *In* "Neuroendocrinology" (L. Martini and W. F. Ganong, eds.), Vol. 1, pp. 565–611. Academic Press, New York.

Davies, I. M., Naftolin, F., Ryan, K. J., and Siu, J. (1975). *Steroids* **25**, 591–609.

Davis, P. G., and Barfield, R. J. (1978). *Neuroendocrinology*, in press.

Debeljuk, L., Rettori, V., Rozados, R. V., and Velez, C. V. (1975). *Proc. Soc. Exp. Biol. Med.* **150**, 229–231.

deKloet, E. R., and McEwen, B. S. (1976a). *Biochim. Biophys. Acta* **421**, 115–123.

deKloet, E. R., and McEwen, B. S. (1976b). *Biochim. Biophys. Acta* **421**, 124–132.

deKloet, E. R., and McEwen, B. S. (1976c). *In* "Molecular and Functional Neurobiology" (W. H. Gispen, ed.), pp. 257–307. Elsevier, Amsterdam.

deKloet, E. R., Wallach, G., and McEwen, B. S. (1975). *Endocrinology* **96**, 598–609.

De Lean, A., Ferland, L., Drouin, J., Kelly, P. A., and Labrie, F. (1977). *Endocrinology* **100**, 1496–1504.

de Moor, P., Van Baelen, H., Verhoeven, G., Boeck, W., Adam-Heylen, M., and Vandoren, G. (1977). *J. Steroid Biochem.* **8**, 579–584.

Denef, C., Magnus, C., and McEwen, B. S. (1973). *J. Endocrinol.* **59**, 605–621.

Denef, C., Magnus, C., and McEwen, B. S. (1974). *Endocrinology* **94**, 1265–1274.

de Vellis, J., and Inglish, D. (1973). *Prog. Brain Res.* **40**, 321–330.

de Vellis, J., McEwen, B. S., Cole, R., and Inglish, D. (1974). *J. Steroid Biochem.* **5**, 392–393.

Diez, J. A., Sze, P. Y., and Ginsburg, B. E. (1977). *Neurochem. Res.* **2**, 161–170.

Döhler, K. D., and Wuttke, W. (1975). *Endocrinology* **97**, 898–907.

Dorfman, R. I., and Shipley, R. A. (1956). "Androgens. Biochemistry, Physiology and Clinical Significance." Wiley, New York.

Drouin, J., LaGace, L., and LaBrie, F. (1976). *Endocrinology* **99**, 1477–1481.

Edwardson, J. A., and Bennett, G. W. (1974). *Nature (London)* **251**, 425–427.

Erdos, T., Best-Belpomme, M., and Bessada, R. (1970). *Anal. Biochem.* **37**, 244–252.

Falvo, R. E., Buhl, A., and Nalbandov, A. V. (1974). *Endocrinology* **95**, 26–29.

Feder, H. H., and Marrone, B. L. (1977). *Ann. N.Y. Acad. Sci.* **286**, 331–352.

Feinendegen, L. E. (1967). "Tritium Labeled Molecules in Biology and Medicine." Academic Press, New York.

Feldman, S., and Sarne, Y. (1970). *Brain Res.* **23**, 67–75.

Fishman, J. (1976). *Neuroendocrinology* **22**, 363–374.

Fleischer, N., and Battarbee, H. (1967). *Proc. Soc. Exp. Biol. Med.* **126**, 922–925.

Flerkó, B. (1966). *In* "Neuroendocrinology" (L. Martini and W. F. Ganong, eds.), Vol. 1, pp. 613–668. Academic Press, New York.

Fox, T. O. (1977). *Brain Res.* **120**, 580–583.

Fox, T. O., and Johnston, C. (1974). *Brain Res.* **77**, 330–336.

Gay, V. L., and Tomacari, R. L. (1974). *Science* **184**, 75–77.

Ginsburg, M., Greenstein, B. D., MacLusky, N. J., Morris, I. D., and Thomas, P. J. (1974). *Steroids* **23**, 773–792.

Ginsburg, M., Greenstein, B. D., MacLusky, N. J., Morris, I. D., and Thomas, P. J. (1975). *J. Steroid Biochem.* **6**, 989–991.

Godefroi, V. C., and Brook, S. C. (1973). *Anal. Biochem.* **51**, 335–344.

Gomez-Sanchez, C., Holland, O. B., Higgins, J. R., Kem, D. C., and Kaplan, N. M. (1976). *Endocrinology* **99**, 567–572.

Gorski, J., and Gannon, F. (1976). *Annu. Rev. Physiol.* **38**, 425–450.

Gorski, J., Toft, D., Shyämalä, G., Smith, D., and Notides, A. (1968). *Recent Prog. Horm. Res.* **24**, 45–80.

Grosser, B. I., and Axelrod, L. R. (1968). *Steroids* **11**, 827–836.

Gustafsson, J. A., and Stenberg, A. (1976). *Science* **191**, 203–204.

Gustafsson, J. A., Pousette, A., and Svensson, E. (1976). *J. Biol. Chem.* **251**, 4047–4054.

Gustafsson, J. A., Eneroth, P., Pousette, A., Skett, P., Sonnenschein, C., Stenberg, A., and Ahlen, A. (1977). *J. Steroid Biochem.* **8**, 429–443.

Hanbauer, I., Lovenberg, W., Guidotti, A., and Costa, E. (1975). *Brain Res.* **96**, 197–200.

Harris, G. W., Michael, R. P., and Scott, R. P. (1957). *In* "Neurological Basis of Behavior" (G. E. W. Wolstenholme and C. M. O'Connor, eds.), pp. 236–254. Little, Brown, Boston, Massachusetts.

Hart, B. L. (1974). *Psychol. Bull.* **81**, 383–400.

Hayashi, S. (1974). *Endocrinol. Jpn.* **21**, 453–457.

Himmelweit, F. (1960). "The Collected Papers of Paul Erhlich," Vol. 3. Academic Press, New York.

Jackson, G. L. (1972). *Endocrinology* **91**, 1284–1287.

Jackson, G. L. (1973). *Endocrinology* **93**, 887–891.

Jensen, E. V., and DeSombre, E. R. (1973). *Science* **182**, 126–134.

Johnston, P., and Davidson, J. M. (1972). *Horm. Behav.* **3**, 345–357.

Jones, M. G., Hillhouse, E. W., and Burden, J. L. (1977). *J. Endocrinol.* **73**, 405–417.

Kalra, P. S., and Kalra, S. P. (1977). *Endocrinology* **101**, 1821–1827.

Kalra, S. P. (1975). *Neuroendocrinology* **18**, 333–344.

Kalra, S. P. (1976). *Endocrinology* **99**, 101–107.

Karavolas, H. J., and Nuti, K. M. (1976). *In* "Subcellular Mechanisms in Reproductive Neuroendocrinology" (F. Naftolin, K. J. Ryan, and J. Davies, eds.), pp. 305–326. Elsevier, Amsterdam.

Kato, J. (1976). *Ann. Biol. Anim., Biochim., Biophys.* **16**, 457–469.

Kato, J. (1977). *In* "Endocrinology" (V. H. T. James, ed.), Int. Congr. Ser. No. 402, Vol. 1, pp. 12–17. Excerpta Med. Found., Amsterdam.

Kelly, M. J., Moss, R. L., Dudley, C. A., and Fawcett, C. P. (1977). *Exp. Brain Res.* **30**, 43–52.

Kier, L. B. (1970). "Molecular Orbital Theory in Drug Research." Academic Press, New York.

King, R. J. B., and Mainwaring, W. I. P. (1974). "Steroid-Cell Interactions." Univ. Park Press, Baltimore, Maryland.

King, R. J. B., Gordon, J., and Steggles, A. W. (1969). *Biochem. J.* **114**, 649–657.

Kizer, J. S., Palkovits, M., Zivin, J., Brownstein, M., Saavedra, J. M., and Kopin, I. J. (1974). *Endocrinology* **95**, 799–812.

Knobil, E. (1974). *Recent Prog. Horm. Res.* **30**, 1–36.

Kobayashi, R. M., and Reed, K. C. (1977). *Soc. Neurosci. Symp.* **3**, abstr. No. 1115.

Korach, K. S., and Muldoon, T. G. (1973). *Endocrinology* **92**, 322–326.

Korach, K. S., and Muldoon, T. G. (1974). *Endocrinology* **94**, 785–793.

Korenman, S. G., Perrin, L. E., and McCallum, T. P. (1969). *J. Clin. Endocrinol. Metab.* **29**, 879–883.

Kubo, K., Gorski, R. A., and Kawakami, M. (1975). *Neuroendocrinology* **18**, 176–191.

Lemaire, I., Dupont, A., Bastarache, E., Labrie, F., and Fortier, C. (1974). *Can. J. Physiol. Pharmacol.* **52**, 451–457.

Lerner, L. J. (1964). *Recent Prog. Horm. Res.* **20**, 435–490.

Lieberburg, I., and McEwen, B. S. (1975a). *Brain Res.* **85**, 165–170.
Lieberburg, I., and McEwen, B. S. (1975b). *Brain Res.* **91**, 171–174.
Lieberburg, I., and McEwen, B. S. (1977). *Endocrinology* **100**, 588–597.
Lieberburg, I., MacLusky, N. J., and McEwen, B. S. (1977a). *Endocrinology* **100**, 598–607.
Lieberburg, I., Wallach, G., and McEwen, B. S. (1977b). *Brain Res.* **128**, 176–181.
Lisk, R. D. (1962). *Am. J. Physiol.* **203**, 493–496.
Litteria, M., and Thorner, M. W. (1974). *J. Endocrinol.* **60**, 377–378.
Lövtrup-Rein, H., and McEwen, B. S. (1966). *J. Cell Biol.* **30**, 405–416.
McDonald, P. G., and Doughty, C. (1973–1974). *Neuroendocrinology* **13**, 182–188.
McEwen, B. S. (1977). *Ann. N.Y. Acad. Sci.* **297**, 568–579.
McEwen, B. S. (1978a). *In* "Mechanisms of Glucocorticoid Action" (G. Rousseau and J. Baxter, eds.). Springer-Verlag, Berlin and New York (in press).
McEwen, B. S. (1978b). *In* "Handbook of Biological Psychiatry" (H. M. Van Praag *et al.*, eds.). Dekker, New York (in press).
McEwen, B. S., and Luine, V. N. (1978). *Colloq. Int. CNRS* (in press).
McEwen, B. S., and Pfaff, D. W. (1970). *Brain Res.* **21**, 1–16.
McEwen, B. S., and Pfaff, D. W. (1973). *In* "Frontiers in Neuroendocrinology" (W. F. Ganong and L. Martini, eds.), pp. 267–335. Oxford Univ. Press, London and New York.
McEwen, B. S., and Plapinger, L. (1970). *Nature (London)* **226**, 263–265.
McEwen, B. S., and Wallach, G. (1973). *Brain Res.* **57**, 373–386.
McEwen, B. S., and Zigmond, R. E. (1972). *In* "Methods in Neurochemistry" (N. Marks and R. Rodnight, eds.), pp. 140–161. Plenum, New York.
McEwen, B. S., Weiss, J. M., and Schwartz, L. S. (1969). *Brain Res.* **16**, 227–241.
McEwen, B. S., Pfaff, D. W., and Zigmond, R. E. (1970a). *Brain Res.* **21**, 17–28.
McEwen, B. S., Pfaff, D. W., and Zigmond, R. E. (1970b). *Brain Res.* **21**, 29–38.
McEwen, B. S., Magnus, C., and Wallach, G. (1972a). *Endocrinology* **90**, 217–226.
McEwen, B. S., Plapinger, L., Wallach, G., and Magnus, C. (1972b). *J. Neurochem.* **19**, 1159–1170.
McEwen, B. S., Zigmond, R. E., and Gerlach, J. L. (1972c). *Struct. Funct. Nerv. Tissue* **5**, 205–291.
McEwen, B. S., Pfaff, D. W., Chaptal, C., and Luine, V. (1975a). *Brain Res.* **86**, 155–161.
McEwen, B. S., Plapinger, L., Chaptal, C., Gerlach, J., and Wallach, G. (1975b). *Brain Res.* **96**, 400–406.
McEwen, B. S., de Kloet, R., and Wallach, G. (1976). *Brain Res.* **105**, 129–136.
McEwen, B. S., Lieberburg, I., Chaptal, C., and Krey, L. C. (1977). *Horm. Behav.* **9**, 249–263.
McEwen, B. S., Krey, L. C., and Luine, V. N. (1978). *In* "The Hypothalamus" (R. J. Baldessarini and J. B. Martin, eds.), pp. 255–268. Raven, New York.
MacLusky, N. J., Chaptal, C., Lieberburg, I., and McEwen, B. S. (1976). *Brain Res.* **114**, 158–165.
MacLusky, N. J., Turner, B. B., and McEwen, B. S. (1977). *Brain Res.* **130**, 564–571.
Mainwaring, W. I. P. (1976). "The Mechanism of Action of Androgens," p. 6. Springer-Verlag, Berlin and New York.
Mandelbrod, I., Feldman, S., and Werman, R. (1974). *Brain Res.* **80**, 303–315.
Mastro, A., and Hymer, W. C. (1973). *J. Endocrinol.* **59**, 107–119.
Miller, A. L., Chaptal, C., McEwen, B. S., and Peck, E. J. (1978). *Psychoneuroendocrinology* **3**, 155–164.
Miller, W. L., Knight, M. M., Grimek, H. J., and Gorski, J. (1977). *Endocrinology* **100**, 1306–1316.

Morris, J. E., and Moscona, A. A. (1970). *Science* **167**, 1736–1738.

Motta, M., Piva, F., and Martini, L. (1970). *In* "The Hypothalamus" (L. Martini, M. Motta, and F. Fraschini, F., eds.), pp. 463–489. Academic Press, New York.

Mowles, T. F., Ashkanazy B., Mix, E., and Sheppart, H. (1971). *Endocrinology* **89**, 489–491.

Naess, O. (1976). *Steroids* **27**, 167–185.

Naess, O., Hansson, V., Djoeseland, O., and Attramadal, A. (1975). Endocrinology **97**, 1355–1363.

Naftolin, F., Ryan, K. J, Davies, I. J., Reddy, V. V., Flores, F., Kuhn, M., White, R. J., Takaoka, Y., and Wolin, L. (1975). *Recent Prog. Horm. Res.* **31**, 295–315.

Neckers, L., and Sze, P. Y. (1975). *Brain Res.* **93**, 123–132.

Neumann, F., and Steinbeck, H. (1974). *Handb. Exp. Pharmakol.* **35**, 235–484.

Nguyen, N. Y., and Crambach, A. (1977). *Anal. Biochem.* **82**, 226–235.

Ogren, L., Vertes, M., and Woolley, D. (1976). *Neuroendocrinology* **21**, 350–365.

Paul, S. M., and Axelrod, J. (1977). *Science* **197**, 657–659.

Pavlik, E. J., and Coulson, P. B. (1976a). *J. Steroid Biochem.* **7**, 357–368.

Pavlik, E. J., and Coulson, P. B. (1976b). *J. Steroid Biochem.* **7**, 369–376.

Peck, E. J. (1978). *Pap., Conf. Ontog. Receptors Mol. Mech. Reprod. Horm. Action, 1977*, in press.

Perez-Palacios, G., Perez, A. E., Cruz, M. L., and Beyer, C. (1973). *Biol. Reprod.* **8**, 395–399.

Perez-Palacios, G., Larsson, K., and Beyer, C. (1975). *J. Steroid Biochem.* **6**, 999–1006.

Pfaff, D. W. (1968). *Science* **161**, 1355–1356.

Pfaff, D. W., and Keiner, M. (1973). *J. Comp. Neurol.* **151**, 121–158.

Pfaff, D. W., Silva, M. T., and Weiss, J. M. (1971). *Science* **172**, 394–395.

Pfaff, D. W., Diakow, C., Zigmond, R. E., and Kow, L.-M. (1974). *In* "The Neurosciences: Third Study Program" (F. O. Schmitt and F. G. Worden, eds.), pp. 621–646. MIT Press, Cambridge, Massachusetts.

Phillips, M. I., and Dafny, N. (1971). *Brain Res.* **25**, 651–655.

Pietras, R. J., and Szego, C. M. (1975). *Nature (London)* **253**, 357–359.

Pietras, R. J., and Szego, C. M. (1977). *Nature (London)* **265**, 69–72.

Plapinger, L., and McEwen, B. S. (1978). *In* "Biological Determinants of Sexual Behavior" (J. Hutchinson, ed.), pp. 153–218. Wiley, New York.

Plapinger, L., McEwen, B. S., and Clemens, L. E. (1973). *Endocrinology* **93**, 1129–1139.

Pohorecky, L. A., and Wurtman, R. J. (1971). *Pharmacol. Rev.* **23**, 1–35.

Purdy, R. H., and Axelrod, L. R. (1968). *Steroids* **11**, 851–862.

Quadagno, D. M., and Ho, G. K. W. (1975). *Horm. Behav.* **6**, 19–26.

Raisinghani, K. H., Dorfman, R. K., Forchielli, E., Gyermek, L., and Genther, G. (1968). *Acta Endocrinol. (Copenhagen)* **57**, 395–404.

Robel, P., Corpechot, C., and Baulieu, E. E. (1973). *FEBS Lett.* **33**, 218–220.

Robinson, J. A., and Leavitt, W. W. (1971). *Proc. Soc. Exp. Biol. Med.* **139**, 471–475.

Rogers, A. W. (1973). "Techniques of Autoradiography." Elsevier, Amsterdam.

Rommerts, F. F. G., and Van der Molen, H. J. (1971). *Biochim. Biophys. Acta* **248**, 489–502.

Roy, E. J., and McEwen, B. S. (1977). *Steroids* **30**, 657–669.

Ruf, K., and Steiner, F. A. (1967). *Science* **156**, 667–668.

Russell, S. M., Dhariwal, A. P. S., McCann, S. M., and Yates, F. E. (1969). *Endocrinology* **85**, 512–521.

Samperez, S., Thieulant, M. L., Mercier, L., and Jouan, P. (1974), *J. Steroid Biochem.* **5**, 911–915.

Sar, M., and Stumpf, W. E. (1977). *J. Steroid Biochem.* **8**, 1131–1135.

Sayers, G., and Portanova, R. (1974). *Endocrinology* **94**, 1723–1730.

Schally, A. V., Bowers, C. Y., Carter, W. H., Arimura, A., Redding, T. W., and Saito, M. (1969). *Endocrinology* **85**, 290–299.

Schwarzel, W. C., Kruggel, W. G., and Brodie, H. J. (1973). *Endocrinology* **92**, 866–880.

Sheridan, P. J., Sar, M., and Stumpf, W. E. (1974a). *Am. J. Anat.* **140**, 589–594.

Sheridan, P. J., Sar, M., and Stumpf, W. E. (1974b). *Endocrinology* **94**, 1386–1390.

Smith, M. S., Freeman, M. E., and Neill, J. D. (1975). *Endocrinology* **96**, 219–226.

Steggles, A. W., and King, R. J. B. (1970). *Biochem. J.* **118**, 695.

Stern, J. M., and Eisenfeld, A. J. (1971). *Endocrinology* **88**, 1117–1125.

Stone, R. T., Maurer, R. A., and Gorski, J. (1977). *Biochemistry* **16**, 4915–4921.

Stumpf, W. E. (1971). *Acta Endocrinol. (Copenhagen), Suppl.* **153**, 205–222.

Stumpf, W. E., and Roth, L. J. (1966). *J. Histochem. Cytochem.* **14**, 274–287.

Sutherland, S., and Gorski, R. A. (1972). *Neuroendocrinology* **10**, 94–108.

Suyemitsu, T., and Terayama, H. (1975). *Endocrinology* **96**, 1499–1508.

Swerdloff, R. S., Walsh, P. C., and Odell, W. D. (1972). *Steroids* **20**, 13–22.

Sze, P. Y. (1976). *Adv. Biochem. Psychopharmacol.* **15**, 251–265.

Tang, L. K. L., and Spies, H. G. (1975). *Endocrinology* **96**, 349–356.

Terkel, A. S., Shryne, J., and Gorski, R. A. (1973). *Horm. Behav.* **4**, 377–386.

Thompson, E. B., and Lippman, M. (1974). *Metab., Clin, Exp.* **23**, 159–202.

Tuohimaa, P. (1970). *Histochemie* **23**, 349–357.

Tushinski, R. J., Sussman, P. M., Yu, L.-Y., and Bancroft, F. C. (1977). *Proc. Natl. Acad. Sci. U.S.A.* **74**, 2357–2361.

Vermes, I., Smelik, P. G., and Mulder, A. H. (1976). *Life Sci.* **19**, 1719–1726.

Vertes, M., and King, R. J. B. (1969). *J. Endocrinol.* **45**, xxii–xxiii.

Vilchez-Martinez, J., Arimura, A., Debeljuk, L., and Schally, A. V. (1974). *Endocrinology* **94**, 1300–1303.

Wade, G. N. (1972). *Physiol. Behav.* **8**, 523–534.

Wade, G. N., and Zucker, I. (1969). *Physiol. Behav.* **4**, 935–943.

Warembourg, M. (1975a). *Brain Res.* **89**, 61–70.

Warembourg, M. (1975b). *Cell Tissue Res.* **161**, 183–191.

Watanabe, H., Nicholson, W. E., and Orth, D. N. (1973). *Endocrinology* **93**, 411.

Weisz, J., and Gibbs, C. (1974). *Neuroendocrinology* **14**, 72–86.

Weisz, J., and Philpott, J. (1971). *In* "Influence of Hormones on the Nervous System" (D. H. Ford, ed.), pp. 282–295. Karger, Basel.

Westley, B. R., and Salaman, D. F. (1976). *Nature (London)* **262**, 407–408.

Westley, B. R., and Salaman, D. F. (1977). *Brain Res.* **119**, 375–388.

Westphal, U. (1971). "Steroid Protein Interactions: Monographs on Endocrinology," Vol. 4. Springer-Verlag, Berlin and New York.

Zigmond, R. E., and McEwen, B. S. (1970). *J. Neurochem.* **17**, 889–899.

CHAPTER 9

Properties of Estrogen Receptor Purified to Homogeneity

Francesco Bresciani, Vincenzo Sica, and Alessandro Weisz

I. INTRODUCTION

One major objective of our work over the last few years has been the purification and characterization of the estrogen receptor from calf uterus. To this end we have applied both classical separation methods (Puca *et al.*, 1971a,b, 1975) and developed affinity chromatography adsorbents (Sica *et al.*, 1973a,b).

We approach the problem of understanding the mechanism of estrogen action by isolating, purifying, and characterizing the component parts of this mechanism. By studying the mode of interaction of these parts under simplified condition *in vitro*, we hope to contribute to the analytical knowledge of how the mechanism works as a whole.

Recently (Sica and Bresciani, 1978), we have overcome remaining difficulties and succeeded in purifying to homogeneity tangible amounts (milligrams) of estrogen receptor from calf uterus. Here we will first briefly describe our method of large-scale purification of receptor protein, which exploits sequential affinity chromatography on heparin–Sepharose 4B and 17β-estradiol-17-hemisuccinyl-ovalbumin-Sepharose 4B; and second, furnish some basic information on physical and chemical properties of the purified receptor.

II. PURIFICATION TO HOMOGENEITY OF ESTROGEN RECEPTOR

A. PREPARATION OF CYTOSOL FRACTION

Uteri from immature calves were collected at the slaughterhouse as described earlier (Puca *et al.*, 1971a), stripped of gross connective tissue, and frozen in liquid nitrogen. Before use they were pulverized in a mortar and, in the typical preparation to be described here, 1 kg of powdered uterine tissue was added to 4 l of ice-cold TED buffer.* The mixture was briefly homogenized in a blender, in order to obtain a slurry which was then homogenized using a Polytron machine, as described earlier (Puca *et al.*, 1971a). The homogenate was centrifuged at 35,000 rpm in a Beckman–Spinco ultracentrifuge L5-75 using rotor heads type 35 (142,800 g max). Two centrifuges were used in parallel to speed up the centrifugation step. After centrifugation, the supernatant fraction (cytosol, about 4 l) was collected and further treated as described below. Protein content and specific binding of [³H]17β-estradiol were assessed on a 1 ml aliquot of cytosol. The data of the typical preparation being described are shown in Table I.

---

*TED buffer, pH 7.4: Tris-HCl, 10^{-2} M; EDTA, 10^{-3} M; dithiothreitol, 10^{-3} M.

TABLE I

PURIFICATION OF ESTROGEN RECEPTOR

Purification step	Total volume (ml)	Protein (total mg)	Bound 17β-estradiol (total moles)[a]	Specific activity (moles 17β-estradiol/mg protein)	Recovery (%)	Purification factor (times)
(1) Cytosol	4350	35,670	3.58×10^{-8}	1×10^{-12}	100	
(2) First heparin–Sepharose	1800	5,760	2.54×10^{-8}	4.4×10^{-12}	71	4.4
(3) 17β-estradiol-hemisuccinyl-ovalbumin–Sepharose 4B	1100	n.m.	n.m.	n.m.	n.m.	n.m.
(4) Second heparin–Sepharose	414	n.m.	2.22×10^{-8}	n.m.	57	n.m.
(5) Sephadex G-50	49	1.225	1.9×10^{-8}	1.55×10^{-8}	53	15,585

[a] Computed from specific activity of [^{3}H]17β-estradiol employed; n.m. = not measurable.

B. FIRST PURIFICATION STEP: AFFINITY CHROMATOGRAPHY
USING HEPARIN–SEPHAROSE 4B

Heparin has been shown to inhibit aspecific aggregation of estrogen receptor in cytosol (Shyämalä, 1971; Chamness and McGuire, 1972; Auricchio *et al.*, 1978) and to interact with estrogen receptor with considerable affinity, a property which can be exploited to achieve severalfold purification of estrogen receptor in cytosol (Molinari *et al.*, 1977). Affinity chromatography with heparin–Sepharose has been used by us as the first step in our purification procedure.

Heparin–Sepharose 4B was prepared as follows. A 1 kg amount of freshly CNBr-activated Sepharose 4B was added to a solution of 75 gm of stage 14 crude sodium heparin (INOLEX Corp., Chicago, Ill.) in 2 l of 50 mM borate buffer, pH 9.0. The mixture was magnetically stirred for 15 hours at 4° and thereafter filtered through a Buchner funnel; the resulting cake of gel was washed first with 5 l of KCl (1 M), then with water, and finally incubated with 1 l of 2 M glycine in water for 2 hours at room temperature, in order to eliminate residual activated agarose sites. The heparin–Sepharose derivative was washed again on a Buchner funnel with 5 l of 1 M KCl, followed by 5 l of water. As judged by the amount of unreacted heparin in the washing solutions, about 25 mg of heparin are covalently coupled per ml of packed Sepharose gel by the above procedure.

To 4 l of uterine cytosol prepared as described above, 600 gm of heparin–Sepharose were added. The heparin–Sepharose was washed with 4 volumes of TED buffer immediately before use. The mixture was magnetically stirred for 1 hour at 4°, filtered through a Buchner filter (coarse), and washed with 6 l of TED buffer. A sufficient amount of TED buffer was then added to the final heparin–Sepharose cake in order to produce a slurry which could be easily transferred into a large nylon filter (20 cm in diameter). After filtration of excess buffer, 1.5 l of TED buffer containing 4 mg/ml of sodium heparin (SIGMA, grade I, sp. act. 170 USP/mg) was filtered through the packed gel by gravity. This operation took about 45 minutes. Preliminary experiments published elsewhere (Sica and Bresciani, 1978) had shown that under the above conditions there is optimal elution of receptor bound to heparin–Sepharose (65–80% recovery).

In the purification experiment being described, elution of receptor from the heparin–Sepharose was monitored by carrying out a [^{3}H]17β-estradiol binding assay of receptor on small aliquots of the eluate fractions collected from the heparin–Sepharose. Also, the protein content of the eluate fractions was measured. The results are presented in Table I and show that an about 4-fold purification of receptor is achieved by this first purification step.

C. Second Purification Step: Affinity Chromatography Using 17 β-Estradiol-17-Hemisuccinyl-Ovalbumin-Sepharose 4B

The affinity adsorbents used in this step was prepared according to a previously described method (Sica *et al.*, 1973b), except that, for economic reasons, ovalbumin instead of poly(L-lysyl-DL-alanine) was used as a macromolecular spacer.

200 gm of 17β-estradiol-17-hemisuccinyl-ovalbumin-Sepharose 4B were washed with about 1 l of TED buffer before being added to the eluate from step 1. The mixture was magnetically stirred for 1 hour at 4°, filtered through a Buchner filter, and washed with 4 l of TED buffer containing 0.5 M KCl. The resulting cake was suspended in 1 l of TED buffer containing 0.5 M NaSCN and 10 mg of [³H]17β-estradiol (sp. act. = 0.6 Ci/mmole) and incubated overnight at 4°. Incubation with NaSCN at 4° achieves a more efficient and less inactivating elution by exchange of receptor (Sica *et al.*, 1978) than the previous method of increasing the temperature to 30° for 20 minutes (Sica *et al.*, 1973b).

After the overnight incubation with 0.5 M NaSCN, the suspensions was filtered through a Buchner filter and the filtrate was diluted by addition of 4 l of TED buffer, in order to decrease NaSCN concentration to a level (0.1 M) that will not interfere with binding of receptor to heparin–Sepharose, as required by the next purification step.

As a consequence of the elution with a very large excess of [³H]17β-estradiol, it is impossible to estimate recovery of receptor in the eluate at this step. Also, extreme protein dilution and presence of NaSCN make it unfeasable to assay protein in this eluate.

D. Third Purification Step: Second Affinity Chromatography Using Heparin–Sepharose 4B

All operations were carried out at 4°. 300 gm of heparin–Sepharose 4B were packed on a nylon filter (10 cm in diameter) and washed with 1 l of TED buffer, at the rate of about 300 ml/hour. The diluted eluate from the previous step, containing the [³H]17β-estradiol–receptor complex, was then filtered through the column at the same rate, immediately followed first by 1.5 l of TED buffer and then by 0.5 l of TED buffer containing 0.17 M KCl. The last washing with 0.17 M KCl can be performed without loss of receptor activity only when receptor is bound to heparin–Sepharose as a complex with estrogen. When receptor is bound to heparin as the estrogen-free form, as in the first purification step, washing with KCl produces considerable inactivation and cannot be applied.

As shown in Fig. 1, radioactivity and adsorbance at 280 nm of eluate were continuously monitored during the above operations. When radioactivity in the eluate decreased to a low value following washing with 0.17 M KCl, specific elution began using TED buffer containing 4 mg/ml of Heparin (SIGMA, grade I, spec. act. 170 USP/mg). The result was elution of a peak of radioactivity which emerged in about 400 ml of eluate. Protein concentration in this eluate was below sensitivity of assay methods. As shown in Table I, based on radioactivity, recovery of receptor is 57% at this stage. Thus, with relatively small loss of receptor (about 14%), this second heparin–Sepharose step achieves (a) elimination of the free 17β-estradiol used for the specific elution in the preceding step, (b) elimination of NaSCN, and (c) concentration of receptor into a manageable volume.

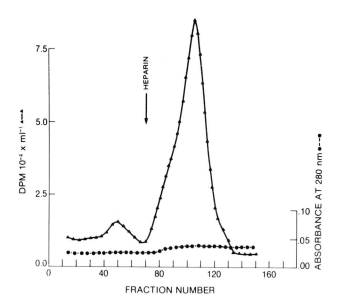

FIG. 1. The third purification step. Diluted eluate from 17β-estradiol-17-hemisuccinyl-ovalbumin-Sepharose was filtered through a column of heparin–Sepharose (300 gm). The column was then washed with 1.5 l of TED buffer to eliminate most of free [^{3}H]17β-estradiol. This figure is the recording of radioactivity and absorbance at 280 nm from the moment at which a final wash was started using 0.17 M KCl in TED buffer, followed by the specific elution with heparin, 4 mg/ml in TED buffer (arrow). The large radioactive peak eluted by Heparin is [^{3}H]17β-estradiol–receptor complex.

E. FOURTH PURIFICATION STEP: CONCENTRATION AND GEL FILTRATION ON SEPHADEX G-50

All operations were carried out at 0°–4°. The eluate from the previous purification step was rapidly concentrated to about 40 ml by filtration under pressure (nitrogen, 60 psi) using an Amicon model 402 stirred cell with a UM 20 Diaflo membrane. No radioactivity passed through the filter or was bound to the membrane.

The concentrate was applied to a Pharmacia K26/100 column containing 400 ml of Sephadex G-50 (coarse) in TED buffer to which 0.01% (w/v) of heparin was added. Heparin was SIGMA grade I (sp. act. 170 USP/mg) and was first filtered on Sephadex G-50; only the included fractions were used for preparation of the TED–heparin buffer. Elution was performed with the same TED–heparin buffer, and the elution pattern is shown in Fig. 2. One can see that virtually all radioactivity is excluded by the gel matrix, together with a peak of absorbance at 280 nm. There is, too, a broad included peak of

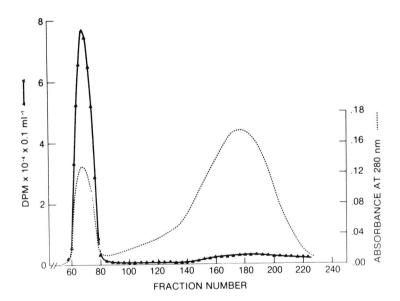

FIG. 2. The fourth purification step: Sephadex G-50 chromatography of eluate from preceding step after concentration to about 40 ml by filtration on a UM 20 Diaflo membrane. Virtually all [³H]17β-estradiol is excluded from the gel matrix, together with a peak of absorbance at 280 nm. The broad included peak of absorbance at 280 nm is oxidized dithithreitol. Heparin is also included. Heparin is transparent at 280 nm. Temperature was 2°–4°. This step achieves elimination of both (a) Heparin used for elution in the preceding step, and (b) other low molecular weight compounds (see text).

optical density at 280 nm caused by oxidized dithiothreitol. Heparin is perfectly transparent at 280 nm.

With this fourth purification step, one achieves (a) concentration to a small volume (40–50 ml) of the purified receptor; (b) elimination of heparin used for elution in the third purification step; and (c) elimination of low molecular weight compounds. Heparin at very low concentration (0.01%) was kept in the buffer used for the Sephadex G-50 chromatography in order to avoid aggregation of receptor; indeed, preliminarly trials had shown that receptor, even at this final stage of purification, is still aggregation-prone when concentrated in the absence of heparin.

As shown in Table I, the total protein content in the final Sephadex G-50 excluded peak is 1.225 mg and the total [^{3}H]17β-estradiol 2.12×10^7 DPM (sp. act. 0.6 Ci/mmole). One may thus easily compute that in the final preparation the ratio of g of protein/mole of 17β-estradiol is 64,450. The purification factor is about 16,000-fold, with 53% recovery of original receptor activity.

F. Proof of Purification to Homogeneity by Gel Electrophoresis Under Nondenaturing Conditions

All operations were carried out at 0°–4°. The Sephadex G-50 excluded peak from the previous purification step was further concentrated to about 7 ml by filtration under pressure as described before (Section I, E), except that the Amicon cell was the smaller model 12 type. The protein content of this final concentrate thus increased to 175 μg/ml. Samples from this concentrate were submitted to disc gel electrophoresis at 5° under nondenaturing conditions, in the presence of a low concentration of heparin (0.02%) to avoid aggregation.

In brief, gel electrophoresis was carried out using the Tris system of Weber and Osborne (1975) with a single modification: heparin, final concentration 0.02%, was substituted for SDS. Glass tubes were 0.55 cm in diameter and 12 cm long. Concentration of stacking gel was 3%, and that of lower gel 5%. After gelification, the tubes were inserted through rubber gaskets into a transparent plastic drum in which water at 5° was continously recirculated throughout the electrophoresis. After a 30 minute initial cooling period, electrophoresis was started. The reservoir buffer contained 0.01% heparin and was precooled to 5°. Sucrose (final concentration 20%) and bromophenol blue (5 μl of a 0.02% solution in water) were added to each sample. After layering the samples (0.2 ml each) on top of the gel with a cold pipette, electrophoresis was carried out for the initial 2 hours at 1 mA/gel and for another 4 hours at 2 mA/gel. At the end of the run, the dye front was marked by inserting a small piece of electric wire into the gel. Duplicate gels were either stained with Coomassie blue or sliced using a Bio-Rad gel slicer into 2 mm thick slices, which were then collected into scintillation vials containing 10 ml of Aquasol II. After overnight extraction, the [^{3}H]17β-estradiol content of slices was assessed in a β-counter.

Both the radioactivity pattern and the Coomassie blue stained gel of a typical duplicate electrophoresis run are shown in Fig. 3. One can see that there is a single large protein band and that [^{3}H]17β-estradiol comigrates with this protein. When heparin was not included in the gel and reservoir buffer, there was no penetration of protein into the gel. The gel was over-loaded with protein (35 μg), and this explains the quite large and somewhat smeared protein band. Overloading was necessary in order to detect possible contaminants. The results show that, with the exception of a very faint band migrating with the dye front, contaminants are absent. The faint band at the front must be low molecular weight material. As shown by scanning the gel at 590 nm, this faint band accounts for less than 1% of total absorbance.

In conclusion, as judged by disc gel electrophoresis under nondenaturing conditions, the estrogen binding receptor has been purified to at least 99%

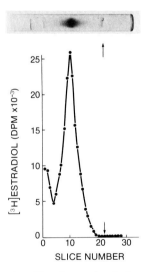

FIG. 3. Disc gel electrophoresis at 5° under nondenaturing condition of [^{3}H]17β-estradiol–receptor complex. Stacking gel was 3% and lower gel 5%. Of a duplicate gel, one was used for measurement of radioactivity and the other was stained with Coomassie blue. The single protein band is somewhat smeared because of overloading of the gel (35 μg protein) for the purpose of detecting contaminants. The faint band at the front accounts for not more than 1% of total absorbance of gel at 590 nm. [^{3}H]17β-Estradiol comigrates with the protein. This electrophoresis is evidence that estrogen receptor has been purified to at least 99% homogeneity (see text).

purity. Further proof of purity is given by the results of gel electrophoresis in SDS, which will be described later.

III. PROPERTIES OF ESTROGEN RECEPTOR PURIFIED TO HOMOGENEITY

A. Stokes Radius as Determined by Gel Filtration

The pure receptor was submitted to gel filtration on a calibrated column of Sephadex G-200 in TD buffer.* The elution pattern of bound $[^3H]17\beta$-estradiol, together with the elution volume of reference proteins, is shown in Fig. 4. There is a single sharp peak, for which a Stokes radius of 6.4 nm was computed on the calibration curve plotted according to Porath (1963). When the elution data are plotted according to Andrews (1964), a molecular weight of about 430.000 is derived for the purified receptor. The broken line in Fig. 4 describes the elution pattern of *crude* calf uterus cytosol, to which 4 mg/ml of heparin were added previous to gel filtration on the same calibrated column used for the purified receptor. It is noteworthy that the elution patterns virtually coincide. This coincidence strongly suggests that we have purified, without modifications, the heparin-stabilized form originally present in the uterine cytosol. We may here be reminded that, in the absence of heparin, receptor in cytosol forms large aggregates. Because we know that heparin interacts with receptor as well as with other proteins of cytosol (Waldman *et al.*, 1975), this stabilizing action of the aminoglycan may be envisaged as formation of a negative electrical shield refractory to protein–protein interaction involving the receptor in cytosol.

Finally, it should be pointed out that addition of heparin (0.02%), NaSCN (0.1 M), or NaBr (1 M) to the TD buffer did not modify the elution volume of purified receptor (data not shown). For NaSCN, this is apparently in contrast with previous results in which the chaotropic salt was added to *crude* or *partially* purified receptor preparations (Sica *et al.*, 1976).

B. Sedimentation Properties on Sucrose Gradients

As shown in Fig. 5, when pure receptor is centrifuged on a 5–20% sucrose gradient in TD buffer, most of it sediments at 8 S (bovine plasma albumin was the internal reference), while some sediments as a shoulder at about 4 S. If 1 M NaBr is present in the sucrose gradient, all receptor sediments at 4.2

*TD buffer, pH 7.4: Tris–HCl, 10^{-2} M; dithiothreitol, 10^{-3} M.

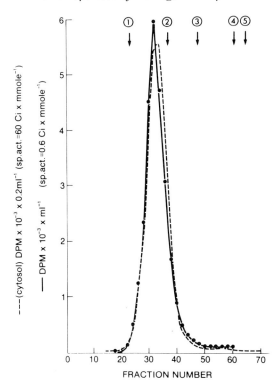

FIG. 4. Chromatography on a calibrated column of Sephadex G-200 of pure receptor (solid line), as compared to uterine cytosol to which 4 mg/ml of heparin were added (broken line). Arrows indicate elution peaks of (1) Blue Dextran; (2) IgG; (3) bovine plasma albumin; (4) myoglobin; and (5) cytochrome c. Stokes radius of receptor computed according to Porath was 6.4 nm. Mol. wt. computed according to Andrews was 430,000. Temperature was 2°–4°. Note coincidence of elution volume of pure receptor with that of heparin-stabilized cytosol form (see text).

S. The effect of NaBr thus shows that the 8 S can quantitatively change into a 4.2 S. It is noteworthy that while 1 M NaBr produces a dramatic change in the sedimentation rate of receptor, it does not, however influence its elution pattern from Sephadex G-200 (see Section II,A). Possibly, hydrostatic pressure may play a role in such difference. Evidence that pressure-induced, or favored, dissociation may play a role during high-speed centrifugation of receptor have been recently produced (Auricchio *et al.*, 1978). This problem will be discussed later in this chapter.

C. ULTRAVIOLET ADSORPTION SPECTRUM

The ultraviolet spectrum of pure receptor was analyzed in an ACTA III double beam spectrophotometer between 240 nm and 340 nm. The spec-

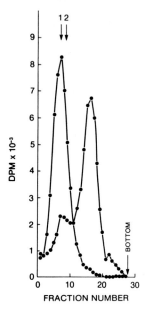

FIG. 5. Patterns of sedimentation of pure receptor on 5–20% sucrose gradients in TD buffer (double peak pattern) or in TD buffer containing 1 M NaBr (single peak pattern). Temperature 2°–4°C. Arrows indicate peaks of BPA, used as internal standard in the TD-buffer tube (1) and in the TD-buffer + NaBr tube (2). Major receptor peak in TD-buffer is at 8 S, and peak in TD-buffer + NaBr is at 4.2 S (see text for further details).

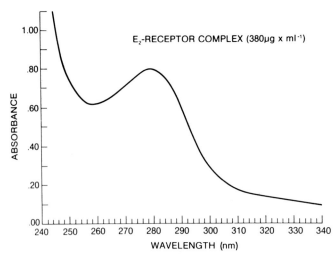

FIG. 6. Ultraviolet spectrum of pure estradiol–receptor complex between 240 and 340 nm. λ_{max} = 278 nm. $E_{280}^{1\,mg}$ = 2.1. Absorbance due to 17β-estradiol is negligible (see text).

trum is presented in Fig. 6 and shows a peak of absorbance at 278 nm. The E_{280}^{1mg} is 2.1. Contribution of bound estradiol to absorbance in the 240–340 nm region is negligible: Although peak absorbance of 17β-estradiol is at 280 nm, there is only 27×10^{-6} mg/ml of hormone in the pure preparation analyzed, and the E_{280}^{1mg} for 17β-estradiol is 1.12.

D. HORMONE BINDING SPECIFICITY

Hormone binding specificity of pure receptor was tested by competition studies at 4°, under conditions of increased ligand turnover brought about by chemical perturbation with NaSCN. Details of the method will be given elsewhere (Sica and Bresciani, 1978). Samples of pure complex (5 μg) were incubated overnight at 4° in TD buffer containing (a) $0.5M$ NaSCN, (b) 50 ng of [^{3}H]17β-estradiol, and (c) 50,000 ng (1000-fold excess) of either 17β-estradiol, estriol, estrone, progesterone, testosterone, or cortisone. The results of these tests are shown in Table II. Only 17β-estradiol and, to a lesser degree, estriol compete for the binding sites. Thus, the binding site is estrogen-specific.

E. SUBUNIT STRUCTURE AND MOLECULAR WEIGHT AS ASSESSED BY SDS GEL ELECTROPHORESIS

The pure receptor was submitted to gel electrophoresis in the SDS-phosphate system of Weber and Osborne (1975). All operations were accord-

TABLE II

SPECIFICITY OF BINDING SITE OF PURE ESTROGEN RECEPTOR. RESIDUALLY BOUND RADIOACTIVE 17β-ESTRADIOL AFTER ADDITION OF 1000-FOLD EXCESS OF COLD STEROID FOLLOWED BY OVERNIGHT INCUBATION AT 4°C IN THE PRESENCE OF 0.5 M NaSCN[a]

	Residually bound [^{3}H]17β-estradiol (%)
50 ng [^{3}H]17β-Estradiol	100
50 ng [^{3}H]17β-Estradiol + 50,000 17β-estradiol	3
50 ng [^{3}H]17β-Estradiol + 50,000 ng of progesterone	115
50 ng [^{3}H]17β-Estradiol + 50,000 ng of testosterone	110
50 ng [^{3}H]17β-Estradiol + 50,000 ng of cortisone	99
50 ng [^{3}H]17β-Estradiol + 50,000 ng of estriol	64
50 ng [^{3}H]17β-Estradiol + 50,000 ng of estrone	94

[a] Buffer: TED. Total volume of incubation mixture: 0.5 ml. Receptor: 5 μg.

ing to Weber and Osborne. Specifically, the receptor sample was dyalysed for several hours against sample buffer and heated for 1–3 minutes in a boiling water bath. Variation in heating time made no difference to the final electrophoresis pattern. After cooling to room temperature, sucrose and bromophenol blue were added to the sample. Electrophoresis was carried out using 5% gel in glass tubes (0.55 cm in diameter, 12 cm long). After 30 minutes preelectrophoresis at 8 mA/gel, the samples were loaded and electrophoresis followed for 4 hours at 8 mA/gel.

At the end of electrophoresis, the gels were cut at the dye front and kept for 2 hours in perchloric acid 10% before overnight staining in Coomassie blue G-250 in 3.5% perchloric acid followed by developing in 7.5% acetic

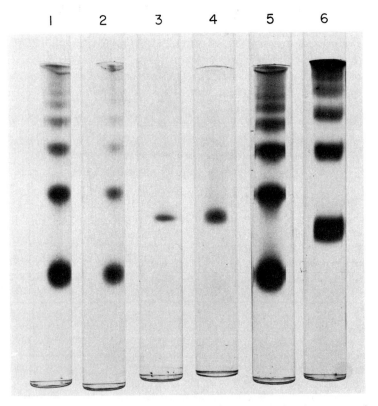

FIG. 7. Parallel SDS disc gel electrophoresis (5 % gel) in the SDS-phosphate system of Weber and Osborne (1975). Ovalbumin and polymers: 1, 2, and 5; pure receptor: 3 and 4; plasma albumin and polymers: 6. Polymers were prepared by cross-linking with dimethylsuberimidate. Amount of loaded proteins was different in different gels. A single receptor protein band is observed, positioned between the plasma albumin monomer and the ovalbumin dimer. Room temperature. Results were consistently reproducible (see text).

acid. Standards for molecular weight determination were ovalbumin and bovine plasma albumin polymers, prepared by cross-linking with dimethyl-suberimidate as described by Carpenter and Harrington (1972). Standards were run in parallel, under conditions identical to those of the samples.

Typical electrophoresis patterns of receptor and of reference proteins run in parallel are shown in Fig. 7. Both receptor and reference proteins were run at two different concentrations, with the same results. A single band of receptor protein is observed, which is positioned between the plasma albumin monomer and the ovalbumin dimer. By interpolation in the semilogarithmic plot of mol. wts. of reference proteins against their R_f's, an apparent molecular weight of 70,000 is found for the denatured estrogen receptor. Assessment of the molecular weight of denatured receptor was repeated many times, always with precisely the same result.

F. NUMBER OF BINDING SITES PER 70,000 DALTON RECEPTOR SUBUNIT

The findings that there is 1 mole of $[^3H]17\beta$-estradiol bound per 64,450 gms of pure receptor protein (Section I,E) and that the molecular weight of the subunit, as shown by gel electrophoresis under denaturing conditions (Section II,E), is 70,000, indicate that there is a single estrogen binding site per receptor subunit. The small discrepancy ($\sim 7\%$) between the weight of the protein subunit as measured by gel electrophoresis (70,000) and as derived indirectly from bound ligand (64,450) cannot be considered significant.

IV. FINAL REMARKS AND CONCLUSIONS

Sequential utilization of heparin–Sepharose and 17β-estradiol-17-hemi-succinyl-ovalbumin-Sepharose as chromatography adsorbents in the purification of estrogen receptor has been instrumental in overcoming the remaining difficulties toward achieving preparation of tangible amounts of homogenous estrogen receptor. Adsorption to heparin–Sepharose followed by elution with heparin offers a gentle method of purification and concentration which has the advantage of avoiding both loss of estrogen binding activity, even when working with estrogen-free receptor, and aggregation of receptor. Furthermore, the preliminary chromatography on heparin–Sepharose eliminates cytosol components which, during incubation of cytosol with 17β-estradiol-17-hemisuccinyl-ovalbumin to Sepharose (V. Sica and F. Bresciani, unpublished results). Most likely, the cytosol components under consideration are proteases and esterases which do not bind to heparin–Sepharose.

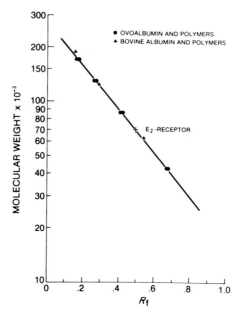

FIG. 8. Semilogarithmic plot of mol. wt. of reference proteins vs. their R_f's on 5% gel in the SDS-phosphate system of Weber and Osborne (1975). By interpolation of R_f of receptor protein run in parallel with reference proteins, an apparent mol. wt. of 70,000 is derived for the denatured receptor. Results are consistently reproducible (see text).

It also seems worth noting that the affinity chromatography method of purification described here has a crucial advantage over methods of purification which apply classical protein separation techniques. Indeed, the affinity chromatography method guarantees that the final purified material is specifically estrogen receptor rather than, possibly, an entire class of proteins with the same, or very similar, physicochemical properties. Such a consideration is important, because organs which contain estrogen receptor generally contain receptors for *all* steroid hormones; furthermore, steroid receptor proteins are "invisible" when their binding site is either filled or inactivated, the latter being a frequent occurrence during purification procedures resulting from high structural instability of these sites.

Table III summarizes known properties of the homogeneously pure receptor. Heat denaturation of pure receptor in the presence of SDS and 2-MCE yelds a single subunit with an apparent mol. wt. of 70,000, as measured by SDS gel electrophoresis. Also, under dissociating conditions as achieved by addition of a chaotropic salt to the medium 1 M NaBr, the sedimentation coefficient of the pure protein is 4.2 S. Based on these values, one may compute the Stokes radius and the frictional ratio of the subunit using the classical equations:

TABLE III
PROPERTIES OF ESTROGEN RECEPTOR PURIFIED TO HOMOGENEITY

Purity of receptor protein[a]	99%	
Hormone specificity	Estrogen	
	Native	Dissociated
Stokes radius (a)	6.4 nm	3.9 nm[b]
Sedimentation coefficient (S) (sucrose gradient)	8 S[c]	4.2 S[d]
Mol. wt. (based on gel filtration only)	430,000[e]	
Mol. wt. (based on S and a)	220,000[f]	
Mol. wt. (SDS gel electrophoresis)		70,000
Frictional ratio		1.2[b]
Axial ratio (prolate)		3[b]
λ_{max}	278 nm	
$E_{280}^{1\ mg}$	2.1	
Number of hormone binding sites per 70,000 dalton subunit		1

[a] Purity expressed as percent of receptor protein/total protein in preparation.

[b] Computed from sedimentation coefficient (4.2 S) and mol. wt. (70,000 daltons).

[c] In view of possible pressure-induced dissociation during ultracentrifugation, it is uncertain that this coefficient corresponds to the undissociated protein with 6.4 nm of Stokes radius.

[d] In the presence of 1 M NaBr.

[e] Measured according to Andrews (1964).

[f] Measured according to Siegel and Monty (1966).

$$M = 6\pi\eta\, Nas/(1 - \bar{v}\rho) \tag{1}$$

$$f/f_0 = a/(3vM/4\pi N)^{1/3} \tag{2}$$

where η = viscosity of the medium, N = Avogadro's number, a = Stokes radius, s = sedimentation coefficient, v = partial specific volume (assumed to be 0.725), and ρ = density of the medium. Axial ratios may be derived from frictional ratios (Oncley, 1941).

The result of the computations are as follows: Stokes radius = 3.9 nm; frictional ratio = 1.2; axial ratio (prolate) = 3. These values agree well with previously found physical parameters of the 4 S receptor form in partially purified preparations (Puca *et al.*, 1971a,b). It can be noted that the SDS gel electrophoresis of pure receptor shows no trace of the smaller estrogen-binding form, about 32,000 mol. wt., which was previously found after addition of NaSCN to cytosol (Sica *et al.*, 1976). Because NaSCN can activate proteases of cytosol (V. Sica and F. Bresciani, unpublished observations), a possible explanation of the NaSCN effect may be a hydrolitic cleavage of the actual subunit into smaller fragments.

Because our starting material is estrogen-free (prepubertal) uterine cytosol, all the binding sites of the final purified receptor preparations are filled with exogenous [^{3}H]17β-estradiol. One of the valuable aspects of having pure receptor homogenously labeled with [^{3}H]17β-estradiol of known specific activity is that the number of binding sites per protein weight can be computed. The result of this calculation is 1 site per 64,000 daltons, clearly indicating that there is a single binding site per receptor subunit.

While the mol. wt. of the receptor subunit can be accepted with confidence to be about 70,000, there is considerable uncertainty about the mol. wt. of the native form of receptor. Indeed, from the elution volume of a protein from calibrated Sephadex columns, one may reliably derive its Stokes radius (Porath, 1963). On the contrary, the mol. wt. of a protein can be derived with confidence from such a filtration study only when the frictional ratio of the protein under study is within the same range of the frictional ratios of the proteins used for calibration of the column (Siegel and Monty, 1966). One may also obtain an unbiased estimate of the mol. wt. for a protein of uncommon axial ratio by measuring the Stokes radius by gel filtration and the sedimentation coefficient by sucrose gradient, and then applying Eq. (1). Further, one can then compute the frictional ratio from Eq. (2). This method of Siegel and Monty (1966) has been extensively applied by us to receptor proteins (Puca *et al.*, 1971a,b; Sica *et al.*, 1976) and also by others (Schrader *et al.*, 1977; Kuhn *et al.*, 1977). The computations generally showed that the larger forms of receptor had an uncommonly high axial ratio; i.e., that the coefficient of sedimentation was smaller than expected of globular proteins with the same Stokes radius.

However, estimation of the mol. wt. of estrogen receptor based on measurement of S by gradient centrifugation and a by gel filtration now seems a hazardous procedure in view of evidence that high pressures, as those developing during ultracentrifugation, have a considerable destabilizing effect on the quaternary structure of proteins (Erickson, 1974; Olmsted *et al.*, 1974; Bairlein and Infante, 1974), including receptor (Auricchio *et al.*, 1978). Subunit interactions may fall apart under high pressure, and therefore we may be dealing with a different protein according to the method being applied, i.e., ultracentrifugation or gel filtration. Dissociation of a protein into smaller components on ultracentrifugation vs. lack of such dissociation on gel filtration would indeed result in erroneous calculation of a smaller mol. wt. and a larger axial ratio than those of the nondissociated protein.

In conclusion, at the moment we can only say that the molecular weight of the native form must be between 220,000 and 430,000, the former value being derived from S (8) and a (6.4 nm) according to Siegel and Monty (1966) and the second directly from the elution volume from a column calibrated with common globular proteins, according to Andrews (1964). Considering that the subunit is 70,000 daltons, the native form should consist of between 3 and 6 subunits.

To summarize, purification to homogeneity of tangible amounts of estrogen receptor from estrogen-free calf uterus has been achieved. There is only one subunit weighing 70,000 daltons. Each subunit is endowed with a single estrogen binding site. Under native condition, subunits are associated into a larger structure with a Stokes radius of 6.4 nm. In view of results casting doubts on the measurement of S, the sedimentation coefficient of this native receptor, by gradient centrifugation, the molecular weight of this larger structure is still uncertain. The use of affinity chromatography in our method of purification guarantees that the purified receptor is truly estrogen receptor, rather than a class of proteins with the same or very similar physicochemical properties. Also, the ratio of estrogen binding sites to receptor protein weight could be measured directly and without uncertainty, owing to the fact that we started with tissue free of endogenous hormone (calf uterus) and that therefore all available sites were filled with $[^3H]17\beta$-estradiol of known specific activity. The availability of pure receptor opens the way to further biochemical characterization and investigation of the role of receptor in the control of gene expression.

REFERENCES

Andrews, P. (1964). *Biochem. J.* **91**, 222–233.

Auricchio, F., Rotondi, A., Sampaolo, P., and Schiavone, E. (1978). *Biochem. J.* **169** (in press).

Bairlein, R., and Infante, A. A. (1974). *In* "Methods in Enzymology" (L. Grossman and K. Moldave, eds.), Vol. 30, Part F, pp. 328–345. Academic Press, New York.

Carpenter, F. H., and Harrington, K. T. (1972). *J. Biol. Chem.* **247**, 5580–5586.

Chamness, G. C., and McGuire, W. L. (1972). *Biochemistry* **11**, 2466–2471.

Harold, P., and Erickson, H. P. (1974). *J. Supramol. Struct.* **2**, 393–411.

Kuhn, R. W., Schrader, W. T., Coty, W. A., Conn, P. M., and O'Malley, B. W. (1977). *J. Biol. Chem.* **252**, 308–317.

Molinari, A. M., Medici, N., Moncharmont, B., and Puca, G. A. (1977). *Proc. Natl. Acad. Sci. U.S.A.* **74**, 4886–4890.

Olmsted, J. B., Marcum, J. M., Johnson, K. A., Allen, C., and Borisy, G. G. (1974). *J. Sopramol. Strct.* **2**, 429–450.

Oncley, J. L. (1961). *Am. N. Y. Acad. Sci* **41**, 121.

Porath, G. (1963). *Pure Appl. Chem.* **6**, 233–239.

Puca, G. A., Nola, E., Sica, V., and Bresciani, F. (1971a). *Adv. Biosci.* **7**, 97–118.

Puca, G. A., Nola, E., Sica, V., and Bresciani, F. (1971b). *Biochemistry* **10**, 3769–3780.

Puca, G. A., Nola, E., Sica, V., and Bresciani, F. (1975). *In* "Methods in Enzymology" (B. W. O'Malley and J. G. Hardman, eds.), Vol. 36, Part A, pp. 331–349. Academic Press, New York.

Schrader, W. T., Kuhn, R. W., and O'Malley, B. W. (1977). *J. Biol. Chem.* **252**, 299–307.

Shyämalä, G. (1971) *Nature (London), New Biol.* **231**, 246–248.

Sica, V., and Bresciani, F. (1978). In preparation.

Sica, V., Nola, E., Parikh, I., Puca, G. A., and Cuatrecasas, P. (1973a). *Nature (London), New Biol.* **244**, 36–39.

Sica, V., Parikh, I., Nola, E., Puca, G. A., and Cuatrecasas, P. (1973b). *J. Biol. Chem.* **248**, 6543–6558.

Sica, V., Nola, E., Puca, G. A., and Bresciani, F. (1976). *Biochemistry* **15**, 1915–1923.

Sica, V., Molinari, A. M., Puca, G. A., and Bresciani, F. (1978). In preparation.

Siegel, L. M., and Monty, K. J. (1966). *Biochim. Biophys. Acta* **112**, 346–362.

Waldman, A. A., Marx, G., and Goldstein, J. (1975). *Proc. Natl. Acad. Sci. U.S.A.* **72**, 2352–2356.

Weber, K., and Osborne, M. (1975). *In* "The Proteins" (H. Neurath and R. L. Hill, eds.), Vol. I pp. 180–226. Academic Press, New York.

CHAPTER 10

Hormonal Regulation of α_{2u} Globulin in Rat Liver

Arun K. Roy

I. INTRODUCTION

Although physiological proteinuria and its sex difference in rodents has been the subject of biochemical interest since 1931, the technical difficulties in those early years greatly limited the scope of the investigations (Addis, 1931; Parfentjev and Perlzweig, 1933; Bell, 1933; Wicks, 1941; Sellers *et al.*, 1950; Finlayson and Baumann, 1958). In 1962 we initiated a study of the various proteins in rat urine that led to the identification of at least 15 different urinary proteins in the mature male rat and established their origin (Roy and Neuhaus, 1966a). The above investigation also showed that approximately half the total protein in the urine of mature male rats could be accounted for by one immunochemically distinct, low molecular weight protein having the electrophoretic mobility of α_2 globulin. This urinary α_2 globulin was distinctly different from the known α_2 globulins of rat serum; therefore, we decided to call it α_{2u} globulin, with the subscript "u" to distinguish it from serum α_2 globulins and to signify its preponderance in urine (Roy and Neuhaus, 1966a; Roy *et al.*, 1966). Because the major urinary protein was found to be absent in the urine of immature male rats and of female rats of all ages, it was felt that this protein would serve as a convenient model for the study of androgen action (Roy and Neuhaus, 1967).

α_{2u} Globulin has been purified from rat urine and partially characterized (Roy *et al.*, 1966; Lane and Neuhaus, 1972). It has a sedimentation coefficient of 2.2 S and a molecular weight of 21,000, and it contains a single peptide chain with 186 amino acid residues starting with an N-terminal glutamine. In addition to its presence in urine, high concentrations of α_{2u} globulin were found in the liver, kidneys, and salivary glands of mature male rats (Roy and Neuhaus, 1966b; Roy and Byrd, 1976). Failure to detect α_{2u} globulin in male rat serum by means of conventional immunoelectrophoresis was later found to be due to its rapid filtration through the kidneys, leaving only trace amounts in the plasma. This protein is present in normal male serum to the extent of only 0.05% of the total serum protein. Organ perfusion and cell culture studies have conclusively proved the hepatic origin of α_{2u} globulin. α_{2u} Globulin is synthesized in perfused rat liver obtained from mature male rats at a rate of 100–150 μg/gm liver/hour (Roy and Neuhaus, 1966b; Geertzen *et al.*, 1973). As a mature male rat excretes daily 25–30 mg of this protein, it could be surmised that at least 80% of the α_{2u} globulin secreted from the liver finds its way into the urine. Immunohistochemical studies with the hepatic tissue have established the parenchymal cells as the cellular source of α_{2u} globulin (Roy and Raber, 1972). Immunofluorescent staining of the section of liver from mature male rats showed that the rhodamine-labeled antibody to α_{2u} globulin was localized in the cytoplasm of all parenchymal cells, indicating the possible involvement of all these hepatocytes, rather than of only some of them, in the synthesis of this protein (Fig. 1). A similar conclusion has recently been reached with immunohistochemical studies of cultured hepatocytes derived from mature male rats.

Besides α_{2u} globulin, there are several other examples of sex hormone-dependent proteins of hepatic origin in the rat, one of which is a cytoplasmic protein first described by Bond (1960). Later studies of Bond and those of Barzilai and Pincus, showed that the sex-associated protein component of the liver tissue could be induced in the female with testosterone and suppressed in the male with estradiol treatment. Immunochemical and chromatographic

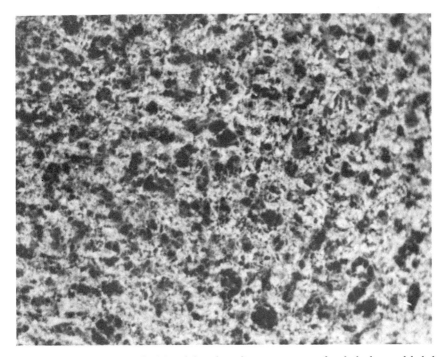

FIG. 1. A photomicrograph of the adult male rat liver section stained with rhodamine-labeled anti-α_{2u}-antiserum. The interwoven, netlike appearance of the immunofluorescence is visible only in the parenchymal cell cytoplasm. Magnification $\times$ 546. From Roy and Raber, 1972.

studies by these investigators have failed to show the presence of this protein in any tissue other than liver, including kidney, brain, testis, and blood (Bond, 1962; Barzilai and Pincus, 1965; Bond, 1966). Although the protein described by Bond has a hormone dependence similar to α_{2u} globulin, immunochemical studies have shown that this protein does not have any generic relationship with α_{2u} globulin (Lane and Neuhaus, 1972). Other notable examples of androgen-dependent hepatic proteins in the rat include steroid sulfatase (Roy, 1958), hexobarbital hydroxylase (Jam and DuBois, 1967), and a specific carcinogen binding protein (Weisburger *et al.*, 1964). In addition, there are several well-documented examples of estrogen-dependent proteins in rat liver. These include the steroid metabolizing enzymes hydroxysteroid dehydrogenase and certain steroid hydroxylases (Denf, 1974; Gustafsson and Stenberg, 1974), and the renin substrate (Eisenfeld *et al.*, 1976).

The above examples of the androgenic and estrogenic regulation of hepatic proteins have certainly led to a change in the status of rat liver as a possible target for the sex hormones. Because the viability and proliferative capacity of the hepatocytes are independent of sex hormone action, these studies have underscored the importance of sex-regulated hepatic proteins as useful models for the study of the androgenic and estrogenic regulation of specific gene activity. The purpose of this article is to review the results of our studies on the androgen-dependent synthesis of α_{2u} globulin in rat liver and the influence of various other hormonal and developmental factors on the process. These studies were designed to elucidate the mechanism of the coordinated multihormonal regulation of a single gene product under physiological conditions. The text which follows will highlight the paramount importance of the age-dependent developmental changes and multiple endocrine interactions in the modulation of androgen response.

II. ANDROGEN-DEPENDENT SYNTHESIS OF α_{2u} GLOBULIN AND ITS MODULATION BY OTHER HORMONAL AND DEVELOPMENTAL FACTORS

A. ANDROGENIC INDUCTION AND ESTROGENIC SUPPRESSION OF α_{2u} GLOBULIN IN MATURE RATS, AND ANDROGEN INSENSITIVITY IN PREPUBERTAL AND SENESCENT ANIMALS

Definitive proof of the hepatic origin of α_{2u} globulin and its almost total excretion into the urine have allowed the use of daily urinary output of this protein as a reliable index of its hepatic synthesis under different endocrine conditions. Quantitative immunodiffusion assay has shown that α_{2u} globulin is absent in the immature male rat and begins to appear at the time of puberty (around 6 weeks of age). Castration of mature male rats also results in a sharp drop in the urinary level of α_{2u} globulin. Androgen dependence of α_{2u} globulin was further shown by the fact that treatment of castrated female rats with either testosterone or 5α-dihydrotestosterone (DHT) resulted in the induction of this protein (Roy and Neuhaus, 1967). Daily androgen treatment of castrated female rats for 2 weeks was found to result in a rise in urinary α_{2u} globulin from an undetectable level to about 15 mg/day (Fig. 2). Maximum induction of this protein could be achieved by daily subcutaneous injections of either testosterone (250 μg/100 gm body weight) or DHT (50 μg/100 gm body weight). Higher androgenic potency of DHT over testosterone has been found to be the case for various reproductive tissues (Williams-Ashman and Reddy, 1972), and the existence of the enzyme testosterone 5α-reductase in rat liver has also been reported (McGuire et al., 1960; Gustafsson and Pousette, 1974). Daily treatment of mature male rats with estrogenic hormones resulted in a gradual decrease, and within 7 days,

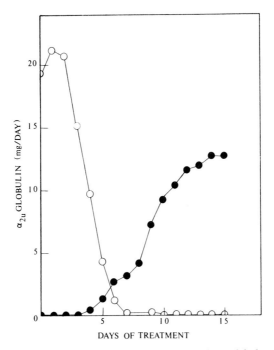

FIG. 2. Androgenic induction and estrogenic suppression of α_{2u} globulin: ●———●, daily urinary output of α_{2u} globulin in castrated female rats treated with DHT (50 μg/100 gm body weight/day); ○———○, daily urinary output of α_{2u} globulin in normal male rats treated with estradiol-17β (25 μg/100 gm body weight/day).

in a complete inhibition of the urinary output of α_{2u} globulin (Fig. 2). Estradiol-17β, estrone, estriol, and estradiol-17α as well as nonsteroidal synthetic estrogen diethylstilbestrol (DES) were effective in completely suppressing α_{2u} synthesis in mature male rats. Estradiol-17β was found to be the most potent and estradiol-17α the least potent estrogen in the suppression of α_{2u} synthesis in these animals (Roy et al., 1975). After complete suppression of α_{2u} synthesis in mature male rats with daily treatments of estradiol-17β for 7 days, withdrawal of estrogen treatment did not result in immediate reinitiation of α_{2u} synthesis. The extent of this lag period was found to be directly proportional to the dose of the hormone; with a daily dose of estradiol-17β of 50 μg/100 gm, the lag period lasted about 20 days. Androgen supplementation of the estrogenized animals within this lag period could not forthwith induce α_{2u} globulin.

In order to explore the possible role of the estrogen-mediated changes in the circulating endocrine factors in the development and maintenance of the androgen-insensitive lag period, the estrogenized animals were joined parabiotically with their normal litter mates. After 18 days of parabiosis, the animals were sacrificed and the cytoplasmic fraction of their hepatic tissue was tested for α_{2u} globulin by immunodiffusion. Unlike the control partners, no α_{2u} globulin was detected in the hepatic tissue of the estrogenized litter mates. These results suggest that the estrogen-mediated androgen insensitivity is due primarily to the effect of the hormone on the liver, rather than to changes in endocrine homeostasis (Roy et al., 1975).

Besides estrogen-treated animals, androgen insensitivity for hepatic synthesis of α_{2u} globulin was also noted as an age-dependent phenomenon— possibly regulated by developmental signals. Normally, α_{2u} globulin is absent in immature male rats and begins to be synthesized around puberty (6 weeks of age). Androgen treatment in prepubertal rats, either normal male or spayed female, does not induce α_{2u} globulin. However, after puberty, both castrated male and female rats respond to androgen with the induction of α_{2u} globulin (Fig. 3). These results show that, besides the low level of circulating androgens in the immature rats, the hepatic tissue of these animals is refractory to androgen action. Castration of male rats at 3 days after birth does not prevent the development of androgen sensitivity at puberty, indicating that the process does not require the action of testicular secretions at prepubertal life (Roy, 1973a).

Because the hepatocytes normally have a very low mitotic index, it was thought that chronological aging of the liver cells might be essential for the development of androgen sensitivity. The above hypothesis was tested by following the daily urinary output of α_{2u} globulin in mature male rats whose hepatocytes were induced to divide by partial (2/3) hepatectomy. In these animals, a close correlation between the degree of hepatic regeneration and

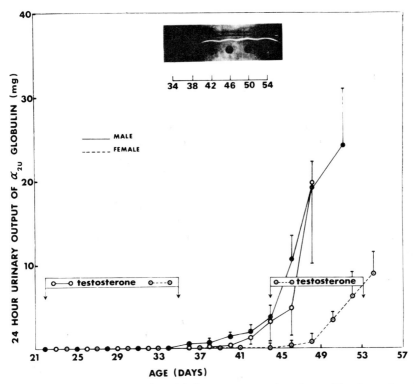

FIG. 3. Daily urinary output of α_{2u} globulin in maturing male and spayed female rats (spayed at 21 days of age). ●———●, Normal control males (no testosterone treatment). ○———○, Male rats treated with testosterone (200 μg/100 gm bw). ⊙———⊙ Spayed female rats treated with testosterone (200 ug/100 gm) at two different periods of life. The duration of testosterone treatment is marked with arrows. Each point is a mean of five individual values, with vertical bars representing standard deviations applicable in both directions. The insert on the top is a photograph of the immunodiffusion plate developed with anti- α_{2u} globulin antiserum and liver extracts from 6 male rats treated with testosterone (1 mg/100 g daily dose) from 24 to 34 days of age. Each antigen well contained liver extracts from rats sacrificed at different ages as labeled on the bottom of the wells. The antiserum was applied in the trough cut along the antigen wells. The precipitin lines can only be seen with liver extracts from rats which are 42 days of age and older. From Roy, 1973a.

the rise in the urinary level of α_{2u} globulin was observed. These results indicate that once the hepatocytes acquire androgen sensitivity at puberty, this faculty can be transmitted to the daughter cells without any lag period (Roy, 1973a). Similar to prepubertal animals, senescent male rats also do not synthesize α_{2u} globulin, nor do they respond to androgen treatment (Roy *et al.*, 1974). From these observations it has been suggested that two independent events—testicular activation/inactivation and appearance/disappearance of androgen sensitivity at the time of puberty/senescence—may be two coincidental phenomena. This hypothesis will be discussed in depth in Section 3,B.

B. Role of Pituitary, Thyroid, and Adrenocortical Hormones in the Regulation of α_{2u} Globulin

Hypophysectomy profoundly restricts the protein synthesis in the liver by limiting the availability of several growth and developmental hormones (Tata, 1968). Early works of Geschwind *et al.* (1950) have also indicated the possibility of a direct effect of the pituitary growth hormone on the hepatic protein synthesis. Preliminary examination of the effect of hypophysectomy on the synthesis of α_{2u} globulin in the mature male rat showed that this operation resulted in complete inhibition of α_{2u} synthesis. Treatment of hypophysectomized and castrated female rats with androgen did not induce α_{2u} globulin (Kumar *et al.*, 1969). As hypophysectomy is known to cause a multiple hormone deficiency, the above results led to the investigation of various other hormonal factors besides androgen that might be involved in promoting the synthesis of α_{2u} globulin.

The idea of a single pituitary factor responsible for controlling the synthesis of α_{2u} globulin did not seem very promising when it was observed that treatment of hypophysectomized male rats with testosterone, along with a single pituitary hormone (such as rat FSH, bovine LH, porcine ACTH, bovine TSH, rat prolactin, and bovine growth hormone), failed to reverse the effect of hypophysectomy (Roy, 1973b). The concept of multihormonal regulation of α_{2u} synthesis was further boosted by the subsequent finding that either adrenalectomy or thyroidectomy resulted in more than 90% reduction in the urinary output of α_{2u} globulin (Irwin *et al.*, 1971; Roy, 1973b). This led to experimentation with the effect of various hormonal combinations on the synthesis of α_{2u} globulin in hypophysectomized animals. Results showed that complete recovery from the effect of hypophysectomy required treatment with a combination of four hormones (testosterone, corticosterone, thyroxine, and groth hormone) (Roy, 1973b).

The effect of hypophysectomy on the urinary output of α_{2u} globulin and its reversal with combinations of various hormones in the male rats are shown in Fig. 4. Administration of one of the above-mentioned hormones with testosterone produced only minor stimulation or none at all on the urinary output of α_{2u} globulin. A combination of two of these hormones, when administered along with testosterone, resulted in considerable induction of α_{2u} globulin, reaching at some combinations up to 50% of the control level. A combination of all four hormones (testosterone, corticosterone, thyroxine, and growth hormone) caused complete restoration of the daily urinary output of α_{2u}

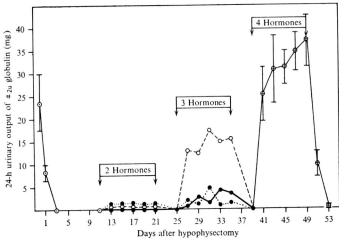

FIG. 4. The effect of hypophysectomy and various hormone treatments on the daily urinary output of α_{2u} globulin in adult male rats. Nine animals were hypophysectomized at day 0 and their daily urinary output of α_{2u} globulin was observed for 10 days, ⊙————⊙. These 9 animals were divided into three groups (3 rats in each group), and each group received daily injections of two hormones for 10 days: ●————●, testosterone + thyroxine; ●·····●, testosterone + corticosterone; ○----○, testosterone + growth hormone. After 4 days of rest, these animals received daily injections of three hormones for another 10 days: ●————●, testosterone + thyroxine + growth hormone; ●·····●, testosterone + corticosterone + thyroxine; ○----○, testosterone + growth hormone + corticosterone. After another 4 days of rest, all the 9 animals received daily injections of four hormones for 10 days: ⊕————⊕, testosterone + thyroxine + growth hormone + corticosterone. The periods of hormone treatments are marked with arrows; each point before the 13th (⊙) and after the 39 (⊕) day is a mean value for 9 animals ± S.D., while the rest of the points represent the mean for 3 animals.

globulin in the hypophysectomized male rats. Withdrawal of the above multihormone treatment resulted in a rapid drop in the urinary output of α_{2u} globulin in these hypophysectomized animals (Roy, 1973b).

In addition to α_{2u} globulin, the role of the pituitary gland in the androgenic and estrogenic induction of several other hepatic proteins in the rat has also been reported. For example, hypophysectomy is known to negate the androgen-dependent stimulation of steroid sulfatase (Burstein, 1968), hexobarbital hydroxylase (Nari et al., 1970) and n-hydroxy-2-acetylaminofluorene sulfotransferase (De Baun et al., 1970). Similarly, the presence of the hypophysis is required for the estrogenic induction of several hydroxysteroid dehydrogenases and 15β steroid hydroxylase in rat liver (Denef, 1974; Gustafsson and Stenberg, 1974; Gustafsson et al., 1975).

There seems to be considerable parallelism between the hypophysial modulation of the estrogenic induction of 15β steroid hydroxylase and the androgenic induction of α_{2u} globulin. The hepatic 15β steroid hydroxylase is a female-specific enzyme. This enzyme could be induced in the liver of castrated male rats after estrogen treatment. Hypophysectomy of the female rats completely abolishes the hepatic hydroxylase activity, and hypophysectomized male rats are unresponsive to estrogen with respect to hydroxylase induction (Gustafsson *et al.*, 1975).

To explain the role of the pituitary gland in the modulation of the hepatic steroid hydroxylase activity by the sex hormones, Gustafsson *et al.* (1975) have postulated the participation of two unidentified factors, i.e., hypophysial "feminizing factor" (FF) and hypothalamic "feminizing factor inhibiting factor" (FFIF). According to this hypothesis, hypothalamic FFIF is positively controlled by the androgens and negatively by the estrogens. Synthesis and secretion of FF will depend on the presence or absence of FFIF. In the female rats or in the estrogenized castrated males, FF will act synergistically with the estrogen to induce the synthesis of the hepatic 15β steroid hydroxylase. Because both FF and FFIF are still hypothetical entities, and no detailed investigation of the effect of various combinations of known pituitary and pituitary-dependent hormones on the estrogenic induction of this enzyme in the castrated male rats has been reported, the possibility of a multihormonal regulation of the estrogen-dependent synthesis of the 15β steroid hydroxylase similar to α_{2u} globulin should not be overlooked. In this connection, it may be mentioned that the female-specific kidney enzyme 17β-hydroxysteroid dehydrogenase in the rat, which is regulated by the sex hormones and hypophysis in a manner similar to the hepatic 15β-steroid hydroxylase, has recently been shown to be under multihormonal regulation involving androgen, estrogen, thyroxine, glucocorticoid, growth hormone, and prolactin (Ghraf *et al.*, 1977).

C. The Role of Insulin

The discovery of the multihormonal requirements for androgen-dependent synthesis of α_{2u} globulin in the hypophysectomized rat led to the search for other possible hormonal synergists in the regulation of this protein. Many publications during the last two decades have shown that diabetes can cause severe impairment of the protein-synthesizing ability of rat liver (Korner, 1960; Penhos and Krahl, 1964; Wool *et al.*, 1968; Baliga *et al.*, 1968). An examination of the effect of alloxan diabetes on the urinary output of α_{2u} globulin showed a sharp drop in the daily output of this protein. Results presented in Fig. 5 summarize the effects of insulin on the daily urinary output of α_{2u} globulin. Induction of diabetes in mature male rats with alloxan resulted in more than 80% reduction in the daily urinary output of this protein. The urinary output of α_{2u} globulin in diabetic rats could be

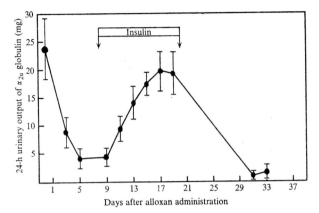

FIG. 5. Urinary output of α_{2u} globulin in alloxan-diabetic adult male rats, and the effect of insulin on the recovery process. The period of insulin treatment is marked with arrows. Each point is a mean value of 5 individual animals. The vertical lines indicate ± S.D. From Roy and Leonard, 1973.

raised to nearly normal and maintained at that level with insulin supplementation. Withdrawal of insulin treatment brought back the daily urinary output of α_{2u} globulin to the pretreatment level (Roy and Leonard, 1973).

These results clearly show that insulin plays an important role in the regulation of α_{2u} globulin. Determination of the precise role of insulin in the regulation of α_{2u} synthesis is complicated by decreased amino acid transport and a general state of enhanced catabolism in the diabetic animal. These aspects of insulin action have been the subject of several excellent articles (Wool *et al.*, 1968; Manchester, 1970; Mortimore and Mondon, 1970) and will be discussed further in Section IV,D.

D. Multiple Hormonal Requirement for α_{2u} Synthesis by Hepatocytes in Monolayer Tissue Culture

Most of the fundamental mechanisms of the hormonal regulation of protein synthesis and gene expression have been elucidated by investigations of hormone action in animal models. However, in certain cases, biochemical and molecular interpretation of the results of such investigation is complicated by interactions of various endocrine factors in the regulation of circulating hormone concentrations. Some of these ambiguities can be resolved by investigating the observed *in vivo* endocrine responses under *in vitro* conditions. On the basis of the above consideration, we have studied the hormonal regulation of α_{2u} globulin in cultured hepatocytes. We have developed a technique for culture of rat hepatocytes in monolayers without any enzy-

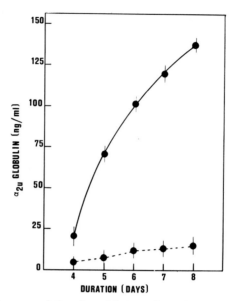

FIG. 6. Cumulative accumulation of α_{2u} globulin in the medium of hepatocytes derived from male rat liver and cultured in minimum maintenance medium (MMM) with and without the addition of growth hormone, T_3, and dexamethasone. Cells were cultured with hormone-supplemented or hormone-deprived medium from the day 1. On day 4 the medium was carefully removed as much as possible and fresh medium was added. Aliquots of the culture medium were removed at different periods and assayed for α_{2u} globulin by radioimmunoassay. Each point represents an average value of 4 experiments ± S.E.M. The values are corrected for minor differences in the number of cells in individual experiments and are expressed as α_{2u} globulin per 5×10^{-3} cells per flask. ●----●, MMM alone; ●———●, MMM + growth hormone, T_3, and dexamethasone.

matic treatment. These cells, when isolated from the liver of male rats, are found to synthesize α_{2u} globulin for more than 2 weeks. When the culture medium (basal maintenance medium containing Dulbecco's medium with 10% male human serum, dibutyryl cAMP, insulin, and glucagon) was supplemented with DHT, no enhancement of α_{2u} synthesis was observed. However, dexamethasone, triiodothyronine, and growth hormone, when added individually, were found to cause significant stimulation of α_{2u} synthesis by these hepatocytes in culture. Fortification of the basal maintenance medium with all the above three hormones caused about 9-fold enhancement of α_{2u} production over those cultured without these hormones (Fig. 6) (Motwani and Roy, 1978). One of the reasons for the failure of DHT to enhance α_{2u} synthesis over the basal level may be due to the adequacy of the androgenic steroids present in the serum component of the culture medium. Alternatively, it could be due to a two-step mechanism for the regulation of α_{2u} gene whereby, after the initial activation by the androgen, continued presence of the hormone is not critical for production and accumulation of α_{2u} mRNA which could be regulated by the synergistic hormones. In summary, the results of the *in vitro* experiments substantiate the multiple hormonal requirement for the hepatic synthesis of α_{2u} globulin as observed in the intact animal (Roy, 1973b).

III. CYTOPLASMIC ANDROGEN BINDING PROTEIN OF RAT LIVER AND ITS POSSIBLE ROLE IN THE REGULATION OF α_{2u} GLOBULIN

A. Properties of the Cytoplasmic Androgen Binding Protein in Rat Liver

Following the initial observation of Jensen and his associates concerning the selective retention of estradiol in the vagina and uterus of the rat, the existence of specific binding proteins for androgens, estrogens, and gestagens in their target tissues has been well documented (Jensen and Jacobson, 1962; Toft and Gorski, 1966; Korenman and Rao, 1968; Bruchovsky and Wilson, 1968; Fang et al., 1969; O'Malley et al., 1971). Although the obligatory role of these specific binding proteins ("receptors") in the mechanism of sex hormone action has received general acceptance, the functional relevance of the different types of receptor proteins in different target tissues, such as α and β forms of androgen receptor in rat prostate (Fang and Liao, 1971), A and B subunits of the progesterone receptor in chick oviduct (Schrader and O'Malley, 1972), and multiple forms and subunit structure of the estrogen receptor in rat and calf uterus (Notides and Nielsen, 1974; Bresciani, this volume) has not been clearly established. Thus, the study of the receptor for sex hormones in different target tissues is still an interesting and rewarding endeavor.

Studies in our laboratory have established the existence of a low-capacity, high-affinity androgen binding protein in the cytoplasmic fraction of rat liver. A strong correlation between the presence of this androgen binding protein and the ability of the liver to respond to androgen for the induction of α_{2u} globulin has also been observed (Milin and Roy, 1973; Roy et al., 1974). The cytoplasmic androgen binding protein of rat liver has a sedimentation coefficient of 3.5 S and binds to DHT in preference to testosterone. This androgen binding protein also possesses additional affinity for estradiol-17β (Fig. 7). Although the presence of excess unlabeled estradiol-17β strongly inhibited the uptake of labeled DHT, the presence of excess unlabeled DHT interfered only very weakly with the binding of labeled estradiol-17β. These results

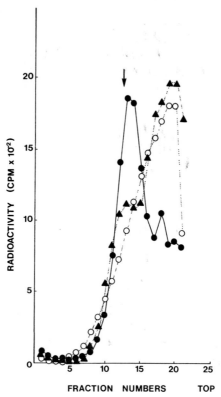

FIG. 7. Distribution profile of the *in vitro* incubation mixture of 5α-[1,2-^{3}H$_2$]dihydrotestos-
terone (DHT) and normal male rat liver cytosol on a 5–15% sucrose density gradient (22 hours
at 216,000 gm). Cytosol preparations in the different gradients were incubated with: ●————●,
^{3}H-labeled DHT alone; ▲————▲, ^{3}H-labeled DHT + excess unlabeled estradiol-17β. Arrow
shows the position of the marker protein ovalbumin in the gradient. From Roy *et al.*, 1974.

indicate that estradiol and DHT may not share the same binding site on the
protein, and it has been suggested that binding of estradiol to a distinct site
interferes allosterically with the androgen binding (Roy *et al.*, 1974).

The hepatic androgen binding protein showed no affinity for progesterone,
corticosterone, and nonsteroidal synthetic estrogen DES. The K_d for DHT
and estradiol-17β were estimated to be 4.5×10^{-8} M and 3.5×10^{-7} M,
respectively. Androgen binding capacity of this protein could be completely
destroyed *in vitro* by exposure to pronase, parachloromercuribenzoate, and
heat (20 minutes at 38°). Optimum binding of DHT was observed at or near
pH 8.5, and no binding activity was noted below pH 4.5 or above pH 10.4.
Its sensitivity to sulfhydryl-blocking reagents and the pH optima at 8.5 may
indicate an involvement for free —SH group in the binding of DHT by this

protein. Although the cytoplasmic androphilic protein of rat liver has certain properties which are distinctly different from those of prostatic androphilic proteins, in order to avoid confusing terminology in this chapter it will henceforth also be referred to as cytosol androgen receptor of rat liver.

One of the interesting differences between the androgen-dependent processes in the male reproductive tissues and in some of the nonreproductive tissues is the differential sensitivity of the competitive androgen analog cyproterone and cyproterone acetate (CA). Unlike male reproductive tissues, where CA strongly inhibits androgen action (Fang and Liao, 1969; Baulieu and Jung, 1970), many androgen-dependent processes in the liver and kidney are insensitive to CA. For example, the androgen-dependent rise of glucuronidase and certain steroid-metabolizing enzymes in rat liver are unaffected by treatment with CA (Kunzel and Muller-Oerlinghausen, 1969; Ghraf et al., 1974). Similar observations have also been reported for mouse kidney glucuronidase by Mowszowicz et a. (1974). These observations have led some investigators to suggest that androgen action in nonreproductive tissues may involve a mechanism independent of cytoplasmic hormone receptors (Ghraf et al., 1977). However, we have found that CA does not inhibit the binding of labeled DHT to the cytosol androgen receptor of rat liver, and this finding accords with the observation that treatment with CA fails to inhibit the androgen-dependent synthesis of α_{2u} globulin in the mature male rat (Roy, 1976). Another unusual property of the hepatic androgen receptor is its ability to bind estradiol but not DES. It is interesting to note that binding of both DHT and estradiol-17β but not of DES to cytosol androgen receptors in mouse fibroblasts (Jung-Testas et al., 1976b), mouse mammary tumor cells (Jung-Testas et al., 1976a), and rat brain (Chamness et al., 1977) has recently been reported. Therefore, there seems to be an emerging pattern of similar ligand specificity among the androgen receptors outside the male reproductive tissues.

B. ANDROGENIC INDUCTION OF THE HEPATIC ANDROGEN RECEPTOR AND ANDROGEN INSENSITIVITY ASSOCIATED WITH RECEPTOR DEFICIENCY IN THE PREPUBERTAL, SENESCENT, TFM, AND ESTROGENIZED MALE RATS

α_{2u} Globulin is not synthesized by female or prepubertal male rats. Treatment of castrated female rats with androgenic hormones results in the induction of this protein. When the hepatic cytosol of castrated female rats, before any androgen treatment, is examined for androgen binding activity by sucrose density gradient, only a minor deflection in the 3.5 S region of the gradient could be observed. However, daily androgen treatment of these animals is found to result in both the gradual rise of the 3.5 S androgen receptor activity and the enhancement of the androgen response, as seen by a sharp rise in the daily urinary output of α_{2u} globulin (Fig. 8). In the prepubertal male rats, no distinct androgen binding peak could be seen when their hepatic cytosol was assayed for labeled DHT binding by sucrose density-gradient centrifugation. In the maturing male rat, a gradual rise in the level of the 3.5 S hepatic androgen receptor could be observed with age, reaching a ceiling at about 48 days of age (Fig. 9). In these animals, the daily urinary output of α_{2u} globulin also follows the rising pattern of the androgen

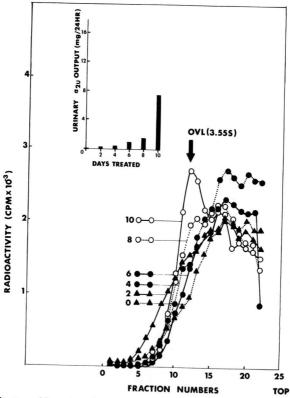

FIG. 8. Induction of hepatic androgen receptor activity in the ovariectomized female rats treated with 5α-dihydrotestosterone (0.5 μg/gm body weight/day, subcutaneous injections). Sucrose density-gradient patterns of the 5α-[1,2-³H₂]dihydrotestosterone binding to the hepatic cytosol by the animals treated with 5α-dihydrotestosterone for various periods are expressed with different symbols: ▲ · · · · ▲, 0-day control; ▲———▲, 2 days; ● · · · · ●, 4 days; ●———●, 6 days; ○ · · · · ○, 8 days; ○———○, 10 days. The inset shows the 24-hour urinary output of α_{2u} globulin of these animals immediately prior to their sacrifice for the receptor assay. From Roy *et al.*, 1974.

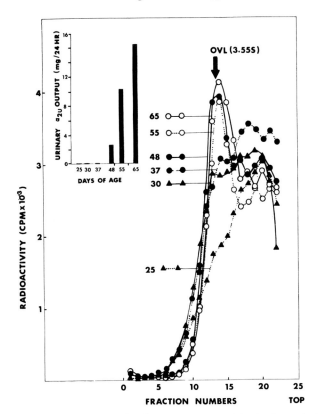

FIG. 9. Development of the cytosol androgen receptor activity in the maturing male rat liver. Receptor activities in normal male rats of prepubertal, pubertal, and early postpubertal ages were assayed on sucrose density gradients. The ages of the animals are represented with with different symbols: ▲····▲, 0-day control; ▲————▲, 2 days; ●····●, 4 days; ●————●, days; ○······○, 55 days; ○————○, 65 days of age. The inset shows the levels of daily urinary α_{2u} output of these animals immediately prior to their sacrifice for the receptor assay. From Roy *et al.*, 1974.

receptor activity. Prepubertal castration of male rats at 21 days of age prevents the age-dependent development of the androgen receptor activity, indicating the obligatory role of the pubertal rise of androgen in the development of the receptor activity in these animals. Daily androgen treatment to prepubertal male rats from 21 to 31 days of age neither induces α_{2u} globulin nor causes any increase in the hepatic androgen binding activity (Roy *et al.*, 1974).

These results support the concept of the androgenic induction of the hepatic androgen receptor. They are also consistent with the view that androgen insensitivity of the prepubertal animals is due to noninduction of the hepatic receptor. However, support of this hypothesis would necessitate an additional postulation for the existence of another yet unidentified type of androgen binding protein in rat liver which is constitutive in nature and appears at the time of puberty. This constitutive receptor in the presence of androgen may induce the 3.5 S androgen binding protein found in the mature male rat which, in turn, may be directly responsible for the induction of α_{2u} globulin (Roy, 1976).

In normal male rats, α_{2u} globulin starts to be produced at around 40 days of age, and the urinary output of this protein reaches a peak (approx. 0.1 mg/g body weight) at about 75 days of age. Depending on the strain of the rat, this high level of α_{2u} globulin is maintained up to 600–750 days of age. Beyond 750 days of age, the animals gradually reach the state of senility, which is associated with rapid decline and complete loss of α_{2u} synthesizing ability.

Similar to prepubertal rats, the synthesis of α_{2u} globulin in senescent animals cannot be induced even with high doses of androgenic hormones (Roy *et al.*, 1974). Examination of the cytosol fraction from the liver of senescent male rats that have stopped producing α_{2u} globulin showed virtual absence of the 3.5 S androgen receptor activity. Daily treatment of these animals with 1 mg DHT/day for 25 days failed to induce α_{2u} globulin and did not produce any detectable rise in the hepatic androgen binding activity (Roy *et al.*, 1974). These results indicate that, similar to the prepubertal rats, noninduction of α_{2u} globulin in the senescent animals is also due to a deficiency of the hepatic androgen receptor.

Despite the similarity between the state of androgen insensitivity in the prepubertal and senescent rats, it is possible that these two states may operate via two distinctly different mechanisms. Whereas the androgen insensitivity in the prepubertal animals may be due to the absence of a critical level of certain developmental signals, in the senescent animals it may involve age-dependent changes in the receptor structure, as indicated by the discovery of certain enzyme alterations in aging animals (Grinna and Barber, 1972; Gershon and Gershon, 1973; Sullivan and Debusk, 1973). However, alternative mechanisms, such as age-dependent changes in the genetic apparatus involved in receptor regulation, may also be possible. Besides rat liver, there are at least two other systems in which evidence for an age-dependent decrease in the level of steroid hormone receptors in their target tissues has been reported. Shain and Axelrod (1973) have reported a decreased uptake of androgen by the aging rat prostate, and uptake of glucocorticoids by the lymphocytes has also been found to be decreased with aging (Roth, 1976). Our findings, and the above results, indicate that receptor inactivation associated with senility may represent one of the primary reasons for the gradual loss of reproductive capacity and hormone responsiveness in the aged animals. Age-dependent changes in androgen sensitivity and the steps which may be involved in the process are summarized in Fig. 10.

Studies of the mechanism of androgen action have been greatly facilitated by the availability of experimental animals with testicular feminization. Testicular feminization is an inborn defect where the affected offspring show complete lack of the androgen-dependent differentiation. Stanley and Gumbreck have developed a strain of Tfm rats with an X-linked recessive mutation. These animals are insensitive to androgen action at the target level (Bardin *et al.*, 1970). The inability of the senescent rats to produce α_{2u} globulin and the lack of the hepatic androgen receptor activity in these animals are, in certain respects, comparable to the androgen insensitivity in testicular feminization (Neuhaus and Irwin, 1972). Stanley–Gumbreck Tfm rats normally produce only trace amounts (<0.21 mg/day) of α_{2u} globulin, and

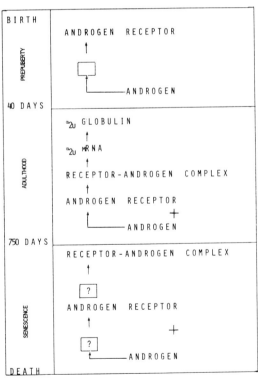

FIG. 10. Scheme for the sequence of events leading to age-dependent changes in androgen sensitivity in rat liver; □ indicates the site of age-dependent block in androgen action. The upward arrows show increase in the level of the entity.

androgen treatment does not stimulate the production of α_{2u} globulin in these animals. Sucrose density-gradient analysis of the cytosol androgen binding activity of the hepatic tissue of the Tfm rats shows only a minor deflection at the 3.5 S region of the gradient as compared to a distinct peak in the case of normal animals (Milin and Roy, 1973). These results accord with the mounting evidence for receptor deficiency as the primary reason for androgen insensitivity in Tfm syndrome (Gehring *et al.*, 1971; Bullock and Bardin, 1972; Smith *et al.*, 1975).

Recently, Naess *et al.* (1976) have reported that the pituitary gland and the brain of the Tfm rats contain about 10–15% cytosol androgen receptor, as compared to their normal litter mates and that a very high dose of DHT (40-fold higher than normal) could elicit normal pituitary response with respect to the androgenic inhibition of gonadotropin secretion. On the basis of these results, we have examined the effect of the daily administration for 10 days of a very high dose of DHT (2.5 mg/100 gm body weight, 50 times higher than optimum) on the urinary output of α_{2u} globulin in the Tfm rats. Even with this massive dose, DHT failed to stimulate the synthesis of α_{2u} globulin in the Tfm rats (A.K. Roy, unpublished). These results point toward the possible differences in the degree of androgen insensitivity among various target tissues in the Tfm animals.

Daily treatment of mature male rats with estradiol not only inhibits α_{2u} synthesis, it also reduces the hepatic concentration of the cytosol androgen receptor (Roy *et al.*, 1974, 1975; Kurtz *et al.*, 1976a). When the daily dose of estradiol-17β is 50 μg/100 gm body weight or higher, withdrawal of estrogen treatment after complete suppression of α_{2u} synthesis does not cause immediate reinitiation of the synthesis of this protein. These estrogenized male rats undergo a lag period of about 3 weeks, during which the animals do not even respond to androgens for the induction of α_{2u} globulin. This temporary state of androgen insensitivity has been found to be due to a complete lack of cytosol androgen receptor activity brought about by the estrogen treatment. Although the exact mechanism of this relatively long androgen-insensitive lag period remains obscure, receptor deficiency emerges as a common denominator among the various states of androgen insensitivity observed in the androgen-dependent synthesis of α_{2u} globulin.

C. BIFUNCTIONAL NATURE OF THE HEPATIC ANDROGEN RECEPTOR AND BOTH ANDROGENIC AND ESTROGENIC INDUCTION OF α_{2u} GLOBULIN IN THE EARLY STAGE OF HORMONE ACTION

Recently, we have developed a very sensitive double-antibody radioimmunoassay for α_{2u} globulin. This procedure allows us to examine the early effects of androgen and estrogen on α_{2u} synthesis in castrated female rats and to correlate it with the hepatic androgen receptor activity (Roy, 1977). These studies have revealed that on first exposure both estradiol-17β and DHT were almost equally effective in inducing α_{2u} globulin. However, on continued treatment, the capability of the liver to respond to estrogen was gradually diminished; ultimately, estradiol became ineffective in promoting α_{2u} synthesis (Fig. 11). On the other hand, daily pretreatment of spayed female rats with DHT increased the sensitivity of subsequent androgen response. The androgen pretreatment also increased the hepatic concentration of the androgen receptor and, conversely, estrogen treatment suppressed cytosol androgen receptor activity (Roy *et al.*, 1974).

Because the cytosol androgen receptor of rat liver is capable of binding both DHT and estradiol-17β, it has been postulated that binding either DHT or estradiol to the bifunctional receptor protein could lead to the induction of α_{2u} globulin. However, uptake of DHT by the receptor would

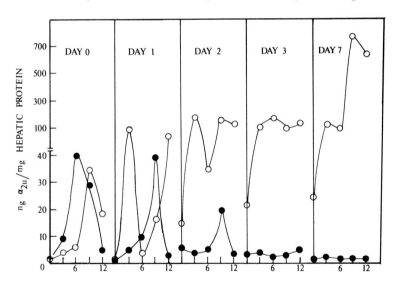

HOURS AFTER LAST INJECTION

FIG. 11. Effect of daily pretreatments with estradiol or dihydrotestosterone on the hepatic levels of α_{2u} globulin in castrated female rats after single final injection of the same hormone. The animals in day 0 did not receive any pretreatment and received only single injections of either estradiol (●————●) or dihydrotestosterone (○————○). Animals in days 1, 2, 3, and 7 received 1, 2, 3, and 7 daily pretreatments with either estradiol (●————●) or dihydrotestosterone (○————○) followed 24 hours later by a single injection of the same hormone. Amounts per injection were 5 μg estradiol/100 gm body weight and 30 μg dihydrotestosterone/100 gm body weight. The animals were sacrificed at various times (hours) after the final injection. Each point represents the average value from 3 experimental animals. From Roy, 1977.

also lead to increased synthesis and build-up of the receptor itself; uptake of estradiol would lead to an opposite effect—i.e., nonreplenishment of the receptor leading ultimately to androgen insensitivity (Roy, 1977). At this point it should be emphasized that the regulation of α_{2u} globulin may also involve the interaction of the specific estrogen receptor of rat liver. The existence of specific estrogen binding protein in rat liver has been reported by several investigators (Chamness *et al.*, 1975; Viladiu *et al.*, 1975; Eisenfeld *et al.*, 1976; Beers and Rosner, 1977). The cytosol estrogen receptor of rat liver binds to both estradiol-17β and DES but does not bind to DHT or testosterone. The fact that DES mimics the effect of estradiol on the hepatic synthesis of α_{2u} globulin but does not bind to the cytosol androgen receptor suggests the possible contribution of the estrogen receptor in the regulation of α_{2u} globulin.

IV. MESSENGER RNA FOR α_{2u} GLOBULIN AND ITS REGULATION BY VARIOUS HORMONES

A. IDENTIFICATION OF THE MRNA FOR α_{2u} GLOBULIN AND ESTIMATION OF ITS MOLECULAR SIZE

In order to understand the molecular mechanism of the multihormonal regulation of α_{2u} globulin in rat liver, it was imperative to explore the role of various hormonal regulators in the transcription and translation of the mRNA for this protein. Since the publication of the first successful translation of mRNA in a reticulocyte cell-free system by Lockard and Lingrel (1969), several efficient systems for the translation of mRNA have been established (Mathews and Korner, 1970; Gurdon *et al.*, 1971; Roberts and Patterson, 1973). We have shown that the mRNA for α_{2u} globulin can be faithfully translated in various heterologous translational systems, such as ascites tumor cell-free system (Sippel *et al.*, 1975), wheat germ cell-free system (Roy *et al.*, 1976b) and in *Xenopus* oocyte (A.K. Deshpande and A.K. Roy, unpublished). Immunoprecipitation of α_{2u} globulin from these translational products and subsequent sodium dodecylsulfate polyacrylamide gel electrophoresis of the immunoprecipitate showed that the mRNA-primed translation product is released as completed α_{2u} globulin chain without any evidence for a larger pro-protein product, as was discovered in the case of several secretory proteins, e.g., growth hormone, insulin, and serum albumin (Sussman *et al.*, 1976; Duguid *et al.*, 1976; Strauss *et al.*, 1977).

Fractionation of the poly(A) containing total hepatic mRNA in either sodium dodecyl sulfate–sucrose gradient or acid–urea agarose gel electrophoresis followed by extraction and translation of the fractions demon-

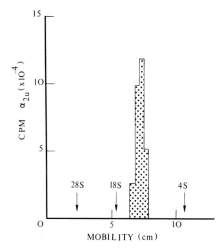

FIG. 12. Mobility of α_{2u} mRNA in agarose–urea gel. Total poly(A) enriched RNA extracted from the liver of mature male rats was electrophoretically separated on agarose–urea gel, and the RNA extracted from different gel fractions was translated in wheat germ cell-free system. The dotted bars represent immunologically and electrophoretically identifiable α_{2u} globulin in the translation product of the wheat germ cell-free system. The α_{2u} mRNA migrated as a 14 S band, as judged by its relative position to the marker RNA's (arrows).

strates that α_{2u} mRNA migrates as a peak in the 14 S fraction (Fig. 12). The above sedimentation coefficient would correspond to a molecular weight of about 500,000, indicating approximately 1200–1400 nucleotide residues (Loening, 1968; Attardi and Amaldi, 1970). Because α_{2u} globulin consists of 186 amino acid residues, it would require 558 nucleotides to code for the protein structure and approximately an additional 200 poly(A) residues at the 3' end of the mRNA. This would account for only about half the estimated nucleotide residues within the α_{2u} mRNA. The mRNA's for several eukaryotic proteins, such as immunoglobulin light chain (Mach *et al.*, 1973), hemoglobin (Morrison and Lingrel, 1976, Ovalbumin (Woo *et al.*, 1975) and αA_2-crystallin (Berns *et al.*, 1974), are known to contain a greater excess of nucleotide residues than could be accounted for by their coding function.

The striking similarity between the estimated size of αA_2-crystallin and its mRNA and that of α_{2u} globulin and its mRNA is of interest. Both of these two proteins are coded by 14 S mRNA, and αA_2-crystallin contains 173 whereas α_{2u} globulin contains 186 amino acid residues. It has recently been reported that under physiological conditions the ovalbumin mRNA may contain secondary structure to the extent of 41% of the molecule (Van *et al.*, 1977). Although the biological significance of the "extra" stretches of nucleotides within the mRNA is still unknown, it is likely that the portions of the mRNA containing base-paired secondary structure may not be available for its coding function.

B. Effects of Androgen and Estrogen on the Level of the mRNA for α_{2u} Globulin in Rat Liver

Extensive and some very excellent studies in several laboratories, especially those of O'Malley and Schimke, which have been reviewed in Volume III of this series, have provided unequivocal documentation of the role of estrogen in the transcriptional regulation of the ovalbumin mRNA in the chick oviduct (Rosen and O'Malley, 1975; Schimke *et al.*, 1975). Unfortunately, comparable evidence on the transcriptional regulation of protein synthesis by other hormones is still scarce. Results from our laboratory have shown that the effect of androgen on the hepatic synthesis of α_{2u} globulin is also mediated by changes in the intracellular concentration of the mRNA for this protein. About 1–2% of all proteins synthesized in the heterologous cell-free system directed by RNA from mature male rat liver could be identified as α_{2u} globulin, and no α_{2u} globulin could be detected within the translational product when the RNA was obtained from the liver of normal female rats (Sippel *et al.*, 1975; Roy *et al.*, 1976b). On the other hand, treatment of spayed female rats with DHT has been found to result in a gradual rise in the urinary output of α_{2u} globulin and also a corresponding rise in the hepatic concentration of the translatable mRNA for α_{2u} globulin. The relationship between the circulating androgens and the hepatic concentration of the mRNA for α_{2u} globulin can best be exemplified in the case of maturing male rats (Roy *et al.*, 1976a).

Figure 13 shows the relationships among rising levels of serum testosterone, hepatic concentrations of α_{2u} mRNA, and the hepatic and urinary concentrations of α_{2u} globulin in male rats immediately before and after puberty. The serum level of testosterone in male rats younger than 42 days of age was found to be less than 2 ng/ml, and no mRNA for α_{2u} globulin could be detected within the hepatic mRNA populations from these animals. A gradual rise in the level of serum testosterone was observed from 42 to 70 days of age. The hepatic levels of α_{2u} mRNA at different ages showed a strong correlation with the rising levels of serum testosterone and the hepatic and urinary concentrations of α_{2u} globulin. Daily treatment of prepubertal male rats with either DHT or testosterone between 25 and 35 days of age failed to induce the mRNA for α_{2u} globulin in the liver.

The above results, and the observed absence of the cytosol androgen receptor in the liver of prepubertal animals, are compatible with the following suggested sequence of events: (a) Puberty in male rats is associated with gonadal maturation and a gradual rise in the level of serum testosterone; (b) coincident with the rising level of serum testosterone, developmental changes in the hepatocytes lead to the appearance of the 3.5 S cytosol androgen receptor; (c) these two events lead to the derepression of the α_{2u}

GEL FRACTIONS

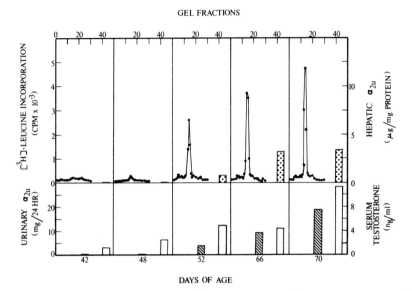

FIG. 13. Relationships among the levels of serum testosterone, hepatic messenger RNA for α_{2u} globulin, and both hepatic and urinary levels of α_{2u} globulin in the maturing male rats. Data in each vertical frame represent average values from same 3 animals. Equal amount of the hepatic tissue from each of these animals was blended together for the extraction of RNA. Other values represent mean of three separate assays. The messenger RNA activity for α_{2u} globulin (●――――●) is represented as the pattern of radioactivity on SDS-polyacrylamide gel electrophoresis of α_{2u}-anti-α_{2u} immunoprecipitate obtained from 2×10^6 cpm of released peptide chains synthesized *in vitro* under the direction of hepatic mRNA. Key to other symbols: dotted bars, hepatic concentration of α_{2u} globulin; hatched bars, 24 hour urinary output of α_{2u} globulin; open bars, serum testosterone. From Roy *et al.*, 1976b.

gene, causing transcription and accumulation of the mRNA for α_{2u} globulin, translation of which results in the rise of α_{2u} globulin.

Initial exposure of castrated female rats to estrogenic hormones results in a small rise in the hepatic concentration of α_{2u} globulin which could be blocked with cycloheximide (Roy, 1977). The magnitude of induction of α_{2u} globulin at this initial response is so small that it is below the limit of sensitivity of the *in vitro* translational assay for α_{2u} mRNA. However, daily treatment of mature male rats with estrogenic hormones brings about a large decrease in the hepatic synthesis of α_{2u} globulin, and it has been possible to examine the molecular basis of the above inhibitory action of the estrogen by a correlative study of the amounts of α_{2u} globulin and its corresponding mRNA in the estrogenized animals.

Results presented in Fig. 14 show that daily treatment of mature male rats with estradiol-17β ($10 \mu g/100$ gm body weight) for 4 days causes more than a

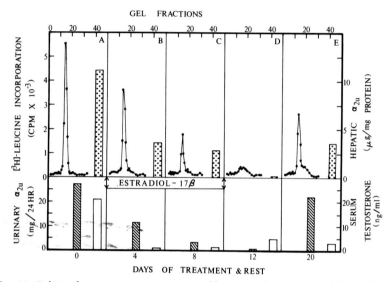

FIG. 14. Relationships among concentrations of hepatic and urinary α_{2u} globulin, hepatic mRNA activity for α_{2u} globulin and serum testosterone in estrogen-treated (10 μg/100 gm body weight) mature male rats. Each vertical frame (A–E) represents average data from three experimental animals. RNA was extracted from pooled liver (3 gm from each animal), and the remainder of the assays were performed separately and results are expressed as mean of the three values. (A), Untreated controls; (B) and (C), animals treated daily for 4 and 8 days, respectively, with estradiol; (D) and (E), animals recovering for 4 and 12 days, respectively, after initial 8 days of daily estradiol treatment. ●, Radioactivity pattern of the sodium dodecylsulphate/polyacrylamide-gel electrophoretogram of α_{2u} globulin-anti-(α_{2u} globulin) immunoprecipitate obtained from samples of released peptide chains synthesized by the wheat germ cell-free system under the direction of hepatic mRNA containing 2×10^6 cpm of incorporated [³H]leucine; stippled bars, hepatic content of α_{2u} globulin; hatched bars, 24 hour urinary output of α_{2u} globulin before death; open bars, concentrations of serum testosterone. From Roy et al., 1977.

50% drop in the hepatic concentration of the mRNA for α_{2u} globulin as compared to the control. The same treatment also reduced the level of serum testosterone to about 10% of the control value. Another 4 days of estrogen treatment caused a further drop in the hepatic mRNA for α_{2u} globulin and both the hepatic and urinary concentrations of this protein. After estrogen withdrawal, the decline in the hepatic levels of α_{2u} globulin and its mRNA still continued, reaching a level of about 5% of the control on the day 12 (8 days of treatment and 4 days of rest). Animals tested after 12 days of hormone withdrawal, following 8 days of treatment, showed partial recovery from the inhibitory effect of estrogen treatment with a parallel rise in the hepatic and urinary α_{2u} globulin and the mRNA for this protein. The level of serum testosterone, however, still remained low (about 20% of the control).

In a separate set of experiments, the levels of hepatic mRNA for α_{2u} globulin and serum testosterone were brought to less than 5% of the control with 8 daily injections of 50 μg estradiol-17β/100 gm/day. In these animals, the low levels of α_{2u} mRNA and serum testosterone were found to be maintained for at least 2 subsequent weeks beyond the last estrogen injection. Treatment of these animals within this 2 week withdrawal period with testosterone (250 μg/100 gm body weight/day, for 8 days) did not increase the hepatic concentration of α_{2u} mRNA (Roy et al., 1977). These results indicate that, although a reduction in the level of circulating androgens may contribute to the inhibition of the hepatic synthesis of α_{2u} globulin in the estrogen-treated male rats, the principal causative factor could still be the decline in the hepatic concentration of the cytosol androgen receptor; further, the estrogenic inhibition is mediated by a reduction in the hepatocytic concentration of the mRNA for α_{2u} globulin.

C. ROLE OF THYROXINE, CORTICOSTERONE, AND GROWTH HORMONE IN THE REGULATION OF THE mRNA FOR α_{2u} GLOBULIN

Androgen-dependent synthesis of α_{2u} globulin is synergistically promoted by several other growth and developmental hormones, such as thyroxine, glucocorticoids, and growth hormone (Roy, 1973b). Because the mRNA for this protein has also been identified, the system has provided us with an unique opportunity to study the interacting role of several hormones on the synthesis of one specific species of mRNA. Our initial efforts were concentrated on the investigation of the effects of the individual hormonal synergist on the regulation of the hepatic concentration of the mRNA for α_{2u} globulin. In later studies we examined the effects of various combinations of androgen, thyroxine, glucocorticoid, and growth hormone on the hepatic level of α_{2u} mRNA in the hypophysectomized rats.

The effects of deficiency and sufficiency of thyroid hormones on the hepatic mRNA for α_{2u} globulin and the urinary output of this protein are shown in Table I. Thyroidectomy in mature male rats resulted in approximately a 90% reduction in the mRNA for α_{2u} globulin, and the urinary output for α_{2u} globulin was reduced to about 3% of the control. Treatment of the thyroidectomized animals with testosterone did not cause any enhancement of either the mRNA for α_{2u} globulin or the urinary output of this protein. However, daily treatment of the thyroidectomized male rats with thyroxine (10 μg/100

TABLE I

QUANTITATIVE RELATIONSHIP BETWEEN THE HEPATIC α_{2u} mRNA ACTIVITY AND THE URINARY
LEVEL OF α_{2u} GLOBULIN UNDER DIFFERENT THYROIDAL STATES[a]

Thyroid status and treatment	Hepatic mRNA activity for α_{2u} globulin		Urinary level of α_{2u} globulin	
	α_{2u} mRNA activity (cpm)	% Control	mg α_{2u} Globulin in 24-hour urine	% Control
Intact thyroid + no treatment (unoperated control)	39,727	100	25.0	100
Thyroidectomized + 8 days of testosterone, 250 μg/100 gm body weight (testosterone-treated control)	4,049	10.2	0.61	2.44
Thyroidectomized + no treatment	5,386	13.5	0.75	3.0
Thyroidectomized + 4 days of thyroxine	5,673	14.2	1.1	4.4
Thyroidectomized + 8 days of thyroxine	37,593	94.6	16.8	67.0
Thyroidectomized + 8 days of thyroxine followed by 4 days of withdrawal	16,781	42.2	6.0	24.0

[a] All animals (300–350 g male rats) received 2 weeks of postoperative rest before any further experimental treatment. 24-Hour urine samples for the determination of the urinary output of α_{2u} globulin were collected just before the sacrifice of the animal for removal of the liver. Post-ribosomal supernatant from the wheat germ translation system containing 300,000 cpm of [³H]leucine incorporated into the peptide chains were used for immunological and electrophoretic separation of the newly synthesized α_{2u} globulin (owing to the differences in counting efficiency, 300,000 cpm on filter paper was found to be equivalent to 1,605,000 cpm in macerated gel; the counts were not multiplied with any conversion factor and are given as original counts per minute). Messenger RNA activity for α_{2u} globulin is expressed as the cpm of [³H]leucine within the α_{2u} band after SDS-polyacrylamide gel electrophoresis of the α_{2u}-anti-α_{2u} immunoprecipitate of the *in vitro* product of translation. Each value is an average of three animals. From Roy *et al.*, 1976a.

gm body weight) resulted in nearly complete restoration of the hepatic mRNA for α_{2u} globulin (Roy *et al.*, 1976a). These results indicate that thyroid hormone regulates the hepatic synthesis of α_{2u} globulin by regulating the hepatic concentration of the mRNA for this protein. Similar conclusions have also been reached by Kurtz *et al.* (1976b).

Recently, two other groups of investigators have shown that thyroid hormones are also involved in the regulation of the mRNA for growth hormone in a rat pituitary cell line (Seo *et al.*, 1977; Martial *et al.*, 1977). Because the existence of specific receptor for thyroid hormones in both rat liver and pituitary cell line has been demonstrated (Oppenheimer *et al.*, 1974; Samuels *et al.*, 1976), the above results point toward a mechanism of thyroxine action not too dissimilar from that of steroid hormones.

Studies concerning the role of glucocorticoid hormones on the hepatic concentration of the mRNA for α_{2u} globulin have shown that although adrenalectomy in mature male rats results in a 95% reduction in the urinary output of α_{2u} globulin, the hepatic level of α_{2u} mRNA is maintained up to 20% of the control. Daily treatment of the adrenalectomized animals with corticosterone produced nearly a 500% increase in the urinary output of α_{2u} globulin, with a corresponding rise in the level of α_{2u} mRNA of about 60% over the untreated adrenalectomized control (Sippel *et al.*, 1975). These results definitely indicate a transcriptional regulation of α_{2u} synthesis by glucocorticoid hormones, at the same time leaving open the possibility of a superimposed control at a level beyond the transcription of mRNA.

Hypophysectomy is known to cause multiple hormonal deficiencies, and the reversal of the effect of hypophysectomy on the synthesis of α_{2u} globulin requires simultaneous administration of DHT, thyroxine, corticosterone, and gorwth hormone (Roy, 1973b). The mechanism of action of growth hormone on the synthesis of α_{2u} globulin was inviestigated by a correlative study on the hepatic and urinary concentrations of α_{2u} globulin and the hepatic concentration of the mRNA for this protein in hypophysectomized male rats treated with DHT, thyroxine, and corticosterone and also DHT, thyroxine, corticosterone plus growth hormone. The results, presented in Fig. 15, show that hypophysectomy leads to complete elimination of the α_{2u} mRNA activity within the poly(A)-enriched hepatic RNA. Treatment of hypophysectomized rats with a combination of three hormones (DHT, thyroxine, and corticosterone) caused only a slight enrichment of α_{2u} mRNA (6% of the normal male) within the total mRNA population of the liver. However, addition of growth hormone to the above three-hormone combination caused more than a 7-fold increase in the hepatic concentration of the mRNA for α_{2u} globulin over the level found in the three-hormone-treated animals. The hepatic and urinary concentrations of α_{2u} globulin in the three-hormone- and three-hormone-plus-growth-hormone-treated animals closely paralleled the levels of hepatic mRNA concentrations (Roy and Dowbenko, 1977). Treatment of hypophysectomized animals with growth hormone alone did not cause any detectable rise in the hepatic concentration of the mRNA for α_{2u} globulin. Growth hormone, when administered alone or in combination with either thyroxine or corticosterone to the hypophysectomized animals, is known to enhance hepatic RNA synthesis (Talwar *et al.*, 1964; Tata and Widnell, 1966). However, examination of the rate of incorporation of labeled orotic

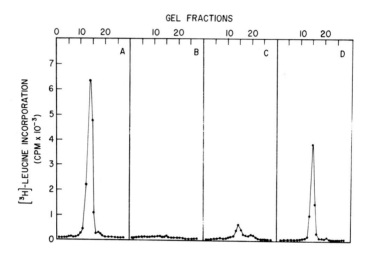

FIG. 15. Effect of hypophysectomy and multiple hormone supplementation on the hepatic concentration of mRNA for α_{2u} globulin. Each frame shows a representative pattern of radioactivity in the sodium dodecyl sulfate/polyacrylamide gel electrophoretogram of immunoprecipitated α_{2u} globulin from labeled proteins (10^6 cpm) synthesized *in vitro* under the direction of poly(A) enriched hepatic RNA obtained from different experimental animals. RNA samples obtained from various experimental animals are represented as follows: (A), unoperated control; (B), hypophysectomized rat without any hormone treatment; (C), hypophysectomized rat treated daily for 8 days with dihydrotestosterone, corticosterone, and thyroxine; and (D), hypophysectomized rat treated daily for 8 days with dihydrotestosterone, corticosterone, thyroxine, and growth hormone. From Roy and Dowbenko, 1977; reprinted with permission from *Biochemistry*.

acid into the poly(A)-enriched hepatic RNA of the hypophysectomized animals treated with a combination of three hormones (DHT, thyroxine and corticosterone) and the above three hormones plus growth hormone showed that inclusion of growth hormone in the hormone combination failed to cause any further enhancement of orotic acid incorporation into the hepatic RNA over those treated with three hormones only (Roy and Dowbenko, 1977).

These results support the argument that growth hormone exerts a specific effect on the hepatic synthesis of the mRNA for α_{2u} globulin rather than a nonspecific stimulatory effect on hepatic RNA synthesis. The complete disappearance of the mRNA for α_{2u} globulin after hypophysectomy and the evidence for individually exerted stimulatory role of DHT, thyroxine, corticosterone, and growth hormone on the hepatic concentration of α_{2u} mRNA may indicate that the pituitary gland coordinates the multihormonal regulation of α_{2u} globulin primarily via regulation of transcription.

D. Levels of Hepatic α_{2u} Globulin and its mRNA in Experimental Diabetes

Pioneering studies in several laboratories have implicated insulin in the regulation of protein synthesis and ribosome function (Korner, 1960; Penhos and Krahl, 1964; Wool *et al.*, 1972). Diabetes is also associated with decreased amino acid uptake and increased protein catabolism (Mortimore and Mondon, 1970; Jefferson *et al.*, 1977). We have shown that the daily urinary output of α_{2u} globulin is drastically reduced in the diabetic rats, and that this defect could be corrected by insulin supplementation (Roy and Leonard, 1973). In order to obtain further insight into the role of insulin in α_{2u} synthesis, we have recently examined the effect of diabetes and insulin treatment on the urinary and hepatic level of α_{2u} globulin and on the hepatic concentration of α_{2u} mRNA. The results (Fig. 16) show that diabetes causes very significant reduction in all these three parameters. However, a large discre-

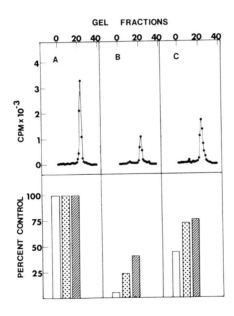

FIG. 16. Changes in the hepatic concentrations of α_{2u} globulin and its mRNA in diabetic rat. (A), Normal male; (B), animals made diabetic by treatment with streptozotocin; (C), diabetic rats treated for 7 days with insulin (2.5 units, twice daily). Upper frame: distribution of radioactivity in the SDS-polyacrylamide gel of the immunoprecipitated α_{2u} globulin from 7.5×10^5 cpm of released peptide chains synthesized *in vitro* which were programed by hepatic mRNA. Lower frame: open bars, daily urinary output of α_{2u} globulin; dotted bars, hepatic α_{2u} globulin; hatched bars, hepatic mRNA for α_{2u} globulin.

pancy between the levels of daily urinary output of α_{2u} globulin and the hepatic mRNA for this protein in the diabetic animals was evident. In addition, the lack of a strict correlation between the hepatic concentration of α_{2u} globulin and its mRNA may indicate both transcriptional and translational regulation of α_{2u} synthesis by insulin. Recently, the role of insulin in the regulation of the mRNA for another hepatic protein, serum albumin, has been reported (Peavy *et al.*, 1978).

V. CONCLUDING REMARKS

One of the most interesting outcomes of our studies on the hormonal regulation of α_{2u} globulin has been the discovery of the close coordination between the age-dependent changes in androgen sensitivity of the hepatic tissue and the changing levels of the circulating androgens. The development of androgen sensitivity of the liver, although initially independent of androgen action (Roy, 1973a; Roy *et al.*, 1974), coincides with gonadal maturation at the time of puberty. Even though the initial development of androgen sensitivity is an androgen-independent phenomenon, the maintenance of the optimum level of hepatic androgen receptor requires adequacy of the androgen status of the animal. The gradual decline and ultimate loss of the androgen receptor activity of the hepatic tissue associated with senescence again highlights the critical role of the age-dependent changes in receptor concentration in the regulation of hormone action. Similar age-dependent appearance in the hypothalamic estrogen receptor activity in the maturing female rats has also been observed by Kato (1971). Examination of the possible changes in the hypothalamic androgen receptor activity in the senescent animals may, therefore, be a rewarding endeavor.

Another important finding with regard to the regulation of hepatic androgen sensitivity is the regulation of the level of cytosol androgen binding protein by its own ligands, the androgen acting as the inducer and the estrogen acting as the antiinducer (Milin and Roy, 1973; Roy *et al.*, 1974). Because uptake of both the androgen and the estrogen can cause the induction of α_{2u} globulin (Roy, 1977), receptor regulation by these two hormones in an opposing manner seems to be a logical and efficient way to exercise their antagonistic action on α_{2u} synthesis. It is of interest to note that Gschwendt and Kittstein (1974) have also observed that estradiol-17β can cause a severalfold increase in the estrogen receptor activity in chicken liver, which is involved in the synthesis of the egg yolk proteins under the influence of this female sex hormone (Greengard *et al.*, 1965; Bergink *et al.*, 1973).

Several investigators have shown the requirement of the androgenic hormones for the maintenance of the protein-synthesizing machinery of the accessory sex organs in the castrated male rat. These observations include androgen-dependent increase in the ability of prostatic ribosomes for incorporation of amino acids into proteins (Liao and Williams-Ashman, 1962), increase in the total cellular RNA in the ventral prostate (Williams-Ashman et al., 1964), increase in the synthesis of ribosomal and transfer RNA in the seminal vesicle (Wicks et al., 1965; Greenman et al., 1965), and an increase in the rate of synthesis of poly(A) containing RNA in the ventral prostate (Mainwaring et al., 1974). Moreover, a reduced level of the prostatic RNA polymerase activity in the castrated rats and its elevation after androgen treatment have also been reported (Mainwaring et al., 1971).

All these results emphasize the generalized nature of the androgen dependence of the accessory sex organs in the male rats but shed only minimal light on the role of this hormone in the differential regulation of specific gene activity. However, observation of the parallel rise in the hepatic concentration of α_{2u} globulin and its corresponding mRNA with the rising level of circulating androgens provides strong evidence for the role of androgenic hormones in the selective regulation of the gene activity. The finding of the androgen-dependent increase in the level of the mRNA for fructose diphosphate aldolase in the rat prostate also points toward a similar conclusion (Mainwaring et al., 1974). The last two observations, along with the established role of estrogens and gestagens in the selective regulation of specific mRNA in their target tissues (Rosenfeld et al., 1972; Palmiter, 1972; Tuohimaa et al., 1972; Chan et al., 1973; Bullock et al., 1976), provide a strong argument for a unified mechanism of the differential regulation of gene activity by the sex steroids, primarily operating at the level of transcription.

Most of the basic information concerning the molecular basis of the steroidal regulation of gene activity has so far been obtained by detailed investigation of the monohormonal systems where the synthesis of a specific gene product is regulated by a single hormonal factor. However, under normal physiological conditions, every cell in the organism is subjected to a multitude of hormonal influences conferring anywhere from synergistic to antagonistic effects on the primary endocrine response. The study of the multihormonal regulation of the hepatic synthesis of α_{2u} globulin and its mRNA, therefore, provides some interesting and physiologically relevant information concerning the molecular mechanism of hormone action. The observation that thyroxine, glucocorticoid, growth hormone, and insulin all contribute in the modulation of the androgen-dependent synthesis of the mRNA for α_{2u} globulin raises some interesting questions as to the site of action of these hormones. Are they all involved in the regulation of the same step in the process of information transfer, or are they acting on independent and sequential steps leading to ultimate activation of the α_{2u} gene? Still another possible mechanism could be the regulation of mRNA processing by various synergistic hormones. With the presently available techniques of molecular biology, these are now feasible subjects for experimental analysis.

ACKNOWLEDGMENTS

This work was supported by a research grant (AM-14744) and a research career development award (KO4-AM-00141) from the National Institute of Arthritis, Metabolism and Digestive Diseases. The author acknowledges criticisms, suggestions, and moral support from several of his students and colleagues, especially Drs. B. Chatterjee and A. K. Deshpande.

REFERENCES

Addis, T. (1931). *Proc. Calif. Acad. Med.* **2**, 38.
Attardi, G., and Amaldi, F. (1970). *Annu. Rev. Biochem.* **39**, 183.
Baliga, B. S., Pronczuk, A. W., and Munro, N. N. (1968). *J. Mol. Biol.* **34**, 199.
Bardin, C. W., Bullock, L., Schneider, G., Allison, J. E., and Stanley, A. J. (1970). *Science* **167**, 1136.
Barzilai, D., and Pincus, G. (1965). *Proc. Soc. Exp. Biol. Med.* **118**, 57.
Baulieu, E. E., and Jung, I. (1970). *Biochem. Biophys. Res. Commun.* **196**, 599.
Beers, P. C., and Rosner, W. (1977). *J. Steroid Biochem.* **8**, 251.
Bell, M. E. (1933). *J. Physiol. (London)* **79**, 191.
Bergink, E. W., Kloosterboer, H. J., Gruber, M., and Ab, G. (1973). *Biochim. Biophys. Acta* **294**, 497.
Berns, A., Janssen, P., and Bloemendal, H. (1974). *Biochem. Biophys. Res. Commun.* **59**, 1157.
Bond, H. E. (1960). *Biochem. Biophys. Res. Commun.* **3**, 53.
Bond, H. E. (1962). *Nature (London)* **196**, 242.
Bond, H. E. (1966). *Nature (London)* **209**, 1026.
Bruchovsky, N., and Wilson, J. D. (1968). *J. Biol. Chem.* **243**, 2012.
Bullock, D. W., Woo, S. L. C., and O'Malley, B. W. (1976). *Biol. Reprod.* **15**, 435.
Bullock, L. P., and Bardin, C. W. (1972). *J. Clin. Endocrinol. Metab.* **35**, 935.
Burstein, S. (1968). *Endocrinology* **83**, 485.
Chamness, G. C., Costlow, M. E., and McGuire, W. L. (1975). *Steroids* **26**, 363.
Chamness, G. C., King, T. W., and Sheridan, P. J. (1977). *Program 59th Annu. Meet., Am. Endocr. Soc.* p. 164.
Chan, L., Means, A. R., and O'Malley, B. W. (1973). *Proc. Natl. Acad. Sci. U.S.A.* **70**, 1870.
De Baun, J. R., Miller, E. C., and Miller, J. A. (1970). *Cancer Res.* **30**, 577.
Denef, C. (1974). *Endocrinology* **94**, 1577.
Duguid, J. R., Steiner, D. F., and Chick, W. L. (1976). *Proc. Natl. Acad. Sci. U.S.A.* **73**, 3539.
Eisenfeld, A. J., Aten, R., Weinberger, M., Hasebacher, G., Halpern, K., and Krakoff, L. (1976). *Science* **191**, 862.
Fang, S., and Liao, S. (1969). *Mol. Pharmacol.* **5**, 420.
Fang, S., and Liao, S. (1971). *J. Biol. Chem.* **246**, 16.
Fang, S., Anderson, K. M., and Liao, S. (1969). *J. Biol. Chem.* **244**, 6584.

Finlayson, J. S., and Baumann, C. A. (1958). *Am. J. Physiol.* **192**, 69.

Geertzen, H. G. M., Ouderaa, F. J. G., and Kassenaar, A. A. H. (1973). *Acta Endocrinol. (Copenhagen)* **72**, 197.

Gehring, U., Tomkins, G. M., and Ohno, S. (1971). *Nature (London), New Biol.* **232**, 106.

Gershon, H., and Gershon, D. (1973). *Proc. Natl. Acad. Sci. U.S.A.* **70**, 909.

Geschwind, I., Li, C. H., and Evans, H. M. (1950). *Arch. Biochem.* **28**, 73.

Ghraf, R., Lax, E. R., Hoff, H. G., and Schriefers, H. (1974). *Acta Endocrinol. (Copenhagen)* **77**, 287.

Ghraf, R., Lax, E. R., and Schriefers, H. (1977). *Hoppe-Seyler's Z. Physiol. Chem.* **358**, 165.

Greengard, O., Sentenac, A., and Acs, G. (1965). *J. Biol. Chem.* **240**, 1687.

Greenman, D. L., Wicks, W. D., and Kenney, F. T. (1965). *J. Biol. Chem.* **240**, 1965.

Grinna, L. S., and Barber, A. A. (1972). *Biochim. Biophys. Acta* **288**, 347.

Gschwendt, M., and Kittstein, W. (1974). *Biochim. Biophys. Acta* **361**, 84.

Gurdon, J. B., Lane, C. D., Woodland, H. R., and Marbaix, G. (1971). *Nature (London)* **233**, 177.

Gustafsson, J. A., and Pousette, A. (1974). *Biochemistry* **13**, 875.

Gustafsson, J. A., and Stenberg, A. (1974). *J. Biol. Chem.* **249**, 1940.

Gustafsson, J. A., Ingelman-Sunberg, M., and Stenberg, A. (1975). *J. Steroid Biochem.* **6**, 643.

Irwin, J. F., Lane, S. E., and Neuhaus, O. W. (1971). *Biochim. Biophys. Acta* **252**, 328.

Jam, K. M., and DuBois, K. P. (1967). *Radiat. Res.* **31**, 315.

Jefferson, L. S., Li, J. B., and Rannels, S. R. (1977). *J. Biol. Chem.* **252**, 1476.

Jensen, E. V., and Jacobson, H. J. (1962). *Recent Prog. Horm. Res.* **18**, 387.

Jung-Testas, I., Bayard, F., and Baulieu, E. E. (1976a). *Nature (London)* **259**, 136.

Jung-Testas, I., Desmond, W., and Baulieu, E. E. (1976b). *Exp. Cell Res.* **97**, 219.

Kato, J. (1971). *J. Biochem. (Tokyo)* **70**, 1051.

Korenman, S. G., and Rao, B. R. (1968). *Proc. Natl. Acad. Sci. U.S.A.* **61**, 1028.

Korner, A. (1960). *Biochem. J.* **74**, 471.

Kumar, M., Roy, A. K., and Axelrod, A. E. (1969). *Nature (London)* **223**, 399.

Kunzel, B., and Muller-Oerlinghausen, B. (1969). *Naunyn-Schmiedebergs Arch. Pharmakol. Exp. Pathol.* **262**, 112.

Kurtz, D. T., Sippel, A. E., Ansah-Yiadom, R., and Feigelson, P. (1976a). *J. Biol. Chem.* **251**, 3594.

Kurtz, D. T., Sippel, A. E., and Feigelson, P. (1976b). *Biochemistry* **15**, 1031.

Lane, S. E., and Neuhaus, O. W. (1972). *Biochim. Biophys. Acta* **257**, 461.

Liao, S., and Williams-Ashman, H. G. (1962). *Proc. Natl. Acad. Sci. U.S.A.* **48**, 1956.

Lockard, R. E., and Lingrel, J. B. (1969). *Biochem. Biophys. Res. Commun.* **37**, 204.

Loening, U. E. (1968). *J. Mol. Biol.* **38**, 355.

McGuire, J. S., Hollis, V. W., and Tomkins, G. M. (1960). *J. Biol. Chem.* **235**, 3112.

Mach, B., Faust, C., and Vassalli, P. (1973). *Proc. Natl. Acad. Sci. U.S.A.* **70**, 451.

Mainwaring, W. I. P. (1969). *J. Endocrinol.* **45**, 531.

Mainwaring, W. I. P., Mangan, F. R., and Peterken, B. M. (1971). *Biochem. J.* **123**, 619.

Mainwaring, W. I. P., Wilce, P. A., and Smith, A. E. (1974). *Biochem. J.* **144**, 413.

Manchester, K. L. (1970). *Biochem. Actions Horm.* **1**, 267.

Martial, J. A., Baxter, J. D., Goodman, H. M., and Seeburg, P. H. (1977). *Proc. Natl. Acad. Sci. U.S.A.* **74**, 1816.

Mathews, M. B., and Korner, A. (1970). *Eur. J. Biochem.* **17**, 328.

Milgröm, E., Atger, M., and Baulieu, E. E. (1970). *Steroids* **16**, 741.

Milin, B., and Roy, A. K. (1973). *Nature (London), New Biol.* **242**, 248.

Morrison, M. R., and Lingrel, J. B. (1976). *Biochim. Biophys. Acta* **447**, 104.

Mortimore, G. E., and Mondon, C. E. (1970). *J. Biol. Chem.* **245**, 2375.

Motwani, N. M., and Roy, A. K. (1978). *Program 60th Annu. Meet., Am. Endocr. Soc.* p. 509.

Mowszowicz, I., Bieber, D. E., Chung, K. W., Bullock, L. P., and Bardin, C. W. (1974). *Endocrinology* **95**, 1589.

Naess, O., Haug, E., Attramadal, A., Aakvaag, A., Hansson, V., and French, F. (1976). *Endocrinology* **99**, 1295.

Nari, V., Brown, T., Bau, D., and Siegel, S. (1970). *Eur. J. Pharmacol.* **9**, 31.

Neuhaus, O. W., and Irwin, J. F. (1972). *Life Sci.* **11**, 631.

Notides, A. C., and Nielsen, S. (1974). *J. Biol. Chem.* **249**, 1866.

O'Malley, B. W., Toft, D. O., and Sherman, M. R. (1971). *J. Biol. Chem.* **246**, 1117.

Oppenheimer, J. H., Schwartz, H. L., and Surks, M. I. (1974). *Endocrinology* **96**, 897.

Palmiter, R. D. (1972). *J. Biol. Chem.* **247**, 6450.

Parfentjev, I. A., and Perlzweig, W. A. (1933). *J. Biol. Chem.* **100**, 551.

Peavy, D. E., Taylor, J. M., and Jefferson, L. S. (1978). *Fed. Proc., Fed. Am. Soc. Exp. Biol.* **37**, 1505.

Penhos, J. C., and Krahl, M. E. (1964). *Am. J. Physiol.* **204**, 140.

Roberts, B. E., and Patterson, B. M. (1973). *Proc. Natl. Acad. Sci. U.S.A.* **70**, 2330.

Rosen, J. M., and O'Malley, B. W. (1975). *Biochem. Actions Horm.* **3**, 271.

Rosenfeld, G. C., Comstock, J. P., Means, A. R., and O'Malley, B. W. (1972). *Biochem. Biophys. Res. Commun.* **47**, 387.

Roth, G. S. (1976). *Endocrinology* **99**, 831.

Roy, A. B. (1958). *Biochem. J.* **68**, 519.

Roy, A. K. (1973a). *Endocrinology* **92**, 957.

Roy, A. K. (1973b). *J. Endocrinol.* **56**, 295.

Roy, A. K. (1976). *J. Endocrinol.* **70**, 189.

Roy, A. K. (1977). *Eur. J. Biochem.* **73**, 537.

Roy, A. K., and Byrd, J. G. (1976). *J. Endocrinol.* **71**, 265.

Roy, A. K., and Dowbenko, D. J. (1977). *Biochemistry* **16**, 3918.

Roy, A. K., and Leonard, S. (1973). *J. Endocrinol.* **57**, 327.

Roy, A. K., and Neuhaus, O. W. (1966a). *Proc. Soc. Exp. Biol. Med.* **121**, 894.

Roy, A. K., and Neuhaus, O. W. (1966b). *Biochim. Biophys. Acta* **127**, 82.

Roy, A. K., and Neuhaus, O. W. (1967). *Nature (London)* **214**, 618.

Roy, A. K., and Raber, D. L. (1972). *J. Histochem. Cytochem.* **20**, 89.

Roy, A. K., Neuhaus, O. W., and Harmison, C. R. (1966). *Biochim. Biophys. Acta* **127**, 72.

Roy, A. K., Milin, B. S., and McMinn, D. M. (1974). *Biochim. Biophys. Acta* **354**, 213.

Roy, A. K., McMinn, D. M., and Biswas, N. M. (1975). *Endocrinology* **97**, 1505.

Roy, A. K., Schiop, M. J., and Dowbenko, D. J. (1976a). *FEBS Lett.* **64**, 393.

Roy, A. K., Schiop, M. J., and Dowbenko, D. J. (1976b). *FEBS Lett.* **70**, 137.

Roy, A. K., Dowbenko, D. J., and Schiop, M. J. (1977). *Biochem. J.* **164**, 91.

Samuels, H. H., Shapiro, L. E., and Tsai, J. S. (1976). *Program 58th Annu. Meet., Am. Endocr. Soc.* p. 189.

Schimke, R. T., McKnight, G. S., and Shapiro, D. J. (1975). *Biochem. Actions Horm.* **3**, 245.

Schrader, W. T., and O'Malley, B. W. (1972). *J. Biol. Chem.* **247**, 51.

Sellers, A. L., Goodman, H. C., Marmoston, J., and Smith, M. (1950). *Am. J. Physiol.* **163**, 662.

Seo, H., Vassar, G., Brocas, H., and Refetoff, S. (1977). *Proc. Natl. Acad. Sci. U.S.A.* **74**, 2054.

Shain, S. A., and Axelrod, L. R. (1973). *Steroids* **21**, 801.

Sippel, A. E., Feigelson, P., and Roy, A. K. (1975). *Biochemistry* **14**, 825.

Smith, A. A., McLean, W. S., Nayfeh, S. N., French, F. S., Hansson, V., and Ritzen, E. M. (1975). *In* "Hormonal Regulation of Spermatogenesis" (F. S. French *et al.*, eds.), p. 257. Plenum, New York.

Strauss, A. W., Donohue, A. M., Bennett, C. D., Rodkey, J. A., and Alberts, A. W. (1977). *Proc. Natl. Acad. Sci. U.S.A.* **74**, 1358.

Sullivan, J. L., and Debusk, A. K. (1973). *Nature (London), New Biol.* **243**, 72.

Sussman, P. M., Tushinski, R. J., and Bancroft, F. C. (1976). *Proc. Natl. Acad. Sci. U.S.A.* **73**, 29.

Talwar, G. P., Gupta, S. L., and Gros, F. (1964). *Biochem. J.* **91**, 565.

Tata, J. R. (1968). *Nature (London)* **219**, 331.

Tata, J. R., and Widnell, C. C. (1966). *Biochem. J.* **98**, 604.

Toft, D., and Gorski, J. (1966). *Proc. Natl. Acad. Sci. U.S.A.* **55**, 1574.

Tuohimaa, P., Segal, S. J., and Koide, S. S. (1972). *Proc. Natl. Acad. Sci. U.S.A.* **69**, 2814.

Van, N. T., Monahan, J. J., Woo, S. L. C., Means, A. R., and O'Malley, B. W. (1977). *Biochemistry* **16**, 4090.

Viladiu, P., Delgado, C., Pensky, J., and Pearson, O. H. (1975). *Endocr. Res. Commun.* **2**, 273.

Weisburger, E. K., Grantham, P. H., and Weisburger, J. H. (1964). *Biochemistry* **3**, 808.

Wicks, L. P. (1941). *Proc. Soc. Exp. Biol. Med.* **48**, 395.

Wicks, W. D., Greenman, D. L., and Kenney, F. T. (1965). *J. Biol. Chem.* **240**, 4420.

Williams-Ashman, H. G., and Reddy, A. H. (1972). *Biochem. Actions Horm.* **2**, 257.

Williams-Ashman, H. G., Liao, S., Hancock, R. L., Jurkowitz, L., and Silverman, D. A. (1964). *Recent Prog. Horm. Res.* **20**, 247.

Woo, S. L. C., Rosen, J. M., Liarakos, C. D., Choi, Y. C., Busch, H., Means, A. R., O'Malley, B. W., and Robberson, D. L. (1975). *J. Biol. Chem.* **250**, 7027.

Wool, I. G., Stirewalt, W. S., Kurihara, K., Low, R. B., Bailey, P., and Oyer, D. (1968). *Recent Prog. Horm. Res.* **24**, 139.

Wool, I. G., Castles, J. J., Leader, D. P., and Fox, A. (1972). *Handb. Physiol., Sect. 7: Endocrinol.* **1**, 385.

Index

A